Conservation
of Natural Resources

Conservation of Natural Resources
Third Edition

Editor: GUY-HAROLD SMITH
The Ohio State University

Contributors:

Marion Clawson
Charles A. Dambach
Oliver D. Diller
Edwin J. Foscue
John H. Garland
H. Bowman Hawkes
Lawrence A. Hoffman
Lowry B. Karnes
Howard H. Martin

Harold H. McCarty
E. Willard Miller
Harold V. Miller
William A. Rockie
Harold M. Rose
Guy-Harold Smith
Stephen S. Visher
Warren C. Whitman
Louis A. Wolfanger

The late Herbert C. Hanson

JOHN WILEY & SONS, INC.
New York · London · Sydney

In memory of E. B. S.

Preface

In the first edition of *Conservation of Natural Resources*, published in 1950, I, taking the backward look, observed that "As the pioneers took possession of the continent they were first overwhelmed by abundance. Great forests stood in the way of the farmer who would cultivate the land. In the rivers and the adjacent seas fish and other seafoods were available in great quantities. The expansive prairies of midland America were among the most productive in the world. The mineral treasures beneath the surface were largely unknown when the outer frontiers of the nation were first established. To possess the land and bring it under cultivation meant the destruction of a great forest resource. Wasteful exploitation was condoned in the midst of such abundance."

By the end of the nineteenth century it was becoming evident that economic development had as a consequence the destructive utilization of a rich heritage. The forest resources had been depleted. The farmlands were declining in productivity because of soil depletion and erosion. The need for conservation was becoming clear to learned men such as George P. Marsh and Charles R. Van Hise and to public officials such as Gifford Pinchot and Theodore Roosevelt. The latter were in positions to do something about the wastage of resources. It was in the administration of President Roosevelt that extensive areas of forest lands were set aside or withdrawn from entry and in time became the National Forests.

In the preface of the first edition I wrote that "World War I and the high production of the 1920's made heavy demands on the resource base to meet the needs of the mass-production economy. Immediately thereafter the difficult times of the 1930's brought on a soul-searching inquiry into the causes and consequences of the economic prostration which had overwhelmed the country and involved much of the world." New leaders appeared on the scene. Hugh Hammond Bennett became the patron saint of the soil conservationists. Franklin D. Roosevelt when he became President called for an inventory of the nation's resources and urged the Congress and the people to search for ways to overcome the effects of the depression.

World War II, fought to achieve a victory over tyranny, made a heavy drain on the material and human resources of the nation. Many people became concerned, even alarmed, at the enormous loss of life and treasure attributable to the war. Before the full impact of the war on the resource situation could be assessed, the nation was called upon to pledge its material wealth and technological strength in the rebuilding of western Europe. On June 5, 1947, General George C. Marshall, then Secretary of State, in an address delivered before an audience at Harvard University urged that the United States contribute economic and financial aid to free Europe. The Congress responded to this request and appropriated 12 billion dollars of Marshall Plan aid to be expended over a period of three and one-half years.

In the preface of the second edition (1958) I noted "That many people in this country became fearful that so much foreign aid would make a heavy drain upon the resources of the nation. Their fears were allayed somewhat by the issue in 1947 of J. A. Krug's *National Resources and Foreign Aid*, a report of the Secretary of the Interior." The material resources had been used to give great strength to the nation and its allies during the war, and their continued use was necessary to accomplish the role of political and economic leadership which had become the responsibility of the United States.

Mid-century concern about the resource situation has been replaced in the 1960's by a more optimistic outlook. Many people cannot escape the conviction that the fund resources will in time be depleted, diminished in quantity, and in some instances be exhausted or destroyed. However, in spite of a number of unfavorable trends in resource use, the nation with its great wealth, its technological capacity, and managerial skills can continue to prosper and provide the basic necessities for comfortable and gracious living. The pollution of streams and lakes can be stopped. The air we breathe can be improved in quality by reducing the wastes that are discharged into the atmosphere. By the time the petroleum reserves are greatly diminished other liquid fuels will be available in quantity and at a price the people can afford. In the fifteen years since the publication of the first edition of this book increasing emphasis is being placed on research and the resourcefulness of man in meeting his needs. Modern science in the hands of an educated populace can defer for decades, perhaps centuries, the eventual destruction of the resource base. This does not mean that blind optimism can be substituted for a perceptive approach to the numerous problems in the general area of conservation that have engaged the attention of many people and organizations for most of the twentieth century.

This contribution to the literature on conservation represents the combined efforts of nineteen different authors. They have been constrained by the publishers not to expand their chapters beyond the limits set for the second edition. This will explain in part why some topics have been presented too briefly or have been omitted.

To the several contributors and to the publishers I wish to express my genuine appreciation for their cooperation. I would like to acknowledge the secretarial help of Linda S. Wilkins, who handled very ably most of the correspondence and to recognize the professional assistance of Vera Luczka Herman, who for many years has been a loyal and highly competent aid.

GUY-HAROLD SMITH
EDITOR

The Ohio State University
Columbus, Ohio

July 1965

Contents

Part Eight   477

Index   517

Part 1

HAROLD M. ROSE*
University of Wisconsin-Milwaukee

CHAPTER 1

Conservation in the United States

Security, an element which is sought by all men, be it social, economic, physical or spiritual, is not always assured within the time spectrum that an individual or group actually occupies an area or can envision its occupation by their progeny. In the absence, or a threat to the existence, of security, men have been led to engage in activity that would result in its initiation or restoration. This type of behavior characterized primitive man, as well as modern man, although the philosophical and operational armaments have varied through the ages. One concept which has grown up in the United States as a means of eliminating the insecurity surrounding the nation's ability to support itself, now and in the future, and at some predetermined level, is the conservation philosophy.

Conservation, as a formal philosophy, is as much American as Jeffersonian Democracy, and at times has proved to be no more flexible. Much difficulty has been encountered in attempts to assign to conservation formal definitions. Much of the difficulty can be attributed to oversimplification, limited focus, and narrowness of scope. Difficulties of definition frequently arise when people attempt to move from the philosophical to the operational level and therefore should be anticipated.

NATIONAL DEVELOPMENT AND THE PRE-CONSERVATION ERA

Land, the Basic Resource. The basic factor underlying the nation's successful development in so short a period of time was the availability of an extensive quantity of land and the ease with which land could be secured by individuals for development. The land factor and all its productive powers, which are commonly referred to as natural resources, thus represented the nation's potential for development.

Once the Appalachian barrier had been penetrated, the frontier was swiftly and continuously pushed westward until the nation's land was inhabited by Americans from the Atlantic to the Pacific. During settlement there was much evidence of land-use mismanagement, which gave rise to the subsequent threat of scarcity and the despoliation of facets of nature's bounty, two factors which were later to give rise to dualisms in conservation philosophy. The dualisms which were later to create persistent conflicts in con-

*Professor Rose succeeds Professor Alfred J. Wright who died on January 14, 1964, as the author of this chapter. Although the textual material differs in many ways from Professor Wright's work, Professor Rose wishes to acknowledge the influence of Professor Wright in the development of his interest in conservation.

3

servation ideology were related to the objectives that natural resources were thought to satisfy. Very early in the twentieth century there evolved one group of conservationists who promoted natural resource development or use and another group who promoted preservation or nonuse. These basic value differences that have been assigned to natural resources have been passed on through time.

By the time of the transcendentalist writers, Ralph Waldo Emerson and Henry David Thoreau, the frontier had been pushed to the base of the Rockies and mountain men were paving the way for settlement beyond the mountains.[1] These writers did much to focus attention on the man-nature relationship,[2] and their influence on both the ethical and aesthetic school of conservation thought has been pervasive.

Early Conservationist Thought. George P. Marsh is often considered the principal forerunner of the modern conservationist in the United States. Marsh, a naturalist, politician, and government servant, had the opportunity to observe man's relationship with nature in both Europe and the Middle East, areas of long settlement. He concluded that the abuse that was evident on these continents would soon prevail in America if some attempts were not made to study the man-nature relationship. Marsh's thesis was that "man disrupts the fundamental harmony or balance of nature."[3] This thinking led to the eventual rise of the ecological philosophy of conservation. Marsh has been referred to as the "fountainhead of the conservation movement,"[4] even though conservation as a formal movement did not get under way before his death.

Legislative Action and Natural-Resource Management. By the close of the Civil War, the nation had acquired the entire territory that now constitutes the forty-eight contiguous states. The Homestead Act of 1862 had been passed to accelerate settlement on this newly acquired land. Within the next 30 years frontier conditions were steadily pushed westward, until at last more than just a series of isolated settlements existed west to the shores of the Pacific. It was among this generation that the nation's future conservation leaders were to originate, both native born Americans and persons of European origin whose training in resource management prepared them well for the task ahead. These men observed with great clarity the problems that had evolved out of the passing of the frontier and their possible effects on the future of the nation's development.

It was during this latter part of the nineteenth century that the battle lines were drawn, which were to lead eventually to the dualisms which were to pervade conservation philosophy from its very beginnings to the present. The growing concern over natural resource abuse has previously been attributed to the intense interest in these matters by naturalists and naturalist philosophers. These individuals can be hailed as the promoters of what was to become the ecological school of conservation.

Another group of individuals, frequently representing persons trained in some area of natural-resource management, was also to come to the fore and promote efficiency in resource utilization. The emergence of this group, represented by Gifford Pinchot, has resulted in Hays identifying the period in which they exerted the dominant influence as one of maximum efficiency.[5] These were the forerunners of what might be thought of as economic and technologic conservationists.

THE ROLE OF THE FRONTIER ON CONSERVATION THOUGHT

There is very little serious writing on the conservation movement in the United States that does not attempt to relate the rise of the move-

[1] Ray Allen Billington, *The Far Western Frontier, 1830–1860*, New York, 1962, pp. 41–68.

[2] Arthur A. Ekirch, Jr., *Man and Nature in America*, New York, 1963, pp. 47–69.

[3] *Ibid.*, p. 75.

[4] Quoted by Stewart L. Udall, *The Quiet Crisis*, New York, 1963, p. 94.

[5] Samuel P. Hays, *Conservation and the Gospel of Efficiency*, Cambridge, Massachusetts, 1959, p. 2.

ment to the passage of the frontier. The frontier hypothesis of Frederick Jackson Turner has done much to promote the idea of the rise of institutions west of the Alleghenies that were peculiarly American. The environment allegedly created men who exhibited strong individualistic traits and who resented seemingly senseless social controls. Thus the character of the frontiersmen promoted unregulated use of the natural resources of the Mississippi Valley. More recent explanations of the influence of the frontier on economic and social development in the West do much to refute the validity of the Turner hypothesis which leans heavily toward environmental determinism. It was recently stated that "the frontier was more than an area or a process; it was, in its deepest sense, an interaction of space as nature and of society as an evolutionary organism to produce those virtues upon which Americans prided themselves most." [6]

The Frontier Concept. The fear of declining abundance associated with the passage of Turner's frontier is held by some to be invalid. A recent definition of a frontier is that it is "the edge of the unused," [7] and therefore "science has its frontiers, industry its frontiers, technology its frontiers, and that so long as Americans can advance their standards of living and maintain the fluidity of their lives and their capacity for change along these frontiers, the disappearance of the agrarian frontier is not at all critical." [8] This change in thought has given rise to the concept of a vertical frontier, which might be as valid as the horizontal frontier in explaining the availability and development of natural resources, as the horizontal frontier was during a prior period.

The Horizontal versus the Vertical Frontier. It is now possible to link the two frontiers with the dualism that pervades the conservation philosophy. Those whose orientation is still the dominance of the horizontal frontier tend to

represent individuals whose conservation views are principally ecological, ethical, and aesthetic. Much writing supporting these views includes the names of Samuel H. Ordway, Jr., Aldo Leopold, Paul B. Sears, F. Frazier Darling, William Vogt, and Fairfield Osborn, although the chief proponent and one of the earlier and most active conservationist was John Muir.

The recent rise of the concept of a vertical frontier and its focus on economic production factors other than land has not resulted in developing as large a body of supporters as in the former case. But as man continues to demonstrate reliance on resources in a broader sense, the voices of this new school will probably grow more insistent.

EVOLUTION OF THE CONSERVATION MOVEMENT

Conservation as a social movement in the United States was not initiated before the turn of the twentieth century, although there was much sporadic action and emphasis on resource abuse growing out of a land policy that had as its principal objective the acceleration of settlement west of the Mississippi. By 1890 it was realized that much of the previous legislation passed during the latter half of the nineteenth century had led to creating problems that were unanticipated at the time of its passage. Some of the earlier laws, such as the Timber Culture Act of 1873, the Pre-emption Act, and the Desert Land Act of 1877, were eventually repealed or in the case of the last-named Act strengthened to prevent further dummy sales that were being promoted by special interest groups.[9]

The germinal concepts that later were identified with conservation were embodied in the writing of an early group of naturalists, teachers, and public servants such as Louis Agassiz, Arnold Guyot, Nathaniel S. Shaler, George P.

[6] Robert F. Berkhofer, Jr., "Space, Time, Culture and the New Frontier," *Agricultural History*, Vol. 38, 1964, p. 24.

[7] David M. Potter, *People of Plenty*, Chicago, 1954, p. 157.

[8] *Ibid.*

[9] Paul W. Gates, "The Homestead Law in an Incongruous Land System," Vernon Carstensen, editor, *The Public Lands*, Madison, Wisconsin, 1962, pp. 315–348.

Marsh, and Major J. W. Powell, the first director of the United States Geological Survey. Agassiz and Shaler taught at Harvard University; Guyot was on the faculty at Princeton University. Major Powell,[10] a disabled veteran of the Civil War, appraised with keen perception the dry lands of the West (Fig. 1). All were familiar with the emerging problems related to the use and abuse of the rich resources of the nation.

While public land continued to be disposed of, some land was being withdrawn from private entry and set aside so that it could be protected and freed from possible abuse. Thus by the turn of the century the stage was set for the initiation of a formal social movement that would focus attention on the situation surrounding the na-

[10] J. W. Powell, *Lands of the Arid Regions of the United States,* Washington, D.C., 1879.

tion's natural resources, which were thought to represent the key to continued national development.

Conservation Under Theodore Roosevelt. The initial phase of the conservation movement in the United States was associated with the administration of Theodore Roosevelt, who himself was an active outdoors man. The idea of promoting a conscious effort to produce change in the area of natural resource management was Gifford Pinchot's, a professional forester (Fig. 2). It was Pinchot who was to become a great influence in the nation's first attempt at organized conservation. Pinchot chose the term conservation to describe the movement in 1907. He had been informed that government forests in India were known as Conservancies,[11] and

[11] Udall, *op. cit.* p. 106.

Fig. 1   Major J. W. Powell published his *Lands of the Arid Regions* in 1879, probably the first realistic appraisal of the land resources of the dry and semi-arid West. Mainly as a result of this investigation an irrigation division of the United States Geological Survey was established in 1888. (U.S. Geological Survey.)

Fig. 2   Gifford Pinchot, at one time head of the Forestry Service and later Governor of the Commonwealth of Pennsylvania, was one of the leading conservationists in the United States. For many years he was closely associated with President Theodore Roosevelt who reserved for public use large areas of forest land. (U.S. Forest Service.)

this term interested him, thus leading him to employ a form of it to describe his own favored program.

The primary emphasis during this period was focused on the problems associated with forestry. Pinchot was opposed to establishing forest reserves which would result only in their preservation rather than their conservation. To Pinchot the concept of conservation connoted use under systematic management. This belief was later to cause him to sever his friendship with another noted personality, John Muir (Fig. 3), whose interest was principally in nature for nature's sake. These two individuals were later to represent the conservation giants of the era, with Pinchot on the inside directing the government's program and Muir on the outside promoting his own following through his many writings on the subject and the organization of the Sierra Club.

During much of the period, 1901–1909, the conservation movement was characterized by much propaganda designed to focus attention on declining resources. Most authorities agree today that the greatest contribution to come out of this era was that of pointing up the problems which characterize the nation's storehouse of natural resources.

One of the last major efforts of the Theodore Roosevelt period was the calling of the governors of each state to Washington to discuss the resource problems existing within their own states; this conference was termed the White House Conference of 1908. Before Roosevelt could spread his influence further afield, and into the international area of conservation, he was no longer in public office. Even though many of Roosevelt's plans for conservation were eclipsed as a result of his leaving presidential politics, he left a legacy to resource-conscious individuals and groups that should not be minimized. The Reclamation Act of 1902, which fostered western development, the concept of multiple-purpose resource development, scientific forestry, a mineral policy for the public lands, and the development of the Inland Waterways Commission represented some of the last-

Fig. 3 John Muir, a scientist and nature lover, as a pioneer in the promotion of the esthetic and the ethical philosophy embodied in the conservation movement. The thinking of Muir continues to influence a number of the nation's leaders in conservation. (Department of the Interior.)

ing effects of the Theodore Roosevelt era that have had more far-reaching effects on national resource development than the much publicized propaganda aspect of his program.

The influence of Roosevelt policy makers was to extend into the administration of President William Howard Taft. But the voices of such individuals as Frederick Newell, W. J. McGee, Charles R. Van Hise, and others were to be less frequently heard and only Pinchot, the giant of the previous administration, was to make his voice felt for another decade.

The Second Phase of the Conservation Movement. The initial phase of the conservation movement is generally regarded as having terminated in 1909. In the following decade there was not within the group in power a strong personality to promote the nation's conservation program. This does not mean that no attempts were made to promote conservation, but much of the period was given over to controversy arising out of policy differences between the Taft administration and the previous administration. The growing conflict on the international scene did much to divert the nation's attention from national resource development to the war in Europe. Thus the latter half of the second decade of the century did not lend itself to the promotion of conservation.

The apparent waning of Pinchot's influence in conservation circles was evidenced by the passage of the Water Power Act of 1920, which did not promote the type of multiple-purpose policy to which he was committed. "By 1921 the way had been cleared for the rapid expansion of resource development on the public lands of the United States, and a new stage in Conservation history had begun." [12]

The second phase of the conservation movement saw three individuals occupying the position of central authority in the national government: Harding, Coolidge, and Hoover. During their era no single personality dominated the stage or provided the type of leadership typical of the previous phase.

The natural resource on which most attention was focused during this period was petroleum. Petroleum had reached new heights in popularity, for it was the fuel that powered allied armies to victory in Europe. The growing automobile market created new demands for this power source in the years following the war, even to the extent that it was thought that the nation's limited reserves might soon be exhausted. The Bureau of Mines promoted a program that attempted to eliminate waste in petroleum production and to increase efficiencies in drilling techniques. A petroleum experiment station was opened at Bartletsville, Oklahoma, in 1920 to aid in promoting the Bureau's policy.[13]

[12] Donald C. Swain, *Federal Conservation Policy 1921-1933*, Berkeley, California, 1963, p. 4.
[13] *Ibid.*, p. 57.

The Teapot Dome scandal which occurred during the Harding administration did little to create a favorable conservation atmosphere. The Teapot Dome was a formation containing petroleum on public land in Wyoming that was to play a major role in weakening the conservation efforts of this period. The appointment of a Federal Oil Conservation Board by President Coolidge was an attempt to overcome the image created during the administration of his predecessor.

The last four years of the second phase of the movement was the most promising in regard to conservation. President Herbert Hoover, had the opportunity to introduce a number of the programs to which he had given attention as Secretary of Commerce during the administrations of Presidents Harding and Coolidge. Hoover's contributions are not too frequently hailed in the general conservation literature, but his zeal for efficiency and his water resource planning program must be recognized as valid contributions.

President Hoover, first as Secretary of Commerce and later as Chief Executive, had a vital interest in the orderly development and control of the water resources of the country. The Flood Control Act of 1928 passed in the Coolidge administration was strongly endorsed by Secretary Hoover. The great dam on the Colorado River which now bears his name was originally known as the Boulder Canyon Project, and the name Hoover Dam was belated recognition of his interest in and support of the project (Fig. 4). It was in his administration that the Federal Power Commission was reorganized and established as an agency that was to play a dominant role in the development of the water power resources of the country.

Hoover's distaste for federal regulation and dependence on voluntary cooperation and action was to reduce the effectiveness of his program. "In certain instances he achieved considerable success by means of cooperation. His oil policy is a good example. But on the whole, cooperative tactics failed in the face of

Fig. 4 Hoover Dam, in the Boulder Canyon section of the Colorado River, is concrete evidence
of President Hoover's leadership in the development of the water resources of the dry Southwest.
(Bureau of Reclamation.)

strong opposition from resource users." [14] This
era saw a movement away from complete dependence on the federal government for developing conservation programs. This was a break
with the Roosevelt-Pinchot theme of conservation as a governmental function.[15]

Conservation and the New Deal. The period
1933–1939 might be thought of as the "golden
age of conservation" in the United States. The

[14] *Ibid.*, p. 162.
[15] H. Bowman Hawkes. "The Paradoxes of the Conservation Movement," *Bulletin of the University of Utah*, Vol. 51,
February 1960, p. 19.

state of the nation's economic situation did
much to remove some of the obstacles to an
effective conservation program that prevailed
during the earlier period. Thus the stage was set
for a strong personality to take over while conservation was on the wane. The problems to be
corrected were both far-reaching and complex,
since they related not only to land but also to
man.

Franklin D. Roosevelt, unlike Theodore
Roosevelt, was not overshadowed by any individual in his administration as the guiding
force in the development of his administration's

Fig. 5   Hugh Hammond Bennett, former Chief of the Soil Conservation Service, a long-time enthusiast and leader in the movement to save the soil resources of the nation from destructive erosion and depletion. (Soil Conservation Service.)

conservation program. Although Franklin D. Roosevelt did enlist a strong professional bureaucracy of experts in bringing about solutions to these multifarious problems the responsibility for leadership was his.

The primary emphasis during this period was on land planning, with a special focus on soil improvement programs. Up to now, the major conservation emphasis had been on a single natural resource. But it was now realized that the diseconomies prevailing throughout most of the nation represented a failure in man-land relationships within an institutional frame of reference. Thus it was necessary to introduce the type of machinery which would result in the realignment of these discordant relations.

The FDR program was characterized by the passage of much legislation and the creation of numerous bureaus and agencies to transform legislation into meaningful action at the grass-

roots level. Some of the more far-reaching legislations were those acts allowing for the establishment of the Tennessee Valley Authority, the Civilian Conservation Corps, The National Resources Board, the Soil Conservation Service, and the Resettlement Administration.

The enthusiasm for soil conservation, both official and personal, was in a large measure related to the leadership of Hugh Hammond Bennett. The Soil Conservation Act of 1933 was the legal basis for establishing demonstration projects across the nation and particularly in those states where soil erosion had already greatly reduced the productivity of the land. Few people in the past century attracted a larger following of devoted conservationists than did Bennett, the long-time Chief of the Soil Conservation Service (Fig. 5).

It was also during this period that the indiscriminate giveaway of land was terminated. The passage of the Taylor Grazing Act in 1934 resulted in the withdrawal from entry the remaining unreserved area of public domain, although at the same time tax delinquent land within individual states was being ceded to the national government for the purpose of creating National Forests and other public holdings.

These various measures enabled the nation to start back on the road to economic recovery, with full recovery following on the heels of the outbreak of war in Europe, for the second time in a single generation. Thus once more the nation's interest was turned from the domestic scene to the international scene and the exigencies of war resulted in turning one's back on problems of a conservational nature which had existed only a short time before, but now seemed to have disappeared.

CONSERVATION IN THE POST-WAR ERA

The years following World War II found the nation deeply committed and active in the area of international economic recovery. The problems of recovery required much in the way of both financial assistance and the temporary employment of many of the nation's top resource specialists. Thus the Point Four Program, the Marshall Plan, and other such programs overshadowed the need to reappraise the domestic resource situation and the problems which were later to evolve.

No Single Overriding Issue. The advent of the Korean crisis occurring on the heels of the period of readjustment did much to hamper strong government participation in sponsoring a unified conservation effort. This does not mean that the government was ignoring its responsibility, for numerous uncoordinated bits of legislation were passed which indicated resource consciousness. The "Paley Report," which was the nation's first postwar effort to appraise the status of its natural resources, is frequently hailed as the first attempt to take a careful stock of the situation of resource adequacy.

The 1950's saw the nation becoming more and more urban, with employment operating at a high level and an apparent absence of threat to material security. The condition of the times made it difficult to generate much public interest in conservation of an emotional type, which had characterized conservation during a prior era.

Professional public bureaucrats were active in promoting the passage of legislation which supported their own specific interests. "The professional forester, engineer, conservationist, and economist are vital to the success of modern government. That hardly seems debatable, but we should raise an issue or two concerning the role of the professional public bureaucrat."[16] It is now apparent that many of the nation's resource programs because of their complexity do not originate at the grass-roots level, but are recommendations made by a group of specialists who desire to initiate some positive change. What is lacking is a central governmental authority that would look at the total field of natural resources as an area of policy and subject it to vigorous analysis as a means of coordinating it with other principal areas of national policy.[17]

The Expanding Role of Private Organizations. This period also saw the beginning of more participation by private organizations in the area of resource management and development. The Conservation Foundation and Resources for the Future, evolving in 1948 and 1952, respectively, are the most active in promoting research and education in this area. The former organization is ecologically oriented, whereas the latter is the chief proponent of the economic-engineering approach to resource problems. Other conservation organizations generally represent special interest groups that are frequently guilty of associating conservation solely with their own special interest. Resources for the Future, on the other hand, has supported numerous outstanding resource studies since its inception in 1952 and tends to focus on the larger resources picture, rather than confining its interest to a narrow spectrum. The role of the private organization in the realm of resource development might be a sign of the times and partially an outgrowth of President Eisenhower's partnership policy.

CONSERVATION TODAY

In the year 1964 we find that the embryonic conservationist thought of George P. Marsh, which is now more than a century old, has reached maturity. The America of Marsh's day or even Theodore Roosevelt's day is a far cry from the America of today, with its concrete landscape, materialistic orientation, and metropolitan dominance. These changes in the nature of the landscape and in its settlement pattern have provided the necessary impetus for a reappraisal of the conservation concept and the subsequent policies and actions which are described or identified as conservational in nature.

The Technological Revolution. The problem of growing unemployment which made itself felt in the latter part of the 1950's occurring at a time when the nation's standard of living was

[16] Ross B. Talbot, "The Political Forces," Howard W. Ottoson, editor, *Land Use Problems and Policy in the United States*, Lincoln, Nebraska, 1963, pp. 149–150.

[17] Charles M. Hardin, "Can We Afford a Separate Resources Policy," Henry Jarrett, editor, *Perspectives on Conservation*, Baltimore, 1958, p. 227.

at a peak, was a bit difficult to understand. It was quite apparent, however, that this situation was not a replication of the situation which confronted Herbert Hoover or Franklin D. Roosevelt. This was an outgrowth of the technological revolution, and its associated minimizing of land as a factor of production, and its expanded emphasis on the role of capital, both physical and human in national development.

The United States emerged from World War II as the free-world leader, and therefore was forced to become more international in its outlook and perspective. The assumption of this role has made it necessary not only to provide domestic security from external threats but to meet the challenge of communism wherever it arises. Thus the technological revolution can be considered an effective scheme which would enable us to reduce our direct dependence on the land factor in order to accelerate the output of security-producing measures. This new revolution has emphasized what Nolan considers man's most important resource—knowledge.[18]

Conservation and the Kennedy Administration. By 1960 the problems produced by the technological revolution had become more pervasive. Solutions to these problems became a major political issue during the presidential campaign of 1960. The election of John F. Kennedy to the highest position in the country is frequently thought to be a reflection of his ability to project a strong personal image, an element that had been missing since the administration of Franklin D. Roosevelt. On the basis of this assumption and subsequent Kennedy involvement in attempts to eliminate the multiplicity of resource problems that confronted the nation, it might be said that a fourth phase of the conservation movement had emerged.

The most recent phase of the conservation movement is focusing special attention on man or human resources. This does not imply that natural resource problems do not exist, but it is finally being acknowledged that the existing state of conservation is influenced by the complex interaction of human, cultural, and natural

resources. In order to satisfy the traditionalist it might be necessary to expand the conservation concept to include man specifically considering that noted scholars fail to recognize directly man as an element in the resource complex. Conservation has traditionally emphasized the development and management of the land factor. It appears sanguine at this point in time to recognize conservation, at least on an operational level, as the optimum allocation of natural, human, and cultural resources in the scheme of national development, whereby maximum economic and social security will be assured.

Attempts to solve the problems of the recent era are reflected in the passage of pertinent legislative acts and the growing role of private enterprise in the arena of public responsibility.

The Area Redevelopment Act of 1961 and the man-power Redevelopment Act of 1962, are among the major instruments designed to reduce the effects of the high rate of unemployment. A number of private firms have been active similarly in promoting job retraining experiences. The proposed Youth Employment Act is an administration attempt to solve an urban problem by employing a technique which is a throwback to a former period.

Although man is now receiving increased emphasis as a means of minimizing internal friction, problems of urban living continue to mount. The demand for land for outdoor recreation, the problems of traffic congestion and slum clearance, and rehabilitation are likewise receiving much increased attention. The work of O.R.R.C. in the outdoor recreation field, increasing numbers of transportation studies, and the continued amending of the Housing Act of 1954 are evidence of attempts to relieve the nation of the problems which have emerged only recently.

Although there has been an increase in the current emphasis on man, this has in no way diminished concern for those elements that have traditionally served as the bases for economic and social development—natural resources. One of the first tasks undertaken by President Kennedy in the conservation arena was to request the National Academy of Sciences to

[18] Thomas B. Nolan, "The Inexhaustible Resource of Technology," Jarrett, *op. cit.,* pp. 49–66.

evaluate the research that had been conducted "on behalf of conservation and the development of America's natural resources." [19]

In the spirit of Theodore Roosevelt, a White House Conference on conservation was held in Washington in May 1962. Five hundred of the leading conservationist in the nation convened at the White House to draw up plans that would aid in facilitating the minimization and elimination of resource problems in some seventeen specific areas of development.

President Johnson and Conservation. The untimely death of John F. Kennedy brought to the presidency an individual who has his roots in the land. Lyndon B. Johnson, a native of the southwest, with an early rural orientation, will probably recommend a balanced conservation effort aimed at eliminating problems arising in both rural and urban settings. President Johnson's contribution in the conservation field has thus far consisted of promoting the rapid passage of legislation supported by President Kennedy. His first major successful effort was gaining passage of the anti-poverty bill. Recently he signed the wilderness bill.[20] A bill authorizing the construction of the Lower Teton Division Water Project has also been signed by the President.

OUTLOOK

The future of conservation as a problem-solving technique is indeed challenging. The former emotional connotation associated with conservation will have to be minimized in order to deal rationally with problems that have far-reaching implications for present and future national development. The time has arrived in which the ecological, ethical, and esthetic philosophies of conservation and the economic-technologic philosophies will have to be integrated in order to receive the maximum results from the works of the biological and natural sciences, and the social and behavioral sciences. The continued promotion of conservation as a separate series of special interest programs will bring about more widespread disparity among the separate parts. Therefore harmony is the key to a successful conservation program which has the interest of both present and future generations as its prime concern.

A broader view of conservation than that which has prevailed in the past is necessary, considering the growing importance of spiritual values in a materialistic oriented society. The technological revolution with its ability to eliminate or at least defer the occurrence of periods of absolute scarcity has not eliminated some of the more serious problems now confronting the nation. There is much evidence that the technological revolution has produced problems in the total resource milieu. The growing concern over stream pollution, unregulated use of insecticides and pesticides, perennial agricultural surpluses, evacuation of the central city, problems associated with increased life expectancy, and persistent unemployment in the midst of abundance can at least be partially associated with unregulated and unidirectional goals of this complex force. Thus in an era of "Big Government," "Big Business," and "Big Unions," the need for a more effective conservation program is apparent, and at the same time should be more easily instituted, providing the parts can come up with a realistic picture of the total complex.

[19] Herbert L. Schiller, "The Natural Resource Base: Where Do We Stand?," *World Politics*, Vol. XVI, July 1964, p. 669.

[20] This bill makes it possible to set aside more than nine million acres of land to be preserved in its primitive state. Fifty-four wilderness sites will be established principally in Forest Service holdings in the west.

References

Barnett, Harold J. and Chandler Morse, *Scarcity and Growth, The Economics of Natural Resource Availability*, Resources for the Future, the Johns Hopkins University Press, Baltimore, 1963.

Berkhofer, Robert F., Jr., "Space, Time, Culture and the New Frontier," *Agricultural History*, Vol. 38, 1964, pp. 21–30.

Billington, Ray Allen, *The Far Western Frontier, 1830–1860,* Harper and Row, New York, 1962.

Carstensen, Vernon R., editor, *The Public Domain,* University of Wisconsin Press, Madison, Wisconsin, 1962.

Duncan, Craig, "Resource Utilization and the Conservation Concept," *Economic Geography,* Vol. 38, 1962, pp. 113–121.

Ekirch, Arthur A., Jr., *Man and Nature in America,* Columbia University Press, New York, 1963.

Hawkes, H. Bowman, "The Paradoxes of the Conservation Movement," *Bulletin of the University of Utah,* Vol. 51, 1960.

Hays, Samuel P., *Conservation and the Gospel of Efficiency,* Harvard University Press, Cambridge, Massachusetts, 1959.

Jarrett, Henry, editor, *Perspectives on Conservation,* Resources for the Future, The Johns Hopkins Press, Baltimore, 1958.

Landsberg, Hans H., Leonard L. Fischman, and Joseph L. Fisher, *Resources in America's Future: Patterns of Requirements and Availabilities, 1960–2000,* Resources for the Future, The Johns Hopkins Press, Baltimore, 1963.

Noggle, Burl, *Teapot Dome: Oil and Politic in the 1920's,* Louisiana State University Press, Baton Rouge, Louisiana, 1962.

Ottoson, Howard W., *Land Use Policy and Problems in the United States,* University of Nebraska Press, Lincoln, Nebraska, 1963.

Potter, David M., *People of Plenty,* University of Chicago Press, Chicago, 1954.

Swain, Donald C., *Federal Conservation Policy 1921–1933* (University of California Publications in History, Vol. 76), University of California Press, Berkeley, California, 1963.

Udall, Stewart L., *The Quiet Crisis,* Holt, Rhinehart and Winston, New York, 1963.

STEPHEN S. VISHER

Indiana University

CHAPTER 2

The Public Domain

The term "public domain" as here used applies to the land owned by the federal government, or formerly belonging to the people as a whole.

Acquisition of Areas. Shortly after the adoption of the Constitution, the thirteen original states ceded to the federal government all or nearly all of their claims to land beyond their borders. Thus the public domain soon consisted of most of the land between the original states and the Mississippi River, except Kentucky, Vermont, and parts of Tennessee and Ohio. Other vast areas were acquired (1) by the Louisiana Purchase, (2) from Mexico, (3) by the Oregon Compromise, and (4) by the purchase of Alaska. Smaller areas were purchased from Spain, Texas, and Mexico.

Figure 1 summarizes broadly the chief additions to the public domain. It reveals that, of the total land acquired, that ceded by the original states comprised nearly one-sixth, the Louisiana Purchase and Alaska each about one-fourth, the land acquired directly from Mexico about one-fifth, and the Oregon Compromise about one-tenth. The land purchased from Texas (to the north of that state's present boundary) made up 4 percent, the purchase of Florida added about 2 percent to the total public do-

main, and land purchased from Mexico added approximately 1 percent.

These lands were purchased very cheaply. The Louisiana Purchase cost about 6.5 cents an acre; Florida, 20 cents; the tract purchased from Texas, 21 cents; the Gadsden Purchase, acquired from Mexico, 68 cents; and Alaska, about 2 cents an acre.

Disposal of Areas. THEIR TYPES AND GENERAL DISTRIBUTION. Slightly more than a billion acres have become private or state property. This is about three-fifths of the approximately 1,800,000,000 acres (almost 3,300,000 square miles) which at one time or another were owned by the federal government. About half of the remaining two-fifths is in Alaska.

The chief methods of disposal of the land are summarized in Fig. 2, which reveals that about 41 percent of the alienated land was sold; about 27 percent was disposed of under the homestead laws; about 19 percent was granted to the states in aid of education or for other purposes; and 13 percent was granted in aid of the railroads, most of which was given directly to railway corporations.

The land sold, except under the Timber and Stone Act (1878), was located largely east of

15

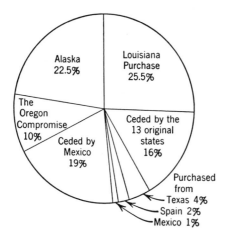

Fig. 1   Sources, percentages.

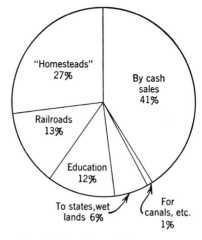

Fig. 2   How disposed of, percentages.

The Public Domain

the Mississippi River or in Iowa, Missouri, and Arkansas. The land sold under the Timber and Stone Act was, however, largely fine timber tracts of the Pacific states or northern Idaho and Minnesota.

Since the first homestead law was not passed until 1862, most of the more accessible land had already been disposed of by sale or grant. The land disposed of under the various homestead laws was therefore mostly in the second and third tiers of states west of the Mississippi River. Almost no land was homesteaded in Ohio, Indiana, Illinois, or Iowa, and none in Kentucky, Tennessee, or Texas. Under the several Desert Acts, which were modified homestead laws, nearly 2,000,000 acres were disposed of in Montana, nearly half as many in Wyoming, and about a fourth to a third as many in Colorado, California, and Utah, with small acreages in the other western states.

The land granted to the states in aid of education was distributed throughout the former public domain, with, however, larger acreages in the less fortunate states. The amount, Alaska being excepted, totaled about 120,000,000 acres, nearly 200,000 square miles, an area nearly four times as large as New England. During the earlier decades of the nineteenth century only one section (640 acres) of each

township was reserved for schools. After 1848, however, two sections to the township were set aside. In 1850 four sections (2, 16, 32, and 36) were reserved for the schools of New Mexico and Utah. In 1864 the same provisions were made for Arizona. Moreover, liberal grants for institutions of higher learning were made after 1852. For example, "agricultural college scrip" (certificates entitling the holder to specified acreages of public land) totaled 8,000,000 acres, a tract about one-fourth as large as Pennsylvania. In addition, about 5,000,000 acres were given to state universities. The educational grants to New Mexico were greater than those to any other state, and totaled 9,600,000 acres, an area nearly half as large as Indiana. The next in declining order are Arizona, Utah, California, and Montana. Twelve other states in the Middle West and West received about 3,000,000 acres each, and twelve others received from 1,000,000 to 2,000,000 acres. All the remaining states received smaller grants, mostly in the form of scrip, chiefly in support of their agricultural colleges.

The land granted to the states for canals was mostly in Indiana, Ohio, and Michigan; grants for river improvement were largely in Iowa, Alabama, and Wisconsin; Oregon received 2,500,000 acres for roads, and Indiana and Ohio received small grants. The total grants to the states for canals, roads, and river improvement were about 10,000,000 acres, an area almost half as large as Ohio. In addition, almost 65,000,000 acres of land classed as "swamp and overflowed land" were ceded to fourteen states. Florida received most, about 20,000,000 acres; Arkansas and Louisiana each received about 8,000,000 acres (roughly one-fourth of these states); and Michigan, Minnesota, Wisconsin, Missouri, and Mississippi each got from 3,000,000 to 6,000,000 acres. Illinois, Iowa, Indiana, and California were each granted 1,000,000 to 2,000,000 acres, and Oregon and Alabama were granted small acreages. A considerable share of the proceeds from the sale of this "swamp land" (much of it well-forested) was added by the states to their endowment for public schools.

The grants in aid of railroads, totaling 38,000,000 acres (60,000 square miles or an area almost as large as New England), were also made chiefly to the states bordering the Mississippi River. However, a few other states, Michigan, Kansas, Alabama, and Florida, each received between 2,000,000 and 5,000,000 acres. Minnesota received most, 8,000,000 acres.

The grants to the railroad corporations, totaling 94,000,000 acres (an area almost as large as the East North Central states), were made in the Rocky Mountain and Pacific states and in North Dakota, Nebraska, and Kansas. Two-fifths went to the Northern Pacific Railway, one-fourth to the Union Pacific, about one-seventh to the Southern Pacific, and nearly as much to the Santa Fe. Because of the large grants to the Northern Pacific Railway, the states through which this line chiefly extends, Montana, North Dakota, and Washington, contained the largest acreages of railroad grants, from 6,000,000 to 9,000,000 acres each. Nebraska, Kansas, and California each had about 5,000,000 acres.

Remaining Public Land. TYPES AND DISTRIBUTION. The public domain of the mid-1960's consists of three main types. (1) Land reserved for specific purposes and presumably to be held permanently for such uses. The chief of these is the national forests; smaller areas comprise the national parks and national monuments. (2) The Indian reservations. (3) The lands which were withdrawn (1934–1936) pending classification and further consideration of what should be done with them. This type (nearly all of it arid or semiarid) includes land usually classed as "unappropriated public land." All three of these principal types of public land are located chiefly in the Rocky Mountain and Pacific states, and in Alaska (Figs. 3 and 4).

Of the Indian lands, the largest areas in 1962 (millions of acres) are in Arizona, 19.4; New Mexico, 6.6; Montana, 5.4; South Dakota, 5.0; Washington, 2.6; Utah, 2.1; Wyoming, 1.9; Oklahoma, 1.7; Nevada, 1.2; Idaho, 0.8; Colorado, 0.7; Minnesota, 0.7; Oregon, 0.7; California, 0.6; North Dakota, 0.4.

A fourth type of public land, at present minor but likely to increase notably, consists chiefly of submarginal tracts formerly privately owned which have been purchased by the federal government to "withdraw them from agriculture," and for reforestation, range control, soil conservation, watershed protection, and wild animal refuges. Many areas of excellent land were acquired for military purposes in 1941–1945; vast expanses of former public domain were closed to entry during the same period and used for proving grounds, bombing ranges, and other military purposes.

Many tracts which had been patented became tax delinquent. These areas have become the properties of the local political subdivisions (the counties and states). Part of this land has been re-ceded to the federal government. Small increases in the public domain are the result of gifts of land, mostly to be incorporated into national parks.

Types of Land Involved. The public domain has included almost all the various types of land in America. Choice agricultural land was well represented; forest land included most of the fine forests of the Middle West as well as the superb Pacific forests; mineral lands included most of the metals of the Far West, iron and copper of the Lake Superior region and also the

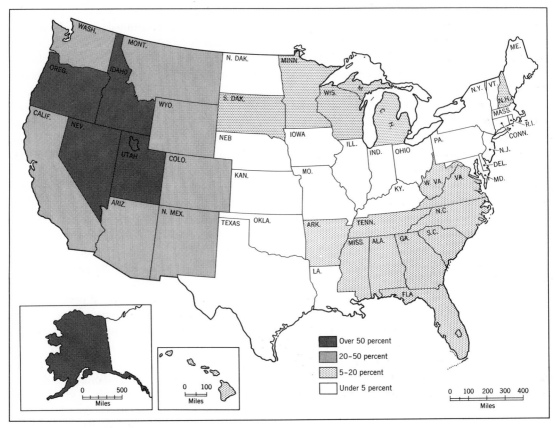

Fig. 3   **Percent of the total area of each state in federal ownership June 30, 1962.** (*Statistical Abstract of the United States*, 1963.)

coal and oil fields of the Interior and the West and Alaska. Grazing lands have been widely represented ever since the acquisition of the Louisiana Purchase, which included much of the Great Plains. The better agricultural, forest, and mineral lands passed out of federal ownership first. Since about 1900 most of the fairly accessible public domain has been grazing land, less valuable forest land, including cut-over and burned-over areas, and wasteland.

CHANGES IN THE POPULAR ATTITUDE TOWARD PUBLIC LANDS

At a time when the seriousness of the problems facing the American people is being widely though vaguely realized, it is desirable to con-

sider what should be the program conerning the remaining public domain. A preliminary step may properly be a survey of the chief historic changes in opinion as to various types of land.

The popular attitude toward the public domain has varied as a result of five chief influences: (1) the growth of population; (2) the spread of the people made possible partly by improvements in transportation; (3) the conspicuous consequences of the exploitation of the land, especially deforestation, depletion of minerals and game animals, and, more recently, the striking effects of soil erosion; and (4) the growing realization that natural resources are limited in amount and many are being used up rapidly. (5) A fifth influence is the growing sense of responsibility concerning the welfare of the people of the future.

Programs concerning the American public domain have varied widely with changes in the popular interest in agriculture, forests, minerals, and outdoor recreation, and with concern for the distant future. Wild land was long considered to have little value. For example, Franklin was criticized by many prominent citizens for extending the national boundary as far west as the Mississippi River when he negotiated the treaty at the close of the Revolutionary War. Similarly, Jefferson's purchase of the Louisiana Territory was widely condemned, and Seward's purchase of Alaska was often called "sheer folly."

Similarly, trees were long inadequately appreciated. The man who cleared the most land was the popular hero, and he who did not completely clear his land was called lazy. The statement, made by those less blind than their fellows, that there would soon be a timber shortage was widely ridiculed. President Harrison was the first president who felt strongly enough the necessity of forest conservation to carve forest reserves out of the public domain (1892). Not until Theodore Roosevelt's terms (1901–1909), however, were large tracts reserved. He withdrew nearly 150,000,000 acres, in contrast to a total of about 45,000,000 acres withdrawn by all his predecessors. He included in national forests substantially all the forest lands then remaining in public ownership. Franklin D. Roosevelt (1933) was the first president to encourage effectively extensive reforestation by means of the Civilian Conservation Corps.

Minerals, too, except gold and silver, meant little to most Americans until after 1850. As a result, except for the reservations by Theodore Roosevelt, little mineral wealth of present value has been retained by the public.

Agriculture was the predominant source of livelihood of Americans until the 1920's. As late as 1880 two-thirds of the people lived on farms. Consequently, the public land was generally evaluated in terms of its agricultural utility. The population spread westward year by year, creat-

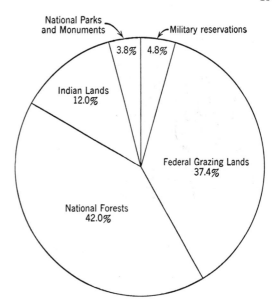

Fig. 4 Land in federal ownership in continental United States, 1962, distributed among the categories shown above. Grazing extends onto many suitable pasture areas in the national forests. Federal grazing lands include approximately 44 percent of the area in federal ownership, a total of 141,912,000 acres in 1962 were in "grazing districts." (*Statistical Abstract of the United States, 1963.*)

ing tens of thousands of new farms and pushing back the frontier. Nevertheless several great westward surges were prominent. The first of these followed the Revolutionary War, when the better lands of Kentucky and Tennessee were occupied. From 1810 to 1850, during the steamboat and canal period, the large families of the first frontier generations, supplemented by many migrants from the area from Pennsylvania to the Carolinas, crossed the Ohio and Mississippi rivers in large numbers. A third great surge into the public domain invovled many people from New England and New York. It followed the completion of the Erie Canal (1825), the establishment of Great Lakes navigation, and the early railroad extension, to 1861. This wave was the first to spread over the prairies. After the Civil War there was a fourth great westward movement, facilitated by the railroads and encouraged by the free homesteads offered by the homestead law. From 1870 to 1886 hundreds of thousands of people, mostly descendants of pioneers or immigrants, moved into the prairie plains and eastern Great Plains. The dry years of the late 1880's and early 1890's checked the spread; indeed, many Great Plains countries were almost depopulated. But, starting about 1900, a series of wetter years, the enactment of legal provisions for enlarged homesteads, and the development of various inventions helpful to farmers led to another great increase in the interest in new farms.

Ten million acres of homesteads were "patented" in 1910—an area twice as large as New Jersey. Dry years, beginning in 1910, checked the spread, but the high prices for agricultural products associated with World War I again greatly increased popular interest in agriculture; but since the land capable of adequately supporting a family on a half-section was "gone," the homestead unit was increased to 640 acres in 1916 for "stockraising" land. Almost a frenzy of filing on land followed, partly because military service reduced the residence requirements for homesteading. The collapse of farm prices after the close of the war chilled the popular enthusiasm for farming, and the droughts and low prices for farm products during 1930–1936 put an end to the frenzied interest in homesteading. Moreover, in November, 1934, and February, 1935, all the remaining unreserved and unappropriated land was withdrawn by executive order.

CHANGES IN THE OFFICIAL ATTITUDE TOWARD PUBLIC LANDS

The popular attitude toward the public domain, just sketched, influenced profoundly the official attitude. Nevertheless the opinions of governmental officials had sufficient independent influence so that a sketch of changes is desirable.

George Washington bought and sold unoccupied lands in New York, Virginia, Pennsylvania, and Kentucky to good effect. Many later government officials likewise considered that

the unoccupied lands provided opportunities for personal gain.

Alexander Hamilton and numerous other financiers of the early years thought of the public lands as potential sources of federal revenue. Many state officials were also interested in having their states receive grants of lands for both the foregoing reasons. Most of the vast tracts granted to states were sold promptly, often to members of the legislature or their friends, many of whom resold at large profits. The funds obtained by the states were used partly to reduce the immediate tax burdens.

Allied to the concept that the sale of public land should help support the government was the realization that such lands could help supply desirable improvements. The first important utilization of public land for this purpose was in 1803, when Ohio was admitted as a state. One full section of each township was set aside toward support of public schools. Other tracts were given, during the early decades of the nineteenth century, to aid in canal and road construction. Before long increases in the grants for schools were made and also grants for colleges. When many railroads were projected into sparsely settled or vacant regions, 1865–1885, vast areas were granted to assist in their construction.

A similar use of public lands was the granting of scrip for 65,000,000 acres as partial compensation for military services. This scrip, which in many instances was sold, may be compared with the bonus payments after World War I.

The sales of public land, however, yielded only relatively small sums—only $60,000,000 during the first half century of the nation's history and approximately $160,000,000 during the second half century, and a total to 1946 of about $250,000,000. This, to be sure, is three times as much as was paid for the land purchased from France, Spain, Mexico, Texas, and Russia. Indeed, a competent authority has concluded that most of the land sold by the federal government yielded only a small fraction of what it was then worth (that is, readily salable for). Almost none of it, even the choicest timber-lands, brought more than $2.50 an acre. All the land sold during 160 years yielded less revenue to the federal government than the taxes on tobacco yield in an average month now.

Similarly, the grants in aid of internal improvements, although locally and immediately helpful, nevertheless yielded disappointing results in many ways. For example, the 350,000 acres granted to Wisconsin in aid of the state university actually yielded less than $600,000. This is much less than one-fortieth of the sum it has received annually in recent years from taxes.

The strong individualism encouraged by frontier life and the conspicuous emphasis placed on real estate, partly as a result of the fact that for generations it was readily possible for any ambitious person to own land, also strengthened the conviction that private ownership was better than public ownership. The fact that public land yielded no local taxes and supported almost no population increased the strong local desire to have all public land pass into private ownership.

The desire for the alienation of public land grew until it became a firm conviction of most of the influential people in America. Numerous steps were taken to facilitate the disposal of public land, and little was done to retard its disposal. An example of this attitude is the fact that when land was sold it was almost always disposed of at the minimum price set by law, regardless of its true value. Likewise, for homesteading, the requirements were the minimum legal conditions in respect to residence and improvements, little concern being shown whether or not the man receiving the title was a bona fide settler or merely the dummy of some grasping corporation or individual.

The demand for decentralization of government and for state control tended to bring about extensive gifts of public land to the states for no specified purpose. The feeling was that the states could dispose of certain public lands to better advantage than the more remote federal government. The gift of 65,000,000 acres of "swampland" to the states in 1850 was an example of this policy.

The several homestead laws with their increasingly generous provisions reflect this popular desire to dispose of the public domain. When the famous homestead law, sponsored by Lincoln, was passed in 1862, the unit was 160 acres; nevertheless settlers were soon permitted to obtain also a "pre-emption" of another 160 acres. From 1873 to 1891 in states then being rapidly settled, a "tree claim" was also possible, giving a possible total of 480 acres. The repeal, because of graft, of the pre-emption and tree claim acts, in 1891, was offset in a way by increases in the homestead unit itself. This was increased to 320 acres for "desert" land in 1877 and for "dry farming" land in 1910; it was still increased further to 640 acres for all land classified as "stock-raising homesteads" in 1916. An earlier act, in 1904, provided for 640-acre homesteads in the "sand-hill country" of Nebraska.

The successive liberalizing of the homestead laws was in accord with the prevailing idea that the public domain ought to be given to bona fide settlers who would make a permanent home on the homestead. That larger acreage of poorer than of good land are required in order to yield a livelihood should have been obvious, but it was largely ignored until seen that few of the homesteads of the poorer agricultural land continued to be the homes of people.

The policy of the disposal of the public domain almost led to the gift to the states in 1931 of all remaining public land. Fortunately, however, there were enough congressmen whose states would have received no such gifts of land to prevent this. However, at almost every session of Congress, efforts are made to have some land now reserved made available for exploitation by lumbermen, cattlemen, miners, or others who are seeking additional personal wealth.

After nearly a century during which prompt disposal was the aim, some public land was finally set aside for permanent federal ownership. The establishment of Yellowstone National Park in 1872 was a momentous event in the history of our public domain and an example to other forward-looking countries. Since then nearly 200 national parks, monuments, and reserves have been created, mostly from the remaining public domain (177 by 1950, 187 by 1963). Notable was the establishment in 1963 of the first three national seashore recreational areas (Several additional sea- or lakeshore recreational areas are being actively proposed).

The establishment of the national forests, commencing in 1892 but most extensive in 1901–1909, was even more important in limiting the alienation of public land.

Another phase of retaining part of the domain for the public was the reservation of various mineral and other rights. President Theodore Roosevelt in 1906–1909 withdrew from entry 80,000,000 acres of possible mineral lands pending their classification. Those found to have valuable minerals have been retained entirely, or the mineral rights at least have been retained to be exploited only under government control on a leasing system. Possible water-power sites were similarly withdrawn in the Pacific states and Alaska.

The alienation of public land has apparently almost run its course. In 1910 more than 10,000,000 acres were transferred to private ownership From 1913 to 1922, inclusive, an average of about 8,000,000 acres a year were patented. Likewise the sale of public land has declined to small proportions, yielding less than $1,000,000 a year since 1921, in contrast to about $2,000,000 a year between 1913 and 1920, and $5,000,000 a year from 1900 to 1912, and about $8,000,000 a year during the 1880's.

The public domain, instead of being disposed of, is now being added to by purchase, tax delinquency, and gift. Moreover, there is much serious official discussion of the desirability of purchase by the federal government of many millions of acres of submarginal lands, especially in the more rugged, sandy, or rocky areas, formerly forested, and in the semiarid Great Plains. A significant advantage expected from govern-

ment ownership of submarginal lands is reduced necessary payments for relief and subsidies for schools and roads in such areas. The removal of the occupants to land on which they could be self-supporting would lighten the tax burden for the rest of the nation. In 1961 nearly 2800 areas, totaling 5,800,000 acres, belonged to state parks. About 2.5 million acres of public land was disposed of in 1962. A considerable part was small tracts located within state forests and state parks. Such gifts of land to the states have been distinctly popular with politicians and various other people.

A recently developed method of disposing of parts of the public domain is for "recreation and public purposes." Under the "Code of Federal Regulations as revised in 1963" it is possible for cities to obtain even sizable tracts of public domain for use as a park. For example, Phoenix, Arizona, has thus obtained "the largest municipal park in the world" (15,000 acres), and many other cities have obtained attractive areas at $2.50 per acre. Some of these recreation areas are far from cities and are sold under specified conditions to groups such as Boy Scout troops, church groups, or organizations especially interested in some recreational activity such as golf, skiing, or boating.

Some Ways in Which the Spirit of the Homestead Laws Was Violated. The several homestead laws were presumed to enable settlers to carve permanent homes out of the public domain. However, a large share of all homesteaded land did not provide a home for settlers. Indeed, in large tracts of the former public domain few settlers continued to reside on the land after receiving title to it. The spirit of the homestead laws was violated in five chief ways. (1) Timber land was homesteaded with no intention of making a permanent home, but merely to sell promptly to some lumber company. (2) Similarly, in the semiarid and arid states, many tracts were homesteaded because of the water on them. As soon as title was obtained, the land was sold to stockmen who could, by owning the available water supplies, monopolize large tracts of public grazing land. Often such homesteading of watering places was done by employees of livestock owners. (3) Although each individual's homestead rights were strictly limited by law, only one homestead being legal, nevertheless many individuals, moving from one land district to another, obtained more free land than they were entitled to, sometimes under assumed names. (4) Homesteading was done by dummies. Federal inspectors, during the rush of homesteading, often could not know that the man who swore that he had made the required improvement, resided on the land, etc., was not the person whose name appeared in the application and subsequently in the deed. Thus a man might "prove up" on a succession of claims, whose deeds he turned over to another person for a fee. (5) The least reprehensible method by which the spirit of the homestead laws was violated was the selling of the homestead, which by itself was inadequate to support a family, to some adjoining settler who needed it to supplement his own too limited holdings. In semiarid regions, several hundred acres are required, on the average, to support a family.

Public Ownership of Minerals under Water. The public ownership of navigable rivers and lakes has long been recognized, but only in recent decades has the problem of the ownership of the minerals beneath such inland waters or under coastal waters been the subject of much discussion. The state's claim to coal, gravel, and oil under rivers that form boundaries as well as those officially declared navigable was first established in Indiana in 1919. Subsequently, many other states have also received substantial sums paid in royalties for gravel and other minerals recovered by permit from under their rivers. When valuable amounts of petroleum were found under some coastal waters, they were similarly claimed by the states. However, after World War II the claim of the federal government to the oil under coastal waters was disputed by Louisiana, Texas, and California. The passage of the Submerged Lands Act of 1953 recognized the claims of these states to the petroleum resources that lie beneath the sea to a distance of 3 miles offshore. Beyond this limit the federal government retains jurisdiction.

SUMMARY

One of the most favored 2,000,000 square miles of the entire earth was spread out before the pioneers who crossed the Appalachians in 1790. The land certainly awaited settlers, and the public policy soon became the encouragement of settlement in almost every possible way. Land was sold cheaply, and vast areas were donated to the states and to corporations. By 1860 most of the better accessible agricultural land had passed into private ownership. Then, to encourage settlement further, homesteads were given free, with the result that by 1890 the frontier was officially declared gone. Nevertheless, the rapidly increasing, land-hungry people pushed on into the poorer lands until by 1920 there remained almost no public land capable of supporting an American family on even three times the original homestead unit. Except in the ephemeral Indian reservations, settlement and exploitation were almost unimpeded as long as fair agricultural land remained. But from 1892 to 1909 vast nonagricultural areas were reserved for national forests, parks, and monuments, and smaller areas more recently. Practically all alienation was stopped in 1935, and a reversal of policy was undertaken—the purchase of lands, largely submarginal, for addition to the reserved public domain.

References

American Forests (American Forestry Association, Washington, D.C.). This magazine has for 70 years published numerous articles dealing with forests.
Bennett, Hugh H., "Adjustment of Agriculture to Its Environment," *Annals of the Association of American Geographers*, Vol. 33, 1943, pp. 163–198. This presidential address

contains considerable of interest to users of this book, as does the same author's *Elements of Soil Conservation*, McGraw-Hill Book Co., New York, 1947, 1955.

Bowman, Isaiah, "The Land of Your Possession," *Science*, Vol. 82, 1935, pp. 285–293.

Brown, Ralph H., *Historical Geography of the United States*, Harcourt, Brace, New York, 1948.

Carstensen, Vernon, editor, *The Public Lands, Studies in the History of the Public Domain* (60 articles). University of Wisconsin Press, Madison, Wisconsin, 1962 (522 pp.).

Clawson, Marion, and R. Burnell Held, *The Federal Lands: Their Use and Management*, Resources for the Future, Johns Hopkins Press, Baltimore, 1957.

Coyle, David Cushman, *Conservation, An American Story of Conflict and Accomplishment*, Rutgers University Press, New Brunswick, New Jersey, 1957.

De Voto, Bernard, "Sacred Cows and Public Lands," *Harper's Magazine*, Vol. 196, 1948, pp. 44–55.

General Land Office, *Reports of the Commissioner*, Washington, D.C. Annual.

Hibbard, B. H., *A History of the Public Land Policies*, The Macmillan Co., New York, 1924, 1939.

Landstrom, Karl S., "Growth and the Public Lands," *A Place to Live*, The Yearbook of Agriculture, 1963, Government Printing Office, Washington, D.C.

Paullin, C. O., and John K. Wright, *Atlas of Historical Geography of the United States*, Carnegie Institution and the American Geographical Society, New York, 1932.

Peffer, E. Louise, *The Closing of the Public Domain: Disposal and Reservation Policies, 1900–1950*, Stanford University Press, Stanford, California, 1951.

Robbins, Roy M., *Our Landed Heritage, The Public Domain 1776–1936*, Princeton University Press, 1942; University of Nebraska Press, Lincoln, Nebraska, 1962 (450 pp.).

Taylor, E. H., "Our Changing Land Policy," *Journal of Soil and Water Conservation*, Vol. 3, 1948, pp. 5–12. This journal contains in almost every issue significant articles on aspects of conservation.

The Living Wilderness. This quarterly, published in Washington, D.C., by the Wilderness Society, presents much of interest especially concerning the wilder areas.

U.S. Census Bureau, *Statistical Atlas*, 1903, 1914, 1924, and *Statistical Abstract*. Annual, Washington, D.C.

U.S. Dept. of Interior, *Community Recreation and the Public Domain*, Washington, D.C., May, 1963 (40 pp.).

Velie, Lester, "The Great Western Land Grab," *Reader's Digest*, Vol. 51, 1947, pp. 109–113.

HAROLD H. McCARTY
The State University of Iowa

CHAPTER 3

Economics and Conservation

The student of conservation soon learns that the subject or concept has been of interest to a great variety of people. He finds it appearing very often in the literature of geography, political science, sociology, and economics, as well as in the writings of the various physical sciences dealing with the earth and its resources. One of the first of these disciplines to become concerned with the problems of conservation was the science of economics. Over a period of almost two centuries writers in the field of economics and political economy have been concerned with problems involving the depletion, the disappearance, or the wise use of man's resources.

Emphasis on the economic aspects of the conservation problem has been especially strong in the United States and in the other countries of the world that have been devoted traditionally to free-enterprise types of economic systems. In these countries the tendency to view the conservation problem as essentially one of managing resources in order to produce a maximum of satisfaction of human wants has frequently been very strong. Not only have the average citizen and public official commonly expressed the problem in economic terms, but

they have also tended to advocate the use of economic measures to bring about those reforms that they consider most important.

Wants and Resources. The student of economics takes, as one of his special problems, the apparently endless conflict between unlimited human wants and the limited means of satisfying them. To him, indeed, the economic drama seems to revolve around this conflict. On the one hand, the economist looks at human nature and discovers that man's effort to satisfy his wants never ends—that as soon as he satisfies one batch of wants, he immediately conjures up a whole set of new ones. Under these circumstances it soon becomes obvious that the means of satisfying those wants can never be adequate. A man's effort will always be directed toward acquiring more and more resources that can be converted into means of want satisfaction. Thus it appears that any organized society must give primary consideration to the manner in which its resources shall be allocated among its people.

Human wants in themselves are not difficult to identify. The economist defines them in much the same way as we do, in such a way as to include all kinds of expressions of desire. Complications begin to appear, however, just as soon as

25

we try to rank these wants, whether they are individual wants, group wants, or wants of the future. A great deal of the science of economics is devoted to the problems of measuring the intensity of individual wants and trying to discover the extent to which the wants of groups of people agree with, or differ from, those of the individual members of those groups. These computations become especially difficult when the economist attempts to project them into the future. It is a well-known fact that wants vary from time to time, as well as from person to person. But it also seems obvious that resources become valuable only to the extent that they are wanted; the entire conservation effort therefore rests on a projection of patterns of human wants into the future.

Early Economic Thought; the Scarcity Principle. The economist, whose central concern is with the manner in which limited means of satisfaction are allocated to the virtually unlimited quantity of human wants, has long been interested in the conservation problem. Among the very early classical economists, such as Thomas Malthus and David Ricardo, the problem was envisioned essentially as a conflict between a continuous expansion of basic human wants, as evidenced by a rapidly growing world population and a strictly static supply of natural resources that could be used in satisfying them.[1] Specifically, their concern was centered in the simple problem of obtaining enough food, clothing, and shelter to satisfy those growing human needs. As a result, their major emphasis was on the available supply of land, and their thinking was in terms of its capacity to produce food, fibers, fuel, forest products, minerals, and related goods required by man to satisfy his basic needs.

To attack these problems, early economists found it necessary to simplify their analyses by introducing certain basic assumptions as to the nature of the phenomena. One of these assumptions, that basic human needs will continue to

[1] An excellent review of the development of economic thought in these matters appears in Harold J. Barnett and Chandler Morse, *Scarcity and Growth*, Baltimore, 1963, Chapters 2 and 3.

expand as population increases, has already been specified. The other assumption, that the fund of resources that may be used to satisfy those needs is specifically limited, merits further examination.

In particular, the limited resources concept is based on the assumption that man's ultimate source of livelihood is the physical earth. The earth can provide only a limited quantity of the items, such as minerals, rainfall, and the components of soil fertility, that can be used to provide those sources of livelihood. When those stocks are exhausted, as in nonrenewable resources such as minerals, man is simply going to be deprived of goods and services whose production depends on their use. Or, in renewable resources, such as the sunshine and rain employed in agriculture, deprivation will begin whenever annual increments are exceeded by human demands. Little wonder that speculations based on these assumptions led people of that day to refer to economics as the "dismal science."

The mechanisms by which these scarcities were to be brought about are worthy of comment. Thomas Malthus, who was among the first to develop and popularize the scarcity concept, felt that man would go ahead willy-nilly, utilizing available land until one day, perhaps rather suddenly, he would come to the end of that conquest and would be faced with the necessity of reducing per capita food and clothing inputs for his growing numbers. And, since Malthus saw no way of halting the then-existing "population explosion," the ultimate consequences to the human population certainly appeared to be disastrous.

The Malthus thesis achieved widespread acceptance among both economists and laymen, although it was modified considerably by later writers. David Ricardo, in particular, who appeared to have somewhat greater confidence in man's perspicacity, felt that the day of ultimate diminishing returns would be foreseen and that there would be a gradual, rather than a sudden, downward adjustment of levels of living that would be spread over a considerable period of time. John Stuart Mill modified further the hypothesis by introducing the notion that man might substitute one form of satisfaction for another and thus alter considerably the process of adjustment to the foreseen condition of scarcity.

In all these speculations of the classical economists, however, there was no provision for the admission of changes in technology or in the general institutional organization of society into the hypothesis. In other words, their world was essentially a world of unchanging patterns of demand and unchanging human abilities to utilize resources more effectively to satisfy those demands. Under those circumstances, a state of diminishing returns, in which man would continue to receive less and less in return for his efforts to satisfy his wants, was inevitable.

Early American Experience. The village economies of Colonial New England had a relatively simple way of handling the wants-resources problem. Members of these communities earned money and spent it bidding against each other for the limited supplies of available goods and services. In such a free-enterprise economy the allocation of resources to individuals was accomplished through the pricing system. Thus it could be assumed that those who had more intense desires for particular resources would gain possession of them simply because they were willing to part with more purchasing power in order to get them. Money was rather evenly distributed among members of these Colonial communities, so that one member had about as much ability to command resources as another, and each one had an opportunity to obtain the goods and services he wanted most.

Despite these early circumstances, however, the pioneer economies did not always produce socially desirable ends. Resource allocation became especially unwieldy in the later years of this period, when some people obtained possession of more purchasing power than others and were willing to use that purchasing power to gain possession of resources. Often these persons used the resources in ways that were felt to be detrimental to the welfare of the group.

And so it came about, in the very early considerations of economic welfare, that restrictions were placed on many of the practices by which resources were utilized (Fig. 1).

Early attitudes concerning the wise use of resources are vividly portrayed in the notions that the Puritans and many of the later pioneers had about "saving for a rainy day." The pioneer family, faced with the rigors of the life on the frontier, quickly learned to avoid waste because daily living was so difficult. Saving was a virtue that was nurtured assiduously. Members of the family who did not use resources wisely were chastised, and these virtues became deeply ingrained into the mores of the American people. It is easy to see how such notions were transplanted into the national culture.

Who was to decide just what kinds of acts would endanger the "welfare" of the group? In the small communities of Colonial New England these questions were easily answered. The groups themselves were small, needs were easily apparent to all members, and consensus concerning the group welfare was quickly obtained. By the same token, the organized group, in town meetings or in other ways, could very easily impose penalties or take other steps to insure conformance by individual members. The idea of husbanding resources for the long, cold winter that was sure to come was readily incorporated into the cultural heritage of the American people.

Social Evolution. We can see in these early attitudes some of the ingredients from which the later conservation movement was made. The movement appeared slowly because there was little realization until near the end of the nineteenth century that unwise use might endanger the future social welfare. Growth and territorial expansion had occupied the energies of the American people, and the rapidly expanding frontier society rarely gave much thought to the future of its resources. These conditions persisted for several generations, but by the decade of the 1890's it had become apparent to many that the conditions of life had changed enormously. The American people still believed in

Fig. 1   Three combines harvesting and threshing the grain in a single operation. In the western Great Plains where extensive grain farming is characteristic of the agricultural economy mechanization has reduced the labor force substantially. Restrictions on wheat production are a feature of current agricultural practices. (Deere and Company.)

thrift and hard work, and they also retained their faith in a price-directed economy. But they began to see that preservation of the public welfare was going to require both a more precise definition of the conservation problem and a program of positive measures. It had become evident that wants were both individual and social.

Individual and Social Wants. Economics, which had long recognized the dual nature of these wants, found it easy to incorporate the more social of the human wants into its analyses of the wants-resources problem. Soon it became common for economists to include in their computations items such as the need for protection from one's enemies and the desire that one's children and grandchildren have enough food and clothing. Wants, said the economist, are not just the day-to-day items that arise out of

ordinary biological needs; they also include a wide variety of items that are more properly related to the social welfare.

The end of the nineteenth century also brought a considerable increase in the number of questions concerning whether the process by which an individual tries to satisfy his own wants necessarily produces a maximum of satisfaction for all the people. There was an increasing tendency to doubt the wisdom of permitting the man with the most money to acquire the most resources. Great attention came to be devoted to questions of how to regulate the acquiring of resources in such ways as to promote the general public welfare. In this situation, the economist became a particularly valuable adviser because he was able to bring all the considerations together and evaluate them in terms of their monetary cost. Thus it occurred that the economic aspects of conservation were brought before the American people at a relatively early date.

Benefits and Costs. In our exploration of the economic aspects of conservation, we should remind ourselves that much of the content of economic analysis consists of a comparison of inputs and outputs. We have traced some of the early developments that underlie the complex pattern of wants which the economist can consider as defining a certain set of goals. We shall soon find it desirable to examine those want patterns in greater detail, but in the meantime let us pause long enough to remind ourselves that the identification of goals is only part of the

economist's task—he is equally concerned with the costs of attaining those goals. In conservation, as in other social affairs, the economist does not tell us what we should want, but he can tell us how much it will cost. He must, however, know what we want before he can tell us how much it will cost and what benefits may be expected (Fig. 2).

Changing Wants. The twentieth century has witnessed many changes in human wants. By 1900, the danger of starvation was no longer a serious threat to the American people. Mechanization had brought tremendous increases in farm productivity, and improvements in transportation had made foods and related products

Fig. 2 An aerial view of the docks at Beaumont, Texas, showing the facilities for loading sulfur, some of it molten, into cargo boats for coastwise commerce and into barges destined for movement along the Intracoastal Canal and up the Mississippi River. Transporting the sulfur in molten form eliminates the necessity of reheating the sulfur. A net economic benefit is derived from this method of transportation. (Texas Gulf Sulphur Company.)

Fig. 3 A refrigerated trailer used to transport perishable commodities in piggyback service. The utilization of the railroad for this type of service takes the big trucks off the highways, is especially advantageous for long-distance movement, and makes possible quick delivery to the consumer who may not live close to a railway freight yard. (Northern Pacific Railway Company.)

accessible to all sections of the country (Fig. 3). It began to be apparent that the greatest dangers to the public welfare would arise from the shortages of metals and of fuels to operate machines rather than of food to nourish the population. These changes in needs were reflected by the placing of metals and fuels higher on the priority list of needed resources. Thus we came to a further realization of the fact that resources cannot be evaluated solely in physical terms but must be considered in the light of human wants.

Immediate and Future Goals. Perhaps the matter of defining and measuring human wants would not give us very much trouble if we were concerned only with immediate wants and not with those that are going to appear in the future. Resources, of course, must be defined as items that are wanted, and the intensity with which they are wanted will govern the value that we

place on the resources. So it is somewhat disconcerting to realize that human wants change considerably from time to time. And since these wants do change, it is difficult indeed to forecast a schedule of wants so that an adequate program of resource provision may be constructed.

All of us know that the structure of human wants is the product of a great variety of forces. Some of these forces are strictly biological and are concerned with the maintenance of man as a human being. Some of the foods we eat and some of the clothes we wear fall in this category, although probably most of our demands for food and clothing arise out of the culture in which we live rather than the biological needs associated with merely staying alive. The culture, on the other hand, changes constantly. We want many things because other people want them, and we do not want the same things that our fathers and grandfathers wanted, nor do we expect to want the same things ten years from today that we want today. So the person who would develop a schedule of wants is faced with a prospect of a very difficult forecast of their characteristics in future years. There is, for example, the whole matter of modern advertising which does a great deal to stimulate various kinds of wants. Other uncertainties are introduced into any forecast by the changing age composition of a population and unforeseeable events such as wars, droughts, and economic depressions.

Yet we would not want to conclude that the forecasting of wants is entirely a matter of guesswork. Certainly we feel that all of us are going to continue to eat. We are going to continue to demand transportation and a considerable amount of recreation, religion, education, and numerous other services. We also know that, regardless of considerable changes in the characteristics of individual items, such as food, clothing, shelter, machines, and other things, the materials from which they will be made have a great deal in common; so that when one gets down to the actual natural resources which lie at the base of the economic process he discovers a rather basic group of chemicals and physical materials that must be considered as basic to the satisfaction of human wants.

The Role of Scientific Progress. This is not to say, however, that we have any very good basis for establishing the relative importance of these basic elemental resources. Who is to say what the relative importance of the various metals, iron, copper, aluminum, and many others, will be 100 years from now; and who is to decide whether it will be best to conserve petroleum at the expense of coal, or vice versa? These are the changes which constantly beset the economist or any other analyst who tries to set down a list of things that are going to be needed in the distant future.

The student of wants and resources soon discovers that these considerations apply to even such fundamental needs as food and clothing and to such basic resources as soil and timber suppliers. Advances in soil chemistry have brought many changes in the economist's classical definition of land as the "inherent and indestructible properties of the soil." Much of our older conservation practice was based on the assumption that such properties of the soil persist. But students of soils point out that a rich soil is basically one that provides water and minerals in the right proportions to sustain plant growth and that neither water nor chemicals are indestructible in any sense of the term.

Role of Diminishing Returns. Modifications in economic thinking that have marked the twentieth-century period in the United States have given increasingly greater weight to sociotechnical variables in the solution of the resources problem. In particular, economists have been troubled by the fact that diminishing returns have appeared only very rarely in the century and a quarter since Malthus first formulated the scarcity principle, and when they have appeared it has been only in very restricted sectors of the economy. Recent studies have shown that in the United States, for example, during the period since 1870, evidences of diminishing returns have appeared only in the forest products industries among all types of production based on natural resources; and even in the forest industries there is good evidence that a substitution of products based on other resources (especially minerals) is rapidly alleviating such conditions of scarcity as may have appeared. In other sectors of the American economy, the per capita availability of suitable goods to meet expanding demands has consistently increased rather than declined in the period of rapidly increasing population that has marked recent decades of American history. Limited evidence points to existence of these same long-run trends in other parts of the world.[2]

Since economists are always eager to modify their models to bring them closer to the conditions of reality, their concern over the assumptions that underlay their classical scarcity model

[2] *Ibid.*, Chapter 1.

has been mounting. Among these assumptions, the most vulnerable seems to have been the notion of technological constancy, the idea that man does not "discover" new resources, does not have the ability to devise new and more economical ways of satisfying his wants. As a consequence, special efforts have been made to revise the classical scarcity model in ways that would include technology as a variable rather than a constant factor in economic growth.

Historical Evidence. In spite of the convincing mass of evidence to the contrary, however, there remains in the economic thinking of many people a strong conviction that absolute general scarcity of resources is inevitable, that diminishing returns must certainly occur in the light of the world's rapidly expanding population and that within the foreseeable future the dire predictions of Malthus and the other early economists that population will outrun its means of subsistence will come to pass. It is clear that this sort of reasoning is not supported by the facts in a world in which hundreds of millions of people have continued to live better and better, rather than worse and worse, in recent decades and in which there is no sound basis for predicting a reversal of that trend.

Economic Change. In addition to recognizing the role of technological progress in the growth of modern nations, economists have also pointed to the need to incorporate elements of changing demand into their resource-use models. Certainly a changing society is constantly developing new products and the demand for them is quite capable of replacing the demand for other products. Productivity has increased to a point where the major portion of the aggregate demand for goods and services in most parts of the world is *not* for the biological necessities of life, as envisioned by early students of the problem, but rather for a great variety of pleasurable, but not necessarily essential, items that make twentieth century living more enjoyable. In addition, man's inventiveness has created many ways of satisfying not only these culturally inspired wants but also the

basic biological wants associated with the maintenance of the human race. Once the basic components of a nutritious and life-sustaining diet have been established, modern consumers quickly discover that they can be satisfied by a very large variety of foods that can be combined in an almost infinite number of interesting ways. Comparable possibilities for substitution are available in the realms of clothing and shelter, in both of which areas we may choose between agricultural products, based on the utilization of climatic and soil resources, and products of the forests or of the mines. Thus it appears that even in the presence of growing scarcity of a particular natural resource, such as timber, there is no appreciable likelihood that the quantity of housing available to mankind will be reduced. It is apparent that these same facilities for substitution exist throughout the entire spectrum of human demand. When these possibilities are coupled with the increasing rate of man's scientific and technological progress, it becomes virtually impossible to forecast general scarcity in the means of life for the people of future generations. Certainly it seems more realistic to forecast a continuance of the presumably temporary surpluses that have plagued the producers of many types of agricultural, mineral, and even forest products in the Western World in recent decades than to predict a general scarcity of all these types of goods. The ability to substitute products derived from one natural resource for those derived from another has made it possible to alleviate impending shortages in one type of resource by replacing products based on those resources with equally acceptable products based on other, more plentiful resources. And, with the promise of continuous new discovery of such resources, the time of ultimate exhaustion of all of the means of satisfying man's wants is pushed further and further into the future—so far, in fact, that we find it impossible to estimate the time of its occurrence.

The Conservation Movement. If we must abandon the general scarcity principle, how then shall we account for the Conservation Movement and its great popularity among the presumably enlightened people of the modern world? In a word, there seems to be no legitimate economic basis for defending programs of "wise use" of natural resources in terms of the *quantities* of goods and services that would be available under alternative systems of resource management. Clearly, that sort of defense cannot be made to stand up. There seem to be excellent possibilities for defending and sponsoring conservation, however, on the basis of forestalling declines in the *qualitative*, rather than the quantitative, aspects of human existence. At this point, we depart from the quantitative, relatively precise and ultimately scientific means of analysis that pervade the discipline of economics and enter into the realm of esthetics, in which identification and measurement of the "true" values of life become much more difficult.

Esthetic Values. Perhaps we may introduce this phase of the conservation issue by posing a specific problem in public policy. A recent case involves a beautifully forested and extremely scenic high valley in the Colorado Rockies of North America. Access to this valley is through a canyon that has long been hailed as one of the most beautiful in the state of Colorado. But the canyon is crooked, and the highway that uses it is narrow, difficult, expensive to use, and somewhat dangerous. A campaign has been launched to widen and straighten that road. Conservation-minded citizens insist that such a construction program would reduce the scenic attractiveness of the area and thereby deprive society of an important source of human satisfaction. Business people, and many other persons who must traverse the canyon regularly, point to the tremendous waste of time and money that could be prevented if the Highway Commission were ordered to apply their acknowledged technical facilities to improve that highway. If you were a member of the commission which must decide such matters, how would you vote?

The Measurement Problem. Whenever we face problems involving a choice between economic and noneconomic values, we immediately encounter difficulties because the latter ordinarily cannot be expressed in quantitative form. How great is the quantum of satisfaction that society would receive from viewing a particularly attractive portion of the natural landscape? And how do those magnitudes compare with the amounts of satisfaction that society would receive if the dis-services imposed by that piece of territory were eliminated? It seems that a fairly adequate estimate of the latter type of benefit could be made by adding together alternative costs of present and prospective users and comparing the totals under present and proposed conditions. These estimates could then be related to estimated costs of the work and an acceptable notion of the economic feasibility of the project could be obtained. Such an estimate could be examined by any interested party and its acceptability could be established, because all values would be expressed quantitatively, probably in terms of monetary cost, and there could be no disagreement as to their magnitudes. But when we turn to the problem of measuring the esthetic costs and benefits of the enterprise how shall we proceed?

Value Conflicts. Actually, of course, the proponents of conservation have been forced to deal in the kinds of values we have just envisioned. As a result, their appeal has been predominantly emotional and they have had great difficulty establishing hierarchies of values when they have found their own desires to be in conflict. Is it more desirable to manage the resources of a particular area so as to maximize its usefulness for hunting and fishing, or shall the area be devoted to other forms of recreation, such as skiing or camping? Or, to introduce an economic motive, shall it be devoted to the production of lumber and timber products, rather than recreation?

Conservationists complain that whenever alternatives such as those we have just considered are presented to legislatures, commissions, and other agencies that must interpret social needs and determine public policy, the verdict is likely to be favorable to the economically expressed needs, simply because they can be quantified. At the same time there is almost universal approval of the goals of the conservationists, especially in the realm of outdoor recreation, and it would be difficult to determine the validity of their complaint.

Recreation. It is precisely in the realm of outdoor recreation, however, that greatest consensus has been achieved among citizens of the United States as to the relative merit of conservation. Surely it cannot be measured, but one of the strongest tenets of American society holds that life in the great out-of-doors is better than life indoors, particularly in the large city. We believe that farming is inherently a better way of life than can be found in the city, and we are willing to subsidize that occupation in the same manner as we provide public and private funds to assure children and adults the facilities for spending a portion of their summers each year in the nonurban atmosphere of the camp, the national park or forest, or other public or private recreation area. If these facilities are to have the desired therapeutic value, we have reasoned, they must be preserved in a manner that somewhat resembles their original natural state; and certainly we must resist alternative courses of action that would impair the usefulness of those areas for recreational purposes. Since nearly all such proposed uses are economic, there is continuous controversy between posited economic and esthetic values. These conflicts are always difficult to adjudicate by public agencies because there are presently no ways of accurately comparing the magnitudes of the two sorts of values. In recent years, however, conservationists have been kept comparatively happy by the decline in the economic need to occupy many portions of our land area and by the increasing affluence of a society which continues to devote more and more of its income to the provision of outdoor recreational facilities. These same tendencies may be observed in virtually every aspect of public policy in which ideological conflict concerning the utilization of resources have appeared.

The Place of Economics in Conservation Programs. In view of these circumstances, it is easy to see why this book should be devoted almost entirely to problems of appraising the importance of various types of physical resources in the light of various interpretations of the structure of the aggregate human demand for goods and services. As a practitioner, the conservationist must reckon continuously with the changing character of human needs and desires, and must devise ways of evaluating them in such a manner as to place them in hierarchies that exhibit varying degrees of social desirability. He must also be able to identify and measure the resources available for use in the satisfaction of human wants. We have already discovered that some of those wants can be evaluated in terms of traditional economic thinking, but that many of them cannot. It is in this larger frame of reference, that includes both pecuniary and nonpecuniary values, that the conservationist must operate when he attempts to contemplate the relative "wisdom" that lies in competing proposals for "wise use" of various types of natural resources.

Inventories of Needs and Resources. Eventually, in the pursuit of the goals of conservation analysis, it becomes necessary to measure both needs and resources. These measurements, as we have seen, are apt to be extremely difficult to accomplish, because our society has not developed very precise ideas concerning the relative importance of either needs or resources. The fact remains, however, that quantitative estimates of both these elements must be provided because of the recurrent necessity for implementing public policy through the enactment of laws and other measures designed to promote the public interest.

Great efforts have been made to forecast future trends in the needs and resources of the American people. The composition of these forecasts is illuminating because it reveals the maze of contradictory forces that must be considered in any forecast of resource utilization. On the demand side we may begin, let us say, with a growing population, and we set about the task of estimating its size and composition at some period perhaps 50 or 100 years hence. Next we go about the task of feeding, clothing, housing, and otherwise caring for that population. What will they need in the way of buildings, automobiles, and battleships, and a thousand and one other goods and services? Eventually we strike a total and begin looking about for means of satisfying those needs. Will we have full employment? How many acres of farmland and barrels of oil will be needed? And what is the probable supply of these commodities? Engineers can estimate the productivity of an acre of farmland or of an oil well with great precision if we permit them to assume that certain techniques of production will be employed. But nobody can tell us how production will be affected if a new kind of fertilizer or a new way of drilling wells is found practicable. So the inventories of needs and resources become obsolete in a short while because of changes in technology and social conditions. And we can begin to see the basis for Erich Zimmermann's statement: Each generation must re-appraise its resources.[3]

The Economic Characteristics of Natural Resources. When we examine resources, we soon discover two very different types. On the one hand, we have fund resources, such as coal and petroleum, which may be used only once and cannot be renewed; on the other, we have flow resources, such as rainfall and sunshine which are renewed continuously. In the former, we must consider ourselves essentially as the custodians of a storehouse in which a valuable stockpile of commodities is housed. This stock cannot be expanded, and our task is to determine the rates at which it may be removed in order to provide a maximum of want satisfaction to the people who own it. We realize, of

course, that these goods have no value whatsoever until we convert them for human use; but we are beset with the problem of deciding which of the many competing uses shall be satisfied. With the fund resources, this problem is especially acute because the dimensions of the stockpile are quite definite, but the time period over which the stock will be needed is impossible to predict. Conservation of the flow resources obviously presents very different problems from the conservation of fund resources. A great many biological resources, such as timber, fish, and game, may be exploited almost to the point of exhaustion; but the stock of these resources may be renewed through proper management practices (Fig. 4). Soils have many of the qualities of both the fund and flow resources and thus present peculiarly complex problems. Soils, for example, will suffer the fate of fund resources if removed by erosion. But, as flow resources, soils may have their productivity reduced or depleted yet still be capable of being restored to their original productivity through proper management practices.

It appears that the conservation of fund resources involves, almost inevitably, some postponement of current consumption in recognition of future needs. With flow resources, on the other hand, the primary problem seems to be obtaining maximum yields without seriously impairing the productivity of the resources. From the economic point of view, the conservation of fund resources is primarily a matter of weighing present and future needs, regulating the rate of exploitation accordingly, and diminishing waste as much as possible.

PETROLEUM CONSERVATION. The changing nature of needs and resources and their puzzling economic consequences are exemplified in the petroleum industry. In the early days of this industry, need for petroleum products was extremely limited, being confined largely to uses for household illumination. Later, petroleum became an essential feature of a new era of transportation that revolutionized human existence. Modern nations would be ineffective in

[3] Erich W. Zimmermann, *World Resources and Industries,* Revised Edition, New York, 1951, Chapter 1.

Fig. 4   An aerial view of the Weyerhaeuser lumber mill at Snoqualmie Falls near Seattle. Note the use of a circular water area for the storage of the timber awaiting processing at the mill. The timber already cut is protected from rapid decay by this method of storage. (Northern Pacific Railway Company.)

peace or war without gasoline and other liquid fuels. Thus the need has expanded enormously and every modern nation is constantly searching for better ways to insure itself a future supply of this commodity.

Petroleum is one of the fund resources—it is exhaustible and nonrenewable. But note what has happened to the fund! An early textbook in conservation quoted the prediction that "at present rates of consumption, petroleum reserves will be exhausted by the year 1925." What has happened? The estimate was authoritative, the best obtainable in 1910. But at no time do estimators have a way of reckoning with

future technological changes that are destined to expand the fund of proven petroleum reserves. Progress has been so steady that we have almost stopped talking about the need of substituting coal and other fuels for petroleum in the interests of conservation. Military experts have virtually abandoned plans to store oil for use in future emergencies—and the only peacetime restrictions on the use of gasoline encountered by the American motorist`are those imposed by the amount of money that is in his pocketbook when he arrives at the filling station!

Incentives to Invention and Exploration. The mechanisms employed by a price-directed economy to promote conservation in cases such as these are worthy of careful study. In the case of petroleum, for example, the expanding needs mentioned previously were reflected in increases in price. Higher prices attracted capital and labor to the petroleum industry and encouraged the development of a great variety of technological improvements that expanded the fund of petroleum reserves enormously. Oil men confidently predicted that they would continue to find more oil as long as the price was high enough to pay them for taking the risks involved in exploration and development. Their predictions came true, and in this fashion the price-directed economy created an ample supply of these resources, enough to care for the expanding needs of the people.

But suppose that the search for new sources of oil had not been successful. How would the economy have reacted? We know that, before this new era of discovery, good progress had already been made in the development of substitutes, so that as soon as the price of petroleum rises to a certain level, a rapid development of industries devoted to the extraction of oil from oil shale, the transformation of coal into liquid fuel, and the probable application of atomic energy to tasks now performed by petroleum products will take place. The development of substitutes has served either to increase the availability or to diminish the need for nearly all the fund resources. In a price-directed economy these developments are presumed to appear automatically whenever scarcity and expanding demand combine to raise prices to levels at which the risk of developing new products appears to be worth taking.

Petroleum is a prime example of a resource for which the fund has been increased at a faster rate than the need has expanded. We are not at all sure that equivalent expansion can be attained in the funds of other minerals, such as tin, lead, copper, and iron. In all these cases, however, the drive to find new sources and to develop substitutes will become strong whenever prices rise high enough.

The Renewable Resources. We have already observed that the primary problem of conserving the flow resources involves measures designed to assure the maintenance of those resources. Some of the simplest examples of the economic aspects of resource utilization of these resources may be found in the studies of problems arising from the needs for supplying present-day societies with water.

WATER. We are familiar with the fact that needs for water have varied enormously, both geographically and historically. Inhabitants of arid lands have generally valued water very highly, whereas the peoples of humid lands have ordinarily considered it either a nuisance or, at best, a "free good," so abundant that it could be used in unlimited amounts by all the people. But in recent years the uses of water have expanded so much that modern nations must now consider how available supplies shall be allocated among a large number of competing users.

Water is a prime example of a renewable resource. There is, in fact, little that we could do to keep our supplies from being renewed through the processes of precipitation. Furthermore, these supplies are mostly free from contamination, so that the product as received has a uniformly high quality. But, except in agriculture, very little rainwater is used directly by man, who depends almost exclusively for his supplies of this commodity on water that is stored on or near the earth's surface. Such storage areas are rather easily contaminated or destroyed, so that the natural product is easily rendered useless to the hordes of nonagricultural users who have developed important needs for it. Thus the flow of this resource continues, but its availability is diminished, and a condition of scarcity has arisen. Some means must therefore be found to determine how these scarce resources shall be allocated to the competing uses and what steps shall be taken to maintain supplies at optimum levels.

BIOLOGICAL RESOURCES. Certainly the most prominent of the flow resources are the biological resources—including forests, animals, and fish—and soils (which also have an essentially biological character). The distinguishing characteristic of these resources is that man can do much to alter their rate of flow. We know, of course, that trees keep growing, that fish continue to spawn, and that microorganisms keep transforming minerals into soil. But the rates at which these changes occur can be altered considerably, so that the supply that becomes available depends to no small degree on how these resources are managed. There is, furthermore, a considerable element of storage in most of these processes, so that man frequently has a choice of cutting trees, catching fish, or utilizing soils rapidly or slowly. In so doing, he can choose between destroying past accumulations, merely consuming current additions, or saving portions of the current production for future use. In all these instances, choices must be made between alternative uses, both present and future, of these resources.

Economic Motivation. To the individual property owner, the social imposition of conservation practices is likely to be considerably more onerous for flow resources than for fund resources. The property owner will often consider the selection of ways and means of managing renewable resources as pre-eminently a matter for exercise of his own individual judgment; he will resent the imposition of social values which forbid him to cut down his own trees or cultivate and plant his land as he sees fit. How shall our society overcome this resistance?

We may approach this problem best by recalling that, in America, the tasks of resource allocation are performed by the pricing system. Other peoples, and we ourselves, have occasionally used rationing or other methods to perform this task, but in America the basic ideology has always stated that resources shall be allocated to those who will pay the highest prices for them. We have seen how these attitudes grew up along with another set that states that individuals shall not be permitted to perform acts contrary to the public interest (even if the pricing system does give them the power to do so).

In general, the American people have preferred those measures that would encourage individuals to act in the public interest to those that would prohibit them from acting against it. That encouragement has generally had a financial character and has been designed to make the socially desirable action more profitable than its undesirable alternative.

Identification of Social Needs. Social needs must be defined, formulated, and measured before intelligent conservation measures can be undertaken. In our society this formulation of definitions of social need is influenced by a variety of agencies, notably the family, the school, and the church. But public attitudes are also influenced by the activities of many public and private agencies whose purposes are to persuade citizens to favor programs and policies that are of special interest to the sponsors and patrons of those agencies. One would expect many of these interests to be in conflict. Even the most ardent conservationists soon discover that to conserve one thing may mean to destroy something else, so that there are many conflicts among those who hold different views of the nature of public interest.

We have seen that, in America, this body of public opinion will certainly be based to a greater or lesser extent on economic considerations. A great variety of wants will have been considered and evaluated in ways that will indicate their relative importance to the American people. These summations of social needs may then be related to lists of resources and the whole matter translated into public policy by governmental agencies. After these needs have been defined and means for satisfying them have been decreed, however, an important question remains to be answered: "How shall these measures be enforced?"

Bonuses, Subsidies, and Benefit Payments. We have already intimated that many of the activities demanded in the public interest cannot be performed at a profit by the private owners of the various resources. We also know that the American people have shown great preference for an economic system in which resources are owned and managed by private individuals. Government ownership and management have been selected in a very few instances, notably in the attempt to care for recreational needs in the National Park system and in a variety of defense activities. Government supervision of leases to private individuals for exploitation has been utilized in connection with national forests and government range lands, But, for most of the translation of public demands into conservation practices, the American people have relied on devices that make the desired practices appear more profitable—and therefore more attractive—to the private owners of those resources. Among these private owners, the largest and most significant group has been in agriculture.

Soil Conservation. Farmers of America have been plagued by many problems, most of which are concerned with low prices for their products and high costs of production. But the farmers are also the owners of the soil: one of the resources that public policy insists must be conserved in the interests of future generations. Soil conservation has therefore become a major interest of federal, state, and local governments in the United States.

We have indicated that the soils problem is complicated by the fact that soils represent both fund and flow resources. The soils "fund" may be completely destroyed through erosion, or the "flow" may merely be reduced by depletion through poor soils management practices. Both aspects of the problem have been attacked by governmental agencies, and in both instances the procedure has been to stimulate conservation practices by making them appear more profitable than alternative practices to the individual farmer.

In implementing these programs, several kinds of subsidies have been provided. In their attempts to reduce erosion, governmental agencies have given extensive financial aid to farmers who would install dams and other preventive devices. They have also given financial encouragement to local agencies that would promote conservation and take steps to enforce locally approved conservation measures by legal means. In the attack on soil depletion, the whole

program has been complicated by the generally accepted thesis that overproduction has kept prices low. There has, nevertheless, been a consistent effort to pay bonuses to farmers who devote part of their lands to those crops that will not induce erosion and that will also arrest depletion. The same result has been sought very often by price-fixing schemes in which the government undertakes to maintain prices at higher levels for soil-conserving crops than for those that have harmful effects on the soil. In all these schemes, however, the primary emphasis has been on making conservation practices appear profitable to the individual landholding farm operator.

OTHER INCENTIVES. Similar incentives are common in other aspects of the conservation program. In forested areas, for example, it is an accepted practice to keep yearly taxes at low levels and substitute a heavy severance tax when the trees are actually harvested. Many states follow this practice in taxing mineral lands. Government services in policing fisheries, forests and other areas, to promote better conservation practices, are well known. The subsidy is a well-established aspect of the American conservation program.

OTHER INDUCEMENTS. The economist is always anxious to point to the fact that the payment of subsidies is not always the most successful or even the most economical way to bring about the adoption of conservation measures by the owners of private properties. He will point out, for example, that in many cases these owners could actually enhance their incomes by practicing conservation and are kept from doing so by sheer ignorance. Under these circumstances the payment of subsidies would be a social waste, and society certainly could get much more for its money if it were to spend it to educate those property holders.

There is also much evidence that wasteful exploitation often occurs because of lack of security on the operator's part. Farm tenants are often led to mismanage the soil so that they can make as much money as possible in a short time and then move to another farm. Renters of mineral claims often behave in the same way. It seems that means taken to lengthen the period of tenancy and to increase the security and level of living of the operators might be very effective in promoting the acceptance of conservation practices. These same effects could also be produced in many cases by reducing other costs of ownership, especially interest rates. All these alternatives must be considered by the economist as he prepares his estimations of how the desired goals may be achieved at minimum social cost.

SUMMARY

By way of summary, we see the interaction of economics and conservation operating at two different levels. On one of these levels, we find the economist defining conservation in terms of the identification of human needs and the allocation of resources to satisfy those needs. On the other level, the economist is concerned with finding the most economical ways of attaining social goals, which have been established to resolve the means-resources problems, discovered in the earlier phases of his investigations. In these ways the science of economics serves first to help people define conservation problems in ways that will provide a basis for the formulation of intelligent public policies; and second, to determine the relative costs of alternative methods of carrying out those policies. In all instances the economist serves essentially as an adviser to those who must determine the content of public policy concerning conservation and all other matters involving conflicts between public and private interests.

References

Barnett, Harold J., and Chandler Morse, *Scarcity and Growth*, The Johns Hopkins Press, Baltimore, 1963.

Bunce, Arthur C., *The Economics of Soil Conservation*, Iowa State College Press, Ames, Iowa, 1942.

Ciriacy-Wantrup, S. V., *Resource Conservation, Economics and Policies*, University of California Press, Berkeley and Los Angeles, 1952.

Ely, Richard T., Ralph H. Hess, Charles K. Leith, and Thomas Nixon Carver, *The Foundations of National Prosperity*, The Macmillan Co., New York, 1918.

Heady, Earl O., *Economics of Agricultural Production and Resource Use*, Prentice-Hall, Englewood Cliffs, New Jersey, 1952.

Heady, Earl O., *Principles of Conservation Economics*, Iowa Agricultural Experimental Station, Research Bull. 382, Ames, Iowa, 1951.

Landsberg, Hans H., Leonard L. Fischman, and Joseph L. Fisher, *Resources in America's Future: Patterns of Requirements and Availabilities, 1960–2000*, The Johns Hopkins Press, Baltimore, 1963.

Malthus, Thomas, *An Essay on Population* (various editions, 1798 to 1816), Ward, Lock and Company, London.

Mill, John Stuart, *Principles of Political Economy*, Longmans, Green, London, 1929.

Proceedings of the Inter-American Conference on Conservation of Renewable Resources, Denver, Colorado, September 7–20, 1948.

Raushenbush, Stephen, "Economic Considerations in Conservation and Development," *UNSCCUR*, Vol. 1: Plenary Meeting, New York, 1951, pp. 202–212, "Discussion," pp. 213–216.

Ricardo, David, *Principles of Political Economy and Taxation*, G. Bell and Sons, Ltd., London, 1922.

Scott, Anthony, *Natural Resources: The Economics of Conservation*, University of Toronto Press, Toronto, 1955.

Spengler, Joseph J., editor, *Natural Resources and Economic Growth,* Committee on Economic Growth of the Social Science Research Council, Resources for the Future, Washington, D.C., 1961.

Van Hise, Charles R., and Loomis Havemeyer, *The Conservation of Natural Resources in the United States,* Revised Edition, The Macmillan Co., New York, 1935.

Zimmermann, Erich W., *Introduction to World Resources,* Henry L. Hunker, editor, Harper and Row, New York, 1964 (paperback).

Zimmermann, Erich W., *World Resources and Industries,* Revised Edition, Harper and Brothers, New York, 1951.

Part 2

LOUIS A. WOLFANGER

Michigan State University

CHAPTER 4

The Great Soil Groups and Their Utilization

The United States ranks above all other nations in its land resources. Although Australia, Brazil, Canada, China, and the Soviet Union are also large countries and have diverse soils, greater proportions of their lands are handicapped by adverse topography, poorer soils, or less favorable climates. Furthermore, none has the counterpart of the productive prairie soils of our Middle West which are such a significant part of our land resources.

SOIL GROUPS

Ranging as our states do from the Arctic area of Alaska to Hawaii in the Tropics, we possess thousands of individually different soils. Like animals and other natural objects, however, they can be arranged into broad classes or groups to facilitate their general study.

Over one hundred such great groups have now been defined in the United States, still too many for us to consider here.[1] As most of these are chiefly local in occurrence, however, we shall select only those that are primarily regional or zonal in character, that is, occupy large continuous areas (such as the American black earths which extend from the Dakotas into Kansas) as the basis for our study. Following their review,

we shall then combine these groups into two very broad groups to secure a comprehensive picture of our soils in their entirety.

Several great soil groups which are chiefly local in extent but have special interest will be either included in the discussion of a zonal group with which they may be conveniently identified or briefly described in separate paragraphs (Tables 1, 2, and 3).

THE PODZOL GROUP

Podzols occupy chiefly the northern borders of the United States, extending from the Upper

---

[1] Soils scientists are now in the process of perfecting a very comprehensive system of classification designed to include every kind of soil the world possesses, but far too complex for this survey.

The most elementary groups are called "soil series." Examples are the Norfolk series of the southern Coastal Plain, the Miami of the Lake States, the Holdrege of the Great Plains, and the San Joaquin of the Central Valley of California.

Soil series that are similar form soil "families," and families make up great soil groups. The student interested in the local soils of his community should consult the county soil survey reports published by the U.S. Department of Agriculture if available, or write to his state agricultural college or experiment station.

45

Table 1. Humid-Forest Groups

Groups	Climate	Native Vegetation	Features	Use
Podzols	Cool, humid	Coniferous, hardwood; or mixed conif. and hardwood	Thin, dark topsoil; gray upper soil; coffee-brown subsoil; strongly acid; low natural fertility	Chiefly forest, wildlife, recreation. Local "islands" of agr. (dairy, beef, root crops, pasture)
Gray-wooded	Same	Same	From fine-text. calc. parent materials; thick, gray upper soil; calc. lower subsoil; often grade into podzols	Forest, recreation, limited agr. (dairy farming, hay, grain). Areas of better land in podzol region
Gray-brown podzolic	Humid, mid-latitude	Decid. forest (oak, hickory, beech, maple); understory: shrubs, herbs	Thin, dark topsoil; gray-brown lighter-colored upper soil; heavier, brown subsoil; mod. acid; productivity high under good management	Highly diversified agr. (grains, forage, root crops, fruit, dairy, beef, etc.); woodlots; forest in rough areas
Brown podzolic	Humid, cool-temperature	Decid., conif., or mixed forest	Faint ashy-gray or coffee brown horizons, or absent; subsoils only slightly heavier; often grade into podzols	Orchard, dairying, truck, woodland, suburban
Sols bruns acides	Same	Hardwoods: beech, oak, maple	Acid soils, from noncalc. formations; low in plant nutrients	Forest, pasture, general farming
Subarctic brown	Short summer, long winter	Boreal forest	Brown, relatively unleached, low in clay; variable permafrost	Forest, limited agr. (grains, vegetables, pasture)
Red-yellow podzolic	Humid, subtropical	Conif., decid., and mixed	Bleached upper soil; red or yellow heavier subsoil; low to medium natural fertility	High prop. in forest; large "islands" in spec. crops (cotton, tobacco, peanuts, fruits, vegetables)
Latosols	Rainy, tropical, and subtropical	Tropic and subtropic forest; in mid-lat.: western pine forest, Douglas fir, redwoods	Red, yellow, and brown; highly friable clays; deep, reticulated subsoils	Tropical agr. (sugar, pineapple, citrus, etc.), tree crops; forest; recreation

Table 2. Low-Rainfall Groups

Groups	Climate	Native Vegetation	Features	Use
Chernozems	Subhumid mid-latitude	Tall grassland changing gradually to short grasses on dry margin	"Black" granular upper soil 3 to 4 feet; brown subsoil; whitish layer of carbonate accumulation at 3 feet or more; high natural fertility	High quality small grains (hard wheat, barley, oats, flax, sorghum, etc.); some livestock; irrigated valleys
Chestnut, including reddish chestnut	Semi-arid mid-latitude to subtropical	Mixed tall and short grasses, with shrubs in South	Dark-brown to reddish-brown upper soil; brown to reddish subsoil; whitish carbonate accumulation at 2- to 4-foot depths; medium natural productivity	High quality small grains; considerable land in range or pasture; irrigated valleys
Brown, including reddish brown	Near-arid mid-latitude to subtropical	Short and bunch grasses	Brown or reddish-brown upper soil; whitish carbonate accumulation at 1- to 2-foot depths; low natural productivity	Chiefly range; some dry farming to grain; irrigated valleys
Desert, including reddish desert, solonchak,° solonetz°	Mid-latitude to subtropical desert	Sparse, desert shrubs, chiefly bare ground	Gray or red surface; carbonate accumulation near surface, locally indurated; low in organic matter	Low quality range; irrigated valleys

° See text for description.

Lake states to the uplands of New England (Map, Fig. 1, page 49).[2]

These soils developed chiefly from sandy formations, principally glacial, under a comparatively cool, humid climate, and a mantle of coniferous, hardwood, or mixed conifer and deciduous forest.

[2] The scale of the map permits showing only major regions of occurrence of each of the great soil groups. Like plants, such as cacti which occur in many places outside of deserts, members of many great soil groups develop locally wherever the combination of soil-forming processes favors their particular formation. For example, local bodies of podzols, not shown on the map, occur at high elevations in the Appalachians, the Pacific Mountains, and Intermountain Plateaus, and on parts of the North Atlantic Coastal Plain (Cape Cod, Long Island, and the Pine Barrens of New Jersey).

Like all soils, podzols are made up of mineral and organic substances. The leaves and other litter which fall to the forest floor were the principal source of organic materials that entered into their make-up. Under the cool temperatures prevailing in podzol regions, the litter decomposed slowly, forming dark-brown humus —an exceedingly complex mixture of organic and inorganic compounds, some of which are highly acid (Fig. 2, page 50).

Rainwaters percolating through the humus became highly acid (acid in terms of soil formation). Entering the soil, the waters leached out most of the soluble nutrients formed, carrying them down into the internal drainage waters. They conveyed dark humus, clay particles, iron, and alumina into the subsoil. The transfer of

Table 3. Others

Groups	Climate	Native Vegetation	Features	Use
Brunizems, incl. reddish prairie	Humid mid-latitude	Tall prairie grasses; locally scattered trees and shrubs	One to 2 feet very dark granular upper soil; brown subsoil, slightly heavier; high natural fertility	"Corn belt" farming in Midwest; cotton, wheat, grain sorghum in southern plains
Tundra	Arctic	Mosses, lichens, shrubs	Dark brown peaty surf.; light brown coarse silt, little clay, mottled sub-soil; permafrost	Reindeer pasture
Grumusols	Humid mid-latitude	Prairie grass	Very dark brown; heavy calc. clays; crumb structure; gilgai relief	Cotton, sorghum, wheat, grazing
Noncalcic brown	Medium to low winter rain; dry summers	Grass with scattered trees	Brown to reddish brown; heavier, noncalc. sub-soils	Grain, grazing; fruit under irrigation
Planosols	Humid, sub-humid; mid-latitude to subtropic	Both forest and prairie grasses	Strongly leached surface; claypan or indurated subsoils	Same crops as normal soils, but yields more limited.
Hydromorphic	Mid-latitude to subtropical humid	Swamp, forest, grasses, sedges	Gleys, marshlands, groundwater podzols, peats, mucks	Forest, wildlife, pasture; special crops (rice, sugar cane, celery, truck, mint, berries, etc.)
Sandhills	Arid to semi-arid	Bare to thin stand of grasses, shrubs	Deep, dry sand dunes; sandy valleys; lakes	Grazing, wildlife
Alluvial lands	Arid to humid	Grasses to forest	Similar, in general, to soils of drainage basin; high fertility	Highly productive; irrigated in low rain-fall areas
Mountainous and rough broken	Arid to humid	Bare to forested	Thin, stony	Forest, grazing, recreation

organic matter and iron left the upper soil bleached and white in color,[3] but made the subsoil a peculiar, dark coffee-brown color (Fig. 3). Moreover, the iron compounds and organic matter often acted as cements to form hard lumps or heavy or hardpan layers in the subsoil; soil scientists call the layers ortstein, from the German word for local stone.

These sandy, ash-gray soils with coffee-brown subsoils contain relatively little clay,[4] are acid in reaction (in terms of soils), and are low in plant

[3] The light gray soil material looks like fine ashes. Podzol, signifying ashlike, is a folk name for similar gray soils in northern U.S.S.R. Soil scientists have adopted it to designate soils of similar character throughout the world.

[4] The clay particles are the chief active mineral components of soils. They have chemical and physical properties which enable them to take up, hold, and release plant nutrients, and to retain water. Their capacity to react depends upon their composition.

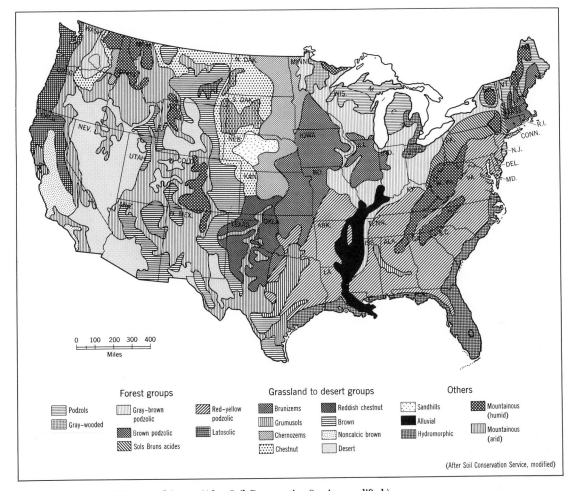

Fig. 1 Soil Groups of the United States. (After Soil Conservation Service, modified.)

nutrients. They occupy both sand plains and rough, morainic, and mountainous topography. Stoniness is common. Many areas include lakes, organic soils, and poorly drained soils.

When the virgin soil is brought under cultivation, the forest litter, the thin dark surface soil, the gray acidic upper soils, and the upper part of the coffee-brown subsoil become mixed in the plowed soil. The soil must then be limed and fertilized to make full use of its agricultural capacity. Most podzols, moreover, are "cold" and "late" soils. They warm up slowly in spring. Where ortsteins occur, the soils may require drainage.

Early Use. The extensive timber resources of the podzols were this soil's first big crop. The New England timber helped develop the great shipbuilding industry of the eastern seaboard. The Great Lakes lumber helped supply and build up the great treeless interior prairie lands south and west of the lakes, being used for homes, buildings, and structures of all kinds.

The agricultural use of these lands in colonial times in New England was almost wholly self-sufficient but of rather short duration. When lands west of the Appalachians were opened for settlement, abandonment was widespread. The sandy acid soils with their low natural fer-

Fig. 2 Accumulation of fresh debris on the forest floor of a podzol, consisting of leaves (chiefly), twigs, branches, flowers, and fruits of both trees and undergrowth. More than a ton of dry weight per acre may fall in a single year.

Fig. 3 Profile of a podzol. An exceptionally thick layer of partially decomposed organic material has accumulated around the roots of the tree. Beneath is the characteristic gray or bleached horizon, one of the distinguishing features of podzols. The dark brown or "coffee brown" subsoil is partially masked by debris fallen on this roadside cut.

Fig. 4 Many areas of New England are still plagued with stones, as in this pasture, although millions of tons have been moved to field edge where they form the picturesque stone fences of the region. (Soil Conservation Service.)

tility, general stoniness, and short growing season were no match for the gray-brown and prairie soils of the Mississippi Valley (Fig. 4).

The first clearings in the Great Lakes podzols were chiefly patchy, and their development was incidental to mining or lumbering. Hay was in great demand for work stock of the lumberman. Many winter lumberjacks took advantage of this nearby market and became hay farmers during the summer. After the lumbering epoch, efforts were made to stimulate farming, but the sandy soils, with their short summers and remote locations, were not generally suited to farming. Much of the land was soon abandoned.

Clearings in the western podzols have been negligible, and those that have been made are chiefly for pasture.

Present Land Use. Today, farming is still limited in the podzol regions. Except for small-scale dairy farms in the less rugged uplands and the Aroostook potato areas of northeastern Maine which have exceptional soils and are heavily fertilized, the rugged Northeastern Highlands are virtually "empty lands" dedicated primarily to forestry, wildlife, and recreation. Here and there are old abandoned farms which nonresidents have purchased for seasonal homes.

Present-day agriculture in the Lake States' podzol region continues to be local and scattered. A very large part of the area is swampy and occupied by lakes. However, the soils are responsive to constructive management. They make good root crop, pasture, and dairy and beef cattle land when properly limed and fertilized.

Forests and Wildlife. Aside from its "islands" of agriculture, the fundamental, long-term value of the podzol region lies in its forestry, wildlife, and recreational resources.

The land is naturally adapted to forests. Millions of acres of forest land, once abandoned after being cut over and ravaged by fire, are now growing a new crop of trees. A considerable acreage is back in public ownership (federal, state, and local) through tax delinquency or purchase. Moreover, much of the land held by large corporations, is now being largely managed on a "crop" and not exploitative basis.

The pulpwood growth which uses chiefly small-sized trees now exceeds the annual cut. The annual growth reaching saw-log maturity, however, is still somewhat below the annual saw-timber cut, since more time is necessary for these trees to become desirable cutting size.

The podzol regions have thousands of habitats favorable for wildlife. Deer and other herbivores now thrive on the grasses, shrubs, and other browse that spring up after forest fires. Paradoxically, however, the new tree growth is making such gains in many places heavily populated by deer that controlled fires, herbicides, and mechanical cutting of nonmerchantable stock are being increasingly used to retard forest regeneration and promote deer range to reduce starvation. Even so, thousands of deer perish annually during the winter for lack of browse.

Gray-Wooded Soils. These soils developed under forest formations similar to the podzols, but mainly from *fine*-textured (loam to silt loam) and calcareous parent materials. Podzolization (acid leaching) was therefore more limited, and the soils are naturally more productive.

They resemble the podzols in having whitish or gray upper horizons,[5] which are, however, generally thicker and more prominent (the basis for their name). They also contrast with the podzols in having medium brown (not coffee brown) subsoils that are moderately heavier than the upper soils and are usually underlain by calcareous lower subsoils.

The largest body of these soils is in northern Minnesota, where the land is generally in second growth in the north but cleared and farmed to grain and hay in the south. Throughout the northern Lake States, gray-wooded soils form local bodies of better land in a region of otherwise relatively poor agricultural soils. They are used chiefly for dairying and livestock.

GRAY-BROWN PODZOLIC SOILS

The principal area of these soils lies immediately south of the podzols in the Eastern States.[6] The soils are termed "podzolic" because the process of formation was similar to that of the podzols, but the action was less intense.

The climate under which the gray-brown podzolic soils developed averaged warmer and wetter than that of the podzols. The natural vegetation was mainly deciduous forest with an

---

[5] Soil students prefer calling soil layers "horizons" because they usually grade into each other or do not have sharp boundaries.

[6] As explained in footnote 2, many local bodies of these soils are also extensively commingled with the regional soils of other areas: on the North Atlantic Plain, in the Piedmont, the Appalachians, the humid prairies, the Rocky Mountains, and the forested valleys and uplands of the Pacific states.

Fig. 5 Profile of a gray-brown podzolic forest soil. The upper 12 inches
is the grayish-brown leached horizon.
The subsoil is a strong, brown silty
clay loam distinctly heavier in texture. Note the nutlike structure. (Soil
Conservation Service.)

appreciable undergrowth of shrubs, herbs, and grasses. As both trees and understory are heavy feeders, they returned a considerable amount of nutrients to the surface each year via their leaf fall. Unlike the hard leaves of the podzols, the soft leaves decomposed quickly and liberated their bases (calcium, etc.) more readily. The bases reduced acidity and favored the development of less-acid humus.

Leaching waters entering the soil were accordingly less acid. The soil was therefore less leached, had a moderate supply of available plant nutrients under virgin conditions, and the subsurface horizons are only grayish-brown, not ash-colored like the podzols. The less acid condition also favored the existence of worms and other soil organisms which are so important in incorporating humus in the soil.

The subsoils are characteristically heavier textured than the upper horizons, for they contain more clay (carried down by percolating waters and are also formed in place). The silt and clay are aggregated, however, forming small, nutlike structures which break up the solidity of the soil mass and facilitate the movement of air and water through the soil (Fig. 5). Even so, the heavier subsoil tends to slow down the intake and internal movement of rainwater and can cause oversaturation of the surface soil, a major cause of erosion. When oversaturated, erosion may set in during even moderate rains unless the soil is protected by appropriate conservation measures.

Agricultural Utilization. The gray-brown podzolic soils are the top-ranking soils developed under a humid climate and forest vegetation in America. Climate and soil favor both subsistence and commercial agriculture. Although the moderate reserve of plant nutrients was presently exhausted, the soils helped materially in carrying the early settler through the difficulties of pioneer occupation. Now, if limed, fertilized, rotated, maintained in organic matter, and protected from erosion, they can be farmed for generations.

One of the more valuable assets of these soils is their marked adaptability. They are easily and cheaply adapted to any crop climatically tolerant of their regions. Most crops we grow seem to prefer mild acidity. The gray-brown soils, with their relatively good physical constitution, can be readily built up to meet the peculiar requirements of almost any crop or cropping system.

The areas with arable soils exhibit highly checkered landscapes of both general and specialized farms. When economic or other conditions warrant, the soils can be readily adapted to grain fields, forage crops, tobacco, root crops, dairy farms, truck patches, vineyards, berries, fruit, orchards, or nut trees. They constitute one of the more valuable groups that the United States possesses (Fig. 6).

Erosion. Although the gray-brown podzolic soils constitute one of our more valuable agricultural groups, thousands of fields in the region have suffered erosion. Most of the soils occupy slopes of some degree. Little of the land is truly flat.

All major types of erosion have taken their toll—sheet, rill, and gully. Some areas have lost part of their subsoil as well as surface horizons. But severe and extensive damage has been chiefly local. On many farms, the system of farming practiced has often, by its very nature, been more or less conservative, although not always completely or ideally so. The use of grass in the cropping system has checked or reduced erosion on thousands of farms.

Three groups of soils that may be considered intermediate between the podzols and gray-brown soils are now examined.

Brown Podzolic Soils. The lowlands of Coastal New England below 1000 feet are occupied by sandy-textured soils in which the acid, podzolic process of soil formation was also less intense. The ashy-gray upper horizon and the coffee-brown horizon of the podzols are absent or only faintly developed. The soils are brown or yellowish brown and, unlike the gray-brown group, have only slightly heavier-textured subsoils. The original fertility was low, but not as low as the upland podzols, and the soils warm up earlier in the spring. Many areas are stony, however.

Like the podzols, these soils were widely abandoned following the opening of the West. But the revival of agriculture which has taken place in New England in recent years—orchards, dairying, market gardening, and others —has generally been on soils of this group, with rough and rocky areas reverting to woodland.

Fig. 6 A gray-brown podzolic landscape. When protected against erosion (note the practice here),
this group of soils is unsurpassed in its agricultural excellence. (Soil Conservation Service.)

Many areas are being suburbanized (Fig. 7).

Sols Bruns Acides (Acid Brown Forest Soils). As the name indicates (adopted from Belgium), these brown soils are characteristically acid. They were formed chiefly from *noncalcareous* formations, such as acid shales and sandstones. Although showing intense weathering, their subsoils, unlike those of gray-brown soils, are not decidedly heavier-textured than the upper horizons. The soils are low in plant nutrients, however.

The main area including these soils, commingled with other podzolic and lithosolic mountain soils, extends from southern New York southwestward through the Appalachians into Tennessee. Topography as well as fertility limits productivity. Much of the land is in forest. Cleared land is used for pasture, dairying, general farming, or specialized crops such as fruit or buckwheat (Fig. 8).

Subarctic Brown Forest Soils. These high latitude soils of Central Alaska resemble the brown forest soils of the middle latitudes and to some extent the podzols. The virgin soils are mantled with mosses and acid organic litter from the Boreal forest, analogous to the podzols. But the soils lack the ashy-gray and coffee-brown horizons of the podzols, although they are often closely associated with them. They are brown in color, relatively unleached, acid, and characteristically low in clay in relation to silt and sand, since chemical weathering is very limited in this climate.

The soils are generally cold below 18 inches. Some are underlain by permafrost. They constitute the chief agriculture lands of Central Alaska. They make good pasture and are surprisingly productive of adapted grains and vegetables under the long day but short summer season of this region (Fig. 9).

Nonagricultural Lands. As already indicated, all these brown forest groups include areas of sandy land, rugged and rocky land, steeply sloping lands, lands costly to clear or drain, land subject to drought or unseasonable frosts, or land isolated from markets. As in the podzols, these lands are best utilized for forestry, wildlife, and recreation, and where accessible to population centers, for rural residence, industry, and commercial enterprises. The greatest concentrations are in the Appalachians, Rocky Mountains, and Pacific areas, but they are scattered everywhere among the good farm lands.

THE RED-YELLOW PODZOLIC GROUPS

Red and yellow soils are typical of the southeastern states. The two soils are allied and frequently closely associated. Each is named after the color of the subsoil.

The red soils have bleached (that is, podzolized) yellow-red or yellowish-gray upper soils and clayey reddish subsoils. They generally mantle the more undulating, sloping or hilly lands of the region. Their original cover was chiefly deciduous forest with local mixtures of coniferous trees.

The yellow podzolic soils have bleached, grayish-yellow upper horizons and yellowish subsoils that are more clayey. They occupy chiefly the level divides of the Coastal Plains and smooth uplands of the eastern Piedmont, extending southward from Pennsylvania. The native vegetation was generally coniferous

Fig. 7 A brown podzolic landscape of New England. The "revival" of agriculture following earlier "abandonment" now makes the Coastal Lowlands a pleasing complex of modern dairy farms, orchards, and suburban homes backed by higher forested ridges. (Soil Conservation Service.)

Fig. 8   Strip cropping in the dissected Appalachian Plateau. The region includes bodies of podzols, red-yellow podzolic, and other groups as well as sols bruns acides, (derived primarily from the acid rocks). Many of the steep slopes have been cleared, limed, and used for pasture. Gentler slopes and ridge tops are in grain and hay. (Soil Conservation Service.)

forest, but it included mixtures with deciduous trees.

Summers in this region average hot and rainy. Winters are moderate to mild and rainy. Chemi-

cal weathering and biologic processes were relatively intense. Both red and yellow soils were subject to strong soil-forming and soil-degrading processes, (degrading from an agricultural point

Fig. 9   Potatoes on the Kenai Alaskan Peninsula. Soils here are chiefly podzols. Hardy vegetables, including turnips, kale, cabbage, and berries do well. Cattle can be pastured for 5 months. (Soil Conservation Service.)

of view). A high percentage of clay particles was formed and concentrated in the subsoils. Leaching waters removed a large part of the soluble nutrients.[7]

The leaf litter and other debris which fell to the forest floor were rapidly decomposed under the attack of the legions of microorganisms which flourish in this warm and humid environment. Hence the virgin soils had only a thin covering or organic matter overlying the surface, and only an inch or two of the dark surface soil became impregnated with humus (Fig. 10).

The soils are medium to strongly acid. Textures range from sandy to loam and clay loam types. The fine-textured types, however, are comparatively well aggregated. Although naturally low in nutrients and acids, both red and yellow soils are relatively easy to till and respond well to lime and fertilizer.[8]

Field and Forest. The South is a combination of forest, cropland, and pasture. Forests and woodlands occupy a large part of the area. In the gray-brown podzolic region, woodlands merely sprinkle the agricultural areas. They do not command as much of the land as they do throughout red-yellow podzolic regions.

Taken as a whole, the red-yellow podzolic soils rank below the gray-brown podzolic soils in natural fertility. The natural fertility of the yellow members is low, especially the sandy-textured soils. The natural fertility of the red members varies from low to medium. Moreover, millions of acres of poorly or imperfectly drained soils are mingled with the well-drained soils of the region, especially on the coastal plains and in the river valleys.

The topography includes countless slopes too steep for the plow. Both topography and many soils of the region tend to favor forest over farm,

Fig. 10   Profile of a southern red podzolic soil. In its virgin state, the upper part of the soil, beneath a thin layer of humus-impregnated surface soil, is a yellowish-brown (podzolized) horizon. The mid-profile beginning at a depth of 18 inches illustrates the darker, heavier red subsoil which slows down internal drainage. The widespread loss of the lighter-textured surface soil by erosion accounts for the red appearance of many fields in the region. (Soil Conservation Service.)

[7] Individual soils may still be relatively high in specific nutrients, however, because the formations from which they are derived were high in particular constituents.

[8] The type of soil formation to which the soils are subject is in part similar to that of the podzols (podzolic) and in part like that of humid tropical soils, latosolic. The red-yellow soils are not highly latosolic, however, although a limited number of such soils occur in the region.

and the southeastern region has two-thirds of the commercial forests of the United States. Unlike the forest-dominated podzols, however, most of the forest land is privately owned. This ownership is divided between lumber and pulp-and-paper companies who own large tracts of land and more than a million farmers and other small-tract owners. Many farmers combine production of forest products, such as lumber, pulpwood, and turpentine and resin, with their farming operations.

Cropland and Pasture. The land utilized for agriculture is mingled island-like with the forest lands, similar to the podzol region. But there are many more such islands and many are much larger, covering several hundred or even thousands of square miles in area except for a sprinkling of woodland. When adequately limed, fertilized, maintained in organic matter, and protected against erosion, both well-drained red and yellow soils may be made highly productive.

The cost of building up and maintaining a high level of productivity averages higher, however, than in the gray-brown podzolic region. Organic matter decomposes more rapidly under this climate. Lime and fertilizers are leached more quickly, requiring more frequent replacement to keep the soils at their maximum productivity. The Southeast consumes one-half of the mineral fertilizers produced in the United States.

Whereas the traditional agriculture of the region has long been cotton, corn, and tobacco, the climate is adapted to a large variety of starch, protein, fat, vegetable, and forage crops: soybeans, peanuts, small fruits, nuts, truck crops, citrus and deciduous fruits, and others. Each is more or less centered in one or more of the agricultural "islands" of the area.

One of the noteworthy agricultural changes in recent years is pasture and forage improvement and the increase in livestock, especially in quality dairy and beef cattle and poultry. Among other improvements, the introduction of new grasses now makes possible extensive and dependable green grazing throughout the year.

Conservation Farming. The rolling and rugged lands of the region have suffered immeasurably from erosion. For years, corn, cotton, and tobacco were planted at all angles across slopes, clean tilled, and then left bare in winter. In a region of heavy rains and relatively mild winters, every river has run muddy and red with soil material stripped from the naked hills.

Strip cropping, contour farming, and terracing are now largely replacing up-and-down-hill row cropping. Forest, grasses, and legumes are slowing down runoff. Soils are being built up with lime, fertilizer, and organic matter. The entire region is now fortunately included in the soil conservation districts.

LATOSOLS

The rainy forested lands of tropical regions are mantled with highly weathered reddish- to yellowish-brown soils which, when typically developed, have clayey subsoils that are remarkably friable and virtually nonsticky in nature.[9] Unlike podzolic soils, there is little difference in texture between surface and subsoil. The lower subsoil is deep, acid, and reticulately mottled.

Water moves through the low-plastic clay so rapidly that the land can often be worked almost immediately after rains. Erodability is accordingly low except on steep slopes. Although the virgin soils are fairly well supplied with nutrients from incorporated decomposed plant remains, they lose them rapidly under cultivation, and the clays have little capacity to "hold" nutrients. Frequent fertilization is therefore necessary to maintain productivity.

Puerto Rico and the Hawaiian Archipelago. Latosols occupy the humid interior uplands of Puerto Rico where rainfall varies from 50 to as much as 150 inches, and elevations range from 300 to 4000 feet. In the Hawaiian Islands, latosols occur under rainfall ranging from 10 to 400 inches and at elevations from sea level to 6000 feet. Unless bedrock is near the surface the soils have great depth.

The soils are highly productive when fertilized. Irrigation is needed where there are dry seasons. Sugar cane, coffee, tobacco, and citrus fruit are major commercial crops in Puerto Rico. The Hawaiian group is noted for pineapples and sugar.[10]

West Coast Types. On the West Coast, brown and reddish latosolic types interspread with

[9] Latosol is from Latin meaning brick. The clays were first described in India where they were used extensively for brick making.

[10] Although latosols feature these islands, they occupy only from one-third to one-fourth of the land. The mountainous topography, coupled with great range in rainfall, has created environments favorable for the local formation of a number of soil groups occurring on the mainland of the United States: podzols, gray-brown, red-prairie, red-brown, red-desert, and others.

podzols, brown-podzolic, sols bruns acides, and other groups[11] occupy the broad mountainous belt extending from the Olympic Peninsula of Washington southward through western Oregon into the Northwest Coast Range and Sierra Nevada of California. Laterization, however, appears less extreme. The soils are noteworthy for the small, rounded, shotlike aggregates or concretions disseminated through their subsoils.

The native forest cover was mainly fir, pine, and redwoods. The rainy season comes in winter, varying from 10 inches in the south to 30 or 40 inches in the north. Summer irrigation is important in the valleys.

Land use varies with topography: recreation and commercial timber in the mountains; tree crops (fruits and nuts) on the lower slopes; grains, hay, and dairying on the lowlands which are chiefly podzolic soils.

Many local bodies of red and brown latosolic soils are commingled with the red-yellow podzolic soils of the Southeastern states. They have about the same productivity as the red and yellow soils and are generally used for the same purposes.

[11] Not shown separately on the map.

PRAIRIE GROUPS

Tall-grass prairies once mantled the Interior Lowlands extending westward from the eastern forests to about the 100th meridian (Fig. 11). Beyond, to the foot of the Rocky Mountains, across the Great Plains, lies the short-grass country, (typically buffalo and grama grasses).

Compared to forests grassland formations have very different effects on soils. They produce great masses of fibrous roots in the upper foot or two of the soils. Many feeder roots go down even deeper. Grasses, moreover, take up large quantities of nutrients.

The leaves of natural grassland formations, however, unlike forest leaves, contribute relatively little to their soils. The roots play the important role. Each year appreciable parts of the roots die off, forming humus and liberating the nutrients brought up. Since the dead roots are in the soil, the humus and liberated nutrients are left *in* the soil body.

Forests deposit their contribution of organic matter and nutrients chiefly *on top* of the soil. Here surface waters continuously carry away both released nutrients and much of the humic

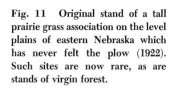

Fig. 11 Original stand of a tall prairie grass association on the level plains of eastern Nebraska which has never felt the plow (1922). Such sites are now rare, as are stands of virgin forest.

substances formed (noticeable in the brownish waters which drain from forests), leaving only a part to be incorporated into the soil body.

The Brunizems. The eastern part of the tall-grass prairies centering on Iowa and Illinois has a humid climate, averaging 30 or more inches of rain annually.[12] The soils which developed here have very dark-grayish brown surface soils, 6 to 20 inches thick, and are known as brunizems (brownish-black). They vary from slightly acid to only medium acid. The return of nutrients helped materially to offset the leaching effects of the humid climate. Unlike forest soils, the subsoils of normal brunizems are but slightly, if at all, heavier than the surface horizons. The soils are rich in plant nutrients.

Brunizems comprise the most productive of our grassland soils. Yet they were scorned by most of the early pioneer farmers migrating westward from the gray-brown forests, even though rainfall was essentially the same. Land incapable of growing trees was deemed too poor for crops! The pioneers preferred the local islands of forested upland scattered through the prairies or the wooded valleys and river bottoms.

However, when settlement finally began in the prairies, the pioneers found a manyfold paradise. They were spared the labor of clearing the forest. They found the rainfall and sunshine near-perfect for their crops. They were able to plant in naturally rich soils. Having nurtured wild grasses and herbs for centuries, the soils were admirably adapted to their domesticated kin, the cereals, and tame hay and pasture grasses. This land is now the heart of the Corn Belt. Its fields of corn, oats, soybeans, hay, and pasture sweep from horizon to horizon. Men can grow bumper crops and fatten many animals on this good land.

Conservation, a Major Problem. Many people who have not seen the prairie region think

the land is level or gently undulating, but many areas are moderately rolling. The prairie region has millions of long, gentle slopes on which the soils have been thinned by sheet erosion. Rivulets have scored many others. Some lands have been gullied, some severely (Fig. 12).

Soil conservation is a major problem in the prairie group—not because the soils have been generally ruined but because of their high agricultural quality. Now that the natural prairie grasses are gone, the soils are no longer enriched by their humus or rejuvenated by the nutrients they annually returned. Thus commercial fertilizer, manure, and such soil-building crops as grasses and legumes must be their substitutes. A few decades ago most farmers regarded their soils as inexhaustible, although no soils are so blessed. One of the striking revolutions in the prairie region in recent years has been the great increase in the use of mineral fertilizers.

Reddish Prairie Soils. Reddish prairie soils occupy central Oklahoma, extending somewhat northward into Kansas and southward into Texas. Because of greater oxidation under the higher temperatures of this area and because of the red color of the formations from which they developed, the soils of this group have brown or reddish-brown surface soils and red or reddish-brown subsoils.

The soils are naturally less productive than the "black" prairies of Iowa and Illinois. The reddish prairies are used chiefly for wheat, oats, grain sorghums, cotton, and forage. The hotter, and often drier, climate is better suited to grain sorghums than corn.

Grumusols. Dark, brunizem-like soils form the well-known Black Belt of Alabama-Mississippi and the Blacklands and Grand Prairies of Texas and southern Oklahoma. These soils were derived from quick-weathering limestone or marl formations originally mantled with grass. Their dark color and high organic matter resemble the Corn Belt prairie soils of Iowa and Illinois, but the soils are calcareous throughout.

The soils are heavy and clayey, show little difference in texture between surface and subsoil, but have a remarkable crumblike structure when

[12] The tall-grass associations are chiefly confined to the level, undissected uplands. Valley slopes and river bottoms and other local sites are occupied by deciduous associations. The prairie region is thus a mixture of two great soil groups—dominantly prairie soils with local bodies of gray-brown podzolics.

Fig. 12   The more rolling topography of the "flat" prairie. In many places the brunizem region is crossed by streams which reduced the smooth uplands to sometimes narrow divides and innumerable slopes. Many of the valleys were originally occupied by oak, elm, hickory, and other trees which gave rise to gray-brown podzolic soils. The "prairie" region is really a mixed combination of brunizems (regionally) and gray-brown podzolic soils (locally). (Soil Conservation Service.)

dry. Owing to marked swelling and shrinkage of the clay, as it takes in water followed by drying, the soils have developed a peculiar low relief of microknolls and microvalleys, known as gilgai.[13]

The Blacklands are famed cotton lands. The Grand Prairies grow small grains, sorghum, livestock, and some cotton. The Rio Grande Plain, the Colorado Mesas, and the California Ranges are chiefly grazing country.

CHERNOZEMS

These soils are the subhumid members of the tall-grass formations of the western plains. Tall grasses predominate in the eastern or more humid parts of the region, changing gradually

[13] Grumusol (from the Latin) signifies hillock. Similar soils are found on the high mesas of the Colorado Plateaus and extend through the Coast Ranges of California under mixtures of grass and scattered oak.

to shorter grasses in the western or drier parts of the plains.

This great soil group is the American equivalent of the renowned Russian black earths, from which this name was derived. Chernozem means "black earth."

Except where interrupted by the Nebraska Sandhills, the principal body of chernozems occupies a 150-mile wide belt immediately west of the brunizems. A much narrower belt borders the eastern edge of the Columbia Plateau. Many smaller bodies are scattered through valleys and uplands of the Western Highlands.

Rainfall averages from 20 to 30 inches. Leaching has accordingly been limited and the soils are high in mineral nutrients. The near-black surface soil contains up to 5 and 10 per cent of humus, often to a depth of several feet, because of the heavy grass cover.

The soils are excellently granulated and the

structural aggregates are very durable. Like all normal grassland soils, both surface and subsoil horizons show little difference in texture.

Carbonate Accumulations. One of the distinguishing features of the chernozems is a layer or horizon of carbonate accumulation in the lower part of their subsoils. In humid regions, rainwater entering the soil body carries the carbonates and other soluble salts that are formed to relatively great depths, if not into the underlying ground-water reservoir. In the chernozem region, however, rainfall is limited. Most of the carbonates and other soluble salts are carried to only the lower subsoil and are there precipitated. The lower subsoils are accordingly light-gray or whitish in color and are often streaked

with grayish or whitish flecks and bands of carbonates.[14] Similar accumulations of carbonates characterize all low-rainfall soils at varying depths[15] (Fig. 13).

A Grain Belt. The chernozems possess the characteristics popularly associated with ideal agricultural soils, although they are best adapted to grain. Because of their naturally high content of soluble plant nutrients, they produce high quality grains—high in the nutrients essential to good health. They are also well adapted for the production of forage crops such as clover and alfalfa.

Unfortunately, the rainfall is not always such that these soils can measure up to their potential productivity. Wet and dry years follow each other in irregular and unpredictable succession. Wet years and good general rains at critical growth and fruiting periods bring bumper crops. But dry years, erratic rains, hot winds, and low-snow years produce low yields or failure.

Because the chernozems are so similar to the prairie soils, the first settlers merely extended the cropping systems that they had followed in the prairie region into the chernozem region. Arriving during a period of good rains, early settlers enjoyed a few good crop years. But when these were followed by a series of dry years, many abandoned the country.

By capitalizing on the large acreages made possible by modern mechanization, the agriculture of the chernozems is now chiefly a combination of grain farming and livestock production. The stock is pastured chiefly on the rough and rolling lands bordering the natural drainageways and streams crossing the region, on the poorly drained basins scattered over the plains, and on

Fig. 13 Profile of a Nebraska chernozem. The rich, granular black surface, often 18 to 24 inches thick, overlies a calcareous, well-developed subsoil to the depth of the spade. The spade rests on the loess formation, the material from which this soil was derived. Note the depth of grass roots. (Soil Conservation Service.)

[14] Carbonates, especially calcium carbonate, or so-called lime, are one of the more abundant chemical salts produced in the decomposition of mineral matter. Magnesium carbonates are common but less abundant.

[15] Chernozems and prairie soils closely resemble each other, except for the layer of lime accumulation due to differences in rainfall. As noted, both are dark colored, are naturally high in available nutrients, have excellent granulation, and show little contrast in texture between the surface soils and subsoils in their natural state.

Fig. 14 Furrow irrigation using siphon tubes to carry water from the main ditch. Parts of the chernozem region are underlain by extensive groundwaters which the "gasoline age" facilitates pumping to the surface for irrigation. The water underlying the region, however, is inadequate for more than relatively local irrigation. (Soil Conservation Service.)

the sandier lands. Forage is produced on the stream bottoms and on terraces under irrigation.

The cropped uplands form a gigantic grain belt whose make-up varies with latitude. The northern part raises a mixture of hard spring wheat, oats, barley, rye, and flax. The central chernozems grow chiefly corn, some oats, and hard, winter wheat. Here the climatic conditions permit a kind of extension of the Corn Belt westward beyond the prairie region (Fig. 14). The southern part forms the chief, hard, winter wheat region of the United States and part of the northern portion of the major grain sorghum belt of the Southwest.

The Palouse Hills. In contrast to the level plains of the mid-continent chernozems, the Columbia Plateau chernozems are predominantly rolling lands. This is the well-known Palouse Hill country. The rainfall approximates

only 20 inches, but most of it falls in the cool seasons of the year. The land is used chiefly for large-scale wheat farming with summer fallowing every few years. The soils are very fertile, but many areas have been seriously eroded. Most of the land is under cultivation and, until recently, was left without a winter cover. Winter and spring rains falling on frozen ground and rapid thaws of heavy snow cause the most damage. Crop rotations, surface mulching, winter cover, and rough tillage now help protect much of the land.

California Prairies. Scattered through the Coastal Ranges of California are many bodies of dark-colored soils,[16] some of which resemble the chernozems and some the brunizems of the Middle West. Rainfall, which averages 15 to 25

[16] Individual areas are too small to be differentiated on the map.

inches annually, falls chiefly during the cool winter. Summers are warm and dry.

These dark-colored soils developed under grasslands with scattered oak. The rolling, hilly character of the land is not well adapted to cropping, but the soils make excellent grazing land. Cultivated areas are usually erosive.

CHESTNUT GROUPS

The name refers to the chestnut or dark brown color of the soils.

These are the soils of the semiarid plains immediately west of the Great Plains' chernozems. A broken belt borders the Palouse chernozems

Fig. 15 Profile of a Great Plains chestnut soil. The dark-colored surface soil containing most of the grass roots overlies the light-colored horizon of lime accumulation at a depth of 10 to 12 inches. Original grasses were short and mid-grasses. These soils take in moisture easily and retain it for crop use when properly handled. (Soil Conservation Service.)

of the Columbia Plateau on the west. Many local bodies are scattered through semiarid valleys, mesas, and plateaus of the Mountain and West Coast states.

Under the semiarid climate, the soils are only slightly leached, and the zone of carbonate accumulation of most soils lies only a foot or so below the surface. The short grasses of the chestnut soils produce less organic matter than the tall grasses of the chernozems, and their root systems are less dense and shallower. The soils are accordingly lower in organic matter and lighter in color than the chernozems. The chestnut-colored or dark brown surface is only about a foot or less in thickness (Fig. 15).

The soils are well supplied with available nutrients, and are highly productive when rains are adequate. Rainfall, as with the chernozems, is the critical limitation of this group, but the hazards are very much greater. The proportion of years when the rainfall is right in amount and distribution is much lower than in the chernozem belt.

Cropped Land and Range. The regions of the chestnut soils, like most of the short-grass country, supported the great buffalo herds as they roamed the Great Plains. They were followed by the range cattle industry which flourished during the latter part of the nineteenth century. Today, the chestnut soils mark the general frontier of crop production that is primarily based upon natural rainfall.

This frontier is a vacillating one, however. It swings eastward or westward as the rain years vary. Yields per acre average low. Land ownership must be large to offset the low yields. Without power machinery to cultivate large acreages, these fertile soils would be little more than rangelands.

Land use viewed from the air presents a complex of cropped land and range (Fig. 16). Except where irrigated—and this is chiefly local—crops are mainly drier-land extensions of those produced on the humid soils immediately to the east: small grains, sorghum, corn, and flax. Although yields run lower, grain quality averages

Fig. 16 Cultivating a young field windbreak planted to check wind erosion. The seven-row planting consists (left to right) of cedar, pine, hackberry, American elm, boxelder, Chinese elm, and Russian olive. Windbreaks afford protection for distances equal to twenty times the height of the barrier. (Soil Conservation Service.)

high, especially in proteins. Cattle are the chief range stock of the plains and foothills; sheep on summer pasture graze in the associated highlands.

The high fertility of these soils, coupled with occasional good rain years, is an ever-tempting urge to overexpand crop production. The *long-time* average rain, however, is the important consideration, especially the amount above that required for any crop at all.

Although relatively well supplied with plant nutrients when compared with soils developed under humid climates, experience is indicating that mineral fertilizers, paradoxical as this may

seem, for these soils help stretch the limited rainfall.

The Columbia Plateau chestnut soils are almost solely a low-rainfall wheat country of large-scale farms.

Reddish Chestnut Soils. Starting in southwestern Kansas, the soils of the Southern Plains become increasingly reddish, and the climate subtropical (Fig. 17). The reddish chestnuts include most of the grain sorghum belt of our Southwest. The Texas Panhandle region is also an important center of wheat and cotton production, some of which has been grown under well irrigation in recent years.

Fig. 17 Profile of a deep, moderately permeable red chestnut soil showing a coarse blocky structure. The horizon of lime accumulation begins around 20 inches and reaches a maximum concentration at 4 feet. (Soil Conservation Service.)

Dust-Bowl Land. The reddish chestnut area includes a large proportion of the dust-bowl country. Dust storms are a natural phenomenon of not only this region but of all our low rainfall regions. They occur year after year with varied intensities, first in one place and then another, scattered irregularly over all the dry plains and deserts.

Dust storms were well known before they attracted national attention in the dry 1930's, when a series of exceptionally low-rainfall years

followed the big plow-up of the late 'teens and 1920's, and the storms reached giant size. There have been several bigger-than-ordinary recurrences since. Control of water and of water erosion is fully as important as prevention of wind erosion in potential dust-storm areas. Water is the key to both cropping and grazing. The chestnut soils are safest for the plow and can carry the greatest livestock population under a system of water conservation. But not all the soils are wholly safe even under such a system. Some blow so easily they should never be plowed and only lightly grazed.

BROWN GROUPS

These soils mantle the drier western part of the Great Plains. They also comprise the transition between the chestnut and desert groups of the Intermountain Region, occupying small plains, valleys, mesas, and plateaus throughout the area.

Short grasses, shrubs, and bunch grasses form the native vegetation with many near-bare areas. The limited plant cover means less organic matter and hence brown-colored soils with surface horizons only 5 to 10 inches thick.

As rainfall averages only about 15 inches, the soils are only slightly leached and are high in

Fig. 18 Cattle on the Great Plains of South Dakota. Small sagebrush and other weeds are beginning to displace the valuable grasses owing to overgrazing.

mineral nutrients. The whitish carbonate zone is only a foot or so deep.

Range and Dry-Farming. The soils are potentially highly productive. However, the low rainfall and hazards of wind erosion make them better adapted as a whole to livestock range. This is primarily the realm of the stockman and the ranch of modern times. The potentials of livestock production under good range management, such as proper rate of stocking, reseeding, and water conservation, are high (Fig. 18).

Dry-land crop production, however, is even more marginal than in the chestnut region. Large areas of these brown soils have been broken and dry-farmed to wheat and sorghums with moderate success during good rain years. But failures have been frequent and good crop years with adequate rains are few and often far between. Crop farming has greatest prospect of success when operated on even a greater scale than in the chestnut region and with modern machinery able to act rapidly at critical crop junctures and under optimum conservation practices.

Reddish-Brown Soils. Similar to the chestnut soils, these brown soils become increasingly reddish in the Southern Plains, as temperatures increase to subtropical and summers become hotter. From western Texas, the soils extend westward into the Southwestern Plateaus and Great Basin Region of the Southwest, including their old alluvial fans. The soils are not differentiated from the Brown Soils on the map.

The vegetation changes to thin, short grass with scattered bunch grass, shrub, and mesquite. The upper subsoils are sometimes tough and heavy, and the calcareous subsoils become pinkish white.

The reddish-brown group is generally unsuited to cropping, especially the loose, sandy soils. When unprotected, the soil is continuously shifted by the wind. On occasion, fence-row dunes up to 10 feet high have piled up in some areas (Fig. 19).

Fig. 19   The result of leaving a sandy soil on the Southern Great Plains without adequate protection against wind erosion following cultivation.

Much of the rangeland has been damaged by erosion brought on by overstocking and in turn overgrazing. When land is overgrazed, less palatable grasses, as well as weeds and shrubs of low feeding value, take the place of the more valuable perennial grasses and herbs, and the stand of vegetation thins out. This opens the soil to erosion. Streams once clear and stocked with fish become subject to floods and silting, and their value for irrigation, recreation, power, and local water supply is reduced.

Noncalcic Brown Soils. The foothills and rolling uplands of California with winter rains (10 to 20 inches) and hot dry summers have brown to reddish-brown soils that lack the carbonate horizons of the Great Plains soils. Such carbonates as are formed are leached out by winter rains, leaving the soils "noncalcic" in character. The surface soils are low in organic matter and the subsoils relatively high in clay.

The native vegetation under which this group developed was grass and brush with a sprinkling of deciduous and coniferous trees. The soils with their winter rains are adapted to both grain and grazing, and also to fruit when irrigation is available.

Fig. 20 Desert shrub on an Arizona red desert soil. The light-reddish surface soil is sprinkled with gravel and underlain by a reddish, heavy subsoil. Note the large percentage of bare ground without vegetation. Since the leaf fall from the shrubs is also inconsequential, the soils receive little or no humus from their open plant cover.

DESERT GROUPS

This group includes the deserts and semideserts of the intermountain plains and plateaus of the West. Rainfall averages 3 to 12 inches. Summers are hot. Winters in the North are cool to cold, but mild in the tropical Southwest.

Vegetation is sparse and open. Bare ground prevails over plant cover. The dominant plants are desert shrubs with scattered bunch grass, brush, and short-lived grasses and herbs that green up after rains.

The soils are only slightly leached, low in humus but rich in mineral nutrients except phosphorus, and often salty. The carbonate zone is very shallow. In older soils it may form an indurated layer called caliche at some depth. Winds pick up fine soil particles, often leaving the surface a residue of pebbles and stones which form the so-called desert pavement.

Three color groups make up most of our desert region: the brownish-gray soils of the semidesert, the gray soils of the central and northern desert, and the red and reddish-brown of the Southwest (Fig. 20).

Grazing Lands. Except where alluvial fan or river valley permits irrigation, these lands are the undisputed home of the sheepman and the cattle rancher. The range can be greatly benefited by reseeding, fire protection, development of water resources, and good management. Improvements can be made by controlled sagebrush burning or chemical sprays to remove low quality vegetation and encourage growth of more palatable forage. The choice rangelands have the best supplies of stock water (streams, springs, accessible well water) and irrigable land, where alfalfa and other feed crops can be grown to supplement the limited natural forage.

Solonchak. Scattered throughout the low-rainfall regions of the West from the desert to the chernozems are many small areas of saline soils having a high concentration of soluble salts. They are known as solonchak soils, from the

Russian term for salt. They are the result of locally poor or imperfect drainage. As water collecting in the areas evaporates, it leaves behind salts which presently accumulate in such quantities that only a sparse growth of salt-loving grasses and shrubs can occupy the soil.

Solonetz. When, for some reason, drainage improves in the course of time and the excess salts are leached out, solonchak soils are converted to solonetz or alkali soils. Unlike solonchak soils, these intrazonal soils are highly alkaline, very dark in color and have hard (when dry) and sticky (when wet) subsoils. During periods of low rainfall, the surface soil of many solonetz areas is blown away exposing the hard clay. The shallow basins form the numerous, peculiar so-called "slick-spots" scattered throughout the Great Plains.

Solonetz areas provide poor to fair grazing. Most of them are merely wasteland, but some can be reclaimed through artificial leaching and the use of calcium and sulfur salts.

ALASKAN TUNDRA

Mosses, lichens, dwarf shrubs, and creeping woody plants form the chief plant cover of large areas of the coastal plain and plateau of Arctic Alaska. As the short, cool summer severely limits organic decay, the soils are mantled with a dark-brown to yellowish turf, matted with the fibrous and woody roots of the plant cover.

As chemical action is also limited, the soil has little clay and is chiefly a mixture of silt, fine sand, humus, and imperfectly decomposed organic matter. Lighter brown, coarse silt loam, streaked with iron stains and black organic matter, forms the lower subsoil. Permafrost may or may not be present. A microrelief of low mounds and shallow depressions, the result of seasonal freeze and thaw, characterizes many local areas.

The land is unexcelled for pastoral nomadism based on reindeer, but as yet is virtually unutilized for commercial meat production because of high transportation costs and undeveloped markets. The reindeer is at home in a snowstorm, contentedly crops the forage of his climate, and needs little care.

PLANOSOLS

Mingled in local bodies in nearly all the zonal soils are areas of near-flat relief mantled with soils having heavier or more strongly "cemented" subsoils than the normal soils associated with them. Soils with such subsoils are known a planosols (soils of flat plains). They develop under both grassland and forest associations.

Although intermixed with nearly all of the great soil groups, they have developed chiefly on flat uplands extending from the forested gray-brown soils of southeastern Ohio westward into northern Missouri, and from the brunizems of southern Iowa and eastern Nebraska southward into eastern Oklahoma.

Soils with even denser subsoils mantle the gently sloping terraces and benchlands bordering the Central Valley of California. These soils have silica-iron cemented hardpans that are often a foot thick and are impermeable to both roots and water.

The flat topography and heavy subsoils restrict drainage, so that the soils tend to be wet in spring and droughty in summer and to retard root penetration. Corn yields average lower than on the dark, normal prairies. Winter wheat, soybeans, and hay are important. Sorghums and cotton are grown on the Oklahoma and Texas planosols. The California planosols are chiefly in wheat, barley, and pasture, except where water for irrigating fruit is available. The claypan is then broken to permit drainage and root penetration.

HYDROMORPHIC SOILS

Intermingled with the normal, well-drained zonal soil groups are also innumerable shallow basins, old lake beds, and other depressional upland and lowland areas occupied by imperfectly or poorly drained soils. The chief concentrations of such soils are on the outer Coastal Plain extending from Chesapeake Bay to Texas, in the Northeastern States, the Great Lake States, and the West Coast lowlands. Excessive moisture played a dominant role in their formation.

The soils are known variously as gleys, groundwater podzols, marshlands, and bog soils, such as peats and mucks. Gley soils develop lower horizons that are sticky and compact and bluish-gray or olive-gray because of their wet condition. Groundwater podzols resemble ordinary podzols: the upper soil is bleached light-gray, and the subsoil is a dark-brown hardpan

irregularly cemented by organic matter or iron. Bog soils develop under swamp or marsh vegetation. Peats comprise partially decomposed organic material that is still identifiable, whereas muck materials are thoroughly decomposed.

The chief uses of these soils are forest, wildlife and pasture. Only restricted areas are cultivated. When adequately drained and fertilized (Fig. 21), they are valued for special crops, such as celery, sugar cane, and truck crops in Florida; rice on the Louisiana-Texas Coastal Plain and the Sacramento-San Joaquin delta; blueberries in the Lake states.

Mucks are especially prized. They contain a

Fig. 21 Artificial drainage is a necessity on imperfectly and poorly drained soils for most crops. This soil is naturally well-drained to a depth of two feet, but requires drainage of the lower subsoil to make most effective use of the thick root zone. (Soil Conservation Service.)

Fig. 22   A mint field on muck land with windbreak erected against prevailing winds to protect the soil from blowing when it dries.

Fig. 23   Nebraska sandhills: a succession of dunes with intervening basins, now generally stabilized with tall grass associations. Yucca plants are in foreground, bunches of little-bluestem grass in middle ground. (Soil Conservation Service.)

high proportion of available plant foods, although additions of lime, potash, and minor elements are beneficial.

Shrinkage, fire, wind erosion, and excessive drainage are major conservation problems. Following drainage, the organic matter decomposes more rapidly and undergoes a more or less long period of shrinkage. Winds readily pick up the dry, fluffy, muck particles from fields unprotected by windbreaks (Fig. 22). Dry muck burns readily, and smoldering underground fires, difficult to extinguish, have destroyed many tons of this limited soil resource. Late spring and early fall frosts are cropping hazards of the northern muck lands.

SANDHILLS

In north-central Nebraska is a huge sand sheet of some 20,000 square miles which has been molded by winds into an irregular succession of billowy and ridgelike dunes with innumerable intervening sandy basins, pockets, and irregularly shaped valleys (Fig. 23). Except in local "blow-outs," the dunes support a mixture of tall and short grasses with scattered sagebrush, yucca, and other drought-resistant plants. The valleys are usually floored with sand con-

taining slightly more clay and support a heavier grass cover. In many valleys, the underlying water table intersects the land surface, creating shallow lakes of various shapes and sizes (up to 1 mile long) with wet, sandy borders.

This great body of sand is a vast, unique, and excellent cattle-ranch country. It is exceptionally suited to grasses. Water supplies are easily obtained from the groundwater. Although

Fig. 24   Overgrazed dune sand showing many bare spots, thin grass, and useless yucca. (Soil Conservation Service.)

droughty in character, the sands absorb water rapidly with little runoff. Water falling in even light rains reaches plant roots before much evaporation takes place. Unless overgrazed or overtrampled, the region will produce a good grass crop year after year (Fig. 24).

ALLUVIAL LANDS

The floodplains bordering the vast network of stream courses draining the United States are made up of water-laid soil material. These materials are sediments eroded from the drainage basins of each stream and deposited during flood periods on the valley floor.[17] Similar materials form the alluvial fans spread out at the base of many mountain slopes of the Western Highlands.

The features of these soils are largely determined by the type of materials laid down and the manner in which the materials were deposited, although in time, the vegetation they acquire and local drainage conditions may modify their character.

The alluvial soils of the arid West are usually light-colored, low in organic matter, and rich in mineral nutrients and lime; whereas those of the humid Northeast are generally brown or grayish-brown with at least moderate amounts of organic matter and plant nutrients.

As a group, the alluvial soils are the most productive of the nation. They are noted for their high yields and durability, although their total acreage is small and they include a number of individual types that are too wet, too sandy, too salty, or too alkaline for ordinary crop production. They generally average higher in plant nutrients than the upland soils with which they are associated, have a good physical constitution, and suffer less from drought. Many older alluvial fans develop hardpans, however, necessitating blasting before crops will do well on them.

[17] Chiefly by natural or geologic erosion. Accelerated erosion induced by man has added only a comparatively thin veneer.

Only the largest area of alluvial soils, the lower Mississippi, is shown in Fig. 1. This is a belt of relatively dark-colored and highly fertile soils whose parent materials were collected from the rich prairie soils, the chernozems, the gray-brown podzolic soils, and the topsoils of every other great soil group in this far-flung river basin. The belt has added advantage of lying in the highly productive subtropical climate of the South: it is a projection of highly fertile land into a region of relatively leached soils. This lowland is one of the more productive areas of the South. Its naturally well-drained lands and those easily drained artificially are intensively planted to cotton, sugar cane, soybeans, and similar high-utility crops.

MOUNTAINOUS AND ROUGH BROKEN LAND

The mountains, plateaus, and rough hill lands of the United States include many areas in which an inch to a foot or two of soil mantles the bedrock. The soils are immature and more or less stony, with frequent exposures of bedrock. They are known as lithosols, from the Greek word for rock, *lithos*. Most of the land is rough and rolling, but there are also areas of smooth or level land where more fully developed soils evolve.

The soils which evolve reflect necessarily the active processes of soil development of their immediate site as well as the effect of the local geologic materials from which they were derived. The rough plateau and mountainous lands of the Appalachians, the Pacific Coast, and the central and northern Rockies, having humid climates and forest formations, promote the formation of many local bodies of podzols, sols bruns acides, gray-wooded soils, and other podzolic types. In turn, the interior highlands of the West, with chiefly low rainfall and vegetation varying from sagebrush, mesquite, and grass to open forest, favor chiefly the formation of vertically zoned desert, brown, chestnut, and chernozemic types.

These rough and rocky lands are of value principally for forests, pasture, grazing, and recreation, depending upon the climate, vegetation, and location. Forests are dominant in the more rugged, least accessible, and rainier lands. Pastures occur chiefly in the humid eastern highlands. Here are numerous small farms which cultivate the smoother, gentler slopes and the deeper soils and which utilize the lithosols for pasture or woodlot. The western unforested lands are chiefly summer livestock range. Their natural carrying capacity is low but, in general, higher than that of the neighboring lowlands.

These highlands comprise one of our major recreational resources. Their rugged terrain and variously sculptured forms have universal appeal. They shelter many forms of wildlife and many varieties of plantlife. Both the desertlike vegetation of the dry mountains and the forests and alpine meadows of the rainier highlands have their enthusiastic followers. Sparkling lakes and clear-flowing streams beautify many valleys. Numerous sites provide breathtaking views.

A COMPREHENSIVE OVERVIEW

We are now ready to combine our zonal soils into two broad inclusive groups to obtain a simple, comprehensive picture of the soils of the mainland of the United States as a whole.

The podzols, gray-wooded, gray-brown podzolic, sols bruns acides, brown podzolic, red-yellow podzolic, and latosols all developed under humid climates and forest vegetation. We may refer to these as our humid-forest soils.

The chernozems, chestnut, brown, and desert soils developed under low rainfall climates and vegetation ranging from grass formations to forest. We may term these our low-rainfall soils.[18]

Viewed broadly, the low-rainfall group comprises our "good" soils as measured by ideal soil characteristics. The soils are relatively high in available nutrients and lime. They have good physical constitutions, except for local hardpans, heavy subsoils, or other local conditions. Excluding the deserts, the soils are well supplied with humus. They are highly productive when rainfall is adequate or the land can be irrigated.

Soils of the humid-forest group, on the other hand, are relatively "poor" soils. They are comparatively low in available mineral nutrients, lime and humus, and are relatively acid in reaction. The virgin soils had only a few inches of dark-colored surface soil beneath the leaf litter, compared with a foot or more of organic-rich surface soil of the chernozem, chestnut, and brown soils. Their subsoils are relatively heavier than the surface soils, and structural aggregates are less durable under cultivation.

Yet the "poor" humid-forest soils comprise our chief agricultural soils because rainfall is as important as soil character in plant growth. We can make up nutrient deficiencies by addition of fertilizers, and we can improve physical imperfections with lime and organic matter. Of course, some members of the group are limited by short growing seasons, such as the podzols and subarctic brown forest soils.

Although the low-rainfall group are inherently more fertile, we cannot as yet make rainfall "to order;" and water resources of low-rainfall regions are wholly inadequate to irrigate more than a small part of the soils. Rivers are few, and depletion of groundwaters is even now a serious problem in many areas.

The brunizems are a happy combination of the desirable qualities of both comprehensive groups. Except for the California prairies, which are limited by dry summers, the brunizems are relatively high in plant nutrients as well as blessed with a generally adequate rainfall. In fact, they comprise one of the more productive soils the world possesses.

Land Use in the Humid-Forest Group. Because settlement of the United States mainland began on the eastern coasts, it was initiated on

---

[18] In an earlier system of classification, the low-rainfall soils were included in a group termed pedocals, and the humid-forest, pedalfers, but these terms are no longer adequately descriptive. See footnote 1.

lands of the humid-forest group. The pioneer-farmer accordingly began growing his crops on our relatively poorer soils. This was true whether he settled in New England on the brown forest soils or in Virginia on the red-yellow podzolic soils. At first, he obtained fair and often large yields (large for his day) on the fresh, virgin soils, and especially in comparison with the yields he had been able to obtain on the worn-down soils of his native country. The average humid-forest soil had a modest supply of available nutrients, a friable structure, and rainfall sufficient for a diversified agriculture.

However, the limited supply of nutrients was soon exhausted, the soils became gradually less friable under the pressure crops put on the land, and yields declined until they were no longer considered very profitable. When this occurred, the pioneer abandoned his fields and cleared a new farm out of the wilderness.

SOIL ROBBERS AND SOIL CONSERVATIONISTS

The pioneer farmer who "exhausted" his soil and his present-day counterpart have been roundly condemned as "soil robbers" and "soil miners." But this is hardly an unqualified fair judgment considering how relatively low in nutrients the soils were to begin with. They had been leached long before any colonist set foot in the New World, and probably before Rome, or Greece, or even Egypt flourished. The colonial farmer did little more than "rob" lands that natural conditions had already reduced to a relatively low state of agricultural fertility.

A far-sighted individual, like George Washington, appreciated the value of crop rotations, manure, keeping up organic matter, erosion-prevention measures, and other good practices. But the average pioneer-farmer knew little or nothing about them. Facts based on careful research were lacking. The first agricultural colleges for research, teaching, and general dissemination of agricultural knowledge were not established until 1855. Furthermore, a huge untilled continent lay before the pioneers. They were few in number, and the virgin land seemed infinite in terms of the simple tools they had—the hand-wielded ax and the horse-drawn plow.

Our humid-forest lands are now a stronghold of soil conservation. They include the majority of our soil conservation districts (nearly 3000) and most farmers in these districts are now soil conservationists in both spirit and practice. Yet, unfortunately, sheet wash, rills, and gullies are still degrading thousands of acres of good cropland. Dissemination of knowledge at all times, and even more its general use, is slow—usually very slow.

COWS OR CAPSULES? One of the distinguishing features of our century is the widespread migration of population taking place into the countryside surrounding our towns and cities. Every day innumerable acres of farmland are sold for suburban homes, commercial enterprises, factories, and other nonfarm uses. Although chiefly on the West Coast and in the humid East, where the majority of our cities and an important part of our good farmlands are located, the movement is nationwide.

This out-to-the-land migration has engulfed millions of acres of good farmland, and it promises to take over millions more during the remainder of the century. Bulldozers are busy uprooting farm after farm to provide space for the new homes, shops, and factories flocking into the country—rich dairy farms in the Lake States and New England, rich corn belt farms in the prairie region, rich cotton farms in the South, and rich orange groves in California. Suburban developments are even taking over good land in the irrigated valleys of our western states, where land suitable for irrigation is at a premium.

Many people still believe that the productivity of our lands is almost limitless, that we need not be concerned over the future. "Science will find an answer." It is true that our agricultural scientists have shown us how to increase our land productivity amazingly. They have also shown us how to convert sawdust and other plant materials into nutritious, and even tasty, concoctions. We can grow food materials in fresh or sea water. We can dispense with cows and chickens and hogs and obtain our proteins from cheaper substitutes.

All these answers are not so attractive, however. Most of us prefer genuine milk, meat, grain, fruits, and vegetables to sawdust *cuisine,* or some sea-grown composite, or a synthetic capsule.

PRIME FARMLAND. Prime farmland in the United States is limited despite the country's great size. Each year as our population and the world's population surge toward the unprecedent numbers it appears destined to attain, we shall feel this limitation more keenly. There is no more to be had, no unconquered wilderness, and prime farmland cannot be made to order. Examples can, of course, be cited where some poor sandy tract or other has been made productive by pouring fertilizer, organic matter, or irrigation water into it. But such reclamation is costly. Far better to keep our good croplands for farming than to spend time and resources patching up poor lands to take their place!

Although we still possess appreciable potential, and all we know about good land management and increasing productivity is not as yet practiced on all of our lands, we should begin to conserve all the good farmland we possibly can and dedicate it to farming, just as we dedicate forest, recreation, and other lands. In cities, good residential areas are protected from invasion by commercial and industrial enterprises. In turn, we reserve prime industrial lands for industry. In the country, good farm communities need similar protection against unnecessary suburban invasions.

Land Use in the Low-Rainfall Group. The humid-forest and the low-rainfall groups are world types, that is, most of the soils of the world could be similarly grouped.

The world's greatest body of low-rainfall soils extends from the dry grasslands and deserts of Africa, across Arabia and central and southern Asia, into western China. For centuries, these natural grazing lands were the domain of the hunter and the nomadic herdsman. The rainfall, like that of the low-rainfall groups of the United States, was too low and too irregular for the limited hoe and/or draft-animal agriculture of the pre-machine age. The cultivator confined himself to the oases or the more humid borders. Even here he had little or no wood for house or fuel. His water supply was limited chiefly to streams, shallow wells, and springs.

FROM RANGE TO FARM. The latter part of the nineteenth century witnessed the beginning of a revolutionary change in the age-old economy of these lands. The cultivator began elbowing his fields farther and farther into the grazing regions, pushing the herdsmen into the drier and desert lands. The Soviet Union's unsuccessful effort to expand its agriculture into the dry lands of central Asia is the closing chapter of the change in that continent.

In the United States, the chernozem, chestnut, and brown soils were chiefly the home of the plains Indian before the advent of the white man. The Indian hunted the buffalo and other herbivores. Then came the stockman, the counterpart of the Old-World pastoral people. But his days were limited. After a few decades of running stock on the open range, he was forced into the drier plains by the pioneer-farmer advancing westward in search of new land.

Beginning with the subhumid chernozems, the farmer-settler turned these rich soils into grain fields, and planted the reddish chestnut of the southern Great Plains to sorghum and cotton. Having nourished wild grasses and herbs for centuries, the chernozems provided ideal conditions for their domesticated relatives, the cereals. Cotton, which is surprisingly tolerant of low rainfall, found the reddish southern grasslands of the Texas-Oklahoma plains naturally far superior to the poorer red-yellow podzolic soils. Livestock have remained in the region chiefly as an adjunct to farming, to graze on local lands unsuited to cropping.

As the frontier moved westward, the chestnut

and then the brown soil groups experienced a similar revolution, except that crops gradually decreased and cattle increased in importance as the land became drier and drier.

A number of converging factors contributed to this over-all change in land use. (1) The building of the railroads and their extension into the region provided cheap transportation. The chief crops—grain, cotton, and livestock—were all bulky crops. The railroads provided low-cost transportation to ship out the bulky crops and to bring in all necessities the region did not have or could grow. (2) The development of agricultural machinery provided the means for cultivating large acreages. Farms in the chernozem belt need to be large—in the chestnut region, still larger—to provide living standards comparable to the humid East. The invention of steel plows with moldboard and share of mirror-like smoothness and with curvature able to cut and invert the entire furrow slice was especially important. (3) The region enjoyed an unusual series of rainy years that were broken chiefly by comparatively short or minor droughts during much of the period of settlement. (4) The invention of barbed wire met the need for fencing where trees and stone were not available. (5) Deep-well drilling solved the water-supply problem on the uplands. (6) Cheap land and good prices for grain and cotton offset all other limitations.

DUST AND DROUGHT. Years of one-crop farming and summer fallowing[19] eventually broke down the soil structure, however. Each year the farmer fitted the land for his next crop, he exposed some of the rich humus of the top soils, with its teeming zoologic life, to a scorching sun. The hot sun gradually oxidized the organic matter and killed the valuable soil population. When soil grains lost the aggregating effects of humus, they fell apart and the soil turned to dust.

---

[19] When land is summer fallowed, it is not seeded but merely cultivated after rains to destroy weeds and to conserve the moisture for the next year's crops by forming a dust mulch. Summer fallowing was a common practice throughout the plains.

The 1930's ushered in the longest and worst drought on record. Great dust storms swept the region. Winds literally blew seeds, and sometimes seedlings, out of the land, shifted loose soil into drifts, or stripped the land to the depth it had been plowed.

Droughts and dust storms had occurred many times before. Records indicate they had taken place again and again at least as far back as the previous hundred years, very irregularly and unpredictably. But in the 1930's the overworked land was in poorer condition than ever before.

Many people faced ruin. Thousands migrated to the wetter and irrigated lands of the Pacific Coast states. The region was not emptied of its population, however. Many stuck it out. Nor were the plains one vast "dust bowl." Thousands of fields did not blow seriously because they had not been overexploited. On land protected with vegetation, dead or alive, or left rough and cloddy, blowing was checked. The subhumid chernozems were least affected by the drought. The arid brown soils were most damaged. Their dry acres should never have been broken during this period.

LOW-RAIN FARMING. Cropland in this low-rainfall country must be carefully sorted from the nothing-but-range land, and then managed conservatively. No acre of rangeland should ever be plowed again. Most of the good cropland is in the chernozem region, the least is in the brown soil region, but both range and farmland are much intermingled throughout the chernozem, chestnut, and brown soil regions.

Most of the blow land of the 1930's and later years is again tacked down. But nature also issues warnings that serious droughts will come again and again. From time to time, ominous dust clouds arise and sweep across parts of the region. The dry-land farmer needs to be as watchful of his fields and protect them against wind as well as water as the humid-land farmer must guard his fields against the raindrop.

The region is now engaged in a long-range program designed to convert all risk land into pasture or rangeland.

SOILS IN YOUR OWN COMMUNITY

These descriptions of the great soil groups of the United States and their utilization constitute a broad picture. To paint it, we brought together numerous soils that are different in many secondary characteristics. Each community is actually made up of many individual kinds of soils.

The best place to start a better land-use program is in one's own community. Here, as in public health, safety, and schools, the average citizen can wield his greatest influence for good. In only a general way can he support regional or national programs.

Every citizen should know the soils on which the well-being of his community is based. He should take the same pride in learning their names and characteristics as he does each kind of tree, flower, weed, bird, and bug. To make the best use of any resource—plant, animal, soil, mineral, or water—we must know its strength and weaknesses.

We must all become more land conscious. Every type of land we have is best suited to some use. Our task is to determine, by careful study, the best use of the lands in our own community and then help dedicate that use, be it for crops, forest, range, suburb, residence, industry, commerce, recreation, wildlife, highways, or any of the other uses that make up our complex life.

References

Allen, Shirley W., *Conserving Natural Resources,* Second Edition, McGraw-Hill Book Co., New York, 1959.

Bear, Firman, *Soils and Fertilizers,* Fourth Edition, John Wiley and Sons, New York, 1953.

Brinser, Ayers, and Ward Shepard, *Our Use of the Land,* Harper and Brothers, New York, 1939.

Cook, R. C., *Soil Management for Conservation and Production,* John Wiley and Sons, New York, 1962.

Clawson, Marion, *Land For Americans,* Rand McNally and Co., Chicago, 1963.

Cline, M. G. et al., *Soil Survey of the Territory of Hawaii,* United States Department of Agriculture, in cooperation with the Hawaii Agricultural Experiment Station.

Dasman, R. F., *Environmental Conservation,* John Wiley and Sons, New York, 1960.

Geographical Review, American Geographical Society, New York. This magazine and other geographical publications, such as *Economic Geography* and *The Journal of Geography,* contain many good articles on soils and land use.

Graham, Edward H., *Natural Principles of Land Use,* Oxford University Press, New York, 1944.

Highsmith, R. M. et al., *Conservation in the United States,* Rand McNally and Co., Chicago, 1962.

Kellogg, Charles E., *The Soils That Support Us,* The Macmillan Co., New York, 1941.

Kellogg, C. E., and I. J. Nygard, *Exploratory Study of the Principal Soil Groups of Alaska,* Agricultural Monograph No. 7, U.S. Department of Agriculture, 1951.

Lutz, Harold J., and Robert F. Chandler, *Forest Soils,* John Wiley and Sons, New York, 1946.

Marbut, C. F., *Soils of the United States,* Part III of the *Atlas of American Agriculture,* Government Printing Office, Washington, D.C., 1935.

Roberts, R. C. et al., *Soil Survey of Puerto Rico,* U.S. Department of Agriculture, 1942.

Soil Conservation Society of America, *Journal of Soil and Water Conservation,* Des Moines, Iowa. A monthly periodical.

Thorp, James, and Guy D. Smith, "Higher Categories of Soil Classification: Order, Suborder, and Great Soil Groups," *Soil Science,* Vol. 67, 1949, pp. 117–126.

United States Department of Agriculture, *A Place to Live, The 1963 Yearbook of Agriculture,* Government Printing Office, Washington, D.C., 1963.

United States Department of Agriculture, *Soil Classification, A Comprehensive System,* 7th Approximation, Government Printing Office, Washington, D.C., 1960.

United States Department of Agriculture, *Soils, The 1957 Yearbook of Agriculture,* Washington, D.C., 1957.

United States Department of Agriculture, *Soil Survey Reports,* 1899—. These reports, usually issued by counties, comprise the most excellent studies of the local soils in the United States.

United States Department of Agriculture, *Land Use and Its Patterns in the United States,* Agricultural Handbook No. 153, 1959.

Wilde, S. A., *Forest Soils,* Ronald Press, New York, 1958.

Wolfanger, Louis A., *Major Soil Divisions of the United States, A Pedologic-Geographic Survey,* John Wiley and Sons, New York, 1930.

WILLIAM A. ROCKIE

Soil Conservationist Emeritus,
U.S. Department of Agriculture

CHAPTER 5

Soil Conservation

Soil conservation is a new applied science. It has many facets, each a segment of some longer established, well-known science. Even the name is new. Its earliest recalled use was in *Farmers' Bulletin* No. 406 from the United States Department of Agriculture, June 16, 1910. At that time, the meaning of the term was limited strictly to the prevention of soil erosion. The science is still so new, however, that it conveys various meanings to different people. Naturally many of the technical terms used in this new field are still in an evolutionary stage. Some of them are not yet listed in our dictionaries. The term *soil conservation* as generally used today includes a multitude of measures and practices which are parts of the broader concept it has come to mean in recent years. Furthermore, since soil and water problems are, in large measure, inseparable, the term necessarily also includes many phases in the conservation of water.

Historically, several crusaders have publicly urged protection of all our resources. Thomas Jefferson was probably the first American to advocate publicly better care of the soil. Theodore Roosevelt was the most noted conservationist in the nation until recently. The first national recognition that soil conservation was important to the nation came with the publication in 1927 of *Soil Erosion a National Menace* by Hugh Hammond Bennett. That bulletin proved sufficiently effective, together with the crusading by its author, that it caused the United States Congress to appropriate $160,000 in 1929 for an initial study of the problem. The writer had the good fortune to initiate and develop the only study under this appropriation in the western half of the United States. Our prior land use in this country had been an ever accelerating campaign of exploitation of our natural resources.

Beginning with the first research done under this initial Congressional appropriation, our knowledge of the subject, together with an almost universal recognition of its need, has grown with miraculous rapidity. As a matter of fact, the changes resulting from this research have really been an agricultural revolution toward better land use in this country. It has reminded us of the terrifying speed with which prairie and forest fires sweep an area. This practically universal recognition of the imperative need for better land use has not been limited to our own country, but has spread to most of the nations of the world. Soil conservation has developed into a profession which is an accepted science in every nation. Simultaneously, its meaning has steadily broadened until it now includes all the various measures, practices, amendments, and treatments involved in the use, development, reclamation, protection, maintenance, improvement, and productivity of our land resources.

The science is still so new that relatively few of the universities and colleges in this country have a four-year course on the subject. All the initial soil conservationists were "made-over" during the 1930's and 1940's from their original training as agriculturists, agronomists, foresters, engineers, soil and range specialists, biologists, horticulturists, geologists, and other scientists. The first college degree with soil conservation as the major subject was granted in 1946, and the first soil conservationist degree was awarded in 1948. Currently, some specific courses on the subject are given at one or more institutions in every one of the fifty states, many are granting degrees with a soil conservation major, and soil conservationist degrees can be earned in every section of the country. Before long all the pioneers who were "made-over" will be gone, and the better prepared personnel will have taken over the task.

THE AMERICAN WILDERNESS

When our forefathers landed on America's shores, the necessity for conservation of soil or water or forests was utterly inconceivable. There was no cultivation, practically no grazing, and no forest denudation, except from an occasional fire.

However, then came the settlers, hunting home sites and ways to make a living. They needed, first of all, food for themselves and their animals, fibers for clothing, logs for building houses in which to live, and fuel to keep them warm. Those were the immediate and most imperative needs of these people. Everything that interfered with those objectives became an enemy. Since most of the early settlements were

made in forested regions, the destruction of that forest was an initial goal. Trees retarded his crops and also provided hiding places for unfriendly Indians. Anything he could do to push back the forests meant greater immediate security for the settler. Although many decades passed before the vast grassland prairies of the interior were similarly settled, the grass cover became a similar enemy of the settler on these lands. So he burned and burned until the grasslands were no more. When the better lands had all been settled, and no really good lands remained for occupancy, the human desire for land reached out to the drier lands. They were either poorly suited or quite unsuitable for cultivation, and so the growing of livestock on the rangelands which proved unsuited for crops dominated these lands having few natural advantages. These range animals have accomplished, on such lands, through almost universal overgrazing, approximately what fire and overcultivation did to the better lands. The virgin plant species on the range, especially those which were the more palatable, were generally destroyed by this widespread abuse of the plant cover. They were replaced by other species which were always less palatable and less nutritious and, almost universally, provided much less protection from erosion.

In their respective virgin conditions of plant cover, most of the many different types of soil found in this country were sufficiently spongelike to absorb the normal precipitation. The duff which typifies the natural forest floor served not only as a sponge and as a filter but also was an excellent insulator against excessive evaporation from the land surface and as a protection against excessive compaction of the soil. In addition, a duff cover is highly effective in the prevention of soil puddling by splash erosion from dashing rains. In the grassland areas of the country, comparable protection to the land was provided by the dead plant litter which fell to the ground each year. That, together with the dense network of living, dead and decaying grass roots, made such a mellow and absorptive soil that it was almost impossible for serious erosion to occur. Whatever the native vegetation was—trees, brush, or grass—the normal rains were readily absorbed by the soil. Only during the once-in-a-century type of storm was surface runoff likely. Even in the storms of greater than normal intensity, any water which did not soak into the soil was at least filtered through the organic duff or litter. A few notable exceptions always had muddy streams, such as the Missouri River in the northern Great Plains and the Red River in the southern Great Plains. This was principally because extensive areas of their watersheds have soils which are predominantly clayey. Fine material remains in suspension in the streams draining such areas.

The settling and clearing of America's agricultural lands were like a westward sweeping fire or flood. It did not stop until it had swept all the way from the Atlantic to the Pacific. The growing of corn, wheat, cotton, tobacco, and many other crops, the raising of cattle, sheep, hogs, horses, mules, and goats all have contributed to the damage that America's farm and range lands have already suffered. Although we have practically ruined some areas of land in different parts of the country, most of our lands are far from ruined. We have damaged most of our lands, since no section of the United States has been immune to, or safe from, such damage.

OUR INEXHAUSTIBLE SOIL

When this country was first settled, the soil was generally considered inexhaustible. Advertisements in early newspapers made such claims on the settlement frontiers as the tide of land-seekers moved westward from the Atlantic seaboard. Such news items appeared, for example, in Virginia as late as 1800, in Ohio from 1820 to 1860, in Illinois beginning about 1830, in Nebraska beginning in the 1860's, and in the Pacific coast states beginning in the 1880's. They usually dominated the news sheets immediately after settlement of a new area began, and often

they could still be seen from 20 to 30 years after settlement had started.

Observational studies have been made several times annually on a tract of 1620 acres which, until 1935, was virgin bunchgrass land that had never felt the plow. During the first 10 years following the initial cultivation in 1935, little and usually no erosion occurred, even on steep 50 percent bare slopes of clean summer fallow. But today, after 30 years, these steeper slopes show sheet erosion every year. The evidence, from all studies and observations made in the United States, indicates that usually erosion does not become a serious problem, except on the steepest lands, in the first 25 years after initial cultivation.

Our Land Problems Today. People all over the nation are becoming conscious of damage to the land. Although our exploitative methods of land use are the primary cause of this damage, the farmer cannot be saddled with all the responsibility. All of us, country and city people alike, must share the blame. The farmer can be charged with neglect for his destructive methods of soil management, but the urban population is also at fault for not merely encouraging but even financing that manner of farming. It is only natural for the farmer to resent the charge that his methods of farming are injuring the land, even when they are the major direct cause. The main indirect cause has been that the United States has never had a constructive, national land policy.

When we look at the lands of other countries, the cause for concern about our own lands becomes more understandable. A few nations present excellent living examples of safe use of their agricultural lands—conservation farming—but the vast majority of the nations of the world present glaring examples of highly destructive use of their land resources. Some outstanding examples of safe land use are found in the British Isles, the Scandinavian countries, Germany, Switzerland, Japan, and other countries. Equally outstanding, but portraying extremes of land abuse, are most of those countries that border the Mediterranean Sea, as well as many parts of the Middle East. In our own Western Hemisphere, we have no nation which portrays safe land use as do those mentioned in northern Europe. One must search diligently to find even a local community that is a living example of conservation farming (Fig. 1). Unfortunately, many large land areas in the United States and Mexico, and lesser areas in many other countries of the New World, present highly eroded landscapes.

What Has Happened to Our Land? Since the lands that we now use for farming were first formed, nature has been continually changing the original raw clays, silts, and sands into soil. Plants have grown, lived, and died each year on these once-inert, mineral materials, adding a bit more humus and organic matter every year to make an ever richer soil.

During the 100 to 150 years that most of America's farmlands have been under the plow, our farming practices have destroyed soil values that took millions of years to build. We first burned off all the organic matter and humus that could thus be disposed of. As if this were not enough, we burned off the crop residues. Then we pulverized and repulverized the soil, with

our efficient farm machinery, from one to several times each year. We have almost completely destroyed the soil structure. The result is that our soils absorb water much less readily, are harder to work, puddle more quickly, and are becoming, in every respect, less suitable for the growth of crops.

The cropland in the United States originally amounted to more than 600,000,000 acres of good, tillable land. In 1957, there were only about 500,000,000 acres of good cropland left. This figure includes, in addition to the nearly 400 million acres of suitable land in crops, nearly 100 million acres which need drainage, irrigation, or other amendments. Of these 500 million acres of good cropland, all but about 100 million are subject to erosion whenever the land is used without protection.

Referring again to this 500 million acres, about one-fourth is being damaged by erosion at a critically rapid rate (Fig. 2). Another one-fourth of our cropland is being eroded at a less critical, but still serious, rate. A third one-fourth is being damaged at a very slow rate, and the remaining fourth is suffering mainly from a heavy decline in fertility.

Some 90 million acres of our present cropland

Fig. 1 Beans have commonly been grown in straight rows without regard to the slope of the land. This Idaho bean field shows the more sensible way of growing beans on the contour. (Soil Conservation Service.)

Fig. 2   Soil washing from wheat lands is one of the most serious erosion problems in the country.
This badly riddled slope, which had been planted to wheat in the autumn, has lost more than
2 inches of topsoil since the planting date 4 months before. Much of the soil eroded from the slope
has been deposited in the light-colored area where as much as 15 inches of new soil covers the old
soil surface. (Soil Conservation Service.)

are not included in the above figures, because they are not at all suited to annual cultivation. They should either be permanently removed from cultivation or, at most, cultivated only once in several years. To offset this loss in cropland, an approximately equal acreage of good land not used for agriculture needs to be brought into cultivation through drainage, irrigation, clearing, or other needed improvements.

We cannot maintain our present standard of living if we continue to destroy land as we have done during the 1920's through the 1950's. In fact, we, as a nation, cannot long survive unless we change our ways. We have been allowing about 400,000 acres of our cropland to be lost by erosion each year, so that our total available area well adapted to cropping purposes has been decreasing each year under the farming practices of the immediate past.

Since the early 1930's, however, the nation's awakening conscience and consciousness have unquestionably slowed down the rate at which we are damaging and destroying land. Possibly it is not too much to hope that, during an equal period of years in the future, the gains may equal or possibly even exceed the annual damage and deterioration.

Why Land Damage Occurs. Croplands have deteriorated from four main causes: loss of the soil itself, loss of organic matter, loss of soil structure, and loss of plant nutrients. These types of land damage have been implemented through the various types of erosion as well as obstructed drainage, improper irrigation, excessive alkalinity, leaching, floods, and various exploitative farming practices.

Rangelands have deteriorated from three main causes: destruction of much of the erosion-resisting, but highly palatable, grass cover through overgrazing (followed by sheet and gully erosion), invasion of the area by unpalatable weeds, and by excessive trampling and packing resulting in accelerated erosion.

Forest land damage has been confined almost entirely to burned-over lands where some sheet and gully erosion usually follow, although only a relatively minor acreage of the land area of the United States currently suffers such damage.

Land Damage Resulting from Cultivation.
LOSS OF SOIL STRUCTURE. When the grassland
was first broken by the plow, the sod was the
bugbear of the farmer trying to make a new
home. The tough chunks of sod made the field
so bumpy for the farm implements of that day
that a good seedbed was almost impossible to
make. These fragments persisted for many
years, but gradually they were broken and torn
to bits by the several cultivations each year.

Most grassland soils have proved highly resistant to pulverization because of their extremely high content of fibrous roots. However,
soils formed beneath drier grasslands contain
much less fibrous material and therefore lose
their structure much more quickly. (The dust
bowl developed where drier grasslands once
prevailed.) Soils formed beneath a forest canopy
are reduced to a powdery status even more
readily, because they contain practically no
fibrous material.

The ultimate result upon all cultivated land,
unless it has had enough crop residues, barnyard
manure, and green manure to offset the losses
from cultivation, cropping, and oxidation, is a
powdered soil that brings decreasing returns
and increasing troubles to its owner with each
added decade of use. It becomes less mellow; it
packs like cement; it puddles with every rain;
and it becomes less desirable with each passing
year. The rich mellow loam which had been
described as inexhaustible has worn out. It
might be said to have hardening of the arteries.
The stage has been set for the terrific soil losses
caused by either water or wind erosion (Fig. 3).

LOSS OF ORGANIC MATTER. Along with the loss
of soil structure goes the loss of organic matter.
Decaying vegetation, especially of grassland
areas, has been adding to the amount of organic
matter stored in the virgin soil for thousands of
years. Only a little is added each year, but in
the aggregate it is enough to transform an originally inert mass of rock fragments into a mellow
living medium. In sandy soils, mellowness is
attained with only 2 or 3 percent organic matter
content, but in heavier textured soils 5 and 6

Fig. 3   Wind erosion has caused the abandonment of millions of acres of farmland in the United
States which formerly were planted to wheat. Clumps of thistles hold on to a small amount of silt
and sand, but when the land is in fallow soil losses by wind erosion are high. (Soil Conservation
Service.)

percent organic matter is needed to make them mellow.

Most of the cultivated soils in the United States have already lost at least half of their long-time accumulation of organic matter through the erosion, stubble burning, leaching, and oxidation that occurred during their first few decades of use. After such a period, loss of organic matter through oxidation usually proceeds at a slower rate, although the loss by erosion tends to become progressively greater.

LOSS OF PLANT FOOD. Erosion, leaching, crop removal, fire, and oxidation all contribute to the loss of plant food, although mineral salts generally are lost only through the first three processes. Plant food deficiencies are almost universal for all lands today, deficiencies of nitrogen, phosphorus, potash, sulfur, and calcium being especially common. The absence of certain trace elements, such as boron and molybdenum, has also proved serious in many areas.

LOSS OF THE SOIL BY EROSION. The soil losses already mentioned are of considerable magnitude, but they are nothing compared to the loss of the soil itself. Each year our average cultivated acre yields from $25 to more than $100— and occasionally several hundred dollars—in newly created wealth. Over one century, at that price, the return from one acre would amount to from $2500 to $10,000—and in the exceptionally high cases much greater returns—and the acre would still be there to continue to produce its annual wealth if it were properly managed and conserved. If we multiply the average annual per-acre return by our 500 million acres of cropland, we have the return in dollars to our country each year.

Erosion by either water or wind may destroy these values. It can remove all, or any portion, of the soil from a given area. If all the soil is lost, the annual harvest of wealth ceases. Its seriousness and its import to every one of us are not yet fully realized.

Most of our soils are practically ruined when they have lost 6 inches of topsoil, and they are generally abandoned before they lose 9 inches of the top layer. Our farm economy is practically dependent upon that topsoil. Wherever we destroy that layer, we destroy the "land bank" on which our agricultural economy has been built. Rebuilding each such acre is an expensive and an extremely slow process.

Land is actually our agricultural capital. Every acre of ruined land is one share of the bank stock thrown away. We have already destroyed about 100 million acres of our land bank, which for 1964, and for every year like it, means $10,585,000,000 of wealth which we should, but cannot, realize.[1]

Land Damage Resulting from Overgrazing. The rangelands of our western states also tell a story of despoliation (Fig. 4). That story is just as dramatic—and just as tragic—as the erosion history of our cultivated lands. It differs only as to detail, for the results have been all too similar. The same land-use principles were violated, and similar land damage was the result.

Essentially, the error involved grazing too many animals on too few acres for too long a time and at the wrong times. The hungry animals gradually ate the most palatable forage species of the virgin cover literally into the ground. The lands were grazed at all seasons, and the range was never rested. Gradually the more palatable plants became weakened, and finally they died. As the good species were eaten out of the stand, other less palatable plants filled the bare spots. Invasion of the area by weed species, which not only were less tasty to livestock but also proved more aggressive on the run-down land than the original virgin species, was the only possible result. With the decrease in the erosion-resisting cover came excessive trampling and packing of the soil. Inevitably, this sequence of events was followed by accelerated erosion. Our western rangelands are potentially capable of a substantial increase in their livestock-carrying capacity, if they are properly managed.

[1] The 1960 Census of Agriculture shows $105.85 average gross agricultural returns for each acre of cropland.

Fig. 4   A heavy rain of 2.8 inches on a freshly plowed field resulted in heavy soil and water losses on this Ottawa County farm in Michigan. Grassed waterways and low terraces on the contour would have prevented the loss of soil from the slopes and the burial of good lands in low-lying areas. (Soil Conservation Service.)

Land Damage from Deforestation. In the land-clearing which has characterized the history of the millions of formerly forest-covered acres of America, no thought was usually given to the land except to get rid of its cover so that it might be farmed. The result was widespread erosion on these former forest lands. Although the damage has been much greater and much faster on the clearings that became cropland, the deforested nonagricultural lands have also contributed greatly to the total land damage in the United States. Most of the logged-off land that is not suitable for cropland now has a protective plant cover, even though it may be inadequate to protect fully the land against erosion. Vegetation on the land, no matter how poor that plant cover may be, does offer at least a measure of protection.

Land Damage from Floods. Most of the long-recognized, highly publicized losses from floods consist of damage not to the lands but to man's physical developments on the land. No effort will be made here to assess such damages. Only flood damage to the land itself will be indicated.

DAMAGE BY STREAM-BANK CUTTING. This type of land damage results in complete destruction of the resource and leaves only desolation behind. Since the annually recurring crop loss from these destroyed acres needs to be capitalized on the basis of its loss to the national economy rather than on its annual loss to the farmer, the average acre of rich bottomland thus lost represents an annual loss of $80 to $400 during all of the years ahead.

DAMAGE BY FLOOD OVERFLOW. This land

damage results mainly from (1) the loss of the current growing crop, (2) the cost and time of establishment of a replacement crop, (3) the task of mixing the new mantle of mud or sand with the soil beneath, and (4) the loss of soil by scouring. The current year's crop is almost always a total loss when inundated by flood. Conditioning of the muddy mantle may delay re-establishment of crops by one and occasionally by two additional crop years. In the event of severe scouring, much depends on the nature of the newly exposed subsoil. If the subsoil is sandy or of mellow silt, it will till readily, but if it is heavy clay, the capital value of the land is badly impaired.

The thin layer of silt deposited annually by the Nile is said to benefit Egypt, but it would be difficult to find a river valley in this country about which its people would consider floods in any way beneficial. After a flood, communities agree that the damages from the flood exceed the benefits many times over. It is doubtful if the people would admit that any sediments deposited in a valley could be sufficiently beneficial to offset the flood damage.

Other Kinds of Land Damage. OBSTRUCTED DRAINAGE. Many thousands of drainage projects have been constructed in the United States, but all too frequently people forget that every drainage enterprise requires constant and perpetual maintenance. The result is that most such projects in the nation have deteriorated far below their top level of performance. Many of them are practically ineffective, chiefly because of the lack of maintenance. Lack of tidal gates, inadequate pumping facilities, silt-filled ditches, insufficient tributary ditches, undersized ditches, inadequate levees, plant-choked ditches, and deteriorated equipment are common in drainage districts which, theoretically, are functioning for the proper drainage of land. Proper maintenance of these already established districts would be an effective means of attaining better land use on many of our lowland areas.

In addition, we have many millions of acres of potentially good cropland on which drainage is needed, but on which no efforts at better drainage have yet been made. We also have other millions of acres of coastal swamps and marshes which could be made into intensive agricultural area at any time that our need for land becomes sufficiently great. Feasibility of such projects has been conclusively and repeatedly proved in Holland and other countries.

IMPROPER IRRIGATION. Altogether there are more than 24 million acres of irrigated cropland in the western half of the United States. Surprisingly little of this vast acreage is sufficiently well irrigated to produce capacity crop yields. Much of this problem is due to (1) application of too much water, (2) water applied in the wrong way, (3) water applied to land that has not been adequately prepared for irrigation, (4) application of water at the wrong time, and (5) shortage of water.

ALKALINITY OR SALINITY. The condition of excessive alkalinity or salinity occurs almost entirely in the western half of the nation and is commonly intimately associated with the irrigation of arid lands. It results from the evaporation of considerable amounts of water from the land surface of regions in which nature provides insufficient precipitation to leach the salts downward beyond the plant-root zone.

Kinds of Erosion. Different kinds of land, when attacked by wind and water, resist erosion in varying degrees and in different ways. Some of these man-induced types of erosion result from washing by water, others from drifting by wind, and still others from the combined forces of water and wind.

Sheet erosion, gully erosion, and badlands are three stages or degrees of soil washing, whereas dust-blowing fields, sand-drifted fence rows between fields, and dunes are somewhat comparable stages of soil drifting.

SHEET EROSION. It has reached an advanced stage over much of the sloping cultivated cropland and over a considerable part of the rangeland in the United States. The structure of the soil has been so completely destroyed on much of the cultivated land that, with every rain, the soil tends to puddle and to seal from the impact of the raindrops. Runoff and rilling are the inevitable results. Lowered production follows, and ultimately gullying and abandonment occur.

On irrigated lands, rill erosion may occur with each irrigation. In certain sections of the country, especially on steep, ditch-irrigated slopes, as much as 20 to 30 inches of soil have been carelessly washed away in a single decade.

Sheet erosion on rangeland results from the same causes as on cultivated areas: inadequate cover, destroyed soil structure, compaction by hooves, and the consequent puddling and sealing of the surface.

SNOWDRIFT EROSION. This is a highly localized, but in places exceedingly severe, type of sheet erosion. It occurs on the downslope side of snowdrifts and on clean-cultivated sloping fields. The snowdrift itself may protect the upper part of a slope from sheet washing but may greatly increase the damage beginning at its lower edge. This type of erosion is most common in the Pacific Northwest, although it also occurs in many other parts of the country.

SOIL SLIPS AND EARTH FLOWS. Soil slips occur only under unusual conditions, mainly when the bottom surface of the sliding mass of soil has become slippery enough and fluid enough to toboggan down the slope. If this sliding material is sufficiently fluid to flow like lava, and often it is, it can also be called an earth flow or mudflow.

GULLY EROSION. In certain highly erosive soils, gullying may occur simultaneously with sheet erosion, but it is more commonly recognized, and it occurs more widely as a succeeding stage of land damage. As gullies develop, they lengthen and deepen so that they truly divide and subdivide farm fields into ever smaller and less practicable land-use areas (Fig. 5). Ultimately gullied land must be abandoned or put to some less intensive use.

BADLANDS. When gully erosion becomes so dominant that raw slopes are everywhere, with none of the original upland surface remaining, with no alluvial bottoms forming, and with all slopes approximately at the angle of repose, the topography known as badlands results. Badlands are usually wholly devoid of vegetation and in such condition are utterly worthless agriculturally.

STREAM-BANK EROSION. When native vegetation covered both the bottomlands along our streams and the uplands that drained into these streams, stream banks did not erode as they do today. Logging, fires, clearing, and cultivation have combined to decrease the reservoir capacity of the formerly forested watersheds; and overgrazing, fire, and cultivation have speeded the runoff from the formerly grass-covered lands. The original fringe of trees along the stream bank proper, much of which is now gone also, further retarded stream-bank erosion.

We have cleared and farmed the usually wooded bottomlands so that, when the increased runoff reaches these lands, the stream banks are undermined and the rich alluvial soil goes down the river. And, even if the bottomlands have not been cleared, the increased flood levels still take them, although at a slower rate.

WIND EROSION. Research studies during the past 30 years in the dust bowl of the 1930's, have proved conclusively that long-continued cultivation of even the best soils under low-rainfall conditions is a hazardous practice. As the soil becomes more and more pulverized with each year of cultivation, it becomes increasingly vulnerable to attack by wind.

Sandy soils break down more quickly than heavier soils, but no soil is too fine textured to blow. Therefore any cultivated land area where strong winds are common—and especially if it is an area of low rainfall—is a potential dust bowl, even including areas under irrigation.

DUNES. As wind erosion becomes more severe, the wind-rippled land surface gradually becomes more dunelike. If adequate corrective measures are not taken, a typical dune topography usually follows.

Fig. 5 After the topsoil is gone, the land has lost most of its value. This slope was formerly fine grassland, but overgrazing reduced it to "badland" condition. Millions of acres of our western range, and hundreds of millions of rangeland in other parts of the world, have been similarly damaged. (Soil Conservation Service.)

FUNDAMENTALS OF SOIL CONSERVATION

The farming methods and practices that have developed in this country during the past 200 years have been many. Some have proved beneficial, others harmful. Some have proved practicable, others impracticable. Some have been profitable, others unprofitable. The objective, especially since the turn of the century, has been to grow the largest amount of salable crops at the lowest possible cost. Too many of the resulting farming practices have proved to be exploitative. When conservation of the soil became an equally important objective—at least

to the nation's economy—it became evident that we must find and develop safer methods of using our lands.

Conservation Farming. The essential fundamentals of conservation farming are (1) to use the land in keeping with its capabilities and (2) to protect the land in keeping with its needs. Actually, the science of conservation farming has been evolving since the early 1900's, although soil conservation was not a recognized objective of most of the earlier beginnings. Many, though certainly not all, of the research projects at our agricultural experiment stations, when adapted to the objective of soil conservation, have proved to be admirable practices and measures.

The long, and successful, search for locally adapted green-manure crops and rotation crops was among the most notable accomplishments in this direction. Some agricultural research project findings and recommendations have proved to be in direct conflict with the principles of soil conservation. Such, for example, are the practices of clean-tilled summer fallow and of stubble burning. Clean bare summer fallow is the antithesis of soil conservation.

When the soil conservation experiment stations were first established about 1930, the principles of soil conservation were little more than a list of theories. However, from the vast store of research done by the agricultural experiment stations, from the work of the newly established soil conservation experiment stations, and from individual experimental efforts by thousands of farmers who had long recognized the need for better farming methods, soil conservationists have developed in less than 35 years a relatively stable science.

During the time of the earliest efforts to get farmers to use conservation practices, it was recognized that good results do not always follow simple, easy changes. The problem proved to be less simple than that. The lands were sick, some in one way, some in another. As with a sick person, a careful, continuing diagnosis of the symptoms was essential. Sometimes the initial diagnosis proved to be inadequate, and modified handling of the case became necessary.

Because of the complexity of the problem and also because the problem differs in detail with every change in the soil, in the slope of the land, or in the climate, progress in applying the best conservation practices to the different farms is necessarily slow.

Before making recommendations of conservation practices for the different parts of any particular farm, the soil conservationist must first be able to classify adequately all the lands in this farm, and second he must be able to prescribe suitable conservation practices for each of the kinds of land he finds.

There are strong indications that the currently increasing need for, and the use of, the dietary phases of medical science may be largely the result of soil deficiencies. Soil and health are being watched more and more closely for their interrelationships.

Principles of Conservation Farming. Ever since the first soil conservation programs were evolved by erosion experiment station personnel in 1930 to 1931, two cardinal principles have stood out.

The first of these is: *Effective prevention and control of soil erosion and adequate conservation of precipitation in any land area require that the various kinds of land be used in accordance with their capability and needs.* Naturally the capabilities, adaptabilities, and facilities of the landowner must also receive consideration.

The second of these two guiding principles is: *Efficient application of conservation measures to various kinds of land requires the assistance of a technician out on the land.* Some farmers have the know-how to be their own technicians, but as yet most farmers do not.

Almost without exception, when these two principles have been carefully adhered to, the recommended use and practices have proved to be sound. On the other hand, when some overzealous worker has attempted to short cut these principles and thereby speed up his work, he has found that his efforts usually brought him more trouble than benefits.

COORDINATED PLAN OF SOIL CONSERVATION. Before making any recommendations for a particular tract of land, the soil conservationist must be able to classify the different kinds of land within the tract and to determine the conservation needs on each kind of land (Fig. 6). He must know how to evaluate the various ecological factors that contribute in any important way to this complicated problem, and then, finally, he must be able to apply or even create remedial measures to correct the unwise uses and methods of land management that he has encountered. In fact, he must be a geologist, soil specialist, geographer, land appraiser, engineer, agronomist, forester, range specialist, biologist,

Fig. 6 Land capability is simply one way to describe the different grades of land within a particular area. In this picture, all of the eight classes except V are shown. Relatively few farms have all of the eight classes of land, usually not more than four. (Soil Conservation Service.)

and several other scientists, all in one. The degree with which he proves able to integrate just the right amount of each science involved partly determines the degree of his success as a soil conservationist. *The soil conservationist must be able to plan properly the integration of the different practices needed for the control of erosion on any given piece of land into a coordinated program.* For example, on a gently sloping field, crop rotation and crop residue utilization may be the only practices needed; a steeper adjoining hillside may need terracing and strip cropping in addition to these; and on a very steep adjoining hillside the needs sound simpler and easier because it should not be cultivated at all. Tree planting and woodland management may be the particular needs for soil protection on the steepest of slopes.

The Conservation Farm Plan. When complicated land problems like these are to be solved, plans must be made for making the necessary changes. Since no two farms are identical and no two farmers alike, no two farm plans should be the same. Different soils cover varying slopes and sites under differing intensities and amounts of rainfall, wind, temperature, humidity, and sunshine.

It must be pointed out that one soil conservation practice alone is not generally adequate to protect land against damage and deterioration. Usually two or three, or even more, practices must be combined to secure the best results. Both sequence and timing of each practice are important and necessary to obtain the maximum benefits.

PLANNING THE FARM. When the soil conservationist undertakes the planning of conservation for a farm, his first step is either to obtain or to make an adequately accurate map of the land. The best possible farm map is a vertical aerial photograph on which the most important physical factors are shown. Usually only four factors are needed: soil, slope, erosion, and cover; but other factors may, in special instances, be shown. From his knowledge of these several contributing factors, he evolves a particular combination of practices for each differentiated unit area on the map. The individual conservation practices, most of which are briefly described on the succeeding pages, are the tools which he suggests that the farmer use to get effective conservation farming.

Land Capabilities. When one thinks of all the kinds of soil, all the different degrees of slope, and all the kinds of climate we have in this country, the variety seems endless. Since the combination of these three things is what makes the different sorts of land we have, we can appreciate why our lands differ greatly in the type of use to which they are best suited. This is defined as their capability; however, this is not necessarily related to their productivity.

More than one system of classification of the land's capability is being currently employed in this country, but only the one in use by the United States Soil Conservation Service is based entirely on capability as to land use. The other classifications mainly emphasize the factor of productivity.

This capability classification places all lands in one of eight classes, which are very briefly described as follows.

CLASS I. Very good land that can be cultivated safely with ordinary good farming methods. It is nearly level and easily worked. Some areas need clearing, water management, or fertilization.

CLASS II. Good land that can be cultivated safely with easily applied practices. These include such measures as contouring, protective cover crops, and simple water-management

operations. Common requirements are rotations and fertilization.

CLASS III. Moderately good land that can be cultivated safely with such protection as terracing and strip cropping. Common requirements also include crop rotation, cover crops, and fertilization.

CLASS IV. Fairly good land that is best suited to pasture and hay, but can be cultivated occasionally—preferably only once in several years. Even when plowed only occasionally the most intensive erosion prevention practices are required.

CLASS V. Suited for grazing or forestry with little or no limitations.

CLASS VI. Suited for grazing or forestry with minor limitations; needs protective measures.

CLASS VII. Suited for grazing or forestry with major limitations; needs extreme care to prevent land damage.

CLASS VIII. Suited only for wildlife or for recreation. This land usually is rough, stony, sandy, wet, or highly erodible.

With these land capabilities as the basis of the farm plan, the conservationist builds his program to fit the particular foundation on which he is working. Then he adds the necessary structural details to brace and strengthen adequately the completed plan. The product of these procedures is a conservation farm plan designed to fit one certain farm. Although it probably will fit no other farm perfectly, it will probably serve other farms having similar measurements and specifications just as a suit made to one man's measure fits another man of similar height and build.

Principal Conservation Practices. The present conservation practices have gradually evolved since the early 1930's by adaptations from research and experience. The current list of conservation practices is still in an evolutionary status and has in no sense become a fixed pattern.

CONTOURING. This consists of plowing, planting, cultivating, and harvesting sloping fields on the level, that is, farming on the contour, around hillsides with curving furrows and rows that fit the lay of the land, instead of with straight up-and-down-hill furrows. The curved furrows retard runoff and allow much of the rain water to soak into the ground (Fig. 7). This conserves water and greatly reduces the amount of soil that is washed away.

CONTOUR FURROWING. This practice consists of making furrows on the level in pastures and ranges to hold rainfall and retard runoff, thus helping the growth of forage plants. Where runoff has been common, this measure decreases the erosion and runoff and virtually increases the effective rainfall.

CONTOUR SUBSOILING. In this practice the hard subsoil is broken so that it can absorb rainfall more readily. This is done most commonly on pasture lands to improve the forage growth, although it is also done on cultivated land. Sub-

soilers follow the contour, and the interval between furrows varies with the land and the cover. This practice gives best results when the subsoil is dry and brittle enough to shatter when the subsoiler passes through it.

TERRACING. It is ridging land on, or nearly on, the contour. This practice builds up low ridges or embankments of soil across sloping fields to intercept runoff. Terraces with a slight grade slow down runoff water, resulting in greater absorption by the soil and in guiding the runoff to a safe disposal at the sides of the fields. This controlled excess water runs off slowly, causing relatively little erosion. Level terraces hold all the rainfall on the land, unless they are overtopped.

DIVERSION CHANNELS. These are channels with a ridge on the lower side. The ridges sometimes are larger than field terrace ridges and are generally farther apart. Otherwise they are

Fig. 7 In Gosper County, Nebraska, the conservation of water and soil is an important objective of the land-management program. Two days after, a 3 to 4 inch rainwater was still held back by the terraces, permitting continued absorption into the soil. (Soil Conservation Service.)

much the same. They are built, with a low channel gradient, across slopes to divert damaging and wasteful runoff.

STRIP CROPPING. This consists of planting strips of close-growing plants, like grass or clover, between strips of clean-tilled row crops on, or nearly on, the contour. The strips of close-growing plants retard the runoff, thus greatly decreasing the erosion on the clean-tilled strip below. They also strain out the soil picked up by runoff water from the plowed strips.

FIELD STRIPPING. This practice places alternate strips of cultivated crops and cover crops roughly at right angles to the main slope of the land (Fig. 8). It is a crude substitute for strip cropping.

WIND STRIPPING. Alternate strips of clean-tilled and thick crops are planted at right angles to the prevailing wind.

STUBBLE-MULCHING. This practice is also sometimes called *trashy fallow*. It involves leaving crop residues and soil-improving crops at least partly on top of the ground instead of burning them or turning them under. These materials include grain stubble and straw, cornstalks, crotolaria, lespedeza, sweet clover, and other protective cover crops. This practice protects the soil from erosion and from baking, cuts down runoff and evaporation, lowers the soil temperature in hot summer weather, helps the soil to absorb more rainfall, decreases the degree of freezing, and aids the growth of useful bacteria in the soil (Fig. 9).

MULCHING. The application of a surface

Fig. 8 Strip cropping on the contour is probably the most picturesque although not necessarily the most beneficial soil-conserving practice now in use. Strips of corn, oats, wheat, and hay characterize the agricultural landscape of Northumberland County, Pennsylvania, shown in this aerial view. (Soil Conservation Service.)

Fig. 9 The standing stubble of the different cereal grains now serves a most useful purpose in the grain-producing sections of the country. Formerly it was either burned or plowed completely under. Now it is mixed with the surface soil and is very effective in minimizing both water and wind erosion. (Soil Conservation Service.)

mulch onto the land is not a general practice. However, the practice is becoming more common in many of the areas where torrential rains cause excessive erosion on the too frequently bare, cultivated fields. Many kinds of plant residues are carried or hauled from the points where they occur in excess to fields that are without protection. Many kinds of straw, rain-spoiled hay, chopped-up tree, cane and vine prunings, sawdust, peat, and chipped wood are in current use for this purpose.

CROP ROTATIONS. This practice involves rotating production of soil-building crops and soil-impoverishing crops. On rich land, it keeps the soil productive, and on rundown land it improves the soil. In a good rotation, the soil-building crop improves the other crops in the rotation. For example, nitrogen is added to the soil by the legumes, such as clover, alfalfa, cowpeas, and lespedeza. The nitrogen left is then used by the crops that do not have the power to fix nitrogen, such as wheat, corn, cotton, tobacco, and potatoes. Rotations often are inte-

grated with strip cropping by shifting the close-growing strips and the clean-tilled strips at fixed periods. In this way, soil-building and erosion control are simultaneously accomplished.

COVER CROPS. Such crops are dense-growing so that they can prevent erosion of cultivated areas at times when there would otherwise be few or no plants on the land to protect it from wind and water erosion. There are summer, winter, and perennial cover crops. Legumes and grasses are the most common (Fig. 10).

FERTILIZING. This is the use of manure or other fertilizer on land that needs additional plant food to stimulate greater plant growth.

DRAINAGE. The practice involves the removal of excess water from wet land by ditches or by tile drains. Such artificial waterways must be kept free of silt, either by protecting the watershed from erosion or by desilting the water as it enters. It may require leveling.

IRRIGATION. In this practice, water is spread on land by safe methods to increase crop yields. Applying water with overhead sprinkler systems

Fig. 10   Although clean cultivation has long been common in the management of fruit and nut orchards in this country, cover crops (some for the entire year and others for only part of the year) in orchards are increasing in both acreage and importance as the landowners endeavor to protect more completely their soils. Turning the crop under as a green manure or harvesting it with sheep are common management methods. (Soil Conservation Service.)

is the safest method, since it is easiest to control. Many other methods are used.

IRRIGATION DEVELOPMENT AND IMPROVE-MENT. This involves management of water for irrigation. The term management includes building and improving water distribution systems on farms; land preparation, such as leveling or draining; measurement and control of water; development or improvement of springs and wells; and the disposal of waste water.

WATER SPREADING. This is the controlled spreading of runoff water in areas of low rainfall, from the foot of slopes and from gullies and washes over the nearby land that needs more water. It is a crude form of irrigation. It is done by dikes, dams, and other means of diverting water from one place to another. The objective is to make use of all water in low-rainfall areas, rather than waste it.

GRASSED WATERWAYS. These are the protected channels and outlets that carry off excess water from farm fields. These waterways are stabilized against erosion by planted grasses, legumes, and vines.

GREEN MANURING. This consists of turning under grain, legume, or grass crops while green to improve the soil by adding to the supply of organic matter. The crop yields, the condition of the soil, and the control of erosion are all bettered by this practice (Fig. 11).

MEADOW DEVELOPMENT. The practice involves using land not suitable for cultivation for the production of hay. The land is plowed only to renew plantings.

PASTURE DEVELOPMENT. New pastures may be developed with selected grasses and legumes, and different combinations thereof. It may include fertilization, liming, drainage, irrigation, fencing, clipping, spreading of droppings, and other measures.

PASTURE IMPROVEMENT. This involves the use of measures that increases growth and improves quality of forage grasses. It includes such measures as deferred and rotation grazing, proper stocking, stock water ponds or wells placed to encourage better distribution of livestock, spacing of salt and bedding grounds for the same purpose, reseeding, liming and fertilizing, basin listing and contour furrowing, water spreading, weed control, clipping, spreading droppings, and fire protection.

RANGE IMPROVEMENT. It involves the same group of measures as pasture improvement. However, it generally uses only those which can be accomplished at low cost, because of the much lower returns from rangeland.

GULLY CONTROL. By using plants and mechanical measures erosion may be stopped in gullies. Such measures reduce the rate of water flow. It is done by using (1) grass, vines, trees, and shrubs; (2) flumes and other devices to lessen the cutting power of falling water; and (3) dams for catching silt.

FIELD AND GULLY PLANTING. This involves planting eroded or erodible land, which is unsuitable for cultivation, to trees, shrubs, grasses, vines, or other useful plants that will help stop erosion and will also conserve rainfall.

WOODLAND HARVESTING AND IMPROVEMENT CUTTINGS. These practices consist of cutting for lumber, pulp, and other uses according to sound forestry practices. Such cutting promotes rapid growth and makes wood a regular crop.

POND MANAGEMENT. This is the use of suitable measures (1) to protect ponds from erosion and from siltation and (2) to aid production of fish and other pond wildlife.

SHELTERBELTS AND WINDBREAKS. The practice involves the planting of trees and shrubs in strips or belts usually one to ten rows wide. The main purpose is to deflect wind currents, thereby reducing wind erosion and snowdrifting. Such strips of trees and shrubs reduce droughtiness to the leeward and also protect people, livestock, fields, gardens, orchards, and buildings from the elements.

This list of practices shows only the most successful methods which are currently in widespread use. Additional practices for conserving soil and water are developing constantly.

WATERSHED MANAGEMENT. Thirty years ago, soil conservationists all over the country tried in vain to get communities to tackle the task of soil conservation on a watershed basis, but it seems in retrospect that the public did not have then an adequate understanding of the problem

Fig. 11 Green manuring with legumes or with grass-legumes mixtures with the dual objective of restoring fertility and improving the tilth is probably the most valuable soil-conserving practice known. (Soil Conservation Service.)

to accept that approach. A few such projects were started, and still fewer were carried through to a successful conclusion.

During the past decade, however, the watershed approach has gained noteworthy momentum, and is currently the most promising aspect of ultimate successful attainment of good land-use in our country. This approach has tended to bring the best interests of the urban and the rural residents into a single focus, because the watershed approach has already shown definite, and sometimes striking, evidence that floods can be materially lessened and possibly eliminated from many of our drainage basins.

To attain success in watershed management, all the people residing in a watershed must work in unison and for the common good. To do this, the interests of the individual must be subordinated to the community's prime needs.

HISTORY OF SOIL CONSERVATION IN THE UNITED STATES

Prevention of soil erosion has been advocated by a few far-seeing persons ever since colonial times, but little was done to accomplish erosion control on the nation's farmlands except by a few zealous missionaries on their own fields. George Washington and Thomas Jefferson advocated and practiced safer use of their croplands.

Only since the late 1920's and early 1930's have such missionaries been more than a voice in the wilderness. Dr. H. H. Bennett made the first impression on the national consciousness when, chiefly through his influence, Congress established ten erosion experiment stations in 1929–1931.

The immediate results of the research started at that time on the experiment farms were so striking that in 1933 the Soil Erosion Service was established, with soil conservation as its primary objective. A number of soil conservation demonstration projects was started in 1933–1935 at key locations throughout the nation. When the Civilian Conservation Corps was started in 1934

to provide employment for our young men, several hundred of the CCC camps were assigned to the Soil Erosion Service. Most of these SES-assigned camps worked either on the projects mentioned or on new projects established specifically for the CCC camps. By these means, a total of several hundred demonstration projects on soil conservation was established in all parts of the country.

In April, 1935, Congress passed the basic Soil Conservation Act (Public Law 46, 74th Congress), declaring it to be the policy of Congress to provide permanently for the control and prevention of soil erosion. Congress, at the same time, authorized the Secretary of Agriculture to establish the Soil Conservation Service to effectuate this policy. In accordance with the wording of the Act authorizing the secretary to "utilize the organization heretofore established," the secretary renamed the old Soil Erosion Service as the Soil Conservation Service. Most of the soil conservation work in the country has been done under that Congressional authority.

In 1936, two lines of attack on the soil conservation problem appeared: the beginning of the soil conservation district movement, and the beginning of subsidy payments by the federal government for establishing of conservation practices.

Since then, and more especially since 1942, the policy of the Soil Conservation Service has been to establish conservation practices on the land through the medium of soil conservation districts (Fig. 12). Although the first state enabling legislation for the creation of such districts was passed only in 1937, the soil conservation district is now a nationwide institution. Each of the fifty states, as well as all our territories, now have enabling legislation. All of this enabling legislation was passed by the state and territorial legislatures during the 1937–1947 decade. Soil conservation districts are legally constituted subdivisions of the states and territories. By July 1, 1964, they numbered 2971, and new districts are still being organized

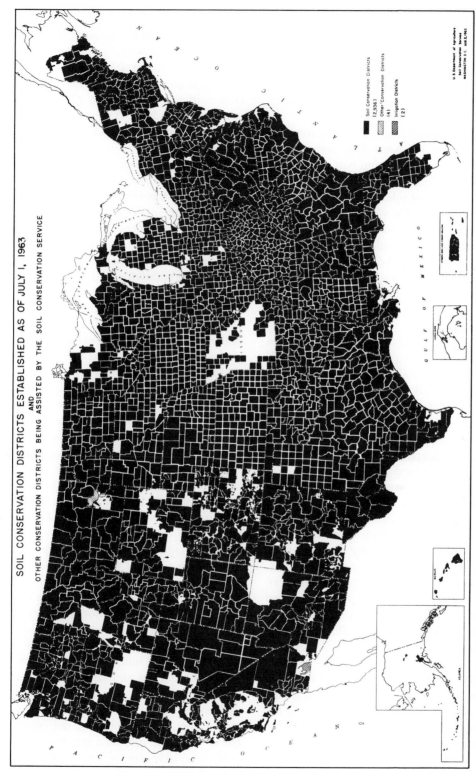

Fig. 12 Although the first soil conservation district came into being in 1937, almost all of the farmland in the United States is in legally constituted districts today. The map shows the districts cooperating with the government as of July 1, 1963. (Soil Conservation Service.)

99

nearly every month. The evolution of the legal soil conservation district of today from the few soil conservation associations organized by farmers in the early 1930's, in connection with the Soil Erosion Service Demonstration Projects, has been an amazing development.

The initial wave of district organization occurred mainly in the areas that were solidly agricultural and where erosion was severe, but, since then, the extent of the district organization has become an almost solid blanket covering the farms of the country. The vast acreage of federal lands, together with the minor percentage of the land area that is agricultural, in the eleven western states, accounts for the large areas without districts in much of the West. The forested areas of northern Minnesota, northern Michigan, northern New York, and northern Maine also have few such districts.

Several predominantly agricultural areas were notably slow in joining the nation-wide landslide in organizing Soil Conservation Districts, especially in California, Oregon, Missouri, Indiana, and Pennsylvania and in the TVA. In spite of official opposition in these areas, Soil Conservation Districts (organized and operated by farmers) have spread over much or all of the areas named. It now appears certain that all the farms in the nation will ultimately be within organized districts.

During the past few years, many hundreds of these districts have had their names changed, either by state legislation or by action of their governing boards, from Soil Conservation Districts to Soil and Water Conservation Districts. They had found that their objectives required this broader concept in order that their name adequately portray their work. This trend may swell into a nationwide rash flood of name changing.

The governing body of each district is elected by the landowners and operators, and it guides (in some states it has the power to control) the type of use for all lands within the district.

The United States government began a cash-subsidy approach to soil conservation in 1936 through the Agricultural Adjustment Adminis-

tration. Since then the name of the bureau has been changed repeatedly. Currently, it is the Agricultural Stabilization and Conservation Service. It pays part of the cost of some of the conservation practices. The payments are administered by local farmer committees after technical approval by the Soil Conservation Service.

Conservation Work on Federal Lands. The several federal agencies which administer large land areas in this country have authority to do soil and water conservation work on the lands under their respective jurisdictions. They are currently carrying on soil and water conservation work on these lands within the limits of their present appropriations.

The farmers of the United States are much better conservationists today than they were 30 years ago. At the same time, the urban people of the nation have a much better comprehension of the need for better land use than they had during the 1930's.

Everywhere one travels today—from the Pacific to the Atlantic and from Canada to Mexico—one sees conservation practices in use by the owners and operators of our several million farms and ranches. Although relatively few farms have attained the ultimate goal of safe land use, most of the nation's lands have one or more conservation practices which were neither used nor believed in 30 years ago. On the other hand, there remain very few land owners who show a complete disregard of the principles of safe land use. Thirty years ago, a vast majority of our farmers displayed an utter disregard of these principles. The evidence proves that there has been tremendous progress during these years toward the ultimate goal (Fig. 13).

Community action, particularly with the watershed as the unit, is currently swelling the tide toward better and safer land use. In hundreds of watersheds across the land, most of them small and wholly within a single conservation district, united action of the entire population has made safe land use their immediate goal. Some have already attained their goal, but most of them are on their way toward it. Some

Fig. 13   Strip cropping is the most extensive and most easily identifiable of the many soil-conserving practices. In many parts of the country, it dominates entire landscapes. (Soil Conservation Service.)

of the watershed projects, however, are much larger and extend across district and even state lines. In watershed work, most of our political boundaries are, too frequently, deterrents to the attainment of safe land use.

Public Opinion. The basic concepts and objectives of the soil conservation program have met with general acceptance by both urban and rural people. This public approval will gradually be expressed by better use of our lands. A serious lag between verbal acceptance and the improved use of the lands will always exist. The length of this time lag varies with different localities, with different degrees of need for better land use, with different types of farming, with different types of people, and with many other factors.

More time and a more complete understanding of the full import of the problem on the part of the land-owning public are needed before the principles, for which soil conservationists are working, become an integral part of our economy.

Importance of Control. Our country has been destroying and damaging too much land at too fast a rate. We must protect our land resource. It must not be left to the indefinite future. Protection of all lands against further damage is of vital importance to our nation and to the generations yet to come.

References

Archer, Sellers G., *Soil Conservation,* University of Oklahoma Press, Norman, Oklahoma, 1956.

Bennett, Hugh Hammond, *Soil Conservation,* McGraw-Hill Book Co., New York, 1939.

Bennett, Hugh Hammond, *Elements of Soil Conservation,* Second Edition, McGraw-Hill Book Co., New York, 1955.

Black, C. A., *Soil-Plant Relationships,* John Wiley and Sons, New York, 1957.

Cook, Ray L., *Soil Management for Conservation and Production,* John Wiley and Sons, New York, 1962.

Graham, Edward H., *Natural Principles of Land Use,* Oxford University Press, New York, 1944.

Jacks, G. V., and R. O. Whyte, *The Rape of the Earth,* Faber and Faber, Ltd., London, 1939. The American edition is entitled *Vanishing Lands: A World Survey of Soil Erosion,* Doubleday, Doran and Co., New York, 1939.

Journal of Soil and Water Conservation, Soil Conservation Society of America, Ankeny, Iowa. A bimonthly magazine.

Kellogg, Charles E., *The Soils That Support Us,* The Macmillan Co., New York, 1941.

Marsh, G. P., *The Earth as Modified by Human Action,* Charles Scribner's Sons, New York, 1907. First Edition, 1864.

Mickey, Karl B., *Man and the Soil,* International Harvester Co., Chicago, 1945.

Sears, Paul B., *Desert on the March,* University of Oklahoma Press, Norman, Oklahoma, 1935; Second Edition, 1947.

Sharpe, C. F. Stewart, *What is Soil Erosion?* Misc. Pub. 286, U.S. Department of Agriculture, Washington, D.C., 1938.

Shepard, Ward, *Food or Famine; the Challenge of Erosion,* The Macmillan Co., New York, 1945.

Soil Conservation, United States Soil Conservation Service, Washington, D.C. A monthly service magazine.

Stallings, J. H., *Soil Conservation,* Prentice-Hall, Englewood Cliffs, New Jersey, 1957.

Stallings, J. H., *Soil: Use and Improvement,* Prentice-Hall, Englewood Cliffs, New Jersey, 1957.

United States Department of Agriculture, *Climate and Man, The 1941 Yearbook of Agriculture,* Washington, D.C.

United States Department of Agriculture, *Crops in Peace and War, The 1950–51 Yearbook of Agriculture,* Washington, D.C.

United States Department of Agriculture, *Grass, The 1948 Yearbook of Agriculture,* Washington, D.C.

United States Department of Agriculture, *Land, The 1958 Yearbook of Agriculture,* Washington, D.C.

United States Department of Agriculture, *Soils, The 1957 Yearbook of Agriculture,* Washington, D.C.

United States Department of Agriculture, *Soils and Man, The 1938 Yearbook of Agriculture,* Washington, D.C.

United States Department of Agriculture, *Water, The 1955 Yearbook of Agriculture,* Washington, D.C.

Vogt, William, *Road to Survival,* William Sloane Associates, New York, 1948.

H. BOWMAN HAWKES

The University of Utah

CHAPTER 6

Irrigation in the United States

A study of irrigation at this time in the nation's economic history must be structured somewhat differently from the approaches of earlier presentations. The rise of irrigation as an institution in the American West must be outlined, but the same historical events will have new connotations when viewed against the problems of this decade. The contemporary scene is one in which old but new shadows are brought into focus. The gap between supply and demand has obviously been present since man began to use water, but today there is an element of anxiety on the part of some resource scientists. As they glance across the gap from the rising curve of current and anticipated water uses and view the prospect of a more stable line of water supply, they have sufficient reason for being apprehensive. It is the shrinking gap that brings the upper limits into focus and with the aroused awareness the old institution of irrigation takes on a new look. And yet there are other resource scientists who recognize the achievements of technology, and they see a century of expanding water use and irrigation ahead. The answers relative to water in general and irrigation in particular are certainly not all in. The purpose of this chapter is to review these trends according to whether they are acceptable, question-

able, understood, or otherwise. There is need for the closest scrutiny along all fronts and the establishment of water policies that reflects the events of the past but dares to look to the future. The use of water for irrigation is caught in this dynamic swirl of thoughts and actions.

EARLY HISTORY OF IRRIGATION

The need to supply the thirsty land with life-giving water certainly antedates recorded history, and this need was undoubtedly satisfied many millenniums before the term *irrigation* was used. There is evidence of irrigation in the Nile area around 3000 to 2500 B.C. The strength of the Babylonian Empire was rooted in a prosperous, irrigated agriculture. The practice of irrigation also flourished in South America before the time of Christ. The Inca culture of Peru was noted for its elaborate canals and aqueducts that were associated with an irrigation system. Irrigation in North America also has had a long history. In the American Southwest there are remnants of irrigation structures that were built shortly after the beginning of the Christian era.[1]

---

[1] Odd S. Halseth, "Arizona's 1500 Years of Irrigation History," *Reclamation Era*, Vol. XXXIII, 1947, pp. 251–254.

103

The intermediate or the pre-pioneer period of American irrigation could be defined as the Spanish Era. It was characterized by the activities of the Spanish missionaries operating in the American Southwest and California. The Roman Catholic padres endeavored to establish among the natives an agricultural way of life based upon improved methods of irrigation.

The modern period of irrigation began on July 23, 1847, when the Mormon pioneers directed the waters of City Creek on the dry pediment slopes of Salt Lake Valley. Other irrigation endeavors by the Anglo-Saxons preceded the 1847 date, such as the irrigation of garden tracts outside Fort Bend on the Arkansas River in Colorado in 1832 and the irrigation of fields by Protestant missionaries near Walla Walla, Washington, and at Lewiston, Idaho, in 1836 and 1847, respectively. It was not the prior date, however, but the institutionalization of modern irrigation that gives to Utah the claim to the title, "Cradle of American Irrigation."[2]

As other groups occupied the land of the arid West, irrigation became an integral part of their activity. The Union Colony at Greeley, Colorado, in 1870, was important since it proved that the method of settlement developed in Utah could be established on a community basis without the theocratic social bond. In the wake of the Greeley success came projects at Boulder, Longmont, Fort Collins, Loveland, and Colorado Springs.

The important issue is not so much where and when irrigation started but why. The primitive peoples who spread waters along the alluvial fans in southwest Asia responded to the same basic need to irrigate the land that prompted the natives of the Salt River Valley in Arizona to construct canals to bring the water to the desired places. The activities of the missionaries in the Walla Walla Country reflected the same needs that prompted the Mormons to spread

water on the pediment slopes. The uniqueness of the issue is the introduction of irrigation in many places and at different times.

IRRIGATION AND PUBLIC LAND POLICY

Irrigation in western America is inextricably tied up with the development of land policies. The Desert Land Act of 1877 was designed to bring land, water, and man together. The Act enabled the settler to purchase 640 acres of land providing he agreed to irrigate it within a period of three years. Several million acres of land entered under the Act of 1877, but most of it went to build up landed estates.

Because of many disappointments and the confusion of ideas growing out of the Desert Land Act, public sentiment was aroused in favor of state intervention in the matter. The first National Irrigation Congress in Salt Lake City in 1891 and the second in Los Angeles in 1893 went on record as endorsing the cession of the public land to the states. The trend culminated in the Cary Act of 1894, which permitted the Government to donate to the western states an amount of land not to exceed 1 million acres. The states in turn assumed the responsibility for the settlement, irrigation, and cultivation of the segregated acres. A total of about 4 million acres were segregated under the Act, but only a trifle more than 1 million were ever patented. The Cary Act of 1894 failed to achieve great success because state officials were without the necessary interests in reclamation projects.

Reclamation Act of 1902. The Reclamation Act of 1902 marks an important guidepost in the history of irrigation. The motivation for the Act stemmed from many sources. There were the failures of earlier legislation to cope adequately with the problems of land and water. For a half century the United States had been able to offer to its citizens, and especially to its war veterans, land that could be easily culti-

---

[2] John A. Widstoe, "A Century of Irrigation," *Reclamation Era,* Vol. XXXIII, 1947, pp. 99–102.

vated; land that was productive and on which independent homes could be built and food provided for family and animals. By 1900, the arable land had been settled, and most of the smaller irrigation projects had been taken up. The only suitable land remaining was the arid West, and its cultivation required irrigation.

The Reclamation Act was also rooted in Theodore Roosevelt's interest in "homes and forests" and a conservation program he fostered. The guiding principle involved in the transfer of public lands to private hands has always been to provide more farms for more people and thereby achieve a wider range of land ownership. Irrigation became a part of a movement concerned with a fuller and wiser use of the nation's resources; it became a legalized method whereby the lands of the western states would become more useful to more people for a longer time.

The National Irrigation Congress of 1900 encountered vigorous opposition, but Theodore Roosevelt prevailed on a stubborn eastern block to cooperate and the Reclamation Act or Newlands Act was signed on June 17, 1902. Reclamation was administered by the Geological Survey as the Reclamation Service until 1907 when a commission was established. Finally, in 1923, the Bureau of Reclamation was established in the Department of the Interior.

The Reclamation Act put the federal government squarely into irrigation business and charged the federal officials with the responsibility of solving the problems of rights, distribution, construction, and settlement. The money for the undertaking was to be derived from a revolving fund which would supposedly be kept alive by the sale of public land.

The Act of 1902 did not resolve the problems of irrigation completely but opened up new difficulties as the program was pushed forward. Reclamation has been under constant scrutiny since its inception. Between 1902 and 1923 there were no less than 550 hearings. In 1923 a Fact Finders' Committee examined and commented on many pertinent problems then existing. The essential issues were:

1. To write off construction costs to land that cannot produce sufficient income.
2. To classify soils in order that a more equitable means of fixing construction charges could be made.
3. To provide a plan of repayment based on average farm return rather than construction costs.
4. To assign agricultural advisors to assist the settlers in farm management.

There were other pertinent recommendations pertaining to new projects:

1. That before a project be authorized a comprehensive survey be made of all pertinent physical and economic factors that may affect the success of the project.
2. That construction costs including land preparation be carefully ascertained and made binding.
3. That settlers be screened thoroughly accordingly to integrity and ability.
4. That financial assistance be provided for improvements in the project.[3]

Some of these findings were enacted into law as part of the Deficiency of 1924. The investigation did point up the mistakes of the past and the needs for the future. Reclamation benefited greatly from this close scrutiny.

More recently hydroelectric power has become irrigation's "partner," but also a subtle competitor along with other water uses within the multiple-use concept. The initial Reclamation Act made no provision for the generation and sale of power. But with Grand Coulee, Shasta Dam, and the Colorado-Big Thompson, the federal government became committed to large-scale public power developments. It is power that will pay much of the reimbursement

---

[3] Senate Document 92, 68th Congress, *The Fact Finders' Report*, Washington, D.C., 1924.

costs of the multiple-purpose projects—within this frame of reference, irrigation benefits. On the other hand and within the same context, irrigation becomes only one of many uses, including power, flood control, navigation, municipal and industrial water, salinity control, sedimentation control, sanitation, recreation, and fish and wildlife. This spectrum of uses certainly gives irrigation a different role in the reclamation program today.

The "Rights" to Use Water. As the federal government wrestled with the problems of land disposal and irrigation, the state governments were involved in creating a most complex set of rules to regulate the rights to use water. These water "rights" became rights to use and not of ownership; they were usufructuary and not proprietary in nature. This is a fundamental principle in all prevailing water laws. The doctrines or rights may be grouped under two major headings: "riparian rights" based on common law and "appropriation rights" based on statutory law.

COMMON LAW DOCTRINE OF RIPARIAN RIGHTS. Legal structure pertaining to water rights in eastern United States has been shaped by the English common law. The demand for water in humid England was largely for domestic needs, livestock requirements, and power; thus the early regulations gave rights to landowners whose property was adjacent to the watercourse. The riparian landowners were entitled to water that was unpolluted in quality and undiminished in quantity, except for the quantity used by upstream riparian owners for domestic purposes. The key to the riparian doctrine is accessibility. Once the land-water connection is severed, by lawful means, the rights are permanently lost. Thus the riparian system is ever contracting.

The riparian landowner may theoretically exhaust the stream to satisfy his domestic need, but such a demand is highly improbable. According to a modified doctrine of riparian rights, the water may be used for purposes other than

domestic, but the users are limited to a so-called reasonable share for artificial needs. When the supply is adequate, the problem of determining reasonable use is not difficult, as has been true in the past, but, when shortages threaten, the common law of riparian rights provides no quantitative guide to apportionment. Bushy recommends that the riparian doctrine be improved by instituting into state legislation new basic policies that contribute to "beneficial use" of water with an equitable division of supply among present and potential users.[4]

STATUTORY OR APPROPRIATION RIGHT. The appropriation doctrine as applied to natural watercourses means the exclusive right to the first appropriation. But it is a right that is conditioned by beneficial use. The doctrine permits the water to be diverted to nonriparian and riparian lands regardless of diminution of stream flow. It was supposedly applied first by the California placer miner in 1848–1849, when the gold seekers followed the expedient course of directing water to the mining claims. It was simply a matter of no water—no placer mining. The California courts have since upheld these actions as valid local laws suited to the immediate problem. Actually, however, California was one of the western states to adopt in 1850 the doctrine of riparian right.

In Utah the doctrine of prior appropriation has been the law in essence since the Mormons entered Great Salt Lake Valley in 1847. Brigham Young made it known early that the streams belonged to all the people. In the homogeneous Mormon communities, the problem of determining beneficial use was minimized; a decision handed down from ecclesiastical leadership was generally sufficient in such temporal matters. Thus, through trial and error, a workable system and a code of water ethics were crystallized: "Those first in time are first in right, but

[4] C. E. Bushy, "Regulation and Economic Expansion," *Water, The Yearbook of Agriculture,* U.S. Department of Agriculture, Government Printing Office, Washington, D.C., 1955, pp. 666–676.

beneficial use is the limit and measure of right."

The appropriation doctrine also has its short-comings. The following suggestions by Bushy point up the weaknesses and offer a plausible improvement of the system.

1. Provide a means whereby a lawful taking of appropriated water may be authorized under a basic water conservation program.

2. Reduce or abolish the law of prescription which permits a person who does not have a lawful right to acquire the right without notice by merely usurping water for a statutory period.

3. Improve the standards whereby beneficial use may be ascertained.[5]

The common law of riparian rights evolved slowly; it is largely judge-made and bound by rules of precedent without consideration of future needs. On the other hand, the statutory rules are formulated by a process of legislation; they have evolved more rapidly on the advice of specialists and layman, and they can be more readily changed in the light of new conditions. Furthermore, the riparian right of common law is based on the ownership of land contiguous to a stream without considering time or actual use of water; the appropriation right of statutory law is based upon the time and actual use without regard to the ownership of land adjacent to the stream. The appropriation or Colorado Doctrine is in vogue in seven intermountain states (Colorado, Idaho, Montana, Nevada, New Mexico, Utah, and Wyoming). In the eight bordering states there is a combination of appropriation and riparian rights which is known as the California Doctrine. Arizona is an exception; the state belongs geographically to the appropriation block but has modified its water laws in keeping with the California Doctrine. In Oklahoma and Oregon, although a riparian code is on the books, the courts are not upholding these rights. The remaining states adhere with mixed degrees to the rights derived from

common law. Where the modified riparian doctrine prevails, it is held that the riparian right includes the right to make use of the water for irrigation.

Figure 1 points up nicely the hard core of the appropriation realm and the transition zone where both doctrines prevail. Furthermore, the figure portrays the relationship between the areas of deficit rainfall and the doctrine of "first in time, first in right."

OTHER WATER RIGHTS.[6] Thus far the discussion has centered exclusively on "rights" as they apply to water in natural stream courses and lakes. These, of course, are the important sources, but as the demand for water continues to mount, the rights to water under other occurrences will require legal interpretations and state legislation.

1. Who is entitled to use the "diffused surface water" or the water that is associated with precipitation and snow melt but has not found its way into a natural watercourse? Can the farmer legally intercept the diffused surface water? Does the farmer, who has been deprived of the water, have any recourse? Water users and state legislators need to be alert to such problems.

2. Rights to groundwater are not clearly defined. The common law of groundwater rests on the theory that the landowner has absolute right to everything above and below his land. The mobile nature of surface water is recognized, and therefore the laws grant usufructuary rights to it. In percolation groundwater, however, the courts and legislative bodies have not consistently taken cognizance of the fact that groundwater may also flow from one property to another.

The "strict rule" places no limitation on the nature or extent of use. A landowner can pump until his well runs dry and the "draw down" extends to adjacent property. Recently, a modification of the strict rule, referred to as "reason-

---

[5] *Ibid.*, p. 673.

[6] *Ibid.*, p. 668.

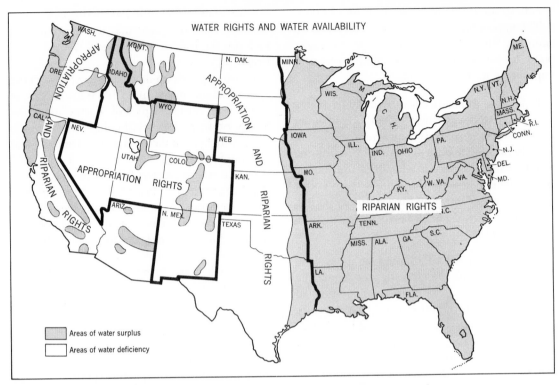

Fig. 1 The relationship between the pattern of water rights and water availability is expressed on the above map. Note the islands of surplus moisture in the area of deficit precipitation. These are, of course, the important mountains and uplands that serve to release the moisture and provide the life-giving water for the adjacent farms, factories, and cities.

able use," has been introduced. In Utah, New Mexico, Washington, and Oklahoma, the doctrine of prior appropriation has been adapted to groundwater with "beneficial use" providing the essence of the right, and with priority in time, the better right.

In California the allocation of a limited supply of groundwater is governed by the doctrine of correlative rights.[7] Accordingly, each landowner is entitled, when the supply is short, to a reasonable proportion of the common supply. The correlative rights for groundwater are an expression of the modified California Riparian Doctrine. It is prompted by a consideration of moral fairness, but the doctrine does not protect

[7] Roy E. Huffman, *Irrigation Development and Public Water Policy*, New York, 1953, pp. 51–52.

the man who came first. Interest in the California line of judicial reasoning has increased as domestic and industrial demands for water have mounted.

3. As yet there are no laws regulating directly the use of water in the air. The few laws that do prevail were set up to license rain making or cloud seeding. If irrigation is defined as the artificial application of water to land for agricultural purposes, then cloud seeding may some day come under that category.

In review it should be noted that water law is a unit in name only. The laws have been established in response to needs that have varied from time to time and from place to place. In large measure each of the needs has been treated separately as it has arisen. At the same time steps are now under way to develop comprehensive, multiple-purpose river basin programs, but without altering the underlying bodies of separate law.

PATTERN OF IRRIGATION IN THE UNITED STATES[8]

In 1959 there were 33 million irrigated acres in the United States, and every state was represented. The acreage, however, ranged from about 400 acres in Rhode Island to over 7 million in California. Table 1 lists all states with more than 100,000 acres. These twenty states include more than 98 percent of the total irrigated acreage.

Table 1. Irrigated Acreage in the United States, 1959

(States with More Than 100,000 acres)

United States	33,021,799 acres
California	7,395,570
Texas	5,655,638
Colorado	2,684,757
Idaho	2,576,580
Nebraska	2,077,926
Montana	1,874,520
Wyoming	1,469,911
Oregon	1,384,284
Arizona	1,152,450
Utah	1,061,683
Washington	1,006,969
Kansas	762,101
New Mexico	731,835
Arkansas	711,812
Nevada	542,976
Louisiana	484,850
Florida	413,526
Oklahoma	197,632
Hawaii	141,179
South Dakota	115,629

[Source: *U.S. Census of Agriculture: 1959.* Vol. III, *Irrigation of Agricultural Lands,* Government Printing Office, Washington, D.C., 1962.]

[8] *U.S. Census of Agriculture: 1959,* Vol. III, *Irrigation of Agricultural Lands,* Government Printing Office, Washington, D.C., 1962.

The 33 million acres represents an increase of 28 percent over 1950. Most of the increase took place on the Great Plains with Texas topping the list. This marked increase is due largely to the development of groundwater supplies in the Plains States (Fig. 2). In Colorado, Nevada, Utah, and Louisiana there was a slight decrease in irrigated acreage during the same period. Groundwater development is not as common in the Mountain States as on the Great Plains and the surface supplies have been utilized for several decades. Furthermore, in 1959 there was a drought in the Great Basin that limited acreage in Nevada and Utah. The decrease in Louisiana was provoked by the decline in rice acreage. Irrigated acreage along the Pacific Coast increased 23 percent during the last decade; in this area both groundwater and surface water developments are important.

About 58 percent of the water used for irrigation comes from the farms where the water is used. This may seem strange since most laymen associate irrigation with federal projects involving huge dams and an elaborate canal system. Of the total amount of irrigation water that originates on the farm, groundwater supplies 42 percent and surface water 16 percent. The remaining 42 percent comes from irrigation organizations, with surface water providing 94 percent of the amount. The striking exception is Arizona where the irrigation companies secure about two-fifths of their water from groundwater sources.

The total number of irrigated farms in the nation has declined about 5 percent. The pattern, of course, is determined by the changes in "irrigation states" where about 90 percent of the irrigated farms are to be found. The decrease in numbers is a result of consolidation that is necessary to accommodate modern mechanization. The exception to the decline is in the northern Plains States and the State of Washington where federal projects have recently opened up new land or converted large dryland farms into smaller irrigated farms.

In the humid areas many variables have en-

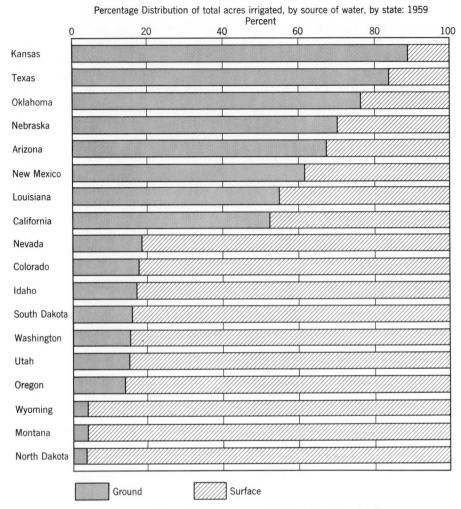

Fig. 2   The importance of groundwater as a facet of irrigation is graphically depicted on the above chart. The regional nature of the pattern is also pointed up; groundwater development along the High Plains contrast sharply with the role of surface water in the Mountain and other western states.

couraged supplemental irrigation.[9] Precipitation is not always dependable as to amount or distribution during the critical growing season. The detrimental effects of drought and their uncertain frequency and duration have prompted the farmers to look on irrigation as a form of production insurance. This is particu-

larly true where high income crops are concerned. Commercial farm producers in the humid area may attain a higher total output by adding increments of other inputs, such as the use of more fertilizer or irrigation. Farm programs that limit acreage have also provoked farmers to strive for higher yields. Thus more fertilizer and denser planting of crops makes irrigation profitable. Truck and garden crops, along with pastures for dairy herds, are the agricultural pursuits that receive supplemental irri-

[9] *U.S. Census of Agriculture: 1959,* Vol. V, Part 2, Irrigation in Humid Areas, Government Printing Office, Washington, D.C., 1960.

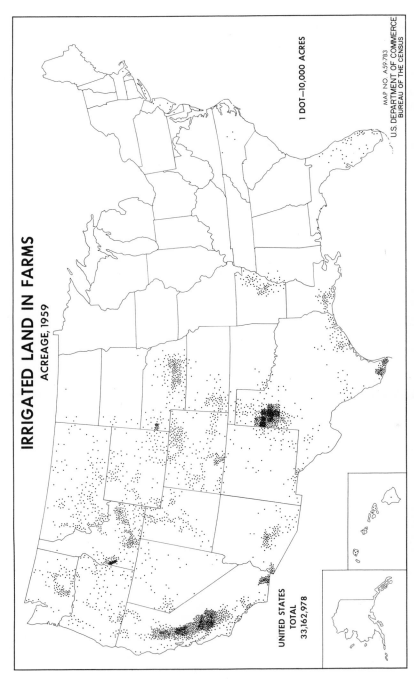

IRRIGATED LAND IN FARMS
ACREAGE, 1959

UNITED STATES
TOTAL
33,162,978

1 DOT—10,000 ACRES

MAP NO. A59-783
U.S. DEPARTMENT OF COMMERCE
BUREAU OF THE CENSUS

Fig. 3 Note how the dot pattern points up the Platte River in Nebraska, the Snake River Plain in Idaho, the Salt Lake Oasis of central Utah, the Yakima Valley of Washington, the Imperial Valley and Central Valley of California, the Salt River Valley of Arizona, and the High Plains of Texas where groundwater is so important. In the humid east the pattern of rice production in Louisiana and Arkansas and citrus and truck crops in Florida are evident. The dots along the east coast are few and far between, but the use of supplemental irrigation for tobacco in North Carolina and for fresh truck crops and dairy pastures between Boston and Washington is expressed. (Bureau of the Census.)

111

gation; the field crops are tobacco, cotton, corn, and soy beans.

North Carolina has more than 20 percent of the total farms of the state equipped with irrigation facilities. Their use depends on prevailing weather and economic conditions that govern the price of tobacco. The largest total acreage, however, is in Arkansas, Florida, and Mississippi. Rice is the leading crop in Arkansas and

Mississippi; citrus fruit and truck crops in Florida. Groundwater provides 62 percent of the irrigation requirements in the humid East.

Along the eastern seaboard, where the demand for fresh truck crops and dairy products is high, brackish water for supplemental irrigation has been recognized as a source of supply. The use of this water requires considerable skill and special storage facilities. Shallow seepage

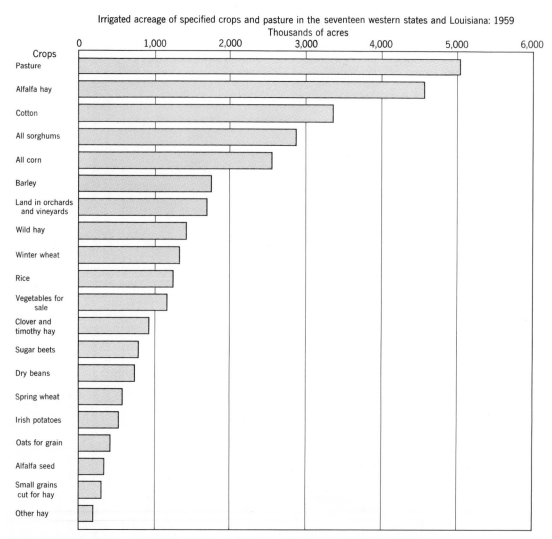

Fig. 4 This figure shows rather clearly the close tie between irrigation and the livestock industry of the west. The high percentage of irrigation devoted to pastures, alfalfa, wild hay, barley, clover, and other forage crops is striking. Even sugar beets and cotton are related to livestock production since cottonseed meal is an important feed in the Southwest, and beet pulp and molasses provide excellent feed for fattening of livestock. (U.S. Bureau of Census.)

ponds are common along the coast to capture subsurface drainage; dammed tidal inlets, bays, sounds, and rivers also serve as storage. The successful use of these brackish coastal waters depends on a knowledge of the salt content at the time of irrigation. This factor varies with rainfall, tides, and winds.[10]

Figure 3 graphically portrays the pattern of irrigation over the nation. The ingredients expressed are rainfall and available water, surface configuration, subsurface structure, good soils, and market.

The irrigated acreage devoted to specific

[10] M. H. Gallatin et al., "Brackish Water Sources for Irrigation Along the Eastern Seaboard of the United States," Agricultural Research Service, Production Research Report, No. 61, Government Printing Office, Washington, D.C., 1962.

crops and pasture is plotted on Fig. 4. The figure lists a variety of crops, but the important theme represented is the close tie between irrigation and the livestock industry as expressed in pastures and forage crops.

Methods of Watering the Land. An adequate irrigation system is one designed to meet the demands of the crops in each field without serious soil erosion. The system must be equipped with conveying and regulatory devices, control structures, drains, and there must be limited interference with tillage and harvesting activities.

SURFACE IRRIGATION. Surface irrigation includes the general methods of flood, furrow, and corrugation. The idea of flood irrigation is to cover the surface with a continuous sheet of water that is held in bounds and directed down a strip between two dikes (Fig. 5). Theoretically

Fig. 5   Flood irrigation or border irrigation. The success of this method depends on land leveling and the gentle grade. Note in foreground the large siphons that are utilized to transfer the water from the lateral to the field. (Soil Conservation Service.)

the water should be standing at every point just long enough for the soil to absorb the required amount. In practice, however, some parts generally receive too much water if all the surface receives at least an adequate amount. The method is well adapted for close-growing crops such as hay, grain, or established pastures.

Furrow irrigation is the most common method employed for row crops, truck crops, orchards, vineyards, and berry patches (Fig. 6). As the water flows down the row, some of it moves through the soil to refill the moisture storage reservoir beneath the plants. If the slope is great and the stream too large, erosion can take place. In such cases the furrow should fol-

low the contour of the land. From a labor standpoint the furrow method is usually rather expensive since the water in each row must be watched.

Corrugation irrigation is best adapted for close-growing crops, such as hay or grain, on rolling topography. The water is conducted to the higher parts of the land swells and then directed downward over the surface in small furrows. The system provides rather uniform wetting and limits erosion on steep lands.

The open ditch, or lateral, is the most common means of conveying irrigation water. For surface irrigation the ditches are generally a permanent feature on the farm, and the struc-

Fig. 6 Furrow irrigation is utilized in this field of pole beans on a farm in Preston, Idaho. The left side of the photo suggests more flooding than furrow. A good leveling job in the field would prevent the ponding of the water. (U.S. Bureau of Reclamation.)

Fig. 7   In this case the farmer is using small siphons to supply water for each row in this sugar beet field at Fruita, Colorado. Note the cement-lined ditch and the metal headgate to control the flow of water in the lateral. (U.S. Bureau of Reclamation.)

tures regulating and directing the stream flow are permanently established. The ditches follow property lines, fences, and edges of the fields. Temporary or secondary ditches are more conspicuous in the irrigated landscape since they are generally newly plowed and thus not hidden beneath a cover of grass and weeds. At the close of the irrigation season these ditches are plowed in order to eliminate them as harvesting obstacles.

Turnouts are used to deliver the water from the open ditch to the area to be irrigated. The simplest turnout is merely a gap cut in the ditch bank; sometimes metal or wooden fixtures are used. More recently siphon tubes have been adopted which transfer the water over the ditch by siphonic action. They come in various sizes

that may carry a gallon per minute to two cubic feet per second (Fig. 7).

The use of pipelines is much less extensive than open ditches since the initial outlay for their installation is extremely high, but the pipelines have many advantages. (1) They may be used to convey the water by gravity or under pressure; (2) losses from seepage and evaporation are eliminated; and (3) the method provides an unsurpassed control of the water. The use of pipelines is gaining favor in areas where water is scarce and crops valuable. The concrete-lined ditch is somewhat a compromise between the wasteful open ditch and the expensive pipeline.

UNDERGROUND OR SUBIRRIGATION. In subirrigation, water is applied beneath the ground rather than on it. The water may be introduced into the soil by an open ditch, through mole drains, or tile drains. Some of the requisites for adequate subirrigation are (1) relatively level land; (2) a layer of permeable soil immediately below the surface that will permit the free movement of water laterally and vertically; (3) a relatively impervious layer in the substratum; or (4) a permanently high, natural water table that can be raised by subirrigation. There are only a few places in the United States where all these conditions are found. The most noted areas are the Sacramento-San Joaquin delta in central California, the Everglades of southern Florida, and the San Luis Valley in Colorado.

SPRINKLER IRRIGATION. Two types of sprinkler systems are in vogue, a sprinkler head and perforated pipe. The sprinkler head with nozzle is used the more widely. These systems may be permanent, but most of them are partially to fully portable. The sprinkler heads are of several kinds. Some are stationary, but the more commonly used type is a revolving head (Fig. 8). The larger, or range, nozzle is set to throw the water to the periphery of the circle while the spreader nozzle applies the water closer to the sprinkler head (Fig. 9). They are activated by the stream itself and rotate about three times per minute. They can be controlled to apply water at rates of 0.2 inch to more than 1.0 inch per hour. The stationary, or fixed head,

Fig. 8 This portable aluminum pressure sprinkler with rotating nozzle is the most common type. In this instance sprinkler irrigation is applied to a field of cabbages. (U.S. Bureau of Reclamation.)

Fig. 9 The sprinkler is known as the "big gun." It will cover a radius of about 150 feet. The sprinkler is operated by a pressure system, using propane gas. This is a field of alfalfa hay in Riverside, Utah. (U.S. Bureau of Reclamation.)

sprinklers when used are best adapted for closely spaced orchards and vegetable plots.

The advantages of sprinkler irrigation over surface irrigation are the following.

1. Erosion can be controlled on steep land.
2. Uniform application is possible on all kinds of soil.
3. The amount of water supplied can be controlled.
4. Land preparation and irrigation structures are not required; thus more land is available for cropping.
5. It lessens the weed problem and excessive tillage.
6. Small streams and ponds can be used.

7. The amount and time of water application can be controlled.

The limitations are the following.

1. Wind can easily disturb the pattern of wetting—some getting too much and other parts too little.
2. The water should be free of sand and debris.
3. The initial costs are extremely high.
4. Power requirements to maintain pressure are high.[11]

[11] Tyle H. Quackenbush and Dell G. Schockley, "The Use of Sprinklers for Irrigation," *Water, the Yearbook of Agriculture,* 1955, U.S. Department of Agriculture, Government Printing Office, Washington, D.C., 1955, p. 267.

IRRIGATION AND THE
TOTAL WATER SUPPLY

The prospects for irrigation become meaningful when viewed in the larger framework of the total water inventory. Thus general concepts will be presented (1) within the broad outline of water resources and then (2) attention will be directed to the immediate and peculiar problems of water for irrigation.

In the quest for increasing the availability of fresh water there are some new or not yet widely applied methods that are significant for all water users. One group of techniques is intended to add to our present supply of water by reaching new sources or obtaining more from the present sources; the second is designed to permit more efficient use of the present supply. Both approaches are presented in the subsequent topics.

Table 2. The Earth's Hydrosphere
(Estimated Quantities of Water Available)

	Millions Acre-Feet	Percent of Fresh Water
1. Oceans	1,060,000,000	---
2. Fresh water	33,016,084	100
a. Polar ice, glaciers	24,668,000	74.72
b. Hydrated earth minerals	336	0.001
c. Lakes	101,000	0.31
d. Rivers	933	0.003
e. Soil moisture	20,400	0.01
f. Ground water		
(1) Fissures to 2500 feet	3,688,000	11.05
(2) Fissures 2500 to 12,500 feet	4,565,000	13.83
g. Plants and animals	915	0.003
h. Atmosphere	11,500	0.035
3. Hydrologic cycle (annual)		
a. Precipitation on land	89,000	
b. Stream runoff	28,460	

[Adapted from *Technology in American Water Development,* Edward A. Ackerman and George O. G. Löf, The Johns Hopkins University Press, Baltimore, 1959.]

New Sources of Water.[12] Considerable fresh water is available in the earth's hydrosphere; the total quantity has been estimated to be 33 trillion acre-feet (Table 2). Three-fourths of this amount is ice and slightly less than one-fourth is groundwater. These two sources constitute 99.6 percent of the total fresh water supply. Some of the remaining allocations are as follows: less than four hundreths of 1 percent is in the atmosphere; about one hundreth of 1 percent of the total supply is found in soil moisture and rivers; a minute amount is derived from lakes; and to complete the inventory a small amount is found in hydrated rocks, plants, and animals.

If new sources of water are to be made available, they must be found some place in the water inventory as identified in Table 2. On the dubious side of the budget would be the very limited fresh water present in plants, animals, and hydrated minerals. The utilization of glaciers and ice fields, although they represent 74.7 percent of the fresh water available, is not too practical. Some consideration has been given to towing and directing icebergs from Antarctica via ocean currents to the coastal cities of southern California. Even if this project were realized, it would do very little to alleviate the need for irrigation water; the costs would be high and agricultural needs are generally far removed from the seacoast.

Soil moisture is certainly singular in the water inventory. It is defined as the water found in the shallow soil layer that is available for plant growth. A negligible amount is picked up in shallow wells but the prospects for increasing this supply is almost nil. The obvious but important fact regarding soil moisture is that all plants are absolutely dependent on it. Irrigation is an expression of an effort to satisfy more nearly the optimum conditions. Few crops, even in the humid East, are grown under ideal moisture conditions. One of the limiting factors is a lack

[12] Edward A. Ackerman and George O. G. Löf, *Technology in American Water Development,* The Johns Hopkins Press, Baltimore, 1959.

of understanding as to what constitutes the optimum and how to measure it.

Rivers are also unique in the inventory; they are not only the most widely used source for fresh water but also serve as the distributive mechanism. The available water at any one time in the system is limited (0.003 percent of the total), but on an average of every 11 days the rivers of the world are completely refilled. Expansion of their use will depend on more diversions and increased precipitation. More diversions of rivers from surplus to deficit areas will undoubtedly be one of the major means of meeting water needs in the next 50 years. (See the NAWAPA story on pages 128–131.)

If precipitation could be increased by speeding up the hydrologic cycle, water available in the streams would be increased. This acceleration of the hydrologic cycle would commence with the water vapor in the atmosphere. Here again the amount at any one time is almost negligible (0.035 percent of the total), but the turnover is tremendous. The challenge, then, is to accelerate the natural mobility of the cycle.

The total amount of groundwater in the earth's hydrosphere is surprisingly large; the estimates place it as the number two source with 24.9 percent of all fresh water available. This is one of the most promising sources for an added supply.

From this inventory and brief appraisal it is evident that there are at least three new water sources worthy of consideration: (1) from the sea by means of salt water conversion; (2) from the atmosphere by acceleration of the hydrologic cycle; and (3) from the ground by improved techniques of locating groundwater and bringing it to the surface. However, the implications of salt water conversion and cloud seeding are limited as far as irrigation is concerned. Thus they will be minimized in the discussion. Groundwater holds a greater potential for irrigation; this source along with river basin diversion will be explored in more detail in subsequent topics.

FROM THE SEA. Conversion of sea water is by no means new. What is significant is the increase in production and decline in cost over the last 15 years. This has been made possible through an ever-improving program of technology. There are several processes involved: the multiple-effect evaporator, compression distillation system, electrodialysis, freezing, and the simple solar evaporator. The costs of production today range from $1.50 to $3.00 per thousand gallons, which is equivalent to $500 to $1000 per acre-foot. Few crops have sufficient value to warrant the use of such high-priced water. The engineers working in the field of salt water conversion believe that with the use of nuclear energy and improved technology the cost will ultimately be reduced to $.50 per thousand gallons. This is still too costly for most irrigation needs. Even if the water were made available with no cost at seaside, the price of lifting and conveying it to the farms would still make it financially prohibitive in most cases.

FROM THE ATMOSPHERE. Two methods are involved in the artificial induction of precipitation. One is to cool a portion of the cloud to a temperature below $-39°$ F with dry ice. At this temperature the droplets present will start to freeze as ice crystals. Crystallization will be propagated and more moisture from the air will be collected until the droplets are large enough to fall. The second method is known as cloud seeding. In this process fine particles such as silver iodide are introduced into a cloud; water vapor and cloud droplets will condense on the nuclei and form ice crystals. These crystals will grow and precipitation may ensue if conditions are suitable.

When this knowledge was made available, commercial cloud seeders moved in immediately to make rain in drought areas. For some time a controversy existed between the Weather Bureau and private operators as to the appropriateness and effectiveness of the cloud seeding projects. Because of its newness and apparent potential, an Advisory Committee on Weather Control was appointed in 1953 to appraise what had been done, what the future might hold, and the role of the federal government in such a program. In 1957 the Committee made the following comments: (1) Seeded storms in the mountainous areas of western United States did increase the total rainfall 10 to 15 percent but (2) in nonmountainous areas no increase could be clearly defined.

FROM THE GROUND. Groundwater as a source of additional water for irrigation is most promising (Fig. 10). The technological advancements in this field are adaptions of methods used in the petroleum industry. For example, the use of seismographs in locating water-bearing formations, electrical resistances to appraise the water content of the near surface layer of soil, aerial photographs to identify groundwater feature at or near the surface are but a few of the well-established surface techniques. When the drilling commences, other methods are applied to investigate the aquifers beneath. A new subsurface innovation is the use of natural radiation. A source of neutrons can be lowered into the well

and the radiation from the neutrons will respond differently to the various elements present. The hydrogen and oxygen in water can be easily identified in the aquifer and recorded by surface instruments.

One of the limitations in groundwater development has been the lack of understanding of groundwater movements. Radioactive tracers can now be used to assist in finding some of the answers. Tritium is such an isotope with a half-life of about 12½ years. It forms naturally in the upper atmosphere under conditions where the cosmic rays collide with other elements; there the tritium unites with oxygen and falls as "heavy, heavy" water in the raindrop. Eventually the tritium will decay. If, for example, a sample of groundwater contains half the tritium found in rainwater, the sample has been in the ground 12 years. The deeper wells will show no trace since the water may have been in the ground a century or more. The applications of this knowledge will contribute to a better understanding of the sources of specific groundwater reservoirs. Tritium can be added in acceptable quantities to the groundwater and thus serve as a tracer in unraveling the enigma of groundwater movements.

The mechanics of drilling and pumping have also improved production. There is an immense amount of groundwater available, but larger and deeper wells are necessary; most of the nation's wells are relatively shallow and small. Ninety-six percent of them are producing about 400 gallons a day and at the going rate of five cents per 1000 gallons this is worth about two cents. Larger investments could be justified if more water were pumped to serve more needs. The "new" water will be secured from depths of 500 to 2000 feet (Fig. 11).

Before groundwater in a basin can be "knowingly" used, it may be necessary to reduce the storage to levels where recharge and withdrawal can be checked against the oscillating water table. Opposition generally arises, however, when State Water Engineers attempt to prepare the basin for better use of groundwater by

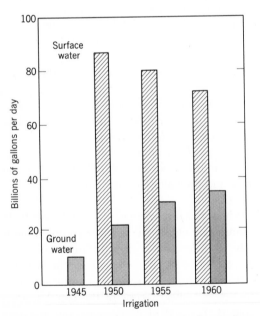

Fig. 10 The ever-increasing importance of groundwater relative to surface water as the basis for irrigation is clearly represented on this chart. Check Fig. 2 and note the development of groundwater in the Plains States.

Fig. 11   Groundwater development for irrigation has progressed rapidly in the Plains States. In the many basins of interior drainage comprising the Great Basin, the groundwater resource has hardly been touched. The scene in the background of a fault-block mountain and an alluvial-filled desert basin is typical. The large well in the foreground is fast becoming more common in the landscape. (Soil Conservation Service.)

lowering the water table or changing the artesian flow to a pump well. Such a move is counter to traditional convictions about underground water. It is not uncommon for citizens to point to the deep wells as a serious threat to the groundwater resource. Obviously, under some circumstances such as salt water invasion, further drilling should be controlled. But the lowering of a groundwater table should not always be misconstrued to mean exploitation of a natural resource.

Once the water table is sufficiently lowered so as to serve as an index, then the administration can proceed on a sustained yield basis or an alternate program of "mining" the resource. If the wiser program of sustained yield is ac-

cepted, then the groundwater would be managed as the forests and rangelands; if mining is adopted, then the groundwater is in the same category as other minerals, such as coal, natural gas, and iron. The practice of mining water may not be undesirable in some instances. It is important, however, to weigh in the factor of water depletion in any planning for the future development of the region dependent on the water. In certain sections of the High Plains of Texas and Oklahoma the "mining" practice proceeded without considering the economic consequences.

The major concern relative to the sustained yield idea is the slow rate of recharge in most basins in contrast with the withdrawal. Groundwater recharge can be enhanced by man through waterspreading devices and removal of nonbeneficial vegetation. We normally think of the porous aquifers as useful only as it contains and yields fresh water. The idea that the space between pores may be a resource in which to store water by artificial recharge is rather new. The U.S. Geological Survey reports that the aquifers in the San Joaquin Valley of California could provide storage for 93 million acre-feet during surplus years. The same practice would certainly be applicable to certain areas in the Southwest.

Efficient Use of Present Supply. The second set of techniques that are important in the quest for increasing the availability of fresh water is designed to permit more effective use of the present supply. This approach has two facets: (1) improved management of the supply already at hand and (2) more effective river basin diversion from surplus to deficit areas.

EFFICIENT USE AND IMPROVED MANAGEMENT. From the vantage point of the present it appears

that the use of water for irrigation is and will be under close scrutiny for some time to come. As the competition intensifies it will be incumbent on agriculture to justify its share. The actual returns on water, in terms of production, range from $3000 to $4000 per acre-foot for industrial use, $250 for recreation, and $51 per acre-foot for agriculture.[13] These facts seem to suggest that crops had better give way to fun and industry. It is not uncommon to find the same message coming through reputable editorials and articles pointing out that "the hard basic facts of hydrology are beginning to force western communities to choose between agriculture with attendant slowdown of economic growth and continued growth at the expense of farming."[14] The problem, of course, is not that simple. When contrasted with other water investments agricultural use looks poor, but the pending needs for food are of such a magnitude that the products of industry will have little attraction for customers with empty stomachs.

It should be noted, however, that as the specialists look ahead, the allocations of water are being drafted by fun and industry (Fig. 12). The total demand for water over the next 35 years is going to increase almost geometrically; from 300 bgd in 1954 to about 900 bgd in the year 2000. On the other hand, irrigation will do well to hold its own. These figures are based on a medium population projection.

Table 3 indicates the same trend but permits a detailed look at the projected changes for irrigation across the nation and in time. There is a noteworthy increase in water allocations for irrigation in the eastern regions. Much of this will be for supplemental irrigation. More importantly, however, it is the projected increase in irrigated acreage from 30 million in 1954 to 56 million in the year 2000. And yet the anticipated increase in water allotment for the same period is from 115 to 137 million acre-feet. Furthermore, the only significant change is in

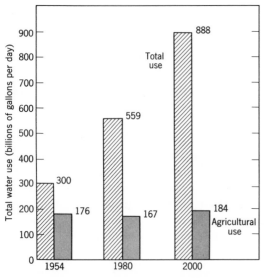

Fig. 12   Irrigation and total water use (1954–2000). Note that in the next decade the projected allocation of water for irrigation is intended to decrease. (Source: Select Committee on National Water Resources, U.S. Senate, 1959–60, Committee Print No. 32.)

[13] Nathaniel Wollman, *Value of Water in Alternative Uses*, University of New Mexico Press, Albuquerque, 1960.

[14] *Christian Science Monitor*, February 26, 1964.

Table 3. Irrigated Acreage and Water Requirements

Year	Irrigated Acreage (1000's Acres)			Water Requirements (1000's of Acre-Feet)		
	East	West	United States	East	West	United States
1954	2,002	27,550	29,552	4,736	109,961	114,697
1980	3,707	32,993	36,700	7,428	106,224	113,653
2000	15,068	40,445	55,513	26,589	110,652	137,241

[Source: *Report of the Select Committee on National Water Resources*, 87th Congress, 1st Session, Report No. 29, Washington, D.C., 1959.]

the water requirements of the east; the requirements in the west changed from 110 million acre-feet in 1954 to only 111 million acre-feet in the year 2000. It is hoped that increased efficiency in the use of water will provide enough to make up the difference.

The critical issue with irrigation is the enormous amount that is consumed. About 46 percent of all water withdrawn is used for irrigation, but 85 percent of all water consumed is by irrigation and, in addition, a sizable amount is lost long before it reaches the farmer's field. A certain amount of loss is to be expected, because it is inherent in the irrigation operation, but the amounts are much too high. Thus the objectives of this phase of the chapter are to appraise the losses and to present the techniques that have had some degree of success in reducing the waste. It is only within this frame of reference that agriculture can justify its allotment; in short, the guiding theme is simply an application of sound principles of conservation to permit more effective and efficient use of the vital natural resource—*water*.

1. Evaporation is one of the greatest offenders in the water loss picture. The losses from the surfaces of 1250 large reservoirs in the seventeen western states are computed to be 6 million acre-feet. But there are literally tens of thousands of small lakes and ponds scattered over the country; no one knows how many or the exact losses, but it has been estimated that 24 million acre-feet of water in the west are lost by evaporation from water surfaces. This is enough

to provide the annual domestic needs of 50 million people.[15]

The seriousness of the situation has attracted considerable research. The use of a monomolecular film that will spread over the water surface is the most widely recognized approach to the problem. Hexadecanol is a compound that will serve the purpose. The problems are associated with applying and maintaining the monomolecular substance over a large reservoir. Dissemination of the substance from a plane has had some success, but maintaining it on the surface is another situation. The film tends to drift with the wind, wrinkle, and sink. On smaller reservoirs agitating boxes along the edges of the body of water have been successful.

In addition to the excessive evaporation from reservoirs and lakes there is an estimated loss by evaporation at the soil surface of about 50 percent of water applied in irrigation. To reduce this loss is not difficult; there are chemicals that would serve as a water repellant, and field tests show that they are not injurious to the plant or the consumer of the plant. The technique has not been widely applied because of the increased erosion potential, cost, and the development of unsightly areas.[16]

2. Seepage like evaporation is subtle and de-

[15] Bureau of Reclamation, "Irrigation, Reclamation, and Other Water Resources Development," Prepared for Committee on Public Works, 87th Congress, 2nd Session, Committee Print No. 5, Government Printing Office, Washington, D.C., 1961.

[16] National Water Resources Symposium, Senate Document, No. 35, 87th Congress, 1st Session, p. 173.

manding. Of the 123 million acre-feet used for irrigation about 32 million are lost in conveyance.[17] A series of controlled studies reveal that in porous soil the loss may be as high as 10 percent per mile. At that rate it would not take many miles to lose it all. This is an extreme case, of course, but surveys indicate that 41 percent of the irrigated water is lost by depletion before reaching the farm. Some of the water that enters the ground may return and can be used at a lower elevation. But it may also damage in the process the lower lying land by bringing up the alkali (Fig. 13).

Ditch lining is the major technique employed to reduce seepage. Concrete lining is effective but expensive. The seepage loss can be reduced by compacting the subgrade of the canal. Butyl sheeting and plastic film have also been successful (Fig. 14). Of the 22,000 miles of canal under the management of the Bureau of Reclamation only 3000 miles have been lined. The work is spotty, however, for in Utah about 35 percent of the total ditch lining has been installed since 1940 and in another 15 years the Soil Conservation Service hopes to complete the remainder.[18]

[17] K. A. MacKichan, "Estimated Use of Water in the United States," U.S. Geological Survey, Circular 398, 1960.

[18] J. A. Libby, "Water Conservation in Utah's Irrigation Agriculture," Mimeographed Report, Soil Conservation Service, Salt Lake City, Utah, 1961.

Fig. 13   The snowlike cover is alkali brought to the surface through irrigation. To get the water on the land is the practice of irrigation. To see that the irrigation water gets away is drainage but a practice of equal importance. Proper drainage and better management of water would prevent this dreaded process of alkalization on the lands of the irrigated west. (U.S. Bureau of Reclamation.)

Fig. 14 Plastic film in canal to stop seepage loss. This sheeting will be covered with earth to protect it from damage by cattle and wind. (Soil Conservation Service.)

It is the evidence of such improvements that is encouraging and suggests that the farmer can expand acreage and production without too much additional water.

3. The phraetophyte is a nonbeneficial plant that requires an immense amount of water for growth. The specialists say that there are 16 million acres of phraetophytes in the nation and they are spreading rapidly. The salt cedar and cottonwood are the two common offenders (Fig. 15). These trees require 50 to 100 percent more water than an agricultural crop on the same area. The estimates of loss by these non-beneficial plants is 25 million acre-feet per year.

The older method of destroying the phraeto-phyte or aquatic weed mechanically is being replaced by the use of chemicals. They have been found to be more effective, convenient to use, and are often less time consuming in appli-cation. The use of 2,4-D is effective for emerged weeds such as cattails and tules. The Bureau of Reclamation survey shows that the chemical method of eradication is $25 to $43 per mile as compared with $400 per mile by drag line. If, however, the water is to be used for irrigating cotton, grapes, or tomatoes, a 2,4-D method is not acceptable since these plants are sensitive to the chemical.[19]

4. The irrigator may not be able to do much about evaporation from the surface of a large reservoir many miles from his farm or the cotton-woods that transpire the water enroute. But poor practices on his farm plot cannot be brushed aside. Through the decades the farmer has brought forward some deeply rooted "mores" about water and its proper use. Perhaps the most

[19] Bureau of Reclamation, *op. cit.*, p. 35.

Fig. 15   The edge of a cottonwood tree is on the left; salt cedars are along both banks; greasewood is on the terraces away from the river channel. When evaporation, seepage, and the
phraetophytes have taken their toll of water, there is little left for the Sevier River. (Soil Conservation Service.)

universal misconception is the conviction that "if a little water is good, more will be better." By that standard there is considerable waste.

An irrigation system should be designed to provide correct distribution, control, and measurement of the irrigation water. And yet 75 percent or more of the water utilized by the farmer is unmeasured. He will measure seeds and fertilizer by pounds per acre and yet fail to convert flow rate to volume applied. The Soil Conservation Service has done much in pointing up the inefficiencies of irrigation and the means of improving the situation. This agency works at a "grass-roots" level; their philosophy is that each community and farm has its own peculiar water supply and demand problems. With this motif they proceed with patience to acquaint the farmer with his faulty irrigation practices; to

point up the advantages of improved methods; and then, if the farmer so desires, they will assist him in a program.

According to Soil Conservation Service engineers, the efficiency of water use throughout the irrigated west is low; in Arizona it ranges from 10 to 50 percent, and in Utah a careful survey indicated that the average efficiency was 18 percent in 1940, 28 percent in 1960, and the agency looks for a 45 percent efficiency in 1980. It will vary from state to state and farm to farm, but the noteworthy issue is that efficiency can be improved.

Labor costs on the farm are relatively high; sometimes they may outweigh the cost of water. Valuable crop, scarce water, and high labor costs mean more efficient use and this will accelerate automation. Clock-operated takeout gates are now in operation in the Boise Valley in Idaho. Machines are being developed that will move along the lateral automatically and introduce water enroute. These are certainly not widespread practices, but will undoubtedly be adopted on more farms in the future.[20]

5. Several of the more experimental techniques have been investigated. Some of these may prove useful and others useless, but only time will tell. Evaporation from reservoirs and canals is enormous, but evaporation and transpiration from the water shed itself may be even greater. Again it has been estimated that in the arid Southwest only 5 percent of the precipitation that falls in the water shed gets into the stream channel. Hexadecanol has been used on the snowpack to reduce evaporation. Such a process delays the melting and increases the final runoff volume. The opposite approach is to use carbon black on the snowpack to accelerate melting and get the water into the storage reservoir as quickly as possible. This process could create a flood hazard. Soils of the watershed have been treated with an asphaltic emulsion that resists weathering. If the soil is anionic in reaction, a cationic emulsion is preferred because it creates a tight bond. The process gets the water off, but the slopes are left unsightly.

The reduction of transpiration from the crop itself has been investigated. Hybrid corn grown in soil enriched by various amounts of fatty alcohols has required up to 40 percent less water. There was no reduction in yield and no known deleterious effects on the consumer.

One of the new innovations is the use of salt water for plants. Some interesting work in this field has been sponsored by the Israel Ministry of Agriculture; they report 180 species of plants growing on salt water with a concentration of 3.5 percent salt.[21]

6. There is one universal recommendation made by the numerous committees and symposia that are concerned with water, and that is —*research*. Agricultural research involving irrigation problems, however, has not maintained a pace comparable with industry. Private enterprise can finance their own programs, whereas agricultural research depends in large measure on piecemeal allotments made annually at local, state, and federal levels. A closer tie between the research scientist, whose assignment is to reduce irrigation losses, and the private research establishment should be encouraged. The limiting factor in the application of many techniques is cost of material and herein the manufacturer could contribute much.

RIVER BASIN DIVERSION. The diversion of water from one drainage basin to another is a practice that is about as old as irrigation itself. It is only the magnitude of the operation that has changed. When the settlers of the West directed the water from one canyon to a tract of land that may have been in the drainage of an adjacent stream, they were engaged in a form of stream diversion on a small scale. When the water of the Sacramento River drainage is transferred southward to the San Joaquin drainage in the Central Valley of California, stream diversion on a large scale is under way. Or when some of the water of the Upper Colorado River drainage is transferred westward across the Wasatch Mountains in Utah to the Great Basin, the diversion involves seven western states.

For many decades this type of diversion has been practiced with a degree of success. And yet the growing demands for water in the arid West challenge the resource engineers' capacity to draft plans of sufficient dimensions to meet future needs. The transfer of water from the Sacramento end of the Central Valley of California to the San Joaquin drainage provokes concern on the part of the citizens to the north. They, too, will need the water soon—so they contend. The transfer of the Upper Colorado drainage to the Bonneville Basin stirs the citizens with expectations and apprehension throughout the entire drainage area. This operation involves a transfer from a deficit to a deficit area regardless of where the water flows. Or, as

[20] *Ibid.*, p. 28.
[21] *Water Newsletter*, May 6, 1964.

the old adage goes, it is a process of "robbing Peter to pay Paul."

NAWAPA.[22] The Ralph M. Parsons Company, a private engineering and construction enterprise with headquarters in Los Angeles, has prepared a plan for developing the water and power potential for the entire North American continent. The project is referred to by the company as NAWAPA—the North American Water and Power Alliance. The plan envisions river basin diversion on a scale beyond the capacity and courage of most resource engineers to consider. If activated only partly, the problems of irrigation tomorrow will be markedly different from those anticipated today. Thus a short review of NAWAPA has been selected as an appropriate conclusion for (1) the immediate discussion of river basin diversion and (2) the general discussion of "Irrigation in the United States"— a chapter heading that may someday read "Irrigation in North America."

The basic idea behind NAWAPA is to capture the surplus waters of the Fraser, Yukon, Peace, and Athabaska river systems in northwestern North America and to direct, via an elaborate system of canals, reservoirs, and tunnels, the surplus water to deficit areas in Canada, the United States, and northern Mexico (Fig. 16). The project is divided into four units (Fig. 17): collect, transfer, distribute surplus water, and waterway improvement.

1. The *collecting* phase starts in eastern Alaska and extends southward through the Yukon Territory and British Columbia to the international border. The 500-mile Rocky Mountain Trench, which runs through northern British Columbia to Montana, is the key feature. This great north-south oriented natural trench will serve as the collecting and stabilizing reservoir.

2. The *transfer* region is immediately south of the collecting area and encompasses Wash-

ington, Oregon, most of Idaho, and western Montana. The water will be lifted from the great Rocky Mountain Trench at 3000 feet another 2500 feet and then by a series of natural channels and man-made canals, siphons and tunnels, the water will cross the Sawtooth and Salmon River uplift of central Idaho. The power necessary to lift the water will be either generated in the NAWAPA collecting area or it will be secured from surplus power that can be generated in the already existing Pacific Northwest power units if additional NAWAPA water is added at critical periods.

3. From central Idaho the water will be *distributed* south into southern Idaho, Nevada, and Utah (Fig. 16). In eastern Utah the canal branches, the western portion flows southward into the Mojave Country and then to southern California; the eastern branch crosses the Colorado Plateau and feeds the much needed water to the rich Gila and Salt River Valley of southern Arizona and a second canal extends to the Pecos and Rio Grande basins of New Mexico and Texas. The states of northern Mexico will receive fresh water at several points along the border.

4. The fourth phase of the project provides for a *bulk freight waterway* from Vancouver on the Pacific eastward across the Rocky Mountains and Great Plains to the Great Lakes and thus to the Atlantic. Enroute eastward some of the water will be utilized on the High Plains of Canada and the Dakotas. The remainder will move through the Great Lakes system, stabilize the water level, relieve the mounting pollution problem around the large industrial and municipal areas, and increase the power potential at Niagara Falls.

The over-all costs, as estimated by the Ralph M. Parsons Company, would be about $100 billion. These costs will be defrayed by the sale of water and power. Enough waterhead is involved to generate about 100 million kilowatts of power; 70 million for sale and 30 million for pumping. The returns on power alone are computed to be $4 billion a year. The downstream

[22] The Ralph M. Parsons Company, *NAWAPA, North American Water and Power Alliance*, Summary Report, June, 1964.

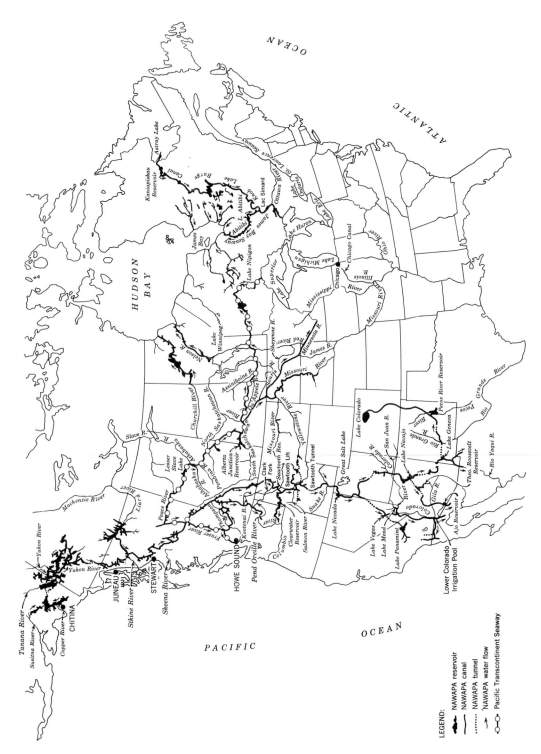

Fig. 16 NAWAPA Plan.

LEGEND:

NAWAPA reservoir
NAWAPA canal
NAWAPA tunnel
NAWAPA water flow
Pacific Transcontinent Seaway

129

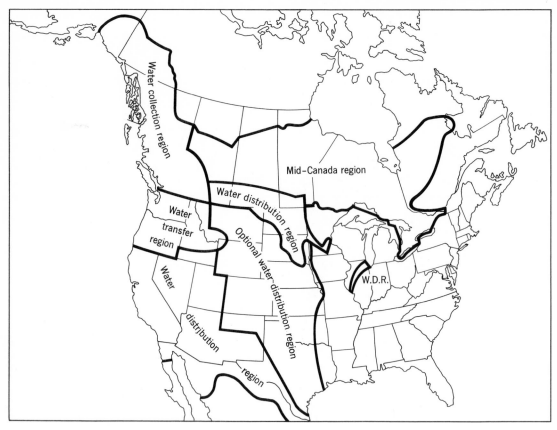

Fig. 17 Units of the NAWAPA Plan. The collecting, transferring, and distributing regions should
be checked against the detailed map shown in Fig. 16.

benefits have not been included in the initial
revenue estimates, but the returns from flood
control, navigation improvement, recreation
fees, and new industries would be sizable.

The time required to complete the program
as outlined has been estimated to be 30 years;
however, some increments could be completed
within 9 years after authorization.

This in brief is the proposal; now the implica-
tion of such a development in specific terms of
irrigation. It is evident from current delibera-
tions about the future use of water that irrigation is going to be receiving, on a percentage
basis, less and less of the water supply available.
NAWAPA introduces an old but greatly expanded variable in the equation of water planning, and the role of irrigation is modified

accordingly. The Ralph M. Parsons Company
has made some arbitrary allocations of water for
study purposes. These allocations must be
viewed strictly as a part of a working model, yet
they reflect an interested and educated opinion
as to what a reasonable allocation could be. According to the somewhat arbitrary figures, the
total assignment for irrigation would be in the
magnitude of 142 million acre-feet for the entire
continent; 25 million to Canada, 97 million to
the United States, and 20 million to Mexico.
This would bring to Mexico eight times as much
water as the new Aswan Dam will provide for
Egypt when completed. The 97 million acre-
feet for the United States is about equal to the
amount used today for irrigation. The 142 million acre-feet of water would bring about 60

million acres of land under irrigation with 41 million acres of the total in the American west. There are currently about 39 million acres under irrigation.

A project of such dimensions will provoke problems, but they will be largely problems of human relations. The technical skill is at hand; it requires no breakthroughs but the application of time-tested engineering achievements represented in present-day canals, tunnels, siphons, locks, dams, and hydroturbine generators.

Some of the human problems of a social, economic, and political nature are as follows: Since the project involves moving a vital resource across the borders of sovereign nations, it will require international arrangements at the top administrative levels. But such agreements are certainly not without precedent. In the field of energy resources the collaboration between Canada and the United States has demonstrated the mutuality of benefits from such an effort. The Columbia River Treaty exports power to Canada; the Hamilton River Project of Labrador will export power to New York; oil and gas flows in either direction across the Dominion at several points.

Perhaps the more complex tasks will be on the inter- and intrastate levels. To resolve the traditional water rights complex between and within states will be no ordinary legal task. The plan does not envision replacing any established or partially completed project. Contrariwise, it is designed to enhance the efficiency of the major water and power operations by providing additional water at critical stages. This move may disturb the *status quo* and legal adjustments must be made. There will also be need for a resolution of the interests of private utilities and government administration.

In addition, there will be minor problems associated with the displacement of some 60,000 people, largely in Canada. In view of the magnitude of the project, however, this number is relatively small. Right of ways will be required from private holdings, but the major traverses are over public lands administered by the Bureau of Land Management, Forest Service, and Park Service.

The development of the project over the next few years will bear watching. It is new, startling, and challenging in scope. The public is not too well acquainted with the idea even though press releases have been published. Key political leaders on the national and state levels have been briefed and technicians have had an opportunity to review reports made available by the Ralph M. Parsons Company. The reactions have ranged across the entire gamut from acceptance to rejection, but the concensus of opinion is highly favorable. When contrasted with other national billion-dollar efforts such as NASA, Interstate Highways Project, or the contemplated California and Southwest Water Plans, NAWAPA becomes more reasonable and perhaps as urgent as any.

NAWAPA is initiated by private enterprise, prompted by a profit motive, and so constituted to utilize the full spectrum of modern engineering techniques. It reflects the far-sightedness and vigor so typical of technological advancement. If the past bears any record to indicate future events, the prediction will be the normal but knotty problems associated with human relations as expressed in prevailing social, political, and economic patterns. There are some "ifs" associated with the project; it will of necessity change to meet technical and human demands; it may even be accomplished someday under another canopy. But it is forward looking and challenging and the idea will undoubtedly be carried forward in some form or another to full fruition.

References

Ackerman, E. A., and George O. G. Löf, *Technology in American Water Development,* The Johns Hopkins Press, Baltimore, 1959.

Bushy, C. E., "Regulation and Economic Expansion," *Water, The Yearbook of Agriculture,*

U.S. Department of Agriculture, Government Printing Office, Washington, D.C., 1955, pp. 666–676.

Golze, Alfred R., *Reclamation in the United States*, Caxton Printers, Caldwell, Idaho, 1961.

Halseth, Odd S., "Arizona's 1500 Year of Irrigation History," *Reclamation Era*, Vol. XXXIII, 1947, pp. 251–254.

Huffman, Roy E., *Irrigation Development and Public Water Policy*, Ronald Press, New York, 1953.

Israelsen, Orson W., *Irrigation Principles and Practices*, Second Edition, John Wiley and Sons, New York, 1950.

Ralph M. Parsons Company, *NAWAPA, North American Water and Power Alliance*, Summary Report, June, 1964.

Thorne, Wynne, editor, *Land and Water Use*, American Association for the Advancement of Science, Washington, D.C., 1963.

United States Senate Document 92, 68th Congress, *The Fact Finders' Report*, Washington, D.C., 1924.

United States Senate Report No. 29, 87th Congress, 1st Session, *Report of the Select Committee on National Water Resources*, Government Printing Office, Washington, D.C., 1961.

United States Senate, Senate Document No. 35, 87th Congress, 1st Session, *Proceedings of the National Water Research Symposium*, Government Printing Office, Washington, D.C., 1961.

United States Bureau of the Census, *Census of Agriculture, 1959*, Vol. III, *Irrigation of Agricultural Lands*, Government Printing Office, Washington, D.C., 1962.

United States Bureau of the Census, *Census of Agriculture, 1959*, Vol. V, *Irrigation in Humid Areas*, Government Printing Office, Washington, D.C., 1961.

Whitaker, J. Russell, and Edward A. Ackerman, *American Resources: Their Management and Conservation*, Harcourt, Brace, New York, 1951.

Widstoe, John A., "A Century of Irrigation," *Reclamation Era*, Vol. XXXIII, 1947, pp. 99–102.

Wollman, Nathaniel, *Value of Water in Alternative Uses*, University of New Mexico Press, Albuquerque, 1960.

LOWRY B. KARNES
Bowling Green State University

CHAPTER 7

Reclamation of Wet and Overflow Lands

The man-land ratio in our country is not nearly as satisfactory as most people believe it to be; effective conservation practices are absolutely essential if we are to maintain an ever-rising standard of living for an ever-increasing number of people.

The drainage or the protection of overflow lands as a phase of the conservation of our agricultural resources is a rather complex problem. This complexity is indicated by sharp disagreement as to whether the drainage or protection of wet lands is a conservation measure at all. If drainage of new land is to be undertaken as a step toward the wise use of the land, it should be inferred that the need for further extension of arable land is sufficiently great that the benefits to be derived from bringing new land into agricultural use will be greater than the cost of the labor and capital involved.

We hear and read a great deal about the destruction of our land and the increasing needs of our people for food, clothing, and industrial raw materials, but during most of this century, one of the most troublesome problems in our national economy has been overcapacity of agricultural productive facilities. There appears to be no immediate necessity for additional land

to supply the needs of the people of our country.[1]

Agricultural drainage refers to the removal, by artificial means, of excess water to improve the condition of land used or to be used for agriculture. Excess water either in or on the soil—whether a permanent or a temporary condition —influences farm production, farm income, and farm values. Too much water in the soil adversely affects crop growth and the timely performance of operations such as tillage, seeding, cultivation, and harvesting.

Accumulation of excess water can arise from heavy local precipitation, runoff from upstream areas, low-lying land in depressions, tidal action in coastal areas, impervious subsoil, buildup of a high water table as a result of irrigation or seepage, or from artesian or other underground movement of water.

The question may arise as to the desirability of draining additional land in order to have it ready for immediate use, when needed, to provide food and fibers for our growing population and industrial raw materials for our rapidly ex-

---

[1] J. Frederic Dewhurst and Associates, *America's Needs and Resources, A New Survey,* New York, 1955, pp. 783–800.

panding industry. There is abundant evidence from all types of land from Michigan[2] to Florida[3] that marshland deteriorates more rapidly after it is drained than it does in its natural state. Several causes contribute to this deterioration, but the most serious one seems to be general subsidence of the land due to settling and accelerated oxidation of the organic matter in the drained soil. Also, fire may completely destroy peat and muck soil, thus lowering the level of the land surface. So long as the water table is maintained at the surface of the ground, little or no deterioration occurs, and the land is more likely to be available for full productive use than it would be if it were drained and thus exposed to the hazards of subsidence and fire.

Although it appears certain that there is no need for additional agricultural land in this country in the middle 1960's it is almost equally certain that the time will come when it will be necessary to bring new land into cultivation. It would be impractical here to attempt to say just when that time will come or to attempt to recount all the means whereby its coming may be postponed.

Importance of Drainage. The drainage of wet lands offers the greatest of all potential sources of additional farmland. Some evidence of the present and potential importance of drainage as a means of adding to or improving our agricultural land is derived from the fact that more than 100,000,000 acres of land have been drained, and it is estimated that a comparable amount of additional land is capable of being drained.[4] The acreage of land provided with irrigation is approximately 25,000,000 acres, and the prospects of doubling this figure by additional developments are far from encouraging. Roughly one-fifth of our best agricultural land has been made available or has been improved by drainage, and, at least theoretically, it would be possible to increase the amount of farmland by a similar amount by additional drainage. However, the quality of much of this additional land is questionable.

The conservation of wet and overflow lands has a twofold significance in that it involves the improvement of lands now in use and the reclamation of lands not now used. The common assumption is that unused land is that not being used for crops, pasture, or forestry and that used land includes all in privately owned farms, ranches, and woodlands. However, it must be recognized that a great deal of undrained land has present value as a habitat for native animal life, as a resting place and a nesting and feeding area for migratory waterfowl, and as a habitat for aquatic life as well as scientific value for studying plant and animal life.[5] Also, before an attempt is made to drain new land, there should be recognition of the potential value of the area as a regulator of stream flow and a source of groundwater supply. Drainage is conducive to rapid runoff, and thus may result in erosion, floods, and the deposition of debris.

Drainage projects should not be undertaken without comprehensive knowledge of the ends sought, the values involved, and the probable results. However, there appear to be some circumstances under which the drainage of new land can be thoroughly justified. Landowners paying taxes on unproductive lands may find it advantageous to drain land to protect their investment or to increase their income. Also, it is probable that some farmers now located on submarginal land might advantageously be moved to more fertile land made available by drainage. Nevertheless, before investing heavily in new drainage enterprises the individuals should know that many such undertakings were never

[2] *State Planning, Review of Activities and Progress*, National Resources Board, Washington, D.C., 1935, p. 156.

[3] Glenn K. Rule, "The Challenging Glades," *The Land*, Vol. XI, 1952, p. 156.

[4] *Land Available for Agriculture Through Reclamation*, Supplementary Report of the Land Planning Committee to the National Resources Board, Part IV, Washington, D.C., 1937.

[5] *Recreational Use of Land in the United States*, Report on Land Planning, Part XI, National Park Service, Washington, D.C., 1934, p. 55.

completed and that some that were completed have been abandoned as economically unsound. Before new land is drained, its potentialities should be studied thoroughly to determine whether the land would be more valuable for recreational and scientific purposes than if put to agricultural use.

LAND IN DRAINAGE ENTERPRISES

Classes of Wet and Overflow Lands. Our wet and overflow lands vary greatly in their productive capacities and in other agricultural advantages and disadvantages.

Wet lands, more or less permanently, have such a high water table that they cannot be farmed profitably. Overflow lands, although not permanently wet, are so situated that inundation is sufficiently frequent that farming is impractical or severely handicapped.

The problems associated with wet and overflow lands are so numerous and they vary so much from place to place that it is convenient to group them into the following classes within which generalizations are possible: (1) the outer Coastal Plain along our Atlantic and Gulf coasts, including tidal marshes; (2) river floodplains, of which the Mississippi River floodplain and delta are the most extensive; (3) glacial lands of low relief and obstructed drainage; (4) alkaline or water-logged areas associated with irrigation enterprises; (5) wet spots on slopes or flat land where the land surface intersects the general water table or a perched water table. No data are available on the amount of land that has been drained or should be drained in the last class, but undoubtedly the total acreage of such lands would reach into the millions of acres.

Extent of Drained Land. No attempt has been made to estimate accurately the amount of land in the United States that should be drained. Reasonably satisfactory data are available concerning the extent and location of artificially drained land and land in drainage enterprises. In 1920, when the first census of drained land was taken, there were 65,000,000 acres reported

in drainage enterprises.[6] The next decade showed a great increase in acreage (to 84,000,000 acres in 1930) related partly to great activity in drainage enterprises and in part to more complete data. The acreage of drained land increased slowly during the decade from 1930 to 1940 because these years were characterized by drought conditions that lowered water tables and capital was not available during the depression years for desirable improvements. The decade from 1940 to 1950 witnessed renewed intensification of activity in drainage as rainfall returned to normal and as wartime and postwar markets brought prosperity to farmers and increases in land values enabling them to improve their land. During this decade the reported acreage of drained land increased from 87,000,000 acres in 1940 to 103,000,000 acres in 1950. The actual increase was somewhat greater than these figures would indicate because the 1950 census did not include drainage enterprises with fewer than 500 acres. Furthermore, the 87,000,000 acres reported in 1940 included the entire area of irrigation developments that had their own drainage; whereas the figures for 1950 included only the land in such developments that was actually drained.

The total area in drainage projects serving agricultural lands according to the 1960 census was 101, 870, 257 acres. This is slightly less than the acreage reported in 1950, but actually represents an increase for comparable categories of land. The 1960 data excluded about 3 million acres of drained irrigated land and about 6 million acres of swamp and waste lands which had been included in the 1950 census. During the decade of the 1950's, drainage was reported as newly established on 5.3 million acres and new works or services on previously established drainage projects amounting to 2.6 million acres. The total cost of drainage works and serv-

---

[6] All the data for this discussion of the expansion of drainage enterprises were taken from *Drainage of Agricultural Lands*, U.S. Census of Agriculture for 1950, Vol. IV, Washington, D.C., 1952, and from U.S. Census of Agriculture, 1959, Vol. IV, Washington, D.C., 1961.

ices during the 10-year period from 1950 to 1959 inclusive was $461,875,000. About 40 percent of this was for new works.[7]

Small-sized enterprises accounted for about 5 percent of the total acreage of artificially drained land reported in 1940. If we can assume that the ratio of land in small drainage enterprises to that in large enterprises was about the same in 1960 as in 1940, it would appear that slightly more than 5,000,000 acres of land in enterprises of less than 500 acres were drained in 1960. This would bring the total acreage of artificially drained land in organized drainage enterprises to about 107,000,000 acres. In addition to organized drainage enterprises, there are large numbers of small undertakings which have never been tabulated.

PROBLEMS ASSOCIATED WITH WET-LAND RECLAMATION

Is It Wise to Drain More Land? The need for drainage appears to be local and personal, since there is no need for increasing the national acreage of farmland at present. As a local and personal problem, the principal aim of drainage is to improve the use of the land and thus promote the welfare of the community and the landowner. This certainly cannot be achieved unless the benefits exceed the cost. Thus, it is advisable, before any drainage project is undertaken, to analyze thoroughly the benefits expected and to weigh them carefully against the expected cost of the project and its maintenance. Furthermore, when estimating the costs involved and the probable benefits to be derived, it should be borne in mind that certain costs will be more or less recurrent and permanent. Therefore, in making comparisons between costs and anticipated benefits, it is necessary to add the probable annual cost of upkeep to the initial cost of the enterprise and to determine whether or not the increase in product from the land will be sufficient to amortize

[7] *Drainage of Agricultural Lands,* U.S. Census of Agriculture for 1959, Final Report, Vol. IV, Washington, D.C., 1951.

the entire cost within a reasonable time and yield a profit. The farmer who undertakes to improve his welfare by the drainage of his land should allow a considerable margin between costs and benefits, or he may find himself losing money during periods of decreasing farm prices.

From a regional or community point of view, the improvement of land through drainage may be expected to yield such benefits as increased land values with higher tax duplicates and all the benefits that come from them, the elimination of mosquito-breeding areas, and the addition of land available for homes. Yet, the greater share of the cost of any land improvement will, in the long run, be borne by the farmer, and he must be concerned with the money value of the benefits as compared with the cost of the improvement. The farmer is interested in increasing the quantity and improving the quality of his product, and it is very difficult for him to know with certainty just what financial returns these may bring.

Certainly no farmer should undertake a major drainage project until he has thoroughly investigated every phase of the problem involved. He must ascertain carefully the quality and depth of his soil. He should determine as precisely as possible the amount of settling that will follow drainage, the effects of the increased rate of oxidation of organic material, and the possibility of fire if his soil has a very high content of organic matter. He should consider alternate uses of the land that would prove profitable with little or no outlay of capital. The land might be used profitably as it is, or with but little improvement, for pasture or forest. It might be adaptable for rice, cranberries, ducks, or aquatic life. If his land happens to be a resting place for migratory waterfowl, perhaps he could realize a net gain by selling hunting privileges. He might combine a drainage project with the development of one or more farm ponds and thus achieve benefits from the drainage of part of the land and at the same time plan to harvest fish or other aquatic life from the ponds. Many farmers report that, acre for acre, the most productive parts of their farms are their ponds. If he decides to drain his land, crops should be grown that are best suited to the soil and the climate of the area and to the market. This list of problems is not intended to be exhaustive, but it is sufficiently long to demonstrate that the drainage of additional land is not something to be entered into hastily.

Methods of Drainage. After a landowner has carefully considered his problem from all angles and has decided to drain his land, he has to face the question of which method of drainage will be most advantageous. First he should determine whether a thorough perforation of the subsoil would permit the surface water to sink into the ground fast enough to give him all the drainage he needs. This procedure probably would be the cheapest method, it would get the water off the land without contributing to increased flow of streams, and it would help to maintain the permanent water table.

If the above method is not feasible and actual drainage installations are necessary, the choice will probably be between open ditches and tile. Tile drains have an advantage over open ditches in that they do not take valuable land out of use. However, open ditches are effective as well as cheap and are simple to install; they are much more extensively used than tile drains. In 1960, there were, in the country as a whole, about three times as many miles of open ditches as there were of tile drains. Moreover, the relative popularity of open ditches appears to be increasing: between 1940 and 1950, sixteen times as many miles of open ditches were constructed as of tile drains (9301 miles of open ditches to 581 miles of tile drains). From 1950 to 1960 the comparable figures were 33,543 miles of open ditches and 2192 miles of tile or covered drains. Open ditches seem to be especially favored in the southeastern states; whereas tile drains are more extensively used in the Corn Belt, a fact which is doubtless related to the higher land values of the latter region. Ohio, Indiana, and Iowa have more than one-half of all the mileage of tile drains in the entire country.

The practice of land grading or smoothing, popularly known as land leveling, is very common in connection with irrigation and the drainage of irrigated land. In recent years this practice has become increasingly popular in the humid eastern states. It is less expensive than tilling and it offers little or no interference with ordinary field operations. No data are available concerning the amount of land now drained by land leveling, but it is reasonable to expect this practice to increase greatly in the future.

In some cases the success of a drainage enterprise is dependent on pumps. The total area served by pumps in 1950 was just under 1.7 million acres. From 1950 to 1960 the number of drainage pumps in use was approximately doubled, but figures as to the acreage benefited are not available.

It is obvious that pumping should be resorted to where topography is such that gravity alone cannot be made to yield the desired results, but pumping is also advantageous in places where it is especially desirable to control carefully the water table, as is the case with peat and muck lands. In such soils most crops will not grow if the water table is too high. On the other hand, if the water table is lowered too far, the results can be serious. The most common of these serious results of excessive lowering of the water table are fire, wind erosion, and rapid decomposition of organic matter.[8] The most extensive areas of land drained by pumping are located in California, Florida, Louisiana, Illinois, and Missouri.[9] Because of the expense involved in pump drainage, it is especially important to weigh carefully the expected benefits.

THE LOCATION FACTOR

Geographic Distribution of Drainage Enterprises. Although some drainage was reported

8 M. S. Anderson, S. T. Blake, and A. L. Mehring, *Peat and Muck in Agriculture*, Circular 888, U.S. Department of Agriculture, Washington, D.C., 1951, p. 27.

9 U.S. Bureau of the Census, *Drainage of Agricultural Lands*, 1959, p. 21.

138   **Conservation of Natural Resources**

in every state in the country in 1950, West Virginia, the Commonwealth of Pennsylvania, Alaska, Hawaii, and the New England states did not report any regularly organized drainage enterprises of more than 500 acres in extent.

In the forty states that did report regularly organized drainage enterprises, the amount of drained land is very unevenly distributed (Fig. 1). The states of Indiana, Michigan, and Minnesota each have approximately 10 percent of the total for the country, whereas Ohio, Illinois, and Iowa together have about 20 percent. Thus six of our north-central states account for about 50 percent of the total acreage of drained land in the country.

The only other states that individually account for as much as 5 percent of the total acreage of drained land are Louisiana, Florida, and Texas, with Arkansas ranking next with about 4.8 percent of the total (Fig. 2). The state of

Louisiana was shown in the census of 1950 to lead all the states in drainage enterprises, but the figures are misleading because they include several million acres of land in enterprises that had been organized late in 1949 and on which work had not yet begun. If the census had been taken a year earlier, before Louisiana adopted the parish-wide system of organization, it is probable that the total acreage in drainage enterprises in that state would have been much less. In 1960 Louisiana reported slightly more than 9 million acres in drainage enterprises and thus ranked fifth in the country, with about 9 percent of the total for the country. In contrast to the nine states which report more than 5 million acres of drained land, there are twenty-nine states (including the ten previously mentioned as reporting no drainage enterprises) that report less than 500,000 acres each. These are distributed in such a way that at least one such state is

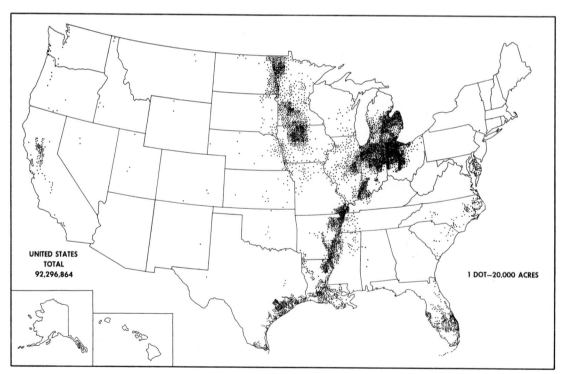

Fig. 1 Map of the United States showing location of drained agricultural lands, 1960. (U.S. Bureau of the Census.)

found in every census division except the East North Central, in which the state of Wisconsin, reporting 587,000 acres, passes the half-million mark by only 87,000 acres.

Although maps of drainable wet lands show extensive areas of such lands along our Atlantic coast, there is only one state (North Carolina) which has more than 400,000 acres in drainage enterprises (Fig. 3). North Carolina's 1,498,892 acres in drainage enterprises account for approximately one-half of all the drained land along the Atlantic coast north of Florida. Florida alone has about six times this acreage in drainage enterprises. Most of the drainage in Florida was developed during the 1920's. The acreage of drained land remained relatively static until about 1950, but it has been increased by about 50 percent since then. Many of the principal drainage canals in Florida seem to have been put through without adequate consideration of the capabilities of the land and with insufficient knowledge of the problems involved.[10]

In the semiarid and subhumid western states drainage is not much of a problem except where it is associated with irrigation. In California, which leads all the western states in both irrigated area and land drained, it was estimated, in 1930, that 85 percent of all land in drainage enterprises was also irrigated land.[11] Although census data are not available to verify the assumption, it is reasonably safe to conclude that a similar relationship exists between drained land and irrigated land in California at the present time.

It may be noted also that California leads all states in the acreage of land drained by means of pumps.[12] Much of the pumping in irrigated areas is so arranged that the water can be pumped back onto the land and used a second, or even a third, time for irrigation.

[10] Rule, op. cit., p. 156.

[11] U.S. Bureau of the Census, Drainage of Agricultural Lands, 15th Census of the United States, 1930, Washington, 1932, p. 64.

[12] U.S. Census of Agriculture, 1950, op. cit., p. xvii.

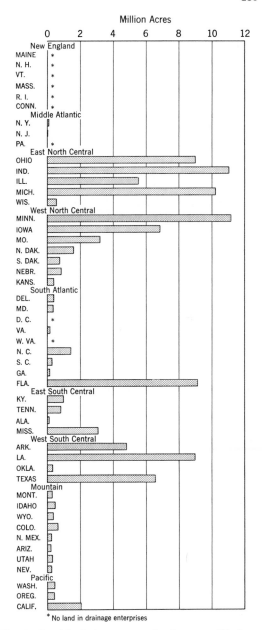

Fig. 2   Land in drainage enterprises by states. (*Drainage of Agricultural Lands*, U.S. Census of Agriculture: 1959, Final Report—Vol. IV.)

Regional Appraisal of Drainage Achievements. About one-half of our drained land is in the Corn Belt and the Spring Wheat Region; without artificial drainage, these regions could

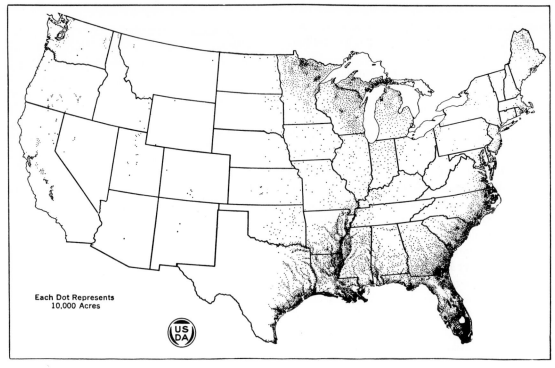

Each Dot Represents
10,000 Acres

Fig. 3 Approximate location of drainable wet lands. (U.S. Department of Agriculture.)

not have attained the high rank as prosperous farming regions that they now enjoy.[13] However, the success of commercial agriculture has been favored in much of this area by such important factors as naturally fertile soil, topography favorable to machine-type agriculture, a stimulating climate that permits the growth of all middle-latitude crops, the world's finest transportation systems, and unexcelled markets for farm products. All these factors have combined to give the farmers of this region competitive advantages that have enabled them to finance costly improvement of their land at considerable financial benefit to themselves. However, there is evidence that drainage was extended too greatly in the northern parts of Michigan, Wisconsin, and Minnesota by includ-

[13] Martin R. Kaatz, "The Black Swamp, A Study in Historical Geography," *Annals of the Association of American Geographers,* Vol. XLV, 1955, pp. 1-35.

ing some land that is better adapted for forest growth, haven for wild life, or for scientific and recreational purposes. Some adjustments have already been made to correct this, especially in Wisconsin.

Other areas of notable achievement in drainage are located in the states of Arkansas, Louisiana, and Texas. In Louisiana and Arkansas, the artificially drained areas lie chiefly on the back slopes of the levees along the Mississippi and Red rivers. These areas have been relatively easy and inexpensive to drain, chiefly by using open ditches extending down the slope away from the main rivers. The soil is fertile alluvium, and the growing season is so long, especially in Louisiana, that off-season crops can be marketed advantageously in the North. Also, the fact that rice, a major crop in both Louisiana and Arkansas, has relatively little competition and that sugar, a major product in Louisiana, has effective tariff protection contributes to the ability of the farmers to operate profitably in spite of the expense of artificial drainage. The artificially drained lands in Texas lie mostly on the eastern coastal prairie where drainage becomes largely a matter of control of water for rice production.

Florida is the only other eastern state in which artificial drainage is extensive. About one-half of the land in drainage enterprises in that state is in the Everglades. Problems resulting from artificial drainage in this area include subsidence of the land, rapid oxidation of organic matter, and burning of the peat and muck soils when they dry out. These problems are combatted by careful regulation of the water table, which, in many cases, involves pumping water off the land during the wet season and pumping it onto the land during the dry season. The problem of regulation is complicated by the fact that the water table should be higher for some crops than for others and it should be as near the surface as possible when the land is not in crops so as to retard oxidation. The difficulty of draining the land in the first place plus the costly problem of regulating the water table precisely make farming in the Everglades precarious. Other areas of artificial drainage in Florida include the west central part of the peninsula, extensive areas along the east coast, and the St. Johns River Basin. In all the drainage districts of Florida, there are extensive areas of infertile soil and unreliable rainfall, and in the coastal areas improper drainage sometimes results in infiltration of salt water. Thus the farming of artificially drained land in Florida is costly and precarious, and it has achieved a reasonable degree of success only because of the unexcelled market for off-season and subtropical fruits and vegetables in the northern and northeastern states.

SHALL ARTIFICIAL DRAINAGE BE EXTENDED?

Arguments for Extension of Drainage. No stronger argument favoring extension of artificial drainage can be offered than the fact that,

on the whole, the artificial drainage of agricultural land has been highly successful. At least one-fifth of our best agricultural land has been made available for crops by artificial drainage. This would seem to indicate the wisdom of proceeding with the drainage of additional land, even if it leads to the abandonment of other land already in use. Much submarginal land is in use that might profitably be retired and be replaced by better land acquired by drainage. This may raise the question of why artificial drainage is the key to the problem of the expansion of agricultural land or of the shift from inferior to more productive land. The answer to this problem is twofold: first, most of the remaining potentially arable land requires drainage, and second, artificially drained land is, with some exceptions, likely to be superior land.

What are some of the advantages of well-drained land which contribute to its superiority? The following advantages are readily apparent.

1. Adequate drainage, by removing surplus water, will lower and stabilize the water table and thus provide a greater depth of the root zone.

2. Well-drained soil warms up earlier in the spring and thus permits earlier planting and germination of crops.

3. Adequate drainage improves the physical condition of the soil, making for a better seedbed and better tillage.

4. On a field that is uniformly well drained, farm work can be done more efficiently.

5. Satisfactory conditions of drainage minimize damage by winter freezing.

6. Effective drainage contributes to improvement of both quality and quantity of crops and thus increases the gross income of the farmer.[14]

In comparing artificially drained land with land that has adequate natural drainage, it may be observed that:

[14] Report on Land Planning, Part IV, *Land Available for Agriculture Through Reclamation,* Prepared by the Bureau of Agricultural Engineering, U.S. Department of Agriculture, for the Land Planning Committee of the National Resources Board, Washington, D.C., 1937, p. 37.

1. The percentage of wasteland on the artificially drained land is relatively low.

2. Erosion is relatively insignificant on artificially drained land.

3. Artificially drained land is less likely to be affected by severe drought than is land that is so situated that it requires no artificial drainage.

4. Artificially drained land is usually so nearly level that labor-saving machinery can be used advantageously.

The student of conservation can doubtless think of additional advantages of artificially drained land, and he may also find exceptions to some of the advantages listed above. However, the list is long enough and reliable enough to suggest that there are sound arguments favoring the artificial drainage of additional land for agricultural use as fast as it can be effectively occupied.

Opposition to Extension of Artificial Drainage. For many years the United States Biological Survey and later the Fish and Wildlife Service pointed out that an undrained marsh might be more profitable than adjacent farmland and that it may provide feeding, breeding, and resting places for birds, fur-bearing animals, and other forms of life. It can yield great quantities of fish, a supply of natural ice, and grasses and other growth that can be used as forage, bedding, rugs and baskets. It may maintain the water table, promote forest growth, insure the flow of springs, and reduce runoff, thus reducing floods and erosion. Furthermore, it can provide areas for educational and recreational uses.[15]

Unfortunate experience in land drainage in a number of states has led to the opinion that: "Unused land should be kept under water until it is needed, to avoid subsidence, fire and oxidation."[16]

In recent years, since several large lumber and paper companies have become interested in maintaining forests on a sustained-yield basis,

some of them have expressed themselves strongly against the extension of artificial drainage. At an open hearing of the United States Army Engineers in Memphis, an executive of one of the largest southern lumber companies pointed out that the drainage of new land usually leads to elimination of forests which often are of more value than any crops that might be raised on the land.[17] At the same hearing representatives of another large lumber company went so far as to express opposition to the drainage of land adjacent to forests. It was their contention that the lowering of the water table in cleared land adjacent to forests would result in the lowering of the water table in the nearby forests and thus make them more susceptible to destruction by drought.[18]

Another segment of our population, represented by both urban and rural dwellers, that voices strong opposition to the extension of drainage includes the inhabitants of low-lying lands in downstream locations who fear that the speeding up of runoff from lands above them would increase the flood hazard in their own communities.

These instances are sufficient to demonstrate that there are some strongly organized groups who have legitimate arguments against drainage of additional land until it is needed for cropland and pasture and that any major project is likely to meet with determined opposition until it has been proved to be fully justified.

CONCLUSION

There is no present need for the drainage of new lands to provide food, fibers, and industrial raw materials for the people of our country. There are, however, many individual farmers and some communities that would profit by the drainage and improvement of agricultural lands in local areas.

Wet lands, subject to drainage, constitute the greatest reserve of new land available for use at

---

[15] U.S. Department of Agriculture, *Yearbook of Agriculture,* Washington, D.C., 1926, pp. 313–314.

[16] *State Planning,* Review of Activities and Progress, National Resources Board, Washington, D.C., 1935, p. 156.

[17] *Memphis Press-Scimitar,* April 12, 1955, p. 1.

[18] *Ibid.,* p. 2.

some future time when our growing population and expanding industry require additional materials. Undoubtedly, the first major step should be the drainage and improvement of land already in farms.

Any major development of a drainage enterprise must be preceded by a thorough study of: (1) need, based on accessibility to actual and potential markets; (2) desirability, based on comparative advantage of the use of the land for agriculture in relation to its use for other purposes; (3) physical condition of the land, to determine whether or not it will be permanently productive; and (4) cost, to determine whether or not the undertaking will be sufficiently profitable to pay for itself.

References

Agricultural Conservation Program; Summary, U.S. Department of Agriculture, Agricultural Conservation Program Service, Washington, D.C. An annual report.

Bartelli, L. J., and C. A. Engberg, "Classification of Michigan Lands According to Use Capability," *Papers of the Michigan Academy of Science, Arts and Letters,* Vol. XXXVIII, Part III, Geography and Geology, Ann Arbor, Mich., 1952, pp. 287–294.

Bourn, W. S., and Clarence Cottam, *Some Biological Effects of Ditching Tidewater Marshes,* Research Report 19, Fish and Wildlife Service, Washington, D.C., 1950.

Clawson, Marion, R. Burnell Held, and Charles H. Stoddard, *Land For the Future,* Resources for the Future, The Johns Hopkins Press, Baltimore, 1960, pp. 432–439.

Dewhurst, J. F., and Associates, *America's Needs and Resources, A New Survey,* The Twentieth Century Fund, New York, 1955, pp. 513–574.

Farm Drainage, Farmers' Bulletin 2046, U.S. Department of Agriculture, Washington, D.C., 1952.

Hewes, Leslie, "The Northern Wet Prairie of the United States: Nature, Sources of Information, and Extent," *Annals of the Association of American Geographers,* Vol. XLI, 1951, pp. 307–323.

Hewes, Leslie, and Phillip E. Frandson, "Occupying the Wet Prairie: The Role of Artificial Drainage in Story County, Iowa," *Annals of the Association of American Geographers,* Vol. XLII, 1952, pp. 24–50.

Kaatz, Martin R., "The Black Swamp: A Study in Historical Geography," *Annals of the Association of American Geographers,* Vol. XLV, 1955, pp. 1–35.

Maintaining Drainage Systems, Farmers' Bulletin 2047, U.S. Department of Agriculture, Washington D.C., 1952.

Peat and Muck in Agriculture, Circular 888, U.S. Department of Agriculture, Washington, D.C., 1951.

Peterson, Elmer T., "Insoak Is the Answer," *The Land,* Vol. XI, 1952, pp. 83–88.

Rule, Glenn K., "The Challenging Glades," *The Land,* Vol. XI, 1952, pp. 155–162.

Saunderson, Mont H., *Western Land and Water Use,* University of Oklahoma Press, Norman, Okla., 1950.

Sears, Paul B., "Comparative Costs of Restoration and Reclamation of Land," *Annals of the American Academy of Political and Social Science,* Vol. 281, 1952, pp. 126–134.

Soil Conservation Service, U.S. Department of Agriculture SCS *National Engineering Handbook,* Section 16, *Drainage,* Chapter 1, "Principles of Drainage," Washington, D.C. 1961.

Supplementary Report of the Land Planning Committee to the National Resources Board, Part III: *Agricultural Land Requirements and Resources,* Part IV: *Land Available for Agriculture Through Reclamation,* Part VI: *Maladjustments in Land Use in the United States,* Part VII: *Certain Aspects of Land Problems and Government Land Policies,* Washington, D.C., 1935.

United States Bureau of the Census, *Drainage of Agricultural Lands, 15th Census of the United States,* 1930, Washington, D.C., 1932.

United States Bureau of the Census, *United States Census of Agriculture*, Vol. IV: *Drainage of Agricultural Land—1950,* Washington, D.C., 1952.

United States Bureau of the Census, United States Census of Agriculture, Vol. IV, *Drainage of Agriculture Land, 1959,* Washington, D.C., 1961.

United States Department of Agriculture, *Land, The 1958 Yearbook of Agriculture,* Washington, D.C.

United States Department of Agriculture, *A Place to Live, The Yearbook of Agriculture, 1963,* Washington, D.C.

United States Department of Agriculture, *Soil, The 1957 Yearbook of Agriculture,* Washington, D.C.

United States Department of Agriculture, *Water, The Yearbook of Agriculture, 1955,* Washington, D.C.

United States Department of the Interior, Fish and Wildlife Service, *Wetlands of the United States,* Circular 38, Washington, D.C., 1956.

HERBERT C. HANSON*
formerly, Catholic University of America

WARREN C. WHITMAN
North Dakota State University

CHAPTER 8

Grassland Resources

When we think of the grasslands of our country, we think first of the great natural grazing grounds lying west of the Mississippi. Throughout a large portion of this area the principal way of making use of the land is by grazing the natural vegetation that grows on it. All this vegetation is not grass, of course, but includes extensive areas of forest, woodland, and shrubby vegetation. Insofar as these latter vegetation types are used for grazing, it is essentially the understory of grasses and other herbaceous plants that provides the forage for livestock and wild animals. The term *range* is often used to describe land on which the vegetation is dominated by various types of plants of different life forms but where grazing of natural vegetation by domestic and wild animals is the accepted land-use pattern. In this discussion of grassland resources, grassland and range will be used largely interchangeably.

Many of the problems associated with our western grasslands have arisen because of long-continued heavy grazing pressure on a scanty vegetation cover developed in a highly variable, semiarid to arid climate, of which recurrent drought is a distinctive feature. Other areas of range in the United States are found in the southern states, Alaska, and Hawaii. In these areas the problems are not those occasioned by a history of past abusive use and inadequate moisture, and these ranges have not been in critical condition, as far as grazing use is concerned, in historical time. Most attention therefore has been directed toward the western grasslands and the problems associated with their conservation and improvement (Fig. 1).

Four facts stand out about our western grasslands. (1) They have been extensively depleted by past exploitation and mismanagement; (2) they have shown substantial improvement under the program of management and rehabilitation developed and applied over the past 30 years; (3) our grasslands can be raised to a much higher state of productivity than they now exhibit; (4) although critical deterioration of our grasslands has been largely halted, most of the job of improvement still lies ahead.

EXTENT OF GRASSLANDS

Of the total land area of the contiguous 48 states of the United States (1902 million acres),

---

* Deceased, March 5, 1962

145

Fig. 1 Typical good-condition mixed grass range in the Northern Great Plains. The trees on the ridge in the background are ponderosa pines. Custer National Forest, southeastern Montana. (U.S. Forest Service.)

about 49.4 percent (939 million acres) is used for pasture and grazing.[1] Included in this grazed area are 66 million acres of cropland used for pasture, 630 million acres of grassland pasture, and 243 million acres of forest land used for pasture and range. Cropland constitutes 20.5 percent of the land area of the 48 states (391 million acres), nonpastured forest and woodland 19.5 percent (371,000,000 acres), and special, urban, and miscellaneous uses make up the remaining 10.6 percent (201 million acres).

Alaska and Hawaii add about a half-million acres of cropland, 3 million acres of grassland pasture and range, 2 million acres of pastured woodland and forest, and 134 million acres of unpastured forest area, most of which is in Alaska. In addition, Alaska has 50 to 60 million acres of potential range not now being grazed. For all 50 states about 28 percent of the total

[1] H. H. Wooten, Karl Gertel, and W. C. Pendleton. *Major Uses of Land and Water in the United States.* Agr. Econ. Rept. 13, U.S. Department of Agriculture, Washington, D.C., 1962.

land area of 2271 million acres is grassland pasture, and 11 percent is forest land used for pasture and range. Thus 39 percent of the total land area of the United States is used as pasture and range. The principal source of forage for livestock on this vast grazed area is the covering of natural grass vegetation occurring as the dominant life form in the true grassland and as an understory layer in the shrub, woodland, and forest areas.

Pastured cropland, for the most part, involves no serious problems in conservation, for the pasture cover can be renewed as needed, the pastures themselves are highly productive, and they are situated largely in noncritical areas from the standpoint of erosion. The pastured areas of natural vegetation, both grassland and forest, are the critical areas, and as such deserve major attention in considering conservation methods and problems.

About 82.5 percent (720,176,000 acres) of the total grassland and forest grazing land of the 48 contiguous states is in the 17 western states.

Another 98,227,000 acres of mainly forested land in 11 southern states is grazed essentially as range.[2] All told, about 93.7 percent of the grassland and forested grazing lands are in the western and southern states. In the western states about 286 million acres of grazing land are public land, with about 237 million acres belonging to the federal government. Another 42 million acres in this area are Indian lands. These lands are not considered public, but belong to the Indians and are held in trust for them by the federal government.[3] In the southern states, on the other hand, most of the grazed range land is owned privately, with only 3,352,000 acres belonging to the federal government.

Grassland and forested range are seldom used solely for the grazing of livestock. This is particularly true in the western states, where forested ranges are especially important as sources of water for urban and agricultural use, and both grasslands and forest ranges are major habitats for wildlife. Lumber is, of course, an important product of forested ranges in both the West and the South, and many kinds of recreational demands are putting increased pressure on both our grassland and forest range resources. It seems likely that the federal government will continue to play an important role in the use and management of our western grazing lands, because of the relatively large acreage of federally owned land, the conflicting demands from groups with different interests, the need for cooperative management efforts in various fields, and the essential need for regulation and control of grazing if the range is to be maintained and improved.

Kinds of Grasslands. In the 48 contiguous states of the United States four major grassland types are commonly distinguished (Table 1).

[2] R. E. Williams, J. T. Cassady, Lowell K. Halls, and E. J. Woolfolk, *Range Resources of the South*, Bull. N.S. 9, Georgia Agricultural Experiment Station, Athens, Georgia, 1955.

[3] M. L. Upchurch. "The Role of Land in Western Ranching," In *Land—the 1958 Yearbook of Agriculture*, U.S. Department of Agriculture, Washington, D.C.

Table 1. Extent of Principal Forage-Producing Types in the Grazing Area of the Western States

	Approximate Area of Virgin Type, Acres	Approximate Present Area, Acres
Grassland Types		
Tall grass	252,000,000	22,000,000
Mixed grass—		
Shortgrass	280,000,000	198,000,000
Semidesert grass	93,000,000	89,300,000
Pacific prairie		
California	22,300,000	10,400,000
Palouse	38,700,000	32,100,000
Shrub Types		
Sagebrush-grass	90,000,000	96,500,000
Salt-desert shrub	42,000,000	40,900,000
Southern desert shrub	25,000,000	26,900,000
Forest Types		
Open forests	130,500,000	126,300,000
Pinon-juniper	74,000,000	75,700,000
Woodland Chaparral	10,000,000	13,400,000
Total—All Types	1,057,500,000	731,500,000

[Adapted from *The Western Range*, Senate Document 199, Government Printing Office, Washington, D.C., 1936 and other sources.]

Subdivisions of some of these types are frequently made, resulting in defining as many as seven major grassland types. Two shrub-grass types are important in the western states, and three major forest types provide tree-grass combinations which are important sources of forage for livestock and big game. The open forests are often subdivided into several different types on the basis of the kind of arboreal vegetation present. Two major grassland types are recognized in the southern states, but the bulk of the grazing in this region is on the grasses associated with the more or less open forest types (Table 2).

TALL-GRASS PRAIRIE. The tall-grass prairie, now mostly plowed, extended through the present midwest agricultural region and along the eastern edge of the Plains from Manitoba into central Oklahoma and eastward into Ohio and southern Michigan. It covered most of the region east of an irregular line along the 97th and 98th meridians. The eastern part of the tall-grass prairie, in which the climate is more typi-

Table 2. Extent of Forage-Producing Vegetation
Types in the Southern Forested Range Area

Vegetation Type	Estimated Acreage
Upland hardwoods—bluestem	46,000,000
Bottomland hardwoods—cane	35,000,000
Shortleaf—loglolly pine—bluestem	66,000,000
Longleaf pine—bluestem	10,000,000
Longleaf pine—slash pine—wiregrass	24,000,000
Cedar—bluestem	1,000,000
Coastal prairie	7,000,000
Marsh	5,000,000
Total	194,000,000

[Adapted from *Range Resources of the South*, Bulletin N.S. 9, Georgia Agricultural Experiment Station, Athens, Ga., 1955.]

cal of deciduous forest than of grassland, was extensively interrupted by forested areas. About 22 million acres of this magnificent grassland remain, with the principal areas of concentration in Kansas, Oklahoma, Nebraska, and North Dakota.

The leading dominants were the bluestems (*Andropogon*), porcupinegrass (*Stipa*), dropseeds (*Sporobolus*), switchgrass (*Panicum*), Indiangrass (*Sorghastrum*), and wildrye (*Elymus*). The average height of the major grasses in this type was 4 to 5 feet, and under good growing conditions big bluestem reached as high as 10 to 12 feet. The roots of many of the grasses normally reached depths of 4 to 8 feet. The tall-grass prairie was and is excellent for grazing, forming a close dense sod of palatable grasses. Included with the grasses were numerous colorful and mainly palatable forbs (broadleaved herbaceous plants native to the vegetation association). Kentucky bluegrass (*Poa pratensis*) has invaded extensively remaining portions of the tall grass.

The coastal prairie is essentially a southward extension of the tall-grass prairie, occupying a strip of land of varying width 5 to 10 miles inland from the coastal marshes of Texas and Louisiana. The major dominants of the coastal prairie are silver beardgrass (*Andropogon saccharoides*),

other bluestems, needlegrass, panicums, Indian grass, and eastern gamagrass (*Tripsacum*). Short-grasses, including grama species (*Bouteloua*), buffalo grass (*Buchloe*), and curly mesquite (*Hilaria*) are common in the western portion of this type.

MIXED PRAIRIE AND SHORTGRASS. The mixed prairie and the shortgrass occupy the area between the tall-grass prairie and the foothills of the Rocky Mountains. Extending from Canada to central Texas, this grassland type is the largest and most important in the United States. A westward extension reaches from Texas across central New Mexico to Arizona. Frequently, this type is referred to as the shortgrass, and less frequently as the mixed grass. In the latter case, a shortgrass phase is usually recognized. Originally considered to have occupied almost 300 million acres, it still is found on almost 200 million acres of grazing land in the northern and southern Great Plains (Table 1).

The mixed prairie portion of the type lies between the shortgrass on the west and the tallgrass on the east and is characterized by dominants from both. The bluestems and tall needlegrasses are of considerable importance but its true character is shown by the mixture of grasses of intermediate height, called midgrasses, with the shortgrasses. Important midgrasses include western wheatgrass (*Agropyron smithii*), needle-and-thread (*Stipa comata*), and prairie Junegrass (*Koeleria*). By far the most important shortgrasses are blue grama grass and buffalo grass. Associated with these are several short sedges, a number of forbs, and in some places an appreciable to heavy development of shrubby species. In the southern area, blue grama and galleta grass become characteristic. The shortgrass portion is considered by some to be a disclimax, caused by overgrazing of the mixed prairie. This phase is most strongly developed in the western and southern portions. The mixed prairie portion is considered to form a transitional strip about 100 miles wide on the east, extending from central Saskatchewan to northern Texas, whereas the shortgrass phase extends from the mixed prairie westward about two-thirds of the way across Montana and one-fourth of the way across Wyoming and Colorado, through the panhandles of Oklahoma and Texas, with outliers westward across New Mexico and into Arizona.

SEMIDESERT GRASSLAND. The semidesert grassland, or desert-plains grassland, extends from central and southwestern Texas across southern New Mexico to southern, western, and northern Arizona and is the driest of the true grassland associations. It resembles the shortgrass type because of its short but more open growth, and indeed some of the species from the shortgrass type are important in the semidesert grassland. The chief dominants are several species of grama grass, especially black grama (*Bouteloua eriopoda*), three-awn grasses (*Aristida*), and curly mesquite (*Hilaria belangeri*). Tobosa grass (*Hilaria mutica*) and alkali sacaton (*Sporobolus airoides*) are important in low sites which are alternately wet and dry. Many desert shrubs, small trees, cacti, and yucca are scattered throughout the type, frequently becoming abundant.

About 89 million acres of this grassland type remain, and despite the much increased abundance of woody species, the semidesert grassland is one of the best yearlong ranges in the country.

PACIFIC PRAIRIE (CALIFORNIA). The Pacific prairie is here considered in two parts because the dominants in the original vegetation of the California prairie and the northern bunchgrass were appreciably different from the vegetation that exists now. The California prairie formerly covered extensive areas in the valleys and foothills of California and Lower California, with the main body of the type occupying the great interior valley. The original dominants were bunchgrasses with purple needlegrass (*Stipa pulchra*) and nodding needlegrass (*S. cernua*) especially important. Associated with these grasses were wildryes (*Elymus*), prairie Junegrass, melic grasses, and a vast number of annual and perennial forbs.

On the portions of the prairie not converted to cultivation, the former bunchgrass dominants have been largely replaced by annual grasses and forbs, mainly of exotic origin. These include wild oats (*Avena fatua*), soft chess (*Bromus hordeaceous*), ripgut (*Bromus rigidus*), red brome (*Bromus rubens*), annual fescues (*Festuca megalura*, *F. myuros*), bur clover (*Medicago hispida*), filaree (*Erodium*), and many others. Major growth of this type begins in late winter or very early spring, and the forage is usually mature and dry by late April or early May. The annual grassland occupies about 10 million acres now, mainly in the foothills around the Central Valley and in the Coast Ranges. It appears almost impossible, and perhaps not desirable, to attempt to restore the original vegetation. Over most of the millions of acres occupied by annual plant species, it seems best to aim at maintaining and using the annual-plant cover in its most productive condition.

PACIFIC BUNCHGRASS (PALOUSE). The northern Pacific bunchgrass, or Palouse prairie, at one time occupied extensive areas in eastern Washington and Oregon, northern Utah, and southern Idaho, with extensions in south-central Montana, southwestern Wyoming, northern Nevada, and western Alberta. The type attained its best development in what is now the wheat-producing area of eastern Washington known as the Palouse country. This type resembles the California prairie in that it is a bunchgrass type with a spring growth pattern, but the dominants are different. The chief dominant of the type is bluebunch wheatgrass (*Agropyron spicatum*). Other important grasses are Idaho fescue (*Festuca idahoensis*), Sandberg bluegrass (*Poa secunda*), western wheatgrass, needle-and-thread, big bluegrass (*Poa ampla*), and prairie Junegrass.

The portions of the type that have not been converted to agricultural production have very often been seriously overgrazed. Consequently, much of the remaining 32 million acres of northern bunchgrass has been extensively invaded by big sagebrush (*Artemisia tridentata*) and annual grasses, particularly cheatgrass (*Bromus tec-*

torum). The annuals have grazing value for only a short period in the spring, and on drying in early summer present a serious fire hazard. The invasion of sagebrush and the large-scale conversion of the grass cover from perennials to annuals has reducedly markedly the grazing capacity of this type.

SAGEBRUSH-GRASS. The sagebrush-grass type is the largest of the western shrub types, and it is believed that originally the grass component of the cover in this type was much more important than it is now. The type has increased in area from about 90 million acres to 96½ million acres in the last 100 years. Most of this increase has been at the expense of the northern bunchgrass in Oregon and Washington and the shortgrass in Wyoming. As the grass component of the cover has thinned out, the sagebrush has thickened, but the type is important to the grazing industry because it provides practically the only source of spring-fall range in the central and northern Great Basin. The type extends from eastern Wyoming to northeastern California and from central Utah and Nevada over the southeastern third of Oregon and the southern half of Idaho. It is also important in east-central Washington, and outliers extend from Colorado, New Mexico, and Arizona to eastern Montana.

The principal shrubs in the type, big sagebrush, rabbitbrush (*Chrysothamnus*), and greasewood (*Sarcobatus*) have little forage value, but the understory perennial grasses, bluebunch wheatgrass, squirreltail (*Sitanion hystrix*), Indian ricegrass (*Oryzopsis*), galleta grass, needle-and-thread, and western wheatgrass provide excellent grazing. Cheatgrass has invaded the understory throughout the range of the type.

SALT-DESERT SHRUB. The salt-desert shrub is closely associated with the sagebrush-grass type and is of major importance in Utah and Nevada. The saltbushes (*Atriplex* spp.) winterfat (*Eurotia lanata*), and black sagebrush (*Artemisia nova*) provide good winter forage for sheep, and the type is primarily valued for its palatable shrubby species. However, there is a thin grass understory that provides considerable forage. Important species here are Indian ricegrass, sand dropseed (*Sporobolus cryptandrus*), squirreltail, galleta grass, blue grama, and saltgrass (*Distichlis*).

SOUTHERN-DESERT SHRUB. The southern desert shrub has very low grazing value, the shrubs themselves being largely unpalatable and the grasses occurring only at higher altitudes and in areas where water accumulates, as in drainage ways or depressions. Low and undependable rainfall combined with high temperatures make this area essentially a desert. The grasses found in the area are principally those from the semidesert grassland. In favorable years a very heavy growth of winter and spring annuals may occur, and some grazing use is made of this crop.

OPEN FORESTS OF THE WEST. The open forests of the West provide a great forage resource for summer grazing by cattle, sheep, and big game animals. Grazing in these forests is on an understory of grasses, forbs, and shrubs beneath rather widely spaced trees or on open parks, mountain meadows, and subalpine grasslands. Open forest types extend on the higher elevations and the mountains from western South Dakota to western California, and from central New Mexico and Arizona to Canada. The ponderosa pine forests are especially important as a grazing resource, and the Douglas fir-aspen forests of higher altitudes also provide good grazing. In the alpine spruce-fir zone the grazing season is very short, but cattle and sheep find the grasses and forbs of these high ranges both palatable and nutritious. The wheatgrasses, fescues, bluegrasses, needlegrasses, pinegrasses, oatgrasses, and a number of sedge species provide much of the forage on these timbered ranges. Numerous palatable forbs and a wide variety of brush species such as serviceberry, snowberry, cliff rose, and mountain mahogany provide additional grazing.

MISCELLANEOUS TYPES. The *Pinon-Juniper* type lies below the ponderosa pine primarily in Colorado, New Mexico, Arizona, Utah, and Nevada, although it has extensive outliers to the south, north, and west of this area. The short coniferous trees that characterize this type have little value as timber, and it is primarily a spring-fall or yearlong range on which wheatgrasses, needlegrasses, grama grasses, and a variety of shrubs and forbs provide grazing for cattle, sheep, and big game, especially deer. The type has been seriously depleted over extensive areas by heavy grazing use.

The *Woodland-Chapparal*, mainly in California, where fairly open, has a cover composed largely of the same annuals that have replaced the perennials in the Pacific prairie. At the higher altitudes and in southern California the dense brush growth may be nearly impenetrable and the type is unfit for grazing.

SOUTHERN FOREST RANGES. A number of forest-grazing types occur on about 182 million acres of land in the area from east Texas and Oklahoma to Virginia, the Atlantic Coast, and Florida. The open and cutover forests of both pines and hardwoods provide good grazing, and much of the land throughout the area has been cultivated and abandoned. In this forested area the associated grasses which provide the bulk of the forage include bluestems and broomsedge (*Andropogon* spp.), wiregrass (*Aristida*), drop-seeds, panicums, paspalums (*Paspalum* spp.), Bermuda grass (*Cynodon*), carpet grass (*Axonopus*), and others. Switchcane (*Arundinaria tecta*) is an important source of forage in the bottomlands and swamps.

GRASSLANDS OF HAWAII. The range lands of Hawaii include roughly about one-fourth of the total area of the islands and are nearly all permanent pastures. Some of the land included in pastures is arable and may be plowed and re-seeded at intervals of several years. Much of the existing pastureland was once heavily forested and trees and shrubs are still of considerable importance in the cover. The types of pastures are mainly related to altitudinal zones, with most of the pastured areas lying below 8000 feet.

At the present time introduced species are far more important than the native grasses. Giant grasses such as Guinea grass (*Panicum maximum*) and Napier grass (*Pennisetum purpureum*) are important at lower elevations, along with Bermuda grass and Dallis grass. A native leguminous shrub, Koa haole (*Lucaena*) and Kiawe, a tree related to the mesquite, are also important here. Intermediate and higher altitudes support such grasses as orchardgrass (*Dactylis*), Yorkshire fog (*Holcus*), ryegrasses (*Lolium*), and bluegrasses (*Poa* spp.). Kikuyu grass (*Pennisetum clandestinum*), and Pangola grass (*Digitaria*) are important at both low and intermediate altitudes. Pili grass (*Heteropogon contortus*) is the only indigenous grass of consequence in the cover.

GRASSLANDS IN ALASKA. The native grasslands of southwestern Alaska, the Alaskan Peninsula, Kodiak Island, and the smaller islands are grazed by cattle and by sheep. Grasslands in southern and south central Alaska also help support a livestock industry. The principal limitation to the grazing use of Alaskan grasslands is the lack of winter feed for livestock. Summer range is readily available, but, except for favored areas such as Kodiak Island, winter grazing of domestic livestock is not possible. Coastal strands, salt marshes, true grasslands and meadows, and upland marshes and bogs are available for grazing. Major forage-providing species include American dunegrass (*Elymus mollis*) along the coast, and alkali-grass (*Puccinellia*) and sedges in salt marshes. Bluejoint (*Calamagrostis canadensis*), red fescue and other fescues, slender wheatgrass, bluegrasses (*Poa palustris* and *P. glauca*), and many other grasses and forbs are important components of grassland and meadows. A number of different sedges characterizes the vegetation of the wetter areas in both lowland and upland positions.

NATURE OF GRASSLANDS

Natural grasslands consist mostly of perennial herbaceous plants, and unless seriously deteriorated, the grasses are dominant over the forbs (broad-leaved, non-grasslike herbs). Frequently, several kinds of grasslike plants known as sedges are associated with the grasses and forbs in the grassland complex. Over 1400 species of grasses are known to occur in continental United States, exclusive of Alaska. Only about a fifth of these would be important as forage for grazing livestock.

In the tall-grass prairie near Lincoln, Nebraska, before the droughts of the 1930's, the flora consisted of a total of 237 species of which 38 were grasses, 18 were sedges, and the rest were broad-leaved flowering plants. The grasses and sedges constituted only one-fourth of the total number of species, but, because of their dense growth and other competitive features, they made up nine-tenths of the vegetation. Only four of the grasses rated as dominants in

the rangeland adjoining the foothills near Fort Collins, Colorado, and of these four, western wheatgrass was the chief, with a total of 109 species. On the rolling hills near the Missouri River south of Mandan, North Dakota, the flora comprised 300 species, of which 60 were grasses (Fig. 2). Two grasses and two sedges provided about 65 percent of the cover and about half of the total yield. Bluebunch wheatgrass (*Agropyron spicatum*) makes up about 95 percent of the vegetation in remnants of the Palouse Prairie in northern Utah. Annuals are usually scarce except in places disturbed by tillage, excessive grazing, erosion, or some other cause. In such cases the annuals may become very

Fig. 2   The effect of overgrazing is seen in the poor condition grassland on the near side of the fence, in contrast to the excellent condition grassland on the far side. Erosion has started in the deteriorated grassland and could become serious. (U.S. Forest Service.)

abundant, indeed, as illustrated by data on the California annual grassland. Here annual populations as great as 7830 mature individuals per square foot have been reported.

Various low shrubs may be scattered among the grasses and forbs, especially in the more arid grasslands. Scattered coniferous and broad-leaved trees also occur in grassland. If the canopy cover of the trees exceeds 10 percent, it is customary to consider the area as woodland or forest, rather than grassland.

Grasses and Erosion. The dense growth of grasses provides excellent cover for the soil, thus reducing runoff and erosion. Their ability to grow in many kinds of soils and to endure long periods of drought, together with their basal habit of growth, makes them the basic resource of the livestock industry. The litter formed by dead stems and leaves is important in many ways, such as protecting the soil from raindrop splash, facilitating the infiltration of water into the soil, and reducing soil temperatures on hot summer days. The litter also provides more favorable conditions than bare soil for the activity of microorganisms, thus aiding in soil development.

The creeping species of both grasses and forbs, with their closely spaced stems and roots, slow down the rate of water flow, hold soil particles against the pressure of the water, and accumulate water-borne debris, which forms tiny dams, thus further retarding the water movement. It is because of these characteristics that sod-forming species are used in seeding terrace slopes, in grassing down gullies, and in other areas over which drainage water from rains and floods flows. In strip farming on slopes, where narrow strips of grass are planted on the contour to alternate with tilled crops, the sod grasses are most effective in absorbing the runoff from the tilled strip above as well as the precipitation received directly.

On cultivated fields subject to wind erosion, grasses may be used in narrow barrier strips alternating with rows of crop plants. The tall and quickly growing bunch grasses are most suitable for this purpose. Cultivated fields that have been damaged by wind erosion can be stabilized and reclaimed by seeding to adapted grasses. Badly depleted rangelands, on which wind action has begun to move the soil, have been successfully reseeded. Wind-eroded rangelands may be reclaimed by natural processes if enough of the former vegetation is left. The scattered remaining grasses spread by means of their rhizomes and anchor the soil with their fine roots.

Grasses are often the first invaders on sand dunes and in "blow-outs." Some of these invade by rhizomes, which may be very long, as in blow-out grass (*Redfieldia flexuosa*). Others, as in sand bluestem (*Andropogon hallii*), invade by seed. Gradually the blowing sand becomes fixed.

Plant-Animal Interrelationships. Interrelationships between plants and animals in the grassland are numerous and varied. The very nature of the grassland appears to be the result of mutual relations that have been occurring throughout the time that grasslands and grazing animals have been developing. A certain degree of grazing is more normal than no grazing whatever. An excessively deep mulch may develop in some ungrazed grasslands, with consequent reduction in kinds of species and in the density of the surviving species. Under moderate use many grasses tend to become more decumbent and provide more ground cover than when they are not grazed. The big question to determine for each kind of range is the usage that is best in the long run for the grassland, the livestock, and the rancher. The proper season and degree of use are major problems of management in every range area. As a rule, maintenance of the desirable combination of plants on a range requires that not more than 35 to 55 percent of the annual growth be grazed. This varies in accordance with the kind of vegetation, soil conditions, physiographic conditions, and the climate.

Specialization in the feeding habits of cattle, sheep, horses, goats, and game animals makes them more efficient in securing and digesting certain kinds of plants. Sheep, for example, prefer weeds, native forbs, and tender grasses. The effects of rodents on the vegetation are usually destructive, but sometimes they are beneficial, as aiding in seed dispersal, mixing of the soil, and in the grazing of some undesirable weeds. Rodents are destructive by consuming herbage and seeds above ground and also underground parts, including roots, rhizomes, and the crowns of plants. In prairie dog towns and about kangaroo rat dens, the original vegetation may be entirely destroyed and remain bare or be invaded by weeds that are not relished by livestock. The establishment of legumes in the southern Great Plains presents a problem because their roots are very palatable to pocket gophers. These rodents may also delay the course of succession by the frequent overturning of the soil, reducing the organic matter of the surface soil by bringing up subsoil to the surface, and providing suitable conditions for the persistence of weedy species.

Insects are numerous in grasslands. It has been estimated that they may reach 9.5 million individuals per acre in Manitoba. Their relations with plants may be beneficial, as in the pollination of flowers, in seed dispersal, and in destroying plants of little value, and other harmful insects. They consume plants, spread diseases, retard succession. Harvester ants, whose burrows penetrate as deep as 10 feet, cause bare areas on the surface. Devastation caused by grasshoppers may be followed by severe soil erosion.

Birds are usually beneficial in their relations to plants. They help in distributing seeds, they destroy insects and rodents, and aid in the disposal of dead animals. Some kinds, as the Texas bobwhite quail, although they prefer grassland for cover and nesting sites, consume for food the seeds of weedy plants. Pheasants in western Nebraska increased during the droughts of the 1930's because of the invasion of weeds, such as ragweed, sunflower, pigweeds, etc., which provided them with suitable food.

Predator-prey relations and their effects on plants are numerous and complex and need to be worked out for each kind of animal. For example, in a study of that much accused predator, the coyote, in Nebraska, the preponderance of its food was found to be wild mammals, especially rabbits, mice, and pocket gophers. The coyote did consume pheasants in certain areas, but this apparently occurred because the pheasant population was sufficiently large to be harvested. Excessive numbers of rodents have occurred in places because of the almost wanton destruction of predators.

HISTORICAL USE OF THE GRASSLANDS

Little is actually known as to the status of our grasslands before the coming of the white man. It is known that the grasslands of the West were used by great numbers of grazing wild animals, with the bison being the most important in terms of forage consumption and exertion of grazing pressure on the grassland resource. Undoubtedly there was damage to the grasslands as the result of overgrazing, excessive trampling, and erosion during long-continued drought over extensive areas. However, the ability of the animals to migrate extensively and the natural reduction in number of animals resulting from a dwindling food supply would tend to minimize destructive grazing effects.

The introduction of cattle, horses, and sheep, primarily under the influence of the Spanish migration from Mexico, beginning over 200 years ago, exerted the first influences of grazing by domestic livestock on the western grasslands. It is likely that before the middle of the 19th century much of the California grassland had been invaded by alien annual species, primarily as the result of heavy grazing use.

Use of the Plains Grassland. The story of the use of the grasslands of the Great Plains east of the Rockies is generally better known than that of the use of the far-western grasslands. Intensive grazing of this great natural grassland did not begin until well into the 19th century.

There are still a few men alive who actually took part in moving livestock into the largely unoccupied ranges of the northern plains.

The final slaughter of the great herds of bison on the plains in the 1870's and 1880's was accomplished by the invasion of the cattleman. Initially many of the cattle came from Texas in the well-known "trail drives." The cattlemen soon recognized the importance of taking possession of streams and springs for watering their stock and thus securing control of adjoining public rangeland. The private land owned by some of the early cattle "barons" formed a fantastic pattern as it followed a meandering stream. Various and devious methods were used to secure title to such streamside "homesteads." As the news spread throughout the eastern states and in Great Britain of the huge profits that could be realized from "free grass," there was a tremendous boom to invest in the cattle business, reminding one of the "gold rushes" to California or Alaska. Sheepmen also appeared on the range, and conflicts occurred between them and the cattlemen. The grasses were nutritious the year round; it was not considered necessary to put up hay for the winter; little or no shelter was provided; expenses were small. It was a bonanza. No wonder the industry expanded by leaps and bounds. But, droughts came; the grass was short; ranges were overstocked; no hay was available. Disaster was not long in coming.

Disaster. The winter of 1885 was very severe in the southern Great Plains. Losses of livestock were unusually heavy, and in the following summer large numbers of cattle were moved to the already heavily stocked ranges of the northern plains. The cattle were in poor condition in the winter of 1886–1887. The cold came early; storm followed storm; the mercury went lower and lower. Temperatures of 60° below zero were reported. The oldest resident had never remembered experiencing such severe conditions. There were no reserves of feed on the range or in the stack. Livestock losses were terrific. More than 90 percent of the livestock died

on some individual ranges. Many operators did not even bother to make the spring roundup. With the coming of spring, most of the operators in this region faced bankruptcy. The days of careless management were over. The summers of 1934 and 1936 and the winter of 1948–1949 were reminiscent of the extreme conditions of the earlier years. Drought conditions on the plains in the 1950's served again to emphasize that the need for careful management is a constant feature of range use on the plains.

Mismanagement Continues. Undoubtedly, many stockmen realized that the boom was over and that those who continued in the business would have to work out proper management methods. There were, however, many difficulties to contend with. The grassland resources had been badly damaged, and new difficulties were arising from the westward march of farmers. They were invading the rangelands. The homestead laws favored acquisition of land by the farmers. Many secured 160- to 320-acre homesteads in areas that were so deficient in soil fertility and soil moisture, had such a short growing season, and were at such a great distance from the market that the only use the land could be put to was grazing. Many of them used ideas and methods of farming that they brought with them from the East or Midwest, not realizing that differences in climatic and soil conditions would not permit their use. After a year, or at the most a few years, during which many depended on the cattlemen for a living, they had to leave their homesteads. But much damage had been done to the grasslands. Small areas were necessarily heavily grazed. The plowing of such rangeland is best expressed by the wondering Indian who remarked, "Wrong side up." The truth of his remark is realized now when one sees so much of the range country still scarred and notes the invasion of numerous weeds and insect pests.

The presence of the farmers in the range country made it difficult for the stockmen to prevent further deterioration of the range. Too often the stockmen did not realize how much damage had already been done by too heavy stocking, by grazing too early and too late in the season, and by failure to distribute stock properly on the range. It was not entirely the fault of the stockman. He had no pattern, guides, or rules to follow. There was no science of range management; grassland ecology was unknown. The first effects of overgrazing are so slight that only careful observations or measurements will reveal them. Often it is difficult to distinguish between the effects of overgrazing and subnormal moisture conditions.

Overuse and mismanagement of the grasslands and the associated shrubby and forest grazing types in the West were not confined to the Great Plains area by any means (Fig. 2). Serious range deterioration was reported from nearly all areas by the early 1900's. The first really quantitative estimate of the status of the western rangelands, however, was the classic report of the United States Forest Service in 1936.[4] This report showed that mismanagement had resulted in the depletion of most of the grassland in the range country, with a considerable decrease in grazing capacity. In its report the Forest Service estimated that the forage on about 55 percent of the range area was so depleted as to have less than half of its original grazing capacity. Another 30 percent was not so seriously depleted, but the forage on this area had far less than its normal grazing value. On only about 15 percent of the total range area was the forage in reasonably good condition. An over-all estimate placed 93 percent of the total range area as being depleted to some extent.

During World War I, because of the need for grain crops, much rangeland was again turned wrong side up, and during the droughts of the 1930's, grasslands, especially those that had been overgrazed, deteriorated considerably. The great dust storms during this period originated in large part in certain mismanaged parts of the range country. The planting of grain in the range country was widespread again during World War II, and after the war, there were serious droughts, especially in the Southwest.

There has been no complete comprehensive report on the status of western rangeland since the 1936 report of the Forest Service. However, the *National Inventory of Soil and Water Conservation Needs*[5] has provided important information on the physical condition of the land and cover in 1958 on about 417 million acres of privately owned range and permanent pasture in the seventeen western states. Federally owned range was not included in the inventory. The results of the survey showed that nearly 75 percent of the privately owned western rangeland (over 307 million acres) was in need of some type of conservation treatment. On the other hand, the survey showed that over 109 million acres had received conservation treatment and were in a generally improved condition.

GRASSLAND CONSERVATION AND IMPROVEMENT

Control of the Range. Fortunately, because many grassland species can take punishment in an excessive degree over a long period and then recuperate when given favorable conditions, improvement measures could be put into effect over extensive areas when the need for such measures was realized. One of the great handicaps to overcome, however, has been the widespread idea that the grass will come back as soon as it rains. Usually, it has taken more than rain to restore depleted grassland.

The first step to range improvement was to bring a halt to unrestricted grazing of the rangelands. The invention of barbed wire in 1873 made it possible for the stockman to exercise some form of range control. After 1880, the use of barbed wire spread rapidly throughout

---

[4] *The Western Range*, Senate Document 199, Government Printing Office, Washington, D.C., 1936, 620 pp.

[5] Summarized by T. A. Neubauer, "The Grasslands of the West," *Journal of Range Management*, Vol. 16, 1963, pp. 327–332.

the range country. By fencing his holding, an operator could keep other livestock from his range and could regulate to some extent the distribution of his own livestock. Without doubt the availability of relatively cheap fencing in the form of barbed wire provided a strong impetus to private ownership and control of grazing lands. Actually, many illegal enclosures of public land were made, which often led to bitterness and conflict. In order to fence, the rancher had to acquire ownership or rights to the land that he put under fence. He naturally secured the most valuable grazing lands and fenced them. Most of the remaining, less valuable, grazing land still continued to exist as public land.

Traditionally, the government agencies with responsibilities for land administration in the western states have provided the primary impetus toward controlled grazing and grassland improvement. Beginning with the setting aside by Congress in 1891 of the first public domain land into forest reserves, later known as national forests, much public grazing land has come under the control of the Forest Service. The grazing on this land has been regulated to some extent for many years, with resulting improvement of the rangeland. In 1962, the total area in the national forests and national grasslands[6] used for grazing was about 62 million acres. The importance of this control and the stimulus to better management of grazing lands provided by the practices advocated by the Forest Service are apparent when it is realized that in 1962 the total number of cattle and horses grazing on national forest land under permit was 1,307,183. The number of sheep and goats was 2,366,858. Livestock graze over 43 percent of the 143 million acres of national forests, national grasslands, and land utilization projects controlled by the Forest Service in the western states.

The Forest Service applies two basic principles in the management of national forest resources in order to meet the objective estab-

lished in 1905 of securing the greatest good for the greatest number of people in the long run. The first of these principles is sustained yield, or the maximum production of forage, timber, or other renewable resources. The other basic principle is multiple use. A certain area of forest land may, at the same time, produce forage for livestock and big game, timber, and serve as an important watershed. Other uses are for recreation, mining, and waterpower sites. The production of water and timber are primary uses, as stated by Congress. Multiple use means the coordinated development and use of all the values of the land.

One of the persisting problems in the administration of the grazing lands is to bring about a proper balance between the forage supply and the livestock numbers so as to improve many ranges that are not in a maximum stage of productivity. For many years the Forest Service has been building up forage production and protecting the land from excessive runoff and erosion by reseeding, other range improvement practices, and by better methods of management. Harmonizing various uses, such as accelerated demands for water, recreation facilities, mining permits, and increased grazing by big game, calls for thorough study and careful judgment.

The Soil Conservation Service, established in 1935, has as a basic objective the use of each acre of land according to its capability and treatment according to its needs. Privately owned grazing land in soil conservation districts, to be managed in accordance with grazing use standards mutually agreed on by the rancher and the district, exceeds 199 million acres. Deferred grazing is being practiced on some 48½ million acres, and over 11 million acres have been reseeded to native or introduced grasses. Other measures that have been adopted to improve many additional acres include: stock water developments; range renovation, including pitting operations; structures to facilitate the spreading and absorption of water, thus controlling erosion and aiding revegetation; control of

---

[6] The national grasslands consist of 19 former land utilization projects now administered by the Forest Service. These areas are mainly in the Great Plains.

undesirable brush and weeds (on about 27 million acres); and improvements in procedures for utilizing range forage (Fig. 3).

Some unique practices are used to secure proper grazing use in the Gulf Marsh ranges of Louisiana and Texas. Large acreages of these marshes are suitable for grazing, but commonly they are interspersed with areas too swampy to support cattle. Walkways, consisting of earth dikes, have been constructed to allow access to usable portions of the marsh. Earth for these dikes is secured from borrow pits, which are staggered rather than continuous, and therefore do not result in marsh drainage. Accumulated rank growth is controlled by periodic burning when the water level is above the ground surface. In many cases flood gates have been constructed to control the inflow of salt water.

Considerable improvement of rangelands has undoubtedly taken place, particularly on the nearly 200 million acres properly used within soil conservation districts. The trend in range condition appears to be upward generally in soil conservation districts, but local conditions, such as prolonged drought, may reverse this trend temporarily. One difficulty in accomplishing range improvement programs is in securing the understanding, interest, and acceptance of range management principles and practices by landowners.

For many years no provision existed for the control of large areas in the public domain, except as individual stockmen were able to exercise it locally. It was widely recognized that depletion of the range forage crop was widespread and continuing, and that accelerated erosion was in progress on some 180 million acres of vacant public lands. To place these lands under control the Taylor Grazing Act was passed by Congress in 1934. The preamble to the act states: "An act to stop injury to the public grazing lands by preventing overgrazing and soil deterioration, to provide for their orderly use, improvement, and development, to stabilize the livestock industry dependent upon the public range and for other purposes." This act

Fig. 3 A watering place on the range. The development of stock-watering facilities is an important aspect of grassland management, since properly spaced watering points promote better grazing use of the range forage crop. (Soil Conservation Service.)

initially authorized the withdrawal from entry of 142,000,000 acres of unreserved and unappropriated public domain and furnished a long-needed basis for measures to improve some of the most badly depleted grasslands. The Act provides for the establishment of grazing districts under the joint management of officials of the Department of the Interior and stockmen.

Over 158 million acres of public lands in 59 grazing districts in the western states are now administered by the Bureau of Land Management of the Department of The Interior. Included in the districts are about 2 million acres of non-federal lands. Grazing on another 18 million acres of public domain not included in districts is controlled by the Bureau under grazing leases. Almost 2½ million head of cattle, 6½ million sheep, and an estimated 1 million big game animals use the public domain lands under the control of the Bureau of Land Management. The management program of the Bureau is designed to bring about the conservation and improvement of the rangelands through controlled grazing, adjustment of stocking rates to the production capabilities of the forage, development of water spreading systems, brush and noxious plant control, and range reseeding.

Important grazing lands are found on the Indian reservations. About 80 percent of the 53½ million acres on the reservations is in grassland, with grazing control under the Bureau of Indian Affairs of the Department of the Interior. These rangelands are managed so as to bring the maximum return to the Indian owners with sustained forage production. Objectives are to preserve the range and water resources through proper grazing practices and to rehabilitate lands that have deteriorated so that the Indians will have an opportunity to earn a living by grazing their own livestock. About 75 percent of the total reservation range land is used to graze Indian-owned livestock.

The National Park Service and the Fish and Wildlife Service of the Department of the Interior administer significant acreages of grassland and forested grazing land in the western states. Almost 14 million acres are in National Parks and about 7 million acres in wildlife refuges. Grazing of domestic livestock is permitted only to a very limited extent on special areas in some of the parks. The objectives in administration are, as set forth by Congress, "to conserve the scenery, and the natural historic objects and wild life therein, and to provide for the enjoyment of the same in such manner and by such means as will leave them unimpaired for the enjoyment of future generations." One of the difficulties encountered at present is the inadequacy of forage, especially during winter months, to keep pace with the natural reproduction of some of the larger animals, such as the bison and elk in Yellowstone National Park and elsewhere. In places, deer and rodent populations are above normal because of the dearth of carnivores.

The wildlife refuges are managed on a multiple-use basis, as far as this is possible without defeating the primary objective for which each was established. In many of them grasslands provide grazing for various kinds of game animals.

PRESENT STATUS OF THE GRASSLANDS

There is general agreement that the true grasslands, the shrub-grass types, and the forested ranges of the western states are depleted in the sense that grazing capacity has been reduced from that of the natural vegetation in the virgin condition. However, it has been questioned whether this depletion is as great as generally pictured.[7] The previously mentioned estimate of range depletion made by the Forest Service in 1936 concluded that the entire west-

[7] Andrew H. Clark, "The Impact of Exotic Invasion on the Remaining New World Mid-Latitude Grasslands," in *Man's Role in Changing the Face of the Earth*, Edited by William L. Thomas, Jr., University of Chicago Press, Chicago, 1956, pp. 737-762.

ern range was depleted by 52 percent. Furthermore 76 percent of the range had declined since the early 1900's and only 16 percent had improved. Federal public domain was in the worst condition, showing a depletion of 67 percent with over 90 percent of the acreage still on the downgrade. Privately owned grazing land was only a little better, with an estimated 51 percent depletion and 87 percent still trending downward. The national forest ranges were considered to be 30 percent depleted, with only 5 percent of the area involved showing a downward trend. It seems likely that the estimates of depletion, made during a period of nearly continuous severe drought, may have been influenced somewhat by the current condition of the forage resource. It should be remembered, too, that the true grazing capacity of our ranges in the virgin state is not known.

A comprehensive re-evaluation of the status of our native vegetation grazing lands has not been made[8], and without the factual data provided by such a survey, the degree of range improvement since the 1930's can only be postulated. Without doubt there has been a marked improvement in the condition of the range forage resource over almost all of the range area during the last 30 years. This improvement has taken place despite the fact that livestock numbers in the seventeen western states have increased substantially during this period. This is not to imply that all range has improved in condition. There are acreages of both public and private rangeland that are still deteriorating, and certainly very little of the rangelands of the west would be considered to be in excellent condition. Renner[9] has estimated that forage production on western ranges can be increased by 150 to 300 percent. Such an increase could not be attained by a stabilization of our range capabilities

at their present level. Rather an all-out effort at range improvement must be made to achieve the goal of more than doubling production from our natural grazing lands. There should not be many acres of range remaining in critical condition by the end of the next decade, but the problems of improving deteriorated grassland and forested ranges will be with us for a long time.

It seems unlikely that there will be much addition of land to the grazing resource of the western states in the coming years. Neither is there likely to be much diversion of present grazing land in this area to other uses. The major possibility for increased grazing capacity of western ranges lies in better management of our present range resource. The primary approach to improvement is through the adjustment of range stocking to the capabilities of the vegetation in relation to (1) intensity of use, (2) season of use, and (3) uniformity of use. Coupled with careful grazing management must be the physical improvements involved in erosion control, water development, reseeding, control of noxious and poisonous plants, and fencing. The magnitude of the improvement task is indicated by the data obtained from the National Inventory of Soil and Water Conservation Needs. Of the 417 million acres of privately owned range in the western states about 307 million acres (75 percent) are in need of conservation treatment. Erosion is a problem of 217 million acres; 46 million acres need reseeding; improvement of plant cover by means other than general reseeding is needed on another 84 million acres; better regulation of stocking to prevent overgrazing is needed on 157 million acres; control of noxious woody plants is needed on 53 million acres.

PRINCIPLES AND METHODS IN GRASSLAND RESTORATION

Plant Succession. Grazing introduces a factor that greatly alters and modifies the competitive relations of species in the grassland complex.

[8] Plans for a nationwide public rangelands appraisal are being made. See Senate Document 119, 87th Congress, 2nd session, Washington, D.C., 1962.

[9] F. G. Renner, "The Future of Our Range Resources," *Journal of Range Management,* Vol. 7, 1954, pp. 55–56.

Defoliation generally results in reducing the carbohydrate reserve needed for the formation of new growth of roots and tops. Grassland species are tolerant of certain degrees of grazing, for grasslands and grazing animals followed the long path of evolution together, but excessive grazing, resulting in repeated defoliation, will greatly reduce the vigor of the plants and the herbage yields and finally result in death.

The grazing by livestock or game animals on grassland containing a mixture of species is seldom, if ever, uniform either in relation to geographical distribution of grazing, time of grazing, degree of grazing, or species utilized. Usually the most palatable and most desirable species suffer the greatest grazing pressure and are the most likely to be seriously weakened or even eliminated from the cover. Thus differential grazing may result in the reduction of one or more of the more valuable species, whereas undesirable species, such as weeds or poisonous plants, may gain the advantage over the other species. These competitive relations have been utilized as the basis of classifying plants into three groups, according to their reaction to continued grazing pressure: (1) decreasers, (2) increasers, and (3) invaders. Under continuous overgrazing, the most desirable forage plants may decrease rapidly, whereas undesirable and unimportant kinds that are already present in the area, or that may invade, increase rapidly. Under moderate or no grazing, the reverse processes may take place, but if overgrazing has continued for a long time, recovery will require a long time.

The determination of the competitive relation of plants under grazing is properly an important field of study in the ecology and management of ranges and pastures. Much information on the general trends of plant succession under grazing in range and pasture grasslands is now available, but many of the intricate relationships of individual species to associated species and to environmental conditions remain to be determined.

Range Condition. In the management of natural grasslands, it is important to determine the condition (successional status) and trend (direction of successional change) of the vegetation in each area being grazed. Management and stocking recommendations are based on the condition or successional status of the vegetation and, where trend can be determined, on the apparent direction of the successional processes currently taking place on the range area. Forage production and conservation values parallel rather closely the condition status of the vegetation.

A range-condition classification essentially represents a statement of the degree of departure of the existing vegetation from the potential climax or near climax vegetation possible for that site. It also represents an approximate statement of the grazing value of the vegetation and the extent of improvement possible as successional processes advance under proper management. In order to determine range condition, a thorough knowledge of the present vegetation as well as the potential climax vegetation is essential. The composition and productivity of climax vegetation can be learned only by careful study of "relict" areas or remnants of the climax vegetation that have survived from earlier days; such areas are invaluable for determining the relative positions of decreasers and increasers in climax or near climax vegetation on many different sites. As these relict areas are discovered throughout the grassland area, their location and a careful description of the vegetation should be permanently recorded. Every effort should be made to preserve these relics for future study and observation.

Range trend in many ways is more difficult to determine than range condition. Differences in rainfall from year to year or differences in grazing use may reverse the trend from one year to the next. Long-range trends either upward or downward will eventually show themselves in the condition status of the range. The condition status will change more slowly than will the trend. In fact, it is possible for the current trend on a range to be downward while the condition status is improving. The interpretation of trend factors is thus very difficult. To arrive at a sound interpretation of trend and to detect relatively small changes in condition, it is necessary to observe small, permanently marked sample areas of the vegetation from year to year. Such observations will give answers to many questions, such as: What is the condition of the plants this year compared to previous years? (Best measured by height and area of plant clumps.) Are the most desirable forage plants increasing or decreasing? Are the less desirable forage plants increasing or decreasing? Are new plants invading and are they desirable or undesirable? This procedure requires but little time each year. It may be considered as taking annual inventory of the chief resource of the ranch—the grassland. The range condition survey and the estimate of trend applied to the specific grazing operation are the primary tools for adjusting grazing use to the capability of the vegetation.

Reseeding. Natural revegetation through plant succession is the chief means used by the

Fig. 4 Range interseeding has been an especially range improvement practice on sandy soils in areas with fairly good rainfall conditions. Here a specially built range interseeder is at work in the Sandhills of Nebraska. (Soil Conservation Service.)

grassland manager to improve the range. Reseeding, however, may speed the process of improvement in many suitable areas (Fig. 4). A great amount of research has been accomplished in determining areas that will warrant reseeding, the species of plants to use, soil conditions that favor reseeding, and costs and returns from seeding efforts. Thousands of plant species have been tested to determine their adaptability for use on specific sites throughout the range area. Crested wheatgrass has been especially outstanding because of its wide adaptability over much of the range region and because of the relatively high degree of success obtained in securing satisfactory stands. Many millions of acres have been reseeded with this grass.

New methods of collecting, threshing, and preparing seeds of native grasses for seeding have been developed. Methods of preparing seedbeds and reducing undesirable plant competition on rangelands to be reseeded have been refined and new implements and methods developed. Brush-choppers and special disc plows have given excellent results for preseeding treatments in range areas where they can be used. Burning has been found to be especially effective in the Intermountain area for the removal of sagebrush prior to reseeding. Specialized machinery for the actual seeding operation has been developed—mainly various kinds of heavy-duty drills with precise seed-flow equipment. Airplanes have been used to broadcast pellets containing grass seed on ranges; such reseeding has been largely unsatisfactory.

The introduction of new species and strains has contributed greatly to the potential productivity of reseeded ranges. Some of these species and strains are the result of introduction from foreign countries. Many of them have been developed and improved from both native and introduced sources by grass breeders working in many sections of the grassland area. The bluestems, panic-grasses, lovegrasses, bromes, ryegrasses, gramas, bluegrasses, needlegrasses, and wheatgrasses have all provided excellent mate-

Fig. 5 Excellent stand of grass in the Nebraskan Sandhills 3 years after the initial seeding with the range interseeder. The rows are 40 inches apart. (Soil Conservation Service.)

rial that has been improved by selection and breeding. Superior strains of many of the groups have been developed and give promise of improved forage production, greater hardiness, or adaptability for special uses.

How many acres of depleted range in the seventeen western states might be profitably reseeded is not really known. Estimates have ranged from as low as 50 million acres to as high as 125 million acres. Perhaps under existing conditions, and taking into account the millions of acres that have already been reseeded and the other millions of acres that have been plowed up, an estimate of 55 million acres might be reasonable. It should be borne in mind that reseeding costs are relatively high in terms of the generally low productive capacity of our western rangelands. Shifting values and land use pressures could make it possible to reseed extensive areas on which the economic returns from grazing at the present time would not justify the cost of the reseeding operation. The actual rate of reseeding on our depleted range-

lands will probably proceed rather slowly through the next decade or so, although we have the equipment, plant material, and technology to achieve a major reseeding job, were is feasible (Fig. 5).

Other Improvement Measures. An important phase of range improvement lies in the control of undesirable plant species, particularly brush and small trees, which severely restrict the production of palatable forage on millions of acres of our western and southern ranges (Fig. 6). The control of brushy invaders is also a problem on Hawaiian ranges. There is probably no limit to the actual amount of control work that can be done, and certainly control of undesirable plant species on our ranges will be no once-over job. The three major brush problems at the present time seem to be with mesquite and junipers in Texas and the Southwest, and with sagebrush in the Mountain states (Fig. 7). Platt[10]

[10] Kenneth B. Platt, "Plant Control—Some Possibilities and Limitations," *Journal of Range Management,* Vol. 12, 1959, pp. 64-68.

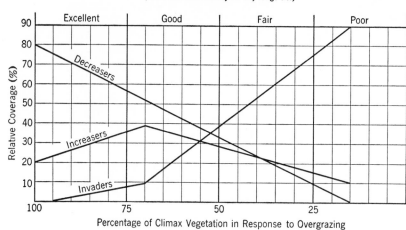

RANGE CONDITION
(Presented schematically for any range site)

Fig. 6 Diagrammatic presentation of the relationships between increasers, decreasers, and invaders in four range conditions. Percentages will differ from place to place in relation to type of vegetation and prevailing grazing conditions. (By E. J. Dyksterhuis, Soil Conservation Service.)

Fig. 7 Southwestern grasslands have been extensively invaded by low-value woody vegetation, especially mesquite and juniper. Here mesquite trees are spreading from the ravine to the hillsides causing range deterioration. Arivaca, Arizona. (U.S. Forest Service.)

estimates that sagebrush is a problem on 87 million acres, mesquite on 93 million acres, and junipers on nearly 64 million acres. Control methods involve burning, chemical treatments, chaining, grubbing, dozing, chopping, root-plowing, and others. Production of grasses is substantially increased following brush removal, but returns are not always economical, and the rate at which brush control is achieved will be largely governed by economic considerations.

Water spreading is an effective way of improving range production, but its application depends on a suitable supply of surface water, an adaptable terrain, and the construction of systems of dikes and dams of varying complexity. Water spreading is being developed as rapidly as possible in those areas where the practice is economical. The actual number of acres to which the practice is applied is small, however.

Range fertilization offers considerable promise for increased production in the less arid portions of the range region. Nitrogen fertilizer has produced excellent returns on portions of the northern plains. Phosphorus and nitrogen have been used effectively on mountain meadows. Responses to sulfur and to nitrogen have been obtained on the California annual ranges. The importance that fertilizers may have in improving western grasslands is only now being evaluated experimentally.

Rodent control is important in many areas, particularly gophers, prairie dogs, and kangaroo rats. Developments for stock water, construction of fences, and building of access roads are improvement measures, because they promote more efficient utilization of the range forage crop.

RANGE RESEARCH

Much of the improvement that has taken place in our ranges can be directly attributed to research in grassland and range problems. If further improvement of our grasslands resource

is to be achieved during the next quarter century, this research activity must be continued and expanded. Scientific range research had its beginnings in the Forest Service as early as 1907. Today the range management research program of the Forest Service is comprehensive. It includes the management and improvement of livestock and big game ranges; the relationships of range to timber production, to watershed values, and to rodents and insects; the study of the ecology, physiology, and productivity of important range plants; techniques to use in measuring and evaluating range condition and trend; and control of undesirable plants on the range. This research is conducted chiefly at four regional experiment stations: the Pacific Northwest Station at Portland, Oregon; the Pacific Southwest Station at Berkeley; the Intermountain Station at Ogden, Utah; and the Rocky Mountain Station at Fort Collins, Colorado. A number of field research centers with experimental ranges are distributed in eight of the western mountain states. In addition, important research on southern ranges is being conducted by the Forest Experiment Station at New Orleans, Louisiana, and the Central States Station at Columbia, Missouri.

The Forage and Range Section of the Agricultural Research Service, U.S. Department of Agriculture, is continuing grassland and range research work at the Northern Great Plains Field Station, Mandan, North Dakota, and the Southern Great Plains Field Station at Woodward, Oklahoma. Range research at these stations had an early beginning under scientists of the old Bureau of Plant Industry (USDA). In addition, this agency now has charge of the range research at the Jornado Field Station in southern New Mexico, the Santa Rita Station in southern Arizona, the Central Great Plains Station at Nunn, Colorado, and the United States Range Livestock Experiment Station at Miles City, Montana. Much additional work is being done in collaboration with state agricultural experiment stations and forest and range experiment stations of the Forest Service. The Soil and Water Conservation Research Division of this agency is also conducting a number of fundamental research studies of direct importance to the management of the western rangelands.

The Bureau of Sport Fisheries and Wildlife of the Fish and Wildlife Service, U.S. Department of the Interior, is conducting investigations on basic conditions that control rodent, rabbit, and predator numbers on western public land ranges. Expanded studies on pesticides-wildlife relations have been begun by this Bureau. The Bureau has also entered into a number of cooperative range research projects with other agencies and some western agricultural experiment stations. Major emphasis in these studies has been on economic considerations in the use of rangelands. Special attention has also been given by this Bureau to the problems of

rehabilitation of pinon pine-juniper infested ranges.

During the period 1935–1952, the Soil Conservation Service was conducting soil and moisture conservation research at a series of erosion-control experiment stations. In November 1952, authority for this work was transferred to the Agricultural Research Service. Particular emphasis has been placed on measures affecting runoff and sedimentation. The effect of various managerial and structural practices on moisture infiltration, soil stabilization, and forage production was studied. The Soil Conservation Service now transmits a list of its research needs to the Agricultural Research Service. It also maintains close liaison with state agricultural experiment stations and carries out numerous field trials and tests.

The state agricultural universities and col-

Fig. 8 This formerly deteriorated grassland has been reseeded to crested wheatgrass and now produces over ten times as much forage as it did before rehabilitation. Glorietta Mesa, New Mexico. (U.S. Forest Service.)

leges and the associated agricultural experiment stations have done much work on grassland, range, grazing, and animal nutrition that has contributed greatly to our knowledge of how to use natural and seeded grazing lands more efficiently in the production of livestock products. Practically all experiment stations in the range area have projects relating directly to the management and improvement of natural rangelands.

Many of the detailed studies of the floristic composition and productivity of our grasslands have originated in state agricultural colleges, universities, and experiment stations. Much of the ecological knowledge that provides the present basis for the science of range management has come from these studies. Studies of this type are still being made on many grassland areas (Fig. 8).

Important phases of the many grassland problems that are currently receiving much attention in state agricultural experiment stations include: value and management of supplementary tame grass pastures, breeding and selection of improved forage grasses and legumes, strain testing and adaptation evaluation, factors affecting forage quality and nutritive value, control of noxious and poisonous plants, role of minor elements in both plant and animal nutrition, range livestock nutrition as related to grazing and feeding practices, the influence of fertilizers on forage composition and production and on the floristic composition of natural grasslands, competition and interaction between game and livestock populations on ranges, stocking rates of both domestic livestock and big game as they affect composition and productivity of natural grasslands, the ecological basis of range condition classification, proper utilization of important native range species, economic factors in rangeland use and in ranching operations, and many others.

References

Agricultural Land Resources (A Digest of the National Inventory of Soil and Water Conservation Needs), Agr. Information Bulletin 263, U.S. Department of Agriculture, Washington, D.C., 1962.

Basic Problems and Techniques in Range Research, A Report of a Joint Committee of the American Society of Range Management and the Agricultural Board, Publ. No. 890, National Academy of Sciences—National Research Council, Washington, D.C., 1962.

Borchert, J. E., "The Climate of the Central North American Grassland," *Annals of the Association of American Geographers*, Vol. XL, 1950, pp. 1–39.

Burcham, L. T., *California Range Lands*, Division of Forestry, Dept. of Natural Resources, Sacramento, California, 1957.

Clawson, Marion, R. Burnell Held, and Charles H. Stoddard, *Land for the Future*, Resources for the Future, The Johns Hopkins Press. Baltimore, 1960.

Dyksterhuis, E. J., "Condition and Management of Rangeland Based on Quantitative Ecology," *Journal of Range Management*, Vol. 2, 1949, pp. 104–115.

Ellison, Lincoln, "Influence of Grazing on Plant Succession of Rangelands," *Botanical Review*, Vol. 26, 1960, pp. 1–78.

Foss, Phillip O., *Politics and Grass—The Administration of Grazing on the Public Domain*, University of Washington Press, Seattle, Washington, 1960.

Grass, The Yearbook of Agriculture, 1948, U.S. Department of Agriculture, Washington, D.C.

Hanson, Herbert C., "Ecology of the Grassland," *Botanical Review*, Vol. 16, 1950, pp. 283–360.

Harlan, Jack R., *Theory and Dynamics of Grassland Agriculture*, D. Van Nostrand Co., Princeton, New Jersey, 1956.

Hitchcock, A. S., *Manual of the Grasses of the United States*, Misc. Pub. 200, Second Edition, revised by Agnes Chase, U.S. Department of Agriculture, Washington, D.C., 1950.

Humphrey, Robert R., *Range Ecology*, Ronald Press, New York, 1962.

Land, The 1958 Yearbook of Agriculture, U.S. Department of Agriculture, Washington, D.C.

Malin, James C., *Grassland of North America, Prolegomena to Its History* (Published by the author), Lawrence, Kansas, 1947.

Malin, James C., "The Grassland of North America: Its Occupance and the Challenge of Continuous Appraisal," in William L. Thomas, Jr., *Man's Role in Changing the Face of the Earth*, The University of Chicago Press, Chicago, 1956, pp. 350–366.

Marschner, F. J., *Land Use and Its Patterns in the United States*, Agriculture Handbook No. 153. U.S. Department of Agriculture, Washington, D.C., 1959.

Oosting, Henry J., *Plant Communities*, Freeman and Co., San Francisco, 1956.

Sampson, A. W., "Application of Ecological Principles in Determining Condition of Grazing Lands," *UNSCCUR*, Vol. 6, New York, 1951, pp. 509–514.

Sampson, A. W., *Range Management, Principles and Practices*, John Wiley and Sons, New York, 1952.

Stoddart, L. A., and A. D. Smith, *Range Management*, Second Edition, McGraw-Hill Book Co., New York, 1955.

The Journal of Range Management, Published by the American Society of Range Management.

The Western Range, Senate Document 199, Superintendent of Documents, Washington, D.C., 1936.

Weaver, J. E., *North American Prairie*, Johnsen Publishing Co., Lincoln, Nebraska, 1954.

Weaver, J. E., and F. W. Albertson, *Grasslands of the Great Plains*, Johnsen Publishing Co., Lincoln, Nebraska, 1956.

Webb, W. P., *The Great Plains*, Ginn and Co., Boston, Mass., 1931.

GUY-HAROLD SMITH

The Ohio State University

CHAPTER 9

The Land We Possess

The development of agriculture in the United States has been marked by an increasing control over a rich land resource and obversely by a wasteful exploitation of the soils. The frontier of settlement, in a little more than two centuries, advanced across the mountains and the plains, across the forests and the prairies, and across the steppe lands and the deserts from the Atlantic seaboard to the Pacific. Progress was not steady or uniform but was characterized by surges of rapid movement alternating with filling in and consolidating the farmlands requisitioned from nature and the aborigines. Changes in the agricultural scene have reflected the progress of scientific advancement, the stultifying effect of depression, the uneasy peace between wars, the cataclysm of war itself, and the challenging opportunities of the postwar period of readjustment. Briefly during the Korean conflict the economy of the nation was again disturbed by war.

Agriculture in the United States today, both as an industry and as a way of life, is related to a variety of conditions. In the utilization and conservation of the land resources the agricultural prospect is linked inextricably with:

1. The trends and changing character of the population.

2. The area of land available, its productivity, and its suitability for the various purposes for which land is required.

3. The level of living, both of the farm population and the nonfarm population who purchase the products of the land.

4. The improvement in rural education and culture.

THE TRENDS AND CHANGING CHARACTER OF THE POPULATION

The agricultural situation at any particular time is closely attuned to the general economic condition of the nation as a whole. The economy is sensitive to both short-range and long-term changes in conditions. When the national economy experiences a wave of prosperity, agriculture generally benefits also, although there may be some differences in timing. For example, in the 1920's farm prices began a downward readjustment while industrial wages still showed little or no decline. In 1948 the prices of many farm products declined months before it was reflected in a lowering of the cost of living or before the decline in employment or in wages. Farm prices rose again in 1950, but at the conclusion of active warfare in Korea in 1953, the prices received by farmers declined sharply, yet the prices they paid remained high or declined only slightly. At the beginning of the decade of the 1960's the prices received by farmers averaged approximately 6 percent below the prices received 10 years before. In the same 10-year period the prices paid by farmers increased 17 percent. All important features of the nation's economy may not move forward simultaneously, but the general level of prosperity and economic progress has an important bearing on the agricultural industry and the farm population.

The total number of people of all ages that collectively makes up the population constitutes a large domestic market. The high standard of living and particularly the desire on the part of the people to improve their living conditions make the American market almost unequaled from the standpoint of its capacity to consume the products of agriculture and industry.

Not only has the number of people increased steadily, but also there have been internal changes of major importance in the population. The birth rate has displayed significant fluctuations; the death rate has declined steadily; and the national policy in respect to immigration has been subject to important changes. Advances in medicine and nutrition have added greatly to the life expectancy of the people.

The population of the United States, subjected to these internal changes over a long period of time, takes on progressively new characteristics that must be examined critically from time to time so that agriculture and other economic activities can be adjusted to the new situation.

The Population Prospect. The population of the United States can be predicted for a few decades in the future with greater certainty than any other factor affecting American agriculture. This high degree of certainty is related to the fact that a very high proportion of the people now living will be counted by the census taker in 1970 and 1980. The birth rate, the death rate, and the net increase in the population can be predicted with great accuracy from year to year. The factors that may be of major importance in the long-range forecast of the total population include a change in the birth rate, the effect of epidemics on the death rate, a long war, and the policy of the federal government in respect to immigration (Table 1).

The most stable of these three factors is the death rate. Birth rates, although variable from year to year, can be forecast for relatively short periods with sufficient accuracy to meet the needs of the school authorities and others in-

Table 1. Population Forecast, 1963–1986

	Slightly Declining Mortality with Immigration°	Rapidly Declining Mortality with Immigration°	Constant Mortality with Immigration°	Slightly Declining Mortality No Net Immigration
1963–1964	189,278,000	189,278,000	189,278,000	189,278,000
1967–1968	200,212,000	200,414,000	199,984,000	198,923,000
1972–1973	215,409,000	216,075,000	214,865,000	212,202,000
1977–1978	233,378,000	234,739,000	232,404,000	227,998,000
1982–1983	253,600,000	255,889,000	252,049,000	245,873,000
1985–1986	266,322,000	269,279,000	264,377,000	257,112,000

° Assumes constant annual net immigration of 300,000.

[Source: Bureau of the Census, *Population Estimates*, Series P-25 No. 286, July, 1964.]

terested in the number of children in the population under 5 years of age. There is less certainty about the number of immigrants who will be admitted to this country from year to year. After 1945 the restrictive regulations and other checks were relaxed and increasing numbers have been admitted to this country. We, as a people, are committed to a policy of selection and consequent absorption of the immigrants so that a degree of homogeneity will result, particularly in respect to an attitude toward American political institutions and traditions. In the middle 1930's, when the decline in the birth rate and the great reduction in immigration became important factors in forecasting the future population, there was a disposition on the part of the forecasters to envision a static or even a declining population a few decades hence. Much of this despair in respect to the population was not dispelled by the increased birth rate of the 1940's.

The Birth Rate. Shortly after World War I the birth rate in the United States began an almost steady decline which continued into the middle 1930's (Table 2). This decline extending over a period of nearly 15 years became the despair of demographers and others who were concerned about the future population of the nation. The lowest rates came in the period from 1933–1936 when unemployment was very high and the marriage rate was relatively low.

Beginning in 1937, there was an upturn in the birth rate which was related partly to improved economic conditions. The uneasy peace in Europe may have influenced some young people to take on family responsibility. The Selective Service Act of 1940 and the prospect of war produced emotional and romantic results, for both the marriage rate and the birth rate increased. The birth rate continued relatively high during the war period, except for 1945 when there was a slight decline. In 1944 and 1945 many young men were separated from their families, and a decline was a natural consequence.

Table 2. Birth Rate and Death Rate, 1920–1962

| Date | *Per 1000 Estimated Population* | |
	Birth Rate	Death Rate
1920	23.7	13.0
1925	21.3	11.7
1930	18.9	11.3
1935	16.9	10.9
1940	17.9	10.8
1945	19.5	10.6
1950	23.6	9.6
1955	24.6	9.3
1960	23.7°	9.5
1961	23.3	9.3
1962	22.4	9.5

° Based on a 50 percent sample.

[Source: *Statistical Abstract of the United States,* 1955, 1963.]

The return of thousands, indeed millions, of young men to their homes and families was followed by an increase in the marriage rate and the birth rate. In 1946 the number of births reached a total of 3,288,672, the first time that the number exceeded three million in a single year.

Because of the upturn of the birth rate in the late 1930's and the 1940's along with the wartime stimulus, agricultural production was greatly expanded. But by midcentury the continued growth in population was not sufficient to offset other unfavorable factors and give renewed vitality to agriculture.

The birth rate and the proportion of children in the population are somewhat higher in the rural than in the urban communities, particularly the larger cities. This long-time difference between the two groups of people has produced a population pressure or differential which has favored and maintained a consistent movement of people from the farms to the cities. Generally, this cityward migration has been a long-time population movement in this country. By this important movement the population of the cities has grown, and the farm population has been held in balance.

In an agricultural community the wife is essential to the success of the farm operations. Her contribution is not that of a wage earner but of a helpmate who shares the work responsibility and rears the family. In the rural area, although children constitute an important cost, they are also a valuable asset and at an early age can make a contribution to the farm income by helping regularly with the daily chores about the farm and during the vacations may help with the more important farm duties. Children, particularly boys of 12 to 15 years of age, may handle certain farm machinery, such as a small tractor, with great skill and may save their father the cost of a hired hand.

In the rural areas the farm produces a large proportion of the food consumed by the family. Self-sufficiency or self-support is a significant feature of the farm economy. In the city, particularly in the larger urban communities, children are unable to make a major contribution to their own support unless the father is engaged in a business where his children may help. On the farm the children are an asset, but in the urban community they are a financial liability. Because of this difference in the birth rate in cities and rural areas the farm families are responsible in a measure for the maintenance and the continued growth of the urban population.

The Death Rate. It is not likely that the death rate can be reduced much more. In fact it may be expected to increase slightly as the population is made up of proportionally more old people whose life expectancy decreases rapidly in the later years.

The lowering of the death rate has increased the number of people in the over-65 group. In 1920 fewer than 9,000,000 people in the general population were 65 or over. In 1963 the number was more than 17,000,000.[1] This older group in the general population still require housing, have an interest in the availability and cost of nursing homes and hospital service. They gen-

erally have reduced desires for food, clothing, transportation, and expensive housing. The drain on natural resources continues but at a reduced rate.

The reduction of the farm population, the selective migration to the cities, and the employment of younger people in occupations other than farming have left many older people in the rural areas. In 1930 only 11.1 percent of the farmers were 65 or over, but by 1960 the percentage had increased to 16.8. These older people who live on the land may take some pride in keeping up the family home and they may be able to produce some of their food. But like other people in the over-65 group they are concerned about their ultimate economic welfare and the availability and cost of hospital and medical service.

Farm Population. The farm population, once a vigorous component of the total population, is feeling the impact of a number of conditions that tend to lessen the attractiveness of farm life. The modernization of the farm home with inside plumbing and electricity has lightened the burden of the housewife. Mechanization of agriculture and good roads have made farming an integral part of the national economy. In balancing the factors that tend to hold people of the land against the attractions of urban life, the declining farm population reflects the relative advantages, real or imagined, in the urban areas of the country.

According to the old definition used to identify and enumerate the farm population, the numbers shown in the last five decennial enumerations are given below.

Year	Million		Year	Million
1910	32.1		1940	30.5
1920	31.6		1950	23.3
1930	30.4		1960	13.4

These data show that the farm population has remained steadfastly attached to the land until recently when the forces related to urban living have strengthened the movement of people

---

[1] *A Place to Live, The Yearbook of Agriculture 1963,* Government Printing Office, Washington, D.C., 1963, p. 45.

away from the farms. In 1950, 15.4 percent of the population lived on farms; by 1960 this proportion had declined to 7.5 percent (Table 3).

Under the new definition used by the Bureau of the Census the farm population was 15.6 million in 1960 and represented only 8.7 percent of the total population. It is now recognized that many people who live in rural areas derive much or most of their income from other sources than from farming. Many may commute to the cities or to nearby industrial plants. Some may have employment on the highways, in the forests, at recreational centers, or in other occupations other than farming. Many farm people may be classed as part-time farmers who find it economically advantageous to derive their income from more than one source.

The Nonfarm Population. In 1960, the Bureau of the Census counted as rural 54 million people, but fewer than one-third of these lived on farms. Many of these nonfarm people lived in towns, villages, and hamlets with a population of under 2500 inhabitants. In these small inhabited places live many people who escape classification as urban, but their activities may be very similar to those of people who live in the larger urban centers. Many professional people such as teachers, doctors, lawyers, butter makers, and others having similar occupations live in homes not unlike those who live in cities. In these small central places the trading or merchandising functions are carried on as they are in the larger urban communities.

Many other occupations help to classify these people as nonfarm, yet their activities may link them with agriculture. Some people utilizing a small tract of land may run chicken hatcheries, provide a dusting and spraying service to farmers and orchardists, many people practice custom harvesting including silo filling, sell crop insurance, operate a small slaughtering plant, and many other service activities closely related to the principal agricultural crops and livestock produced on the nearby farm lands.

Approximately one-eighth of the rural population live in small towns of 1000 to 2500 in-

Table 3. Total, Rural, and Farm Population of the United States

	Total Population	Rural Population	Farm Population
1910			32,077,000
1920			31,974,000
1930	123,202,624	54,042,025	30,445,350
1935°	127,057,000		32,161,000
1940	132,164,569	57,459,231	30,546.911
1945°	139,583,000		25,293,000
1950	151,325,798	61,197,604	23,331,738
1954°	161,763,000		21,890,000
1960	179,323,175	66,266,822	13,444,898

° Data from Alaska and Hawaii not included.

[Source: *1959 Census of Agriculture*, Vol. II, General Report, p. 13.]

habitants. Included in this number are many people over 65 years of age who have moved from the farm to the nearby village. The farm they have moved from may be rented or sold to a son or daughter who is taking the first steps toward eventual ownership of the land. The older people retain an interest, financial and sentimental in the farm on which they spent many years of their life. Many people who live in these small towns are basically rural people and their chief interests center around problems of the agricultural community. Most of the residents of the small towns and hamlets have a vital interest in the farming enterprise and will respond to the various programs aimed at maintaining the productivity of the land, the availability of fish and game in easily accessible areas, the development of recreational facilities such as swimming pools and picnic grounds, and the preservation of forested areas. Many of these people may not be directly involved in the action programs to conserve and protect these natural resources, but they can join with the people in leadership positions to encourage the people who own and work the land to practice conservation and protect the land resource from deterioration and destruction.

Some Implications of Population Change in Respect to Agriculture. A dynamic and growing population provides an expanding market for agricultural products. "Prior to the Civil War the population of the nation, and doubtless its consumption of farm products, increased a third each ten years. After the Civil War the rate of increase lessened, until during the World War I decade, and the decade of urban prosperity that followed, the increase was less than one-sixth each ten years." [2]

As the population changes in respect to numbers, age distribution, and other important characteristics, it is clear that agriculture will be affected. An increasing number of young children in the population requires in due course an expansion of school facilities from the kindergarten to the university. Agriculture will be called upon to provide its share of the products required to meet the needs and wants of this productive group.

LAND RESOURCES

The United States as a nation contains within its national boundaries 2271 million acres of land or 6.9 percent of the land area of the world. Only the Soviet Union, China, and Canada are larger. The 3,615,211 square miles which make up the area of the fifty states and the District of Columbia contain, in addition to the 2271 million acres of land, 42.2 million acres classed as inland water areas including lakes, reservoirs, rivers, canals, and coastal waters such as estuaries, bays, sounds, and lagoons. The land resources distributed widely across the nation differ greatly, depending on climatic conditions such as the length of the growing season, the amount of precipitation, the relief of the land, the character of the soil, and the nature of the vegetation. Under natural conditions the qualities of the land developed over a long interval of time but during the period of settlement, human use has altered locally the physical character of the land resource (Fig. 1).

[2] O. E. Baker, "Significance of Population Trends to American Agriculture," *The Milbank Memorial Fund Quarterly*, Vol. 25, 1937, pp. 121-134.

In the early seventeenth century when the first settlers were establishing their homes on the Atlantic seaboard, the natural cover of this thinly occupied land consisted of the following categories of vegetation.

	Million Acres	Percent
Forest and woodland	1065	47
Grassland	726	32
Desert shrub	266	12
Tundra	214	9

After 350 or more years of settlement, clearing, agricultural readjustment, and economic development the categories of cover or land use show some striking changes.

	Million Acres	Percent
Cropland	458	20
Grassland pasture and range	633	28
Forest and woodland (excluding reserved forest areas)	746	33
Special use areas	157	7
Miscellaneous other land (including 214 million acres of tundra)	277	12

It required the clearing of 320 million acres of virgin forest and woodland and the plowing up or breaking the sod of millions of acres of grassland to create the cropland of 458 million acres. Some of the land converted earlier to cropland has been returned to woodland or to permanent pasture or has been taken over for other uses. The areal expansion of urban communities, the building of highways, railroads, and airports, and the requisitioning of large areas for the defense of the nation have wrought significant changes in the use of the land. The discerning observer can note readily the changes that are continually taking place. On an abandoned farm the uncultivated fields may be invaded by weeds, grasses, shrubs, and trees if a source of

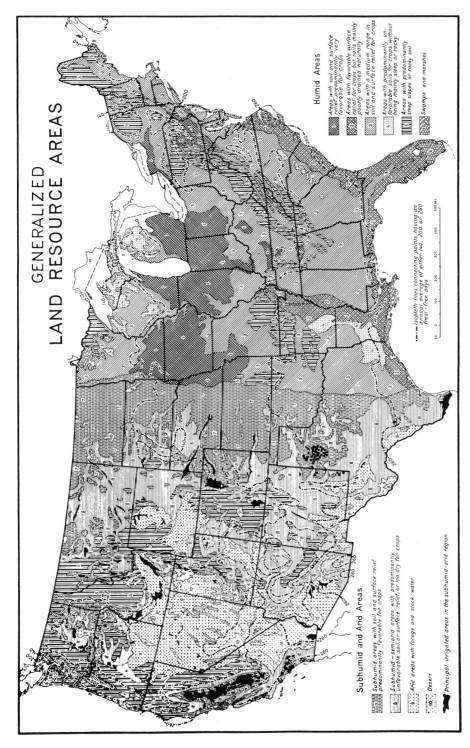

GENERALIZED LAND RESOURCE AREAS

Humid Areas

1. Areas with soil and surface relief predominantly very favorable for crops

2. Areas with favorable surface relief for crops but soils mainly poorly drained naturally

3. Areas with a medium range in soil and surface relief for crops

4. Areas with predominantly unfavorable soils for crops without being mainly steep or rocky

5. Areas with predominantly steep slopes or rocky soil

6. Swamps and marshes

Subhumid and Arid Areas

7. Subhumid areas with soil and surface relief predominantly favorable for crops

8. Subhumid – semiarid areas with predominantly unfavorable soil or surface relief, or too dry for crops

9. Arid areas with forage and stock water

10. Desert

Principal irrigated areas in the subhumid-arid region

Isopleth lines connecting points having an annual average of either 140, 200 or 260 frost-free days

50   100   200   300   400   500 MI.

Fig. 1 This map of the land resource areas is highly generalized but is shows the location and extent of ten major land areas and indicates in the legend something of the character of each area in respect to soil, relief, drainage, and climatic conditions. (Economic Research Service and Bureau of the Census.)

175

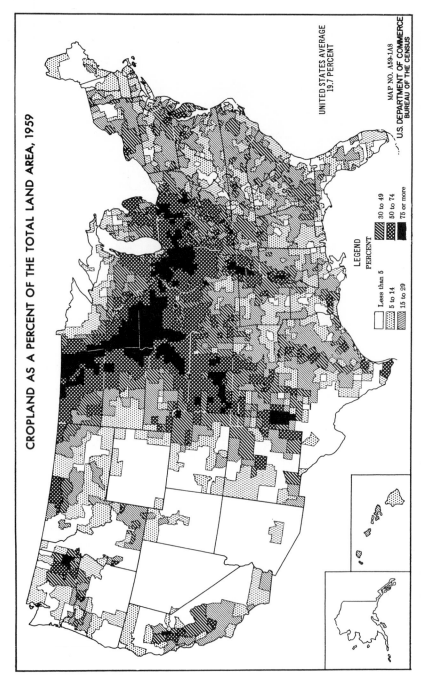

Fig. 2 The distribution of cropland in relation to the total land area is an important means of identifying the sections of the 48 contiguous states that are highly suitable for agricultural use. The corners of the important agricultural triangle are centered in North Dakota, Ohio, and Texas. Other important cropland areas can be identified in the East, in the South, and in the West. (Bureau of the Census.)

seeds is nearby and other conditions are favorable. Some of the areas that once were classed as shrub have been converted into pasture and range by removal of the shrubs and the planting of palatable grasses. A wilderness area may be set aside as a game refuge, which is then protected from despoliation by man. In the name of progress it may be necessary to take over high-quality cropland for developing a residential suburb, an industrial community, or a new municipal airport. These and many other changes are continually taking place in those parts of the country that show economic vitality. In some areas where the economic and social forces are rather weak, changes or trends may not be easily identified.

Cropland. Cropland may be defined as the area in harvested crops, crop failure, cultivated summer fallow, soil improvement crops, idle cropland, and cropland used only for pasture (Fig. 2). Each year important areas fail to yield a crop because of winter kill in the case of autumn-sown crops such as winter wheat or because other conditions such as drought, flooding, hail, or wind make it uneconomical for the farmer to reap a harvest. If the weather hazards recur too frequently and if crop failure is coupled with continuing low prices, marginal cropland areas may be abandoned. On the dry frontier, land once cropped may be restored to the grassland and range category.

Trends in Land Utilization. From the time of settlement until the early decades of the 20th century the areas classed as cropland steadily increased. Between 1900 and 1920 more than 90 million acres were added to the cropland area. This was the last period when significant areas were brought under cultivation. During the 1920's the cropland area remained relatively stable. Farm prices had declined from the levels attained during the period of World War I; surpluses had become an unfavorable factor in the market; but the prices which the farmers had to pay for machinery, household equipment, clothing, and other essentials remained

high. Under these conditions the land in the cropland classification tended to become stabilized.

During the 1930's when the country experienced a serious depression the agricultural sector of the national economy was in serious trouble. Many farmers were unable to continue their mortgage payments and the banks and other money-lending agencies foreclosed and acquired title to the land. Under the economic stress of the times there was little incentive to increase the cropland. The area in cropland declined from 480 million acres in 1930 to 467 million acres in 1940. The economic stresses of the 1930's brought about a number of significant changes in American agriculture. Many areas that had depreciated in value because of soil erosion, depletion of the plant nutrients, and for other reasons were withdrawn from the cropland category and converted to other uses.

In the decade of the 1940's cropland increased to 478 million acres. The stimulating effect of higher prices for agricultural products, and the war-time demand for more food not only for the American market but to satisfy the need of our allies induced the farmer to put forth the necessary effort to expand the cropland and to increase yields.

After 1950 and continuing into the 1960's the area in cropland declined (Fig. 3). In 1959, the cropland area was reported to be 458 million acres. Extensive areas of agricultural land are retained in the cropland category in spite of their low productivity. Areas of low capability cannot be made to yield abundantly without the expenditure of large sums for commercial fertilizer and the practice of farming techniques which in the long run are beyond the means of the farmer. In spite of the fact that large areas of marginal land are still used for agriculture, the lands best suited for farming make up the immense area known as cropland. Anyone concerned about the land resources especially in relation to their availability and adequacy should be encouraged by the fact that produc-

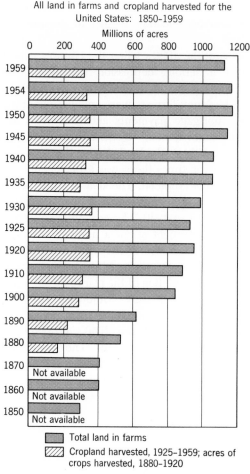

All land in farms and cropland harvested for the
United States: 1850-1959

Millions of acres

Fig. 3   The land in farms and the area in harvested crops
began to level off or decline in the late 1940's or early
1950's reflecting the high productivity of the smaller area of
land and the high skills of the agricultural population.
There appears to be little reason for concern about the
adequacy of the land resource to meet the needs for food
and fiber over the next several years. (Economic Research
Service and Bureau of the Census.)

tivity of the land remains high and surpluses a
continuing threat while the total population increases and the area in cropland declines. There
is no immediate danger that the land resources
will be inadequate to meet the needs of the
United States for food and fiber.[3]

    [3] Marion Clawson, R. Burnell Held, and Charles H. Stod-
dard, *Land for the Future*, Resources for the Future, The
Johns Hopkins Press, Baltimore, 1960, p. 266.

High productivity of the land in crops reflects the retention of lands of high capability
and the withdrawal of marginal farms from production. The application of fertilizers has made
a contribution toward increased yields. The
selection of high quality seed, the use of insecticides and disease-controlling chemicals, and
the practice of modern techniques have made it
possible to increase yields and at the same time
reduce the number of acres under cultivation.
Increased production in the 1920's and 1930's
was related in a large measure to the substitution of mechanical power for horses and mules.
Land long needed and used for the production of
food for horses and mules became available for
other crops. Half the increase in livestock and
crops is directly related to the mechanization of
agriculture. Increased yields per acre accounted
for a third of the increase. In the 1940's when
mechanization was an achievement, less than a
quarter of the increase in production can be
ascribed to the continued substitution of
mechanical power for horses and mules. Much
of the gain in production was related to increased yields per acre, which in turn reflected
the higher prices that induced the farmers to put
forth their best efforts to meet new production
goals. In the 1950's the same factors were operative to increase still further farm output. Mechanization is credited with nearly 20 percent of
the increase. Somewhat less than half the gain
was derived from increased yields. The increased contribution of livestock accounted for
nearly a third of the gain in production.

LAND IN FARMS. The Bureau of the Census has
used several definitions of a farm, so data from
the decennial enumerations are not exactly comparable. The acreage of land in farms in 1959
was 1123 million acres or about 38 million acres
below the acreage reported for 1954. Between
5 and 6 million acres of this decrease was related
to a change in the definition of a farm. The remaining decline included losses of farmlands to
urban expansion, the construction of highways,
the building of factories and shopping centers in
rural areas, and the expansion of nonfarm activities onto land previously used for agricultural

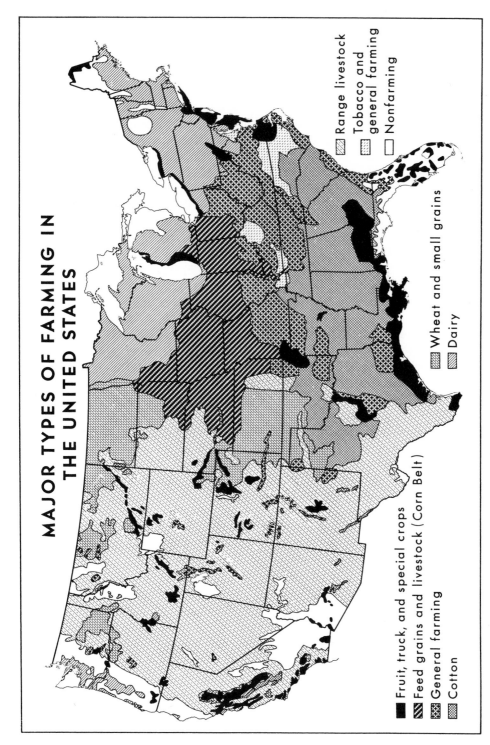

MAJOR TYPES OF FARMING IN THE UNITED STATES

Fruit, truck, and special crops
Feed grains and livestock (Corn Belt)
General farming
Cotton

Wheat and small grains
Dairy

Range livestock
Tobacco and general farming
Nonfarming

Fig. 4 This map shows the eight major types of farming and one nonfarming area in the 48 contiguous states and the location and geographical extent of the several crop and livestock areas. (Economic Research Service and Bureau of t

179

purposes. This decline in land in farms reflects also the trend toward lower farm prices or stabilized prices that tend to make farming less attractive.

The land included in the farms of the nation consists chiefly of the highly productive cropland areas but lands in other categories are also included. Since the cropland area of the United States was only 487 million acres in 1959 and the land in farms totaled 1125 million acres, the farms included large areas of land in other use categories. Grassland used for permanent pasture and range, forest and woodland, and limited areas of unusable lands are included in the farms of the nation. The Census of Agriculture for 1959 reported that 624 million acres of pasture lands were in farms. Of this 66 million acres were cropland used only for pasture. In the same year 164 million acres of woodland were in farms.[4]

The practice of agriculture, especially the development of distinctive crop combinations with the associated livestock industries, has resulted in an agricultural regionalism commonly recognized as the major types of farming (Fig. 4). In areas where the predominant type of farming may be feed grains and livestock (Corn Belt) there are farmers who have developed a specialty such as fruit and vegetable growing. In the Northeast where dairying gives the region its distinctive characteristics there are individual farmers who may raise poultry or sheep or use their land for other purposes. But in spite of considerable diversity several farm types can be identified in the forty-eight contiguous states.

The Agricultural Regions. The distribution of crops in this cropland area reflects the character of the climate, the physical nature of the land in respect to relief, and the productivity of the soil. Economic conditions, particularly market demand and prices, function as important factors in production. The combination of

crops and the farm animals raised in any area is related to both the physical and economic conditions that give distinctive character to the agricultural regions of the United States.

The chief cropland area of the United States is essentially triangular in shape. A straight line drawn from central Ohio to the forty-ninth parallel in northwestern North Dakota, thence southward into the Panhandle of Texas, and thence northeastward to central Ohio encloses a great triangular area of cropland that is probably unequaled by any other agricultural area in the world. Within this area are included parts of the spring wheat region, the hay and pasture belt, the corn belt, a part of the corn and winter wheat belt, and a small section of the Cotton Belt (Fig. 5). East and west across the central section of the triangle extends the corn belt centered on what Transeau has called the prairie peninsula.[5] Most of this great cropland area was originally an expansive tall-grass prairie of slight relief and under the economy of the Amerinds remained a grassland. The aborigines, by the use of fire, may have helped to maintain the prairie against the encroachment of the forest and may have extended the prairie area locally by the same means. This moot question need not be debated here. It is important, however, that the white settlers came into possession of one of the greatest agricultural areas in the world as they dispossessed the natives and, in due course of time, broke the prairie and substituted cultivated crops for the natural grasses which for thousands of years had been building the agricultural heartland of America, known as the Middle West.

In certain counties in this great triangular area as much as 75 percent of the total area was classed as cropland in 1959, and locally more than 75 percent of the land was actually in crops.[6] In the areas of slight relief the mechani-

[4] *United States Census of Agriculture 1959, A Graphic Summary of Land Utilization,* Vol. V, Part 6, Chapter 1, Government Printing Office, Washington, D.C., 1962, pp. 5-19.

[5] E. N. Transeau, "The Prairie Peninsula," *Ecology,* Vol. 16, 1935, pp. 423-437.

[6] *United States Census of Agriculture 1959, A Graphic Summary of Land Utilization,* Vol. V, Part 6, Chapter 1, Government Printing Office, Washington, D.C., 1962, p. 12.

Fig. 5 This stand of corn near Eureka, Illinois, is representative of the major crop grown throughout much of the Middle West. The luxuriant vegetative growth and the high yield of corn as a grain give some indication of the favorable conditions, both physical and economic, under which this crop is grown. (Catepillar Tractor Co.)

zation of agriculture had reached a high stage of development. This is the great granary area of the United States, and in favorable years it can contribute great quantities of food to the hungry peoples of the world.

Locally in other sections of the United States there are important cropland areas that make up a great acreage of productive land, but nowhere are the fertile lands so expansive or continuous as in the Middle West.

In the South the irregularity of the terrain, infertile soils, swamps, and other unfavorable factors function collectively to limit the areas suitable for crops. In the more favored areas such as the inner Coastal Plain, the Piedmont, the valleys of the Ridge and Valley Province of

the Appalachians, the alluvial lowlands of the Mississippi, Arkansas and Red rivers, and the black prairies of Texas and Oklahoma, the proportion of farmland devoted to crops locally may exceed 50 percent. This region of heavy rainfall, erodible soils, clean cultivated crops, notably cotton, corn, and tobacco, cultivated by people not fully aware of their responsibility, is one of the great problem areas of the United States (Fig. 6). The land resource of this area can be saved from destructive exploitation, but the proportion of the land in row crops should be reduced. The agriculture of the South may require many important changes before the area attains its proper place in the farm economy of the United States.

Fig. 6   Parallel terracing on this Georgia cotton field gives a good yield, increases the efficiency
of the mechanical picker, and reduces soil losses. (Catepillar Tractor Co.)

Scant rainfall and extensive mountain systems restrict the croplands in the West to local
areas of adequate precipitation or with water
for irrigation. Large areas in the Great Plains
and in the Palouse country are classed as cropland, but the practice of fallow farming reduces
the area harvested each year (Fig. 7). The Puget
Basin and the Willamette Valley of Oregon carry
on agriculture without the benefit of irrigation.
The areas where the highest proportion of the
lands is in crops include the irrigated valleys of
the Columbia and its tributaries, the Colorado
and its tributaries, and the Central Valley and
coastal valleys of California.

The Use of Fertilizer. The maintenance of
the productivity of the soils of the United States
and the upbuilding of soils that are low in plant
nutrients require the application of fertilizer
materials. Because new lands seemed always to
be available as the frontier of settlement moved

across the country, the soil resources were
allowed to decline by erosion and leaching that
insidiously reduced the physical base on which
the industry of agriculture was built. Many
farmers were slow to realize that their lands had
depreciated in quality, and productivity could
be maintained only by the application of
fertilizer.

In comparison with the older agricultural
areas of the world, fertilizer in the United States
is relatively less important. In the period just
before World War II, Europe and Asia required
"80 percent of the nitrogen, 70 percent of the
phosphates, and more than 80 percent of the
potash used as fertilizer . . ." [7] In the old agricultural areas of Europe and Asia, high produc-

[7] K. D. Jacob and F. W. Parker, *Fertilizer in World
War II,* Proceedings of the Twenty-Second Annual Meeting
of the National Joint Committee on Fertilizer Application,
1946, p. 31.

tivity has been maintained by the long-continued practice of supplying the essential plant nutrients through the application of mineral fertilizers. In the United States the fertilizer industry has been expanding to meet the needs of agriculture. During World War II one of the important contributing factors in attaining new high levels of agricultural production was the increased application of mineral fertilizer. In recent years the nitrogen needs of the nation have been met by the importation of nitrate of soda from Chile, the expansion of the synthetic ammonia industry, the recovery of by-product ammonium sulfate, and the utilization of other nitrogen-containing substances. The large resources of phosphates and sulfur have been exploited to meet the needs for superphosphate.

Also, the loss of potash from Germany was offset by the development and expansion of a domestic industry[8] in the Southwest. During World War II the production and use of fertilizers attained new levels, and agriculture under favorable weather conditions responded abundantly.

The geographical distribution of fertilizer consumption shows a relationship to the regional deficiencies of the soils, the crops grown, and to the availability of the fertilizer materials locally. For example, phosphates and sulfur are produced chiefly in the South, and the soils of the South require the repeated application of fertilizer for high production. Where soil depletion has not become serious, fertilizers remain of less

[8] *Ibid.*, p. 35.

Fig. 7   This field of Texas oats on sloping ground is protected by terracing. It is important that these areas that were originally prairie be protected from wind and water erosion when brought under cultivation. (Catepillar Tractor Co.)

importance than in the older agricultural areas of the east and the south Atlantic.

The increased use of fertilizers in the United States explains in large measure the continued high productivity of the land while erosion diminished the quality of the farmlands. In 1959 nearly 20 million tons of commercial fertilizer were applied on 133 million acres of farmland, an increase of 10 million acres over the area fertilized in 1954. Areas devoted to corn represented 38.3 percent of the land fertilized, wheat represented 13.1 percent, hay and pasture 10.0 percent, and cotton 6.4 percent. Many other crops receive commercial fertilizers in large amounts such as tobacco and the vegetable crops, but the total area is small when compared with the three or four major crops grown.[9]

The Minor Elements. In addition to nitrates, potash, and phosphates, which may be regarded as the great triumvirate of fertilizer minerals, lime is of great importance, and a number of minor or trace elements are known to be essential in plant and animal nutrition. These minor elements include magnesium, manganese, boron, iron, sulfur, copper, and zinc. Deficiencies of one or more of these elements in the soils have been found to be responsible for abnormalities in both plants and animals that fed on the vegetation. Where the farmers are largely dependent on manures and other organic wastes, the deficiencies of these minor elements are less serious than in the areas where mineral fertilizers are used.[10]

GRASSLAND PASTURE AND RANGE. Originally 32 percent of the land area of the United States was classed as grassland and consisted of immense tall-grass prairies of the Middle West and the shortgrass prairies of the Great Plains and other areas in the West. Locally along the Gulf of Mexico coastal prairies can be included with the grasslands. In the long process of converting the land area into cropland large areas of grassland remain in grass. The Census of Agriculture for 1959 showed that 28 percent of the land area of the nation is grassland pasture and range. Woodland pastures particularly in the South and West are utilized for livestock and make a significant contribution to the grassland resources of the country. (For a fuller treatment of the grassland resources see Chapter 8.)

FOREST AND WOODLAND AREAS. When the United States was first settled, 1065 million acres or 47 percent of the land consisted of forest and woodland. In the process of settlement clearing the land for agriculture reduced the forest and woodland to 33 percent of the area excluding reserved forest lands. Lumbering in the virgin forests followed by repeated harvesting of second-growth timber has reduced the quality of the timber resources of the country. Cutover land where the remaining trees have been reduced to less than 10 percent of the original stand is classed as woodland if the land has not been converted to other uses. Areas that have been planted to trees (afforestation) are also included in the forest and woodland category. Most of the land now classed as cropland resulted from the clearing of immense areas of what was originally forest land or the plowing up of the fertile prairies of the Middle West.

Major tracts of forested land have been set aside as national forests, state forests, and publically owned woodland areas. These forest reserves and the immense woodland areas in farms and the great forest lands held by private interests make up the forest resources of the nation (see Chapters 10 and 11).

WOODLAND PASTURES. In the United States including Alaska and Hawaii 93 million acres of pastured woodland were reported by the Census of Agriculture for 1959. On the cutover lands largely in the eastern part of the country native grasses have invaded the once-forested areas or

[9] *United States Census of Agriculture 1959, A Graphic Summary of Agricultural Resources and Production,* Special Reports, Vol. V, Part 6, Chapter 3, U.S. Department of Commerce, Government Printing Office, Washington, D.C., 1962, pp. 19–20.

[10] Matthew Drosdoff, "The Use of Minor Elements," *Science in Farming, The Yearbook of Agriculture,* 1943–1947, Government Printing Office, Washington, D.C., 1947, pp. 577–582, reference on page 578.

have been planted in woodland areas to provide pasture for livestock so essential in the agriculture of the nation. In the drier West and along the transitional zone between the forests and the prairie the open forests provide pasture of great value to the ranchers and farmers who are in a position to utilize these pastures chiefly for cattle and sheep. In the West the carrying capacity of the grasslands must be respected to prevent overgrazing. If the grass cover is destroyed or seriously damaged by overgrazing, not only is a grassland resource reduced in value but the soil becomes more susceptible to wind and water

erosion; also water that might be retained on the land is permitted to flow rapidly to the stream channels carrying with it a burden of silt that may reach reservoirs, and reduce eventually their water-holding capacity.

LAND FOR SPECIAL PURPOSES. Seven percent of the land area or 157 million acres are used for various special purposes such as highways, railroads, airports, parks, wildlife refuges, farmsteads, urban areas, and other land-requiring developments (Fig. 8). The extension of highways to meet the transportation needs of the nation requires usually that the right of ways be

Fig. 8   As the nation undertakes to extend the network of limited-access highways, throughways, parkways, turnpikes, and tollways across the country great strips of land, largely farmland, must be requisitioned for this purpose. In the open country the two multilane highways may be widely spaced but in urban areas, because of the cost of the land, the median strip may be very narrow. (Garden State Parkway, New Jersey Highway Authority.)

withdrawn from other use categories. The establishment of new parks and recreational areas to serve the people who have leisure to enjoy these facilities requires land that was previously used for some other purpose.

Land for Urban Use. Living in urban communities is an ancient way of life, but in the United States urbanism has taken on some aspects of newness. The spread of home building on the fringe of the older urban communities has produced what many people know as urban sprawl. In 1950, 64 percent of the population in the United States lived in cities of more than 2500. By 1960 the proportion had increased to 69.9 percent. The increasing number of city dwellers makes it necessary for lands to be withdrawn from other uses and converted for urban purposes. The casual observer may get the impression that the areal expansion of cities may reduce substantially the land in other use categories, particularly valuable cropland.

In the inner sections of the principal cities vacant or unused lots are available for future developments. Along the urban fringe urban and rural land may be intermingled to the extent that delineating the urbanized area becomes very difficult. Because the internal lands are not fully used, most urban areas would be able to absorb great numbers of people without expanding their corporate boundaries. Many of the significant features of land use in urban communities have been investigated by Clawson, Held, and Stoddard.[11]

The intensified use of the land for urban purposes has resulted in many unfortunate economic and cultural consequences. In some areas an attractive natural landscape has given way to an unsightly assemblage of man-made structures of doubtful esthetic quality. Urbanization is inevitable and the expanding city with its attendant problems must be accepted. The major highways and freeways that interlace the countryside and tie the urban communities together attract commercial and industrial establishments and help to create what Gottmann calls a mega-

[11] Clawson, Held, and Stoddard, *op. cit.*, pp. 51–123.

lopolis.[12] Ribbons or bands of closely settled areas join the suburbs of one town with those of another and the traveler gains the impression that most of the land has become urbanized. Urban areas expand and engulf rural land and rural people, but the total area occupied by urban communities is only about 1 percent of the land area of the country.[13]

The urban areas of the United States, while requiring only limited areas for their homes, factories, commercial establishments, and the other appurtenances of urban life, make heavy demands on the rest of the country for food, the raw materials of industry, recreational facilities, water supply, power, and other materials and facilities. The urban centers have become great consumers of resources and at the same time they provide goods and services required by all the people.

MISCELLANEOUS LANDS. Twelve percent of the land area of the United States or 277 million acres classed as miscellaneous lands include marshes, sand dunes, bare rock areas, deserts, and tundra. It would not be entirely accurate to refer to these areas as wastelands. Expansive areas of desert in the Southwest and the tundra of Alaska may be regarded as wilderness areas, and many people who live most of their lives in crowded urban areas derive satisfaction from viewing or penetrating briefly such wilderness areas. The desert areas of Nevada, New Mexico, and other states in the West have been used as testing areas for both atomic and conventional weapons. The tundra and marshlands are natural refuges and breeding grounds for wild animals and waterfowl. These expansive open areas have utility as do other land areas, but the return may be largely esthetic.

Land Use in the Years Ahead. It would be difficult to identify and list all the factors and conditions that will operate over the next few years to change the use of land in the United States (See Table 4). By applying science in all

[12] Jean Gottmann, *Megalopolis*, The Twentieth Century Fund, New York, 1961.

[13] Clawson, Held, and Stoddard, *op. cit.*, p. 53.

Table 4. Needed Shifts in Major Land Uses, 1959–1980

	Used in 1959, Million Acres	Shifted to Other Uses, Million Acres	To be Added from Other Uses, Million Acres	Net Change, Million Acres	Projected Use in 1980, Million Acres
Cropland	458	68	17	−51	407
Grassland pasture and range	633	30	49	+19	652
Forest land	746	32	27	−5	741
Recreational	62	0	23	+23	85
Farmsteads and farm roads	10	0	0	0	10
Special purpose uses	85	0	25	+25	110
Miscellaneous other uses	277	11	8	−11	266

[Source: U.S. Department of Agriculture, *Food and Agriculture, A Program for the 1960's*, Washington, D.C., 1962, p. 2.]

its various aspects, the utilization of more fertilizer, the selection and use of more productive plants and animals, the selection and use of the most productive farmlands, and by other means the area of cropland required to produce the foods and fibers required by a growing population can be reduced from 458 to 407 million acres. The results of research carried on at the Agricultural Research Laboratories at Beltsville, Maryland, at the regional research laboratories, at the state agricultural colleges, at the state agricultural experimental stations, and at the laboratories of industrial firms engaged in the manufacture of fertilizers, the formulation of insecticides and fungicides, and the food processing industries are available to facilitate the impending readjustments in land use.

Increased yields per acre will make it possible to transfer some of the land now in crops to other use categories. Some cultivated land can be restored to grass and permanent pasture. Not only will the additional grassland areas help support the livestock needed to feed the increasing population but lands planted or restored to grass will protect the land from erosion, prevent excessive runoff, and preserve a basic resource until it is required by future generations.[14]

More Land to Meet the Needs of Urbanization. The continuing growth of the urban population and the decline of the farm population in the United States are conditions that produce important changes in the use of the land. By 1980 as much as 25 million acres will be required to provide space to meet the needs of the urban population. An important proportion of this will be withdrawn from the cropland category of land use. Good farmland with fertile soil may not be needed for streets, factories, and shopping plazas, but good agricultural lands with fertile soil and good drainage are excellent for residential areas. Urban communities will expand into marshland after extensive land-fill operations, into woodland areas, and onto desert or near desert areas, providing water is available. The high value placed on urban land makes it possible to spend large sums on drainage, grading, and platting to make an area suitable for urban development. Unfortunately, not all prospective urban areas are so carefully selected or well prepared for development, and as a consequence many homes have been built in areas subject to floods and other hazards.

Over the next several years the urban communities will expand areally, but when the resistances to further expansion develop the vacant areas within most cities will permit internal settlement and redevelopment.

More Land for Recreation. Urbanization has created the need for recreational opportunities for the people who live in the cities and towns. The relatively short work week, relatively good

[14] For an extended statement in praise of grass see *Grass, The Yearbook of Agriculture, 1948*, Government Printing Office, Washington, D.C., 1948.

wages and salaries, and vacations have made it possible for great numbers of urban dwellers to seek recreational opportunities in accessible parks, picnic areas, resorts, and playgrounds. It is estimated that 23 million acres will have to be added to the 62 million acres now used for recreational purposes.

Leisure time is now the privilege of the average family, and outdoor recreation is the preferred way to spend this available time. The responsibility for providing the recreational facilities must be shared by the government and the private sector of the economy. The larger parks will be provided out of public funds, but substantial sums have been invested in golf courses, stadiums, swimming pools, and other facilities where the cost may be amortized by the collection of admission fees extending over a period of years. (For a more extended discussion of recreation see Chapter 20.)

THE LEVEL OF LIVING

The consumption of farm products, particularly the food crops, in the United States depends on (1) the future population of the nation, (2) the per capita consumption of food, and (3) the net exports or imports of edible products. Of these three factors the most important in the immediate future, as in the past, will be the total number of people in the nation. The market for food crops is closely related to the number of mouths to feed. With the present population and the productive capacity of the arable land available for food crops the American people are well fed, but there still remains an important number whose diet is inadequate in some respect. Improving the living standard of this segment of the population will require readjustments in the production of food crops, but the rising level of living will not increase the overall demand for food so rapidly as will the normal increase in the population.

The Level of Living and the Market for Agricultural Products. The market for agricultural products is related not only to the number of consumers but to the consumption capacity of the population. People with a high standard of living and with a high effective purchasing power can provide a very large market for the products of the land. It is recognized, however, that the consumption of certain foods does not seem to bear any significant relationship to the family income. Certain long-time trends have been established, and a change in income has little or no effect on the general trend. For example, the per capita consumption of wheat flour averaged 224 pounds in 1880, and for more than 80 years the consumption declined until it reached an average of only 120 pounds in the 5-year period, 1957–1959. The general decline in flour consumption continued and reached 116 pounds per person in 1964.

This change in the dietary habits of the nation is certainly related to the improvement of the diet of the American people, but it does not show a close relationship to the purchasing power of the consumer's dollar.

It is clear and significant, from the standpoint of the total economy and the conservation of the basic resources, that the higher the level of living the greater will be the quantity of goods required to satisfy the wants of the people. Enormous sums of money have been spent on advertising, propaganda, and education, all intended to stimulate or create a desire for a particular product. As long as the people of the United States have available a large and productive acreage for agriculture, have access to large mineral treasures, employ fully the power resources available, and apply intelligence in the development and utilization of resources, the present high level of living can be maintained and improved particularly for many underprivileged groups in the population. To say that all these things can be done does not mean that they will be achieved immediately. For one or many reasons the economy may fail to make the necessary readjustments, and fear may grip the people. In spite of the opportunities for progress, economic prostration may overwhelm a people, and temporarily a depression may wipe out many of the gains. But when prosperity returns new levels of consumption may be attained and the stimulating effect of an expanding economy once more may bring hope to the people.

An Adequate Dietary Standard for the People of the United States. Providing an adequate diet for the people of the United States can be examined from a number of viewpoints. The diet of a family reflects somewhat the level of income or the amount of money available for the purchase of essential foods. For many families the inadequacy of the diet can be remedied by increasing the income so that more money will be available in the food budget. But an increase in income will not always provide a solution, for bad food habits tend to persist. Established culinary practices are altered slowly. By education and demonstration, progress can be made particularly among the young women who may be induced to depart from the outmoded methods of their mothers. It should be a major objective of every family where there is responsible leadership to see that adequate quantities of the essential foods are available.

The farmers generally have a dietary advantage over many of the people who live in the urban communities. Because they are producers of a variety of food products including dairy products, fruits, and vegetables, the farm families, with many exceptions among the renter class particularly, are well fed. People who live in the major cities have access to the large markets, and if the income is adequate and other conditions are favorable their families may have an adequate diet. Although many farmers may have adequate supplies of a number of foods, certain protective foods may not be available in sufficient quantities or at all times of the year to maintain the physical well-being of the family. The poor farm families, especially the sharecroppers and the farm laborers, usually are inadequately fed, and the cash income of these poor families is often so low that they are unable to supplement in any substantial way their home-grown food crops. Where the land resources are suitable food production for home consumption should be sufficiently diverse to provide adequate diets. Surpluses of certain farm products may be available for sale in the market so that the cash can be used to purchase other essential foods. The farmers in the poor areas need supplementary sources of income which will permit them to purchase food that cannot be produced locally. In many instances limited land resources could be used to greater advantage if the people were adequately informed about their dietary needs and had sufficient energy and ambition to meet their food requirements.

In the cities the poor, underprivileged families live in the midst of plenty but, because of low income and little knowledge of what constitutes an adequate diet, are ill fed. These people, however, although much too large a group to receive adequate assistance, are the beneficiaries of the good works of the organized charities and the tax-supported relief agencies.

Consumption of Food per Person. The character of the diet consumed by a people greatly affects the area required to feed the population. In the United States in 1959 only 312,000,000 acres of harvested cropland were used to produce the foodstuffs and fibers used by a population of nearly 180,000,000, or approximately 1.8 acres per person. In this are included the areas used to produce fibers and other inedible products and the exportable surpluses.

Because of the high standard of living the area required to supply the various food products is comparatively large. The relatively low density of the population permits the use of extensive areas with relatively low average yields as compared with the older agricultural areas of Europe and the Orient.

The Food Groups. For convenience the several food items that make up the diets of the American people are grouped as follows:

Milk
Potatoes, sweet potatoes
Dry beans, peas, nuts

Green and yellow vegetables
Tomatoes, citrus fruits
Other vegetables and fruits
Meat, poultry, fish
Eggs
Grain products
Fats, oils
Sugar, sweets

These are the foods that in combination provide the inadequate, the staple, and the quality diets of the people. From these the people secure the essential nutrients of proteins, carbohydrates, fats, minerals, vitamins, and the food energy expressed in calories. Slowly and progressively, in peace and in war, in good times and bad, and as greater knowledge of foods becomes available, these several food groups increase or decrease in relative importance.

From the accompanying data it is clear that there has been a number of significant changes in the diet of the American people (Table 5). Generally the changes indicate an improvement in the level of living. Since World War II there have been notable increases in the consumption of meat and poultry products. The carbohydrate content of the American diet has declined ex-

cept for sugar. Fats and oils have changed little during the past 20 years.

Food Energy. In the United States where the quantity of food is relatively abundant the number of calories per day is high as compared to the standards of other countries. In the 40-year period from 1909 to 1949 the energy represented by the average disappearance of food varied from 3170 to 3560 calories per person per day. The average for 1956–1958 was 3200 calories. The highest totals were attained in the period from 1909 to 1912 when the food energy consumed exceeded 3500 calories per day. A low of 3120 calories was reached in 1935 when economic conditions limited the quantity of food purchased by the American people. In the period just before World War II the foods consumed were equivalent to 3250 calories per person per day. During the war the calories increased slightly to 3370 in 1945. No doubt the number of calories would have been somewhat higher except for rationing which greatly reduced the per capita consumption of sugar.

The high levels of food consumption over a long period of years may be expected to continue as a distinctive feature of the family economy. Although many people may be living

Table 5. Apparent Per Capita Consumption

	Fluid Milk and Cream, Pounds	Potatoes and Sweet Potatoes, Pounds	Fresh Vegetables and Melons, Pounds	Citrus Fruits, Pounds	Meat, Pounds	Eggs, Number	Wheat Flour, Pounds	Fats and Oils, Pounds	Sugar, Pounds	Poultry Products, Pounds
1935–1939	330	149.3	140	48.5	125.3	296	157	44.8	96.0	–
1947–1949	359	126.6	147.9	54.8	148.5	385	137	42.4	95.2	22.0
1957–1959	335	110.2	129.4	33.5	156.6	356	120	45.3	96.1	33.5
1961	311	107.6	129.9	30.4	161.0	326	118	45.3	97.7	37.6
1962	309	105.6	126.0	28.9	163.1	323	115	45.6	97.2	37.0
1963°	308	104.9	126.9	21.8	169.9	315	116	46.4	96.6	37.5
1964°	306	103.4	126.0	27.1	172.0	313	116	46.6	96.2	38.7

° Preliminary

[Adapted from *National Food Situation*, Agricultural Marketing Service, U.S. Department of Agriculture, Washington, D.C.]

and working on diets that are inadequate in some significant way, the energy available from the food consumed is relatively high. A decline in food energy need not be regarded as an unfavorable trend provided the diets are improved in other respects. High standards of health and nutrition can be maintained with a static or a slightly reduced caloric intake per person per day.

The Protective Foods. As knowledge about nutrition has increased in the United States, dietary standards have been established which involve more than calories, proteins, carbohydrates, fats, and oils. It is now recognized that certain minerals, such as calcium, phosphorus, and iron, and vitamins are essential ingredients of a proper diet. Foods that contain these necessary substances are classed as the protective foods, which, if consumed in proper quantities, prevent the insidious deficiency diseases. These protective substances include vitamin A and ascorbic acid (vitamin C) which are available in green and yellow vegetables, thiamine and niacin which are contained in meat, poultry, and fish, and riboflavin contributed by milk. A suitable diet must include the foods that will supply the necessary quantities of protein, carbohydrates, fats, minerals, and the protective substances so necessary to meet the energy requirements of the individual consumer and at the same time maintain his physical well-being over the years.

In planning for a permanent agriculture for the United States many programs and objectives must be considered. But the agricultural use of the land should be so organized that adequate quantities of food are produced to meet the dietary needs of the people. Where inadequacies exist the national economy must provide for the importation of the essential foods such as sugar and other tropical products from overseas source areas.

Food Consumption and Income. There is a significant relationship between the money income of the family and that of the consumption of food. The people with the lowest incomes are unable to purchase the various food products that make up a quality diet but must be content with the less expensive foods that constitute the so-called staple diet. The more nutritive and protective foods usually require more money in the food budget than the families in the lowest income classes can afford. The relationship between food consumption and money income is characterized by complexities.

The consumption of individual foods differs greatly among the several income classes. After a family receives a sufficient income to purchase adequate quantities of fluid milk, an increase in income does not step up the consumption of milk. The quantity of meats consumed, or at least the money spent, increases with the family income. Not only is there an increase in consumption of meat among families with the large incomes, but there is generally a shift from pork to beef and lamb. In the case of grain products, particularly flour, an increase in the family income usually means a decrease in the consumption of bread. The lowest income classes consume flour and meal because they cannot afford the more expensive quality foods. Families with large incomes do not consume proportionately large quantities of fats. Apparently the level of income does not affect greatly the quantity of fats consumed, but people with larger incomes probably buy the more expensive fats such as butter. The per capita consumption of butter in the 3-year period from 1947 to 1949 averaged 10.6 pounds per year, but by 1963 consumption had declined to 6.7 pounds. In the same period the per capita consumption of margarine increased from 5.6 to 9.3 pounds.

The dietary use of large quantities of refined sugar has long been a significant feature of American food habits. Between 1935 and 1939 the per capita consumption of sugar averaged 96.5 pounds annually. During the war period the quantity was reduced substantially by rationing and in 1945 was only 73.6 pounds. In 1963, however, the consumption was up to 96.6 pounds. Sugar has long been so cheap in the United States that most families are able to buy the quantities needed. Over half the sugar consumed in the United States is imported from overseas sources; whereas essentially all the wheat and potatoes consumed in the domestic market are produced at home. This situation poses a significant land-use problem, for the continued importation of large quantities of sugar must be counterbalanced by exports. In effect we may be exporting carbohydrates in the form of wheat in order to purchase sugar, a very digestible carbohydrate.

Fruits and vegetables are of major importance in the diet. With an increase in the family income the quantity increases. This is especially true of the protective foods such as the green vegetables and citrus fruits. Between 1935 and 1939 the per capita consumption of citrus fruits averaged 48.9 pounds annually. The quantity consumed declined to 25.3 pounds in 1964. In the same period the use of canned and frozen fruit juices increased substantially. Much of this increased consumption probably benefited the people of the middle and higher income groups, but these protective foods are available in limited quantities to the families of the lowest income groups.

During World War II when rationing was in effect, meat products were in short supply and it was suggested that grain products, particularly bread, be substituted for meat. Enriched white bread and whole wheat bread could partially replace meat and at the same time maintain high nutritive standards at much lower costs to the consumer. However, when the family income is high, people in the United States prefer more meat and less bread in their diet. Under such conditions it usually is profitable to use the grain to increase the supply of meat which is in demand by the high-income families. In 1963, the per capita consumption of meat was 170 pounds.

RURAL EDUCATION AND CULTURE

In maintaining the high production on the arable lands of the United States it is important that the people who live on the farms enjoy and share with the city dweller the comforts and advantages of our material culture. As the farmer assumes the responsibility for extending the cultivated areas by draining the wet lands, clearing the forests, and irrigating the dry lands, he must secure for himself better educational opportunities for his children and improved dental and medical services for his family. Pioneer conditions of living have lasted too long in the farming areas. Farm people are anxious to have the benefits of electricity, running water, indoor plumbing, power machinery, and the automobile, so that life on the farm will be attractive, healthful, and satisfying to all members of the family. The radio, television, and other means of communication have overcome much of the isolation so long characteristic of life in the country. Farm families can participate in and enjoy the attractions of the city and still retain a strong attachment to the land which is so necessary in a long-range program of soil conservation and the maintenance of high productivity of the land.

Direction of Migration as a Factor. The prospect for rural culture, like that for a high standard of living, depends in large measure on the character, extent, and direction of rural-urban migration. If migration from the farms to the cities attains the magnitude of the pre-depression or wartime movement there will be important readjustments in the agricultural economy. Except for a brief interval in the middle 1930's and immediately at the end of World War II when demobilization returned many servicemen to the rural areas, the cityward migration has been relatively more important than the movement from the cities to the rural areas. The relatively higher birth rate in the rural areas, particularly in the poor farming areas, has tended to maintain the more or less steady migration of people from the rural areas to the urban communities.

Although people of all ages are involved in the migration to the city, it is the loss of the youth from the farms that is regarded as most serious both economically and culturally. The retirement of elderly farm couples to the cities is a logical culmination of a long period of productive work on the land. In such a situation usually a son and his wife or a daughter and her husband take over the farm and continue the family enterprise. When whole families including the young children move to the city, they relieve the population pressure on the land. But when the youth from the farms migrate to the cities when they attain the working age the rural areas suffer a serious loss. The farm families and the rural community have shared in the cost of their rearing and their education, and the cities become the beneficiaries without assuming a fair share of the costs. The migration of the farm youth to the cities without a counter movement of city youth to the country results in an important net loss to the rural areas.

The farm areas lose in other ways also, particularly when the farmer and his wife die and the estate is divided among their children. In many instances part of the estate goes to the children who live in the city and part to those who remain on the farm. It usually becomes necessary for those who retain the farm to mortgage the land to pay off the brothers and sisters who have moved to the city. The interest payments represent a further drain from the farm for the benefit of city people.

Not all the benefits accrue to the urban areas. In many states the rural areas still control or wield considerable influence in the legislature. As a consequence farm areas secure important benefits. School funds and appropriations for improved highways commonly exceed the taxes collected in the rural areas. It is a good investment on the part of the cities to make an important contribution to the support of the school foundation program, for many of the children who are the beneficiaries of improved rural schools will migrate to the cities.

This regular outflow from the rural areas helps to maintain the general upward trend of the urban population. At the same time it tends to reduce the pressure of population in the rural areas. If high farm incomes as well as production can be maintained, there is an opportunity to improve the standard of living. If the income is not needed to provide the creature comforts of a large family, funds will be available for electrification of the farm, modernization of the home, an automobile, and other labor-saving equipment. Simultaneously, the rural areas with higher fertility can make a significant contribution to the labor force of the urban communities and perhaps secure better living conditions for those who remain on the land.

Rural Electrification. Electricity, like good roads and the automobile, has been one of the most important factors in improved living conditions in rural areas. Electricity in the home means more than better lighting. It lightens the work of the housewife by making available to her many labor-saving appliances. The farmer's work is greatly facilitated by electric grinders, drills, feed mills, and other current-using machines. The operation of a home water system is made possible by the availability of electricity.

In the period of 30 years, from 1935 to 1965, electricity became readily available to the rural population. Not all farmers and other people who live in rural areas can afford to use this available electrical energy. After the Rural Electrification Administration was created by Executive Order on May 11, 1935, electrification in rural areas moved forward. Electrical energy is supplied from both government financed and the privately owned utilities.[15] The small generators which many farmers had installed were inadequate to meet their many needs, so they welcomed the electrical service from the large and more reliable central stations. "A quarter century of progress has put electricity at the door of nearly every farmer in America." [16] The Rural Electrification Administration, a somewhat controversial agency, can take some credit for the extension of power lines

[15] John H. Pixse, Jr., "Electricity Comes to Farms," *Power to Produce, The Yearbook of Agriculture, 1960,* Government Printing Office, Washington, D.C., pp. 69-75.

[16] *Ibid.,* p. 69.

to the rural areas, but the private utilities are the principal distributors of electric energy to the farmer-consumer.

The Migratory Farm Laborer. The benefits of improved living conditions have been unevenly distributed among the rural people. The farm owner and the tenant, where tenancy is the first important step to ownership, have made important progress in securing the advantages of electricity on the farm, water systems, an automobile, and labor-saving appliances and equipment. But the poorer tenants, where tenancy is a way of life, and the migratory farm laborers commonly live under primitive conditions. Many of the seasonal farm laborers, often involving whole families, have a very low annual income, are ill housed, and are denied many of the benefits of a well-established community in respect to schooling, medical service, and public relief in case of need. In 1939, John Steinbeck, in *The Grapes of Wrath,* called the nation's attention to the people of the dust bowl who were driven from their land by drought and low prices of the depression years of the 1930's. The seasonal laborer who moves from one straw-berry area to another and from one fruit-picking area to another and who moves into the sugar-beet area at peak periods of work has received sympathetic consideration by Carey McWilliams.[17] These migrants as well as the land owners must share in the improved conditions of life that are spreading into the rural areas.

Economic Security. Land ownership, owner-operated farms, and the integrity of the farm family are the foundations of farm life in rural America. From time to time adverse forces have been operative and the stability of the agricultural industry has been in doubt. Farm tenancy has increased alarmingly in many areas. Corporate ownership of farmlands and large-scale operation have become a challenge to the small owner-operated farm. As new patterns of agriculture are introduced into the farming areas, the farmer retains his basic political and human rights to participate in the new developments and movements and to share with the other citizens the material and cultural benefits that accrue to the nation.

[17] *Ill Fares the Land,* Little, Brown and Co., Boston, 1942.

References

Ackerman, Joseph, Marion Clawson, and Marshall Harris, editors, *Land Economics Research,* Farm Foundation, Resources for the Future, Distributed by The Johns Hopkins Press, Baltimore, 1962.

Agricultural Statistics (Annual), U.S. Department of Agriculture, Government Printing Office, Washington, D.C.

Barlowe, Raleigh, *Land Resource Economics,* Prentice-Hall, Englewood Cliffs, New Jersey, 1958.

Carter, Hugh, editor, "Reappraising Our Immigration Policy," *The Annals,* Vol. 262, 1949. 192 pages.

Clawson, Marion, R. Burnell Held, and Charles H. Stoddard, *Land for the Future,* Resources for the Future, Inc., The Johns Hopkins Press, Baltimore, 1960.

Crops in Peace and War: The Yearbook of Agriculture, 1950–1951, U.S. Department of Agriculture, Government Printing Office, Washington, D.C., 1951.

Dewhurst, J. Frederic, and Associates, *America's Needs and Resources, A New Survey,* The Twentieth Century Fund, New York, 1955.

Farmers in a Changing World, The Yearbook of Agriculture, U.S. Department of Agriculture, Government Printing Office, Washington, D.C., 1940.

Food and Agriculture, A Program for the 1960's, U.S. Department of Agriculture, Government Printing Office, Washington, D.C., 1962.

Food, The Yearbook of Agriculture 1959, U.S. Department of Agriculture, Government Printing Office, Washington, D.C.

Grass, The Yearbook of Agriculture 1948, U.S. Department of Agriculture, Government Printing Office, Washington, D.C.

Harris, Chauncy D., "Agricultural Production in the United States: The Past Fifty Years and the Next," *The Geographical Review,* Vol. XLVII, 1957, pp. 175–193.

Haystead, Ladd, and Gilbert C. Fite, *The Agricultural Regions of the United States,* University of Oklahoma Press, Norman, Okla., 1955.

Higbee, Edward, *The American Oasis, The Lands and Its Uses,* Alfred A. Knopf, New York, 1957.

Higbee, Edward, *Farms and Farmers in an Urban Age,* Twentieth Century Fund, New York, 1963.

Land, The Yearbook of Agriculture 1958, U.S. Department of Agriculture, Government Printing Office, Washington, D.C.

Mighell, Ronald L., *American Agriculture: Its Structure and Place in the Economy,* Census Monograph Series 1, For the Social Science Research Council in cooperation with the U.S. Department of Agriculture, Agricultural Research Service, and the U.S. Department of Commerce, Bureau of the Census, John Wiley and Sons, New York, 1955.

A Place to Live, The Yearbook of Agriculture 1963, U.S. Department of Agriculture, Government Printing Office, Washington, D.C.

The Research and Policy Committee, *Economic Policy for American Agriculture,* New York, January 1956.

Science in Farming, The Yearbook of Agriculture, 1943–1947, U.S. Department of Agriculture, Government Printing Office, Washington, D.C., 1947.

Tisdale, Samuel L., and Werner L. Nelson, *Soil Fertility and Fertilizers,* The Macmillan Co., New York, 1956.

United States Census of Agriculture 1959, A Graphic Summary of Agricultural Resources and Production, Special Reports, Vol. V, Part 6, Chapter 3, U.S. Department of Commerce, Government Printing Office, Washington, D.C., 1962.

United States Census of Agriculture 1959, A Graphic Summary of Land Utilization, A Cooperative Report, Vol. V, Part 6, Chapter 1, U.S. Department of Agriculture and U.S. Department of Commerce, Government Printing Office, Washington, D.C., 1962.

United States Department of Agriculture, *Farm Population, Net Migration from the Rural-Farm Population,* 1940–1950, Statistical Bulletin 176, Government Printing Office, Washington, D.C., 1956.

Part 3

OLIVER D. DILLER

The Ohio Agricultural Experiment Station

CHAPTER 10

Our Forest Resources

Forests are our greatest renewable natural resource. Unlike oil and minerals, forests, if properly managed, are self-perpetuating. In addition to their importance as a source of raw material, forests also have far-reaching public benefits wholly divorced from wood substance. Over a vast portion of our land surface, forests conserve irrigation water, protect the soil, regulate stream flow, provide places of public recreation, and offer a suitable environment for wildlife. Under proper management forests provide not only these multiple uses but also employment and security for millions of people.

THE ORIGINAL FORESTS

At the time of the landing of the Massachusetts colonists in 1620 the vast expanse of original forest and woodland covered almost one-half the total area of the country and is estimated to have comprised 1,065,000,000 acres. This great forest area contained over 1100 varieties of trees of which about 100 have been found to have broad economic significance.

America's virgin forests were so magnificent that our pioneer ancestors considered them inexhaustible. Consequently, great quantities of high-quality timber were destroyed during the process of clearing land for agricultural purposes. However, not all this timber was wasted. Billions of board feet were used for building houses, schools, and churches, and in developing a wide variety of industries. Our extensive forests have been important in making America great, but it was not until the 1890's that we began to realize that our forests, unless properly managed, would soon be exhausted, and a national movement of forest conservation began.

FOREST REGIONS

The forests of the United States occur in five broad regions (Fig. 1). Three of these are east of the prairies: the Northern Forest, the Central Hardwood Forest, and the Southern Forest. The Rocky Mountain and Pacific Forests are west of the Great Plains, extending from Canada south to Mexico.

The Northern Forest. The Northern Forest region, shown in Fig. 1, covers almost all of New England, New York, Minnesota, Wisconsin, and Michigan. Also, it extends an arm to the southwest in the Adirondack Mountains of New York and southward along the Appalachian Highland

199

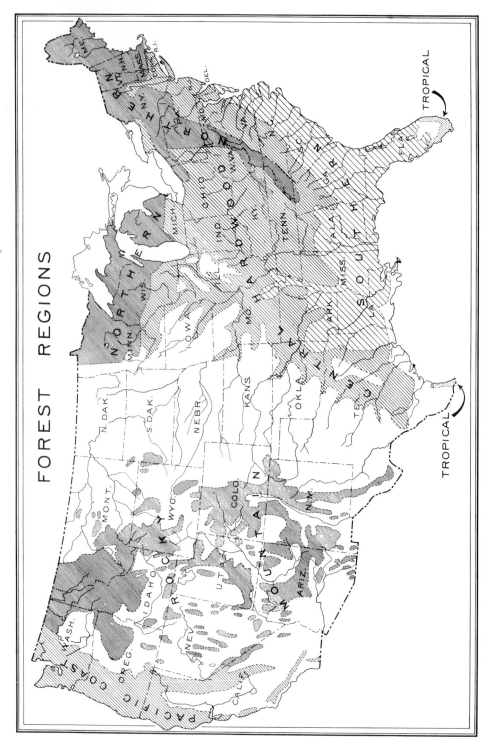

Fig. 1   Map showing the natural forest regions of the United States. (U.S. Forest Service.)

200

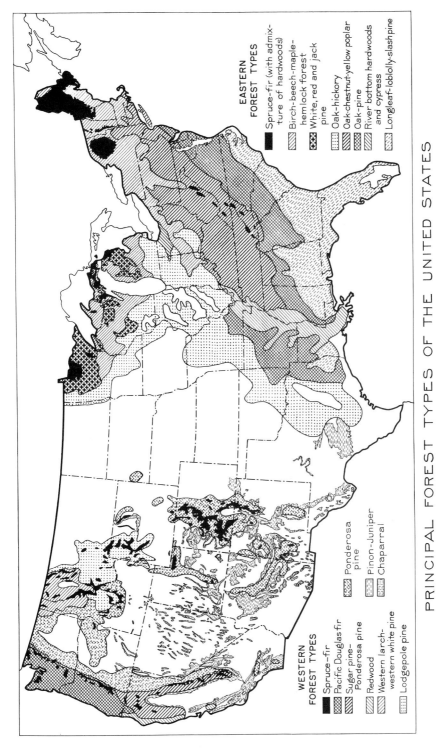

PRINCIPAL FOREST TYPES OF THE UNITED STATES

Fig. 2 A regional forest map of the United States based on a grouping of forest types. (U.S. Forest Service.)

EASTERN
FOREST TYPES

- Spruce-fir (with admixture of hardwoods)
- Birch-beech-maple-hemlock forest
- White, red and jack pine
- Oak-hickory
- Oak-chestnut-yellow poplar
- Oak-pine
- River bottom hardwoods and cypress
- Longleaf-loblolly-slash pine

WESTERN
FOREST TYPES

- Spruce-fir
- Pacific Douglas fir
- Sugar pine-Ponderosa pine
- Redwood
- Western larch-western white pine
- Lodgepole pine
- Ponderosa pine
- Pinon-Juniper
- Chaparral

to northern Georgia. Eastern white pine, red pine, and jack pine forests are native to areas in Minnesota, Wisconsin, and Michigan. In scattered spots in the northernmost parts of these states and in the Adirondack Mountains of New York, forests of spruce-fir occur. Over most of the region hemlock is associated with sugar maple, beech, and yellow birch. Other hardwoods of lesser extent are black walnut, basswood, red oak, hickories, elms, and ashes. In the southern part of the region the shortleaf, pitch, and Virginia pines are found. Before 1910 the American chestnut formed more than half of the stand in the Appalachians, but the chestnut blight has eliminated this species as a commercial tree (Fig. 2).

The Central Hardwood Forest. This forest, principally of deciduous trees, is located in nineteen states in the central eastern half of the United States, and much of it is in forest tracts intermingled with agricultural land. Its forest area represents less than 20 percent of the total area in the region.

The Central Hardwood Forest consists of a wide variety of species, and, since the region covers such a wide range of soils and climate, not all of them are found throughout the region. Certain northern oaks are replaced by other species of oaks in the southern part of the area, white oak having the widest distribution (Fig. 3). American beech and sugar maple have a wider range north and south than most other species in the region. American elm is the most widely distributed tree of the deciduous forest, extending the farthest north and west. Other species in this region include wild black cherry, cottonwood, tulip tree, shagbark hickory, red oak, yellow oak, black oak, burr oak, white ash, black walnut, red maple, silver maple, and cucumber tree.

The deciduous forest was most highly developed in the Ohio and Wabash valleys and in the lower levels of the Appalachian Highland.

The Southern Forest. This forest extends from Virginia through the eastern half of Texas, and from Oklahoma to the Gulf of Mexico. This vast area is characterized by four important pines: shortleaf, longleaf, loblolly, and slash. They are often referred to as hard pines because their wood is harder than that of other trees in the pine family. Of the four principal species, longleaf and shortleaf are the best known (Fig. 4). These once stood in extensive virgin forests of fabulous value, but now they occur mainly in smaller second-growth forests.

The Southern Forest is also known for its cypress swamps and bottomland hardwoods (Fig. 5). The moist lowlands support heavy stands of red and black gums and many species of southern oaks, including water, laurel, and live oak, pecan, cottonwood, ash, elm, sycamore, and soft maple.

The Southern Forest is an important source of forest products, producing more than two-thirds of all the naval stores of the world. The South produces more than one-half of the total

Fig. 3   Stand of virgin hardwood in Ohio. The large trees are all white oak. (Ohio Agricultural Experiment Station.)

pulpwood consumed in the United States, which amounted to 13.2 million cords in 1952.[1] Lumber and fuelwood production amounted to twice as much in wood volume as pulpwood.

Although not so widely distributed as the Central Hardwood Forest, the Southern Forest exceeds 197,265,000 acres on which approximately 18 percent of this country's saw timber is now growing.

The Rocky Mountain Forest. The forests of this region extend from Canada to Mexico and are primarily coniferous, with ponderosa pine the most common tree. In the northern part of the region the forests occur in the valleys as well as on the mountains, but in the southern portion they are limited to the higher elevations because of arid conditions in the lowlands.

At the higher elevations, Colorado blue and Engelmann spruce and Alpine and Douglas fir are dominant. At lower elevations magnificent forests of western white pine, western larch, western hemlock, and ponderosa pine flourish in various combinations. The forests of the Rocky Mountain region have been subjected to severe burning in the past, and in the burned-over areas lodgepole pine commonly has replaced the species of the original forest. Quaking aspen is the most prominent broadleaf tree in this region, but owing to its short life it is not important as a saw-timber tree.

About 11 percent of the total commercial forest land of the United States, or some 54 million acres, is located in the Rocky Mountain region. Since this is a region of low rainfall, the forests are characteristically open and the saw-timber stand is relatively light.

In spite of the fact that only 60 percent of the area is considered to have timber that can profitably be harvested, these scattered forests are of great importance locally not only for timber products but also in the protection of watersheds for irrigation. More than fifty of our na-

Fig. 4 Longleaf pine north of Brunswick, Georgia. (U.S. Forest Service.)

tional forests and eight national parks have been established in this region.

Pacific Coast Forest. On the west coast from Washington to southern California occur the heaviest forest stands in America and probably in the world. The three Pacific coast states contain only one-seventh of the forest area of the country, but it is estimated that they contain 50 percent of the total saw timber.

The California forest forms a natural forest unit, distinguished from the forests of Washington and Oregon. In California, east of the Cascades and the Sierra Nevadas, the forest is largely an extension of the ponderosa pine forest

---

[1] *Timber Resource Review*, U.S. Forest Service, Washington, D.C., 1955, Chapter III.

of eastern Oregon and merges with the south Rocky Mountain forest (Fig. 6). On the west slopes, which have higher rainfall and humidity, redwood, giant sequoia, Douglas fir, and sugar pine are important forest trees. The magnificent redwood forests contain trees varying from 175 to 225 feet in height and from 3 to 10 feet in diameter, but many monarchs attain considerably larger sizes: heights up to 300 feet and diameters in excess of 15 feet. Although some of the virgin redwood stands have been assured continued existence through inclusion in state and county parks, most of them are in the paths of logging operations.

The Douglas fir forest of western Washington and Oregon extends 480 miles from north to south and varies in width from 100 to about 150 miles. This area covers 35,000,000 acres, of

Fig. 5   Cypress brake in Louisiana containing tupelo and red maple as well as cypress. (U.S. Forest Service.)

which 83 percent is forest land. The Douglas fir forms 60 percent or more of the stand on more than half of the forest land. Important species commonly associated with Douglas fir are western hemlock, western red cedar, Sitka spruce, Pacific silver fir, and Noble fir.

The eastern-slope forest of Washington and Oregon occupies the interior of these two states and extends into Idaho and Montana, where it merges with the Rocky Mountain forest. The major species in this forest are western white pine and ponderosa pine.

In addition to supporting a tremendous volume of high-quality timber, the Pacific coast forests are important for recreational purposes and for the conservation of water for irrigation, power, and municipal use.

THE FOREST INVENTORY

Economic planning and formulation of forest policies by both public and private agencies depend on adequate information regarding our forest resources. The U.S. Forest Service under authorization provided in the McSweeney-McNary Act of 1928 has conducted general surveys, and additional studies have been made by individual states, the TVA, and various other agencies.

Extent of Forests. Some 774,000,000 acres, or one-third of the total area of this country, are primarily useful as forest land. Approximately one-fourth of this area is noncommercial, including forest land that is in rugged, mountainous country or located where climate is unfavorable or the soil is shallow. Such forests, although not suited to the production of timber of economic importance, are of great public importance in watershed protection, prevention of erosion, furnishing cover for wildlife, and providing an environment for recreation.

Of the 489,000,000 acres of forest land classed as commercial, or available and suited to economic production of timber and other forest products, more than three-fourths lie in

Fig. 6 Virgin stand of ponderosa pine in the Deschutes National Forest, Oregon. (U.S. Forest Service.)

the Northern, Central, and Southern Forest regions.

Forest Conditions. The fact that 489,000,000 acres, or one-fourth of the area of the United States, are commercial forest land does not indicate that there will always be an abundance of timber.

Our forest lands can be readily divided into five main classes: old-growth saw timber, second growth saw timber, poles, seedlings and saplings, and nonrestocking.

The old-growth forests are those in which no systematic lumbering has taken place and old timber predominates. Nearly 10 percent of our total commercial forest area is in old-growth stands mostly in the Pacific coast and Rocky Mountain regions.

In Table 1, which shows the amount of com-

mercial forest land in the United States and Coastal Alaska by character of growth and by region, the total saw-timber area, including both virgin and second-growth timber, makes up 38 percent of our commercial forest area.

The most serious deficiency in second-growth saw-timber stands is the lack of growing stock. In a well-managed forest there is not only a good stand of merchantable timber but also a good stocking of poles that provide the basis for future harvests. Stands with more than half the saw-timber trees over 18 inches in diameter occupy only 1 percent of the commercial forest area in the South, and one may drive for miles in some parts of the North without seeing any merchantable saw timber. Obviously, we need to increase the proportion of large saw timber in both the northern and the southern forest re-

Table 1. Total Commercial Forest Area by Character of Growth and by Region, 1953
(United States and Coastal Alaska)

| Region | Total | | Saw-Timber Stands, 1000 Acres | Pole-Timber Stands, 1000 Acres | Seedling Sapling Stands, 1000 Acres | Nonstocked and Denuded Areas, 1000 Acres |
	1000 Acres	Percent				
North°	174,041	35.6	47,722	65,513	44,191	16,615
South†	193,288	39.6	60,502	78,376	38,338	16,072
West‡	117,011	23.9	70,392	25,519	12,180	8,920
Continental United States	484,340	99.19	178,616	169,408	94,709	41,607
Coastal Alaska	4,269	0.09	4,092	75	75	27
All regions	488,609	100.0	182,708	169,483	94,784	41,634

° Includes New England, Middle Atlantic, Lake, Central, and Plains regions.
† Includes South Atlantic, Southeast, and West Gulf regions.
‡ Includes California, Pacific Northwest, and Rocky Mountain regions.

[Source: *Timber Resource Review*, U.S. Forest Service, Washington, D.C., 1955.]

gions if we are to build up the output of good quality timber. More than 50 percent of our poorly stocked stands are in these two regions, indicating the degree to which the nation's forest productive capacity is underdeveloped.

The areas covered with poles (5 inches or more in diameter), too small for saw-log operation, make up 35 percent of our total forest land, and satisfactory sapling reproduction makes up 19 percent, indicating the potential increase in timber-crop yields 25 to 50 years hence if sound forestry practices are followed. The column in Table 1 headed Nonstocked and Denuded shows that 8 percent of our commercial forest land is virtually nonproductive.

Volume and Growth of Standing Timber. The forests of the United States are now growing annually at the rate of 14.2 billion cubic feet, including 47 billion board feet of saw timber. It has been suggested that an annual growth of 20 billion cubic feet of all timber and 72 billion board feet of saw timber is required for an economy of full employment in which consumers would have a free choice of readily available materials, including timber and timber products.

It is significant that the over-all growth-cut ratios are now favorable in both the North and

South. In the West, drain exceeds growth by a wide margin because of the virgin timber that is now being harvested (Fig. 7).

Although an analysis of Table 2 indicates an apparently favorable relation between all timber growth and drain in the North and South, this balance by itself is not satisfactory because of the fact that most of these stands are in the pole stage and contain much low-grade timber. In

Table 2. Comparison of Growth and Cut of All Timber and of Saw Timber on Commercial Forest Lands of the United States in 1953

| Saw Timber | Billion Board Feet | | Ratio of Growth to Cut |
	Growth	Cut	
North	12.1	6.7	1.86
South	24.0	19.6	1.22
West	11.2	22.4	0.50
United States	47.3	48.7	0.97
All Timber	*Billion Cubic Feet*		
North	4.7	1.9	2.50
South	6.8	5.1	1.33
West	2.7	3.7	0.73
United States	14.2	10.7	1.32

[Source: *Timber Resource Review*, U.S. Forest Service, Washington, D.C., 1955.]

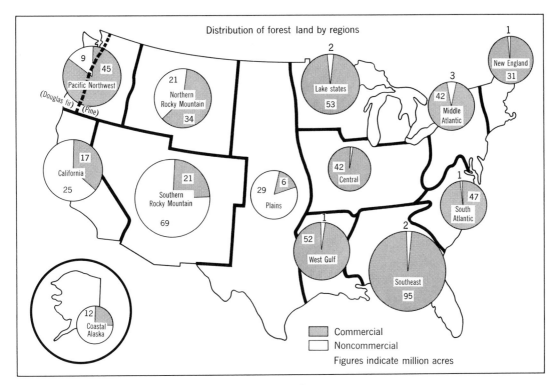

Fig. 7   Distribution of forest land by regions. (U.S. Forest Service.)

Table 3. Ownership of Commercial Forest Area and of Live Saw-Timber Volume, 1953

Ownership	All Sections Area in Percent	All Sections Volume in Percent	North Area in Percent	North Volume in Percent	South Area in Percent	South Volume in Percent	West and Central Alaska Area in Percent	West and Central Alaska Volume in Percent
Private								
Farm	34	15	35	38	46	40	11	5
Forestry industry and other	39	37	46	50	45	50	22	32
Total	73	52	81	88	91	90	33	37
Public								
National forest	17	37	6	5	6	7	53	51
Other federal	4	7	2	1	2	2	10	8
State and local	6	4	11	6	1	1	4	4
Total	27	48	19	12	9	10	67	63
All ownerships	100	100	100	100	100	100	100	100

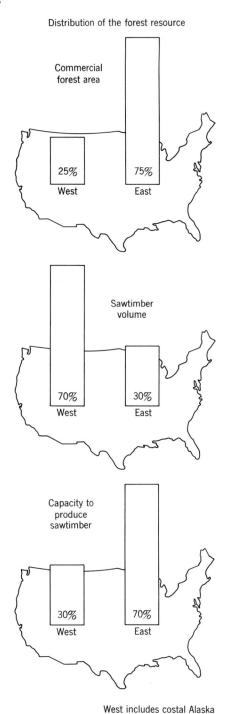

Fig. 8 **Distribution of the forest resources including coastal Alaska.** (*Timber Resources for America's Future*, U.S. Forest Service.)

fact, one of the major problems in the North is to find satisfactory markets for much of the inferior quality, small-size timber that should be removed from the forest to make room for more valuable growth.

In order to meet the goals that were suggested earlier, it will be necessary to increase all timber growth 50 percent and to double sawtimber growth. The long-range solution to the problem lies in the constructive management of our second-growth forests. No nation with vision can afford to let a renewable resource that is so vital to its welfare deteriorate (Fig. 8).

FOREST OWNERSHIP

The character of ownership of forests is an important factor in the development of a sound forestry program. A stable type of ownership is essential because of the time element in producing trees of high quality. In the long run, the interest and ability of the landowners in the growing of trees will determine our success or failure in meeting our future timber requirements.

Private Ownership. Of the 489,000,000 acres of forest land available for commercial timber crops, approximately 366,000,000 acres or three-fourths are privately owned. About 40 percent of the private forest lands is in farm ownership; another 40 percent is in small nonfarm holdings; and 20 percent is in industrial or other large holdings. As shown in Table 3, which presents the pattern of commercial forest land ownership, small ownerships are the rule in privately owned forest lands.

As shown in Table 3, the proportion of privately owned forest land is low in the West, where large untouched areas of the original public domain were set aside as national forests. Private holdings make up 81 percent of the commercial forest land in the North and 91 percent in the South.

In the early days of settlement our land policy had as its objective the building of a nation of small home owners, assuming that each owner would safeguard and develop his home property. However, our land-use history has shown that, in general, these individual property owners failed to recognize that not all their land was suitable for agricultural purposes, and the result was that vast areas of forest land wholly unfit for farming were cleared. The present intermingling of private properties, some small and some large, presents difficult problems in bringing about satisfactory over-all forest management.

The future output of forest products will be more closely related to volume of standing timber on private land than to acreage. Judged by current cutting practices, the small holdings stand out as the crux of the problem of increasing our timber growth. According to the most recent over-all timber appraisal conducted by the U.S. Forest Service during the period 1952–1955, the key to the nation's future timber supplies lies with the millions of farm and "other" private holdings. These have the poorest cutover conditions, are largest in total area, largest in number of owners, and potentially the largest in total timber volumes. The 3.4 million farm owners and the miscellaneous group of 1.1 million other private owners control well over half of the nation's commercial timberland and they must continue to supply a substantial portion of the raw materials for forest industry.[2]

About half of the acreage in small holdings is on farms averaging only 41 acres of woodland each. Although such small forest acreage cannot provide the main source of income to the owner, it can and often is handled as an integral part of the farm business supplying fuel, posts, or lumber for home use as well as providing a supplementary cash income. Unfortunately, in many sections the perennial need for cash has resulted in overcutting and liquidation of the timber. However, small holdings, especially family-size farms, will continue to be an essential feature of the American scene, and we must find ways and means of helping the small woodland owner to practice better forestry if this important segment of our forest resource is to

[2] *Ibid.*

contribute its share of desirable timber products and other values.

Community Forests. The term "community forest" is applied to those wooded areas owned and maintained for public use by any of the subordinate units of government in given states. Local public forests have a high social value because they bring forests and forestry close to the people of the community and create a better appreciation of the relation of forests to our national economy.

The 1953 Census figures reported over 3000 established community forests, with an aggregate area of about 4,000,000 acres. Community forests vary in size from small woodland tracts, such as the town forests in New England, to large county forests in Wisconsin. Massachusetts, a pioneer state in the community forest movement, has 129 town forests aggregating 40,000 acres. In addition to these forests, about 160,000 acres are owned by other municipalities mainly for water protection. Wisconsin, through its county zoning laws, has acquired nearly 2,000,000 acres in county forests and has 210 school forests ranging from 20 acres to over 800 acres per school.

State Forests. During the first decade of this century the growing conservation movement gave stimulus to state activities in forestry, centering on control of forest fires, studies of local forest conditions and problems, and education of the public to the importance of conserving forests. Eight states during this period passed legislation pertaining to acquisition and administration of state forest land.

Since 1933, considerable progress has been made in the establishment of state forests and parks. Thirty-eight states have adopted a policy of establishing and maintaining state forests, and forty-three states have one or more state parks. The aggregate area of state forests is now more than 19,000,000 acres. In 1935 the National Resources Committee recommended that state ownership be eventually expanded to include 77,000,000 acres, mostly in the densely populated states.

In addition to state forests, many states maintain a system of state parks, which include areas of special scenic, historic, or recreational value. Here the emphasis is on the preservation of natural and historic features rather than commercial timber production. In some states there is an effort to preserve areas of virgin forests as examples of original conditions. An outstanding example is the California State Redwood Park, which has great scenic, scientific, and inspirational value. New York and California lead in the number of state parks and total area in parks; Minnesota, New York, Michigan, Washington, and Pennsylvania lead in area of state forests with a total of over 13,000,000 acres.

National Forests. The national forests with their 186,260,000 acres lie in forty-four of the 50 states. Of the total forest area 84,800,000 acres or 46 percent are classed as commercial. The national forests contain 17 percent of the nation's commercial forest land and 37 percent of the saw-timber volume. Most of the national forests are in eleven western states. These lands, including 55,000,000 acres of grazing or other nontimbered land, were permanently set aside by acts of Congress and are administered by the Forest Service of the U.S. Department of Agriculture.

The Forest Service is especially charged with the acquisition, development, and management of these public forests for economic as well as social uses.

One of the original purposes for establishing national forests was protection of watersheds. Achievement of this objective requires adequate ground cover to retard excessive surface runoff of water and to check erosion. Consequently, it has been the policy of the Forest Service to prevent overgrazing of forest and rangeland by livestock and to maintain a productive stand of timber on the lands devoted to forestry.

In the early days of federal land acquisition the federal forests were called "forest reserves." It is significant that in 1907 the name forest reserve was changed to "national forest," indi-

cating that these lands were to be managed for the production of forest products rather than as mere reservations. The fact that the national forests make a substantial contribution in timber production is shown by the record for the fiscal year 1955. Timber harvest from the national forests during that year was the highest on record. Reports from Forest Service field offices show an increased harvest through the country, bringing the total cut to 6,328,229,000 board feet. The value of the timber cut in 1955 was $70,760,440.

Many factors contributed to the increased harvest. A stepped-up, road-building program by timber purchasers and by the government in recent years has opened up for harvest stands of timber that previously have been inaccessible. Also, the comparatively light snowfall in many heavy timber-producing forests permitted logging for a longer time than usual.

Other federal forests not under the jurisdiction of the Forest Service include 20,000,000 acres which still remain in the public domain, 250,000 acres of forest land on watersheds of reservoirs constructed by the Tennessee Valley Authority, 2,500,000 acres in western Oregon recovered by the government from the former Oregon and California Railroad and Coos Bay Wagon Road grants, some 12,000,000 acres in Indian forests, some 6,000,000 acres in national parks, and several million acres in wildlife refuges and military reservations. Commercial use of timber and other resources in the national parks is prohibited because the purpose is to preserve areas of distinctive scenic, historic, educational, and scientific importance in their natural condition.

INCREASING USEFULNESS OF WOOD

Since colonial times, wood has performed a vital role in the development of the United States. Wood is an extremely adaptable material. An attempted census once listed 4500 uses without even approaching a full and exhaustive classification.[3] No other material provides fuel, fiber, food, and chemical derivatives while serving in addition a wide variety of structural uses. A few of the principal products of the forest harvest are shown in Fig. 9.

World War II provided an increased appreciation of the merits and adaptability of wood and stimulated research which resulted not only in the improvement of established products and manufacturing processes but also in the development of new and improved production techniques, new wood derivatives, and modified wood products[4] (see Chapter 11).

DIVERSIFIED RESOURCES IN FORESTS

Previous discussion has dealt mainly with the extent, character, condition, and ownership of our commercial forests; the relation between growth and depletion of our standing timber; and the importance of wood as a raw material. Although high standards of living require the abundant use of wood, forests include other resources of great economic and social significance that in some regions transcend their value as wood producers.

Forests conserve and regulate inland waters essential for irrigation, navigation, power, aquatic life, and domestic use; they are the protecting cover that controls erosion; they are the natural home of wildlife; and, by becoming increasingly important for outdoor recreation, they promote the health and spiritual well-being of our people.

Forests in Relation to Soil and Water. In some sections of the country the value of forest cover as a regulator of stream flow far exceeds that of any other forest product or service. About

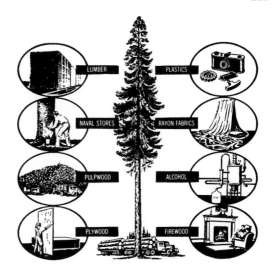

Fig. 9 Principal products of the forest harvest. (American Forest Products Industries, Inc.)

four-fifths of the total forest cover of the nation is classed by the Forest Service as valuable for the protection it furnishes to watersheds. The protective ground cover of vegetation greatly aids infiltration and checks the rate of runoff from the ground surface.

The relation of forests to runoff is well illustrated by a spectacular example in the California mountains where two canyons received 12 inches of rainfall during the last days of December 1934. One of the canyons was covered with chaparral; the other had been denuded by fire. Flood waters in the burned canyon destroyed 200 homes and took 34 lives, whereas in the unburned canyon there was no serious water damage.[5]

Burning of the brush-covered hills and mountains of southern California has become almost an annual occurrence. Losses from fire are high where the building or expensive homes has been extended into areas protected inadequately against fires. The burned-over areas, then without vegetative cover, are subject to floods and

[3] J. A. Hall and T. J. Mosley, *Products of American Forests,* Forest Service, U.S. Dept. of Agriculture, Washington, D.C., 1939.

[4] *Problems and Progress of Forestry in the U.S.,* Report of the Joint Committee on Forestry of the National Research Council and the Society of American Foresters, Washington, D.C., 1947.

[5] Raphael Zon, *Forests in Relation to Soil and Water,* Proceedings of the American Philosophical Society, Vol. 89, 1945, pp. 399–402.

mud flows that may bring serious losses to people who live in the valleys and adjacent plains.

The hydrological functions of the forest vary with the topography, with the climatic conditions such as the amount, distribution, and intensity of rainfall, and with geologic and soil conditions. In certain parts of the United States it appears that removal of the forest cover increases water yield, whereas in other regions when precipitation occurs during the early spring while the ground is frozen, the amount of water stored in the ground is practically zero. Much more research is needed to determine the influence of the forest cover and forest-land management on flood control and water yield.

The processes involved in the regulation of runoff by forests may be explained largely by the fact that a well-managed forest is an integrated biological community with its own special climate, characteristic undergrowth, and topsoil.[6] The forest floor is protected by the crowns of trees and shrubs at different levels. The ground surface is a mat of dead leaves and twigs, and beneath this litter is a layer of organic matter in various stages of decay, in which there is an abundance of soil fauna and flora. All this biologic activity keeps the soil porous and gives it a crumbly structure, ideal for absorbing and filtering large amounts of water.

Snow accumulation and melt are also influenced by good forest cover. Protected against sun and wind, snow remains on the forest floor from a few days to several weeks longer than in exposed areas nearby. Also, the interception of snow by forests has received special attention because, usually, a considerable amount will stick to the trees. Measurements taken in the dense forests of Idaho show that about 25 percent of the snowfall on the average is caught by the crowns.

Another important relation between forests and water is that forests help to hold the soil open in winter. When the surface of open fields is frozen so solidly as to be virtually impervious, that of the forest soil is still fairly open and receptive. Consequently, in cold regions, as deep snows melt, much of the water percolates gradually into the forest soil.

In addition to the above-mentioned effect of the forest in reducing runoff is the control of erosion and the consequent prevention of the silting of streams and reservoirs. Silt will eventually ruin the storage capacity of any retention reservoir.

Federal legislation has been passed in recent years which extends federal programs in water production and conservation beyond the management of federal lands. Under Public Law 566 the expanding small watershed program of the United States Department of Agriculture is making a significant contribution to reducing flood damages and providing additional capacity for storing water for domestic, industrial, agricultural, and recreational use. Of 467 projects approved to date, 281 require special forestry measures aimed at protecting the water resource.[7] Awareness at the federal level of the important relationships existing between forestry and water was expressed by the late President Kennedy in his special message to Congress on natural resources on February 23, 1961. He said, "This administration accepts the goal urged by the Senate Select Committee to develop comprehensive water basin plans by 1970 in cooperation with the individual states." During 1963 the U.S. Forest Service participated in comprehensive river-basin studies by developing the forestry phases for eighteen basin and sub-basin plans.

Forests in Relation to Wildlife. The forest, when properly managed, furnishes an ideal home for many kinds of wildlife. The forest indirectly provides safe breeding places, water, food supply, shelter, and protection.

That the management of our national forests on a continuous-production basis since the early

[6] Bernard Frank and Clifford A. Betts, *Water and Our Forests*, Misc. Pub. 600, U.S. Forest Service, Washington, 1946.

[7] "Wood, Water, and People," *Proceedings*, Annual Meeting of the Society of the American Foresters, Boston, Mass., 1963.

years of the century has materially aided wild-life is indicated by the fact that one-third of all our big game animals and myriad smaller ani-mals and birds claim the national forests as their home. The main objectives of the Forest Service in wildlife management are to build up the habitat, to increase wildlife population in some areas, and to keep wildlife populations in pro-portion to the land's productive capacity. Many state and private agencies have a similar policy.

Another important program that has contrib-uted greatly to the restoration of wildlife is the federal system of wildlife refuges. President Theodore Roosevelt set aside the first national wildlife refuge in 1903. Since then, and espe-cially during the past decade, this program has expanded to the point where over 280 areas totaling nearly 14,000,000 acres have been set aside for this purpose under the administration of the federal Fish and Wildlife Service (see Chapter 18).

Value and Use of Forests for Recreation. Recreation is an increasingly important use of forest land. Before World War II no less than 40,000,000 persons visited the national forests and national parks each year. In the 12 years from 1950 to 1962 the number of visits to the national forests for all kinds of recreation in-creased from 27 to 113 million. The records from the national parks, state parks, and private oper-ations all show the same trend. Management for recreation is an equal partner with management for timber or other purposes for which national forests are administered.

The two most common outdoor recreational activities in the summer time, according to the Outdoor Recreation Resources Review Com-mission, are driving for pleasure and swimming. The third is walking for pleasure. Insofar as the first is concerned, the scenic roads and parkways in the national forests are serving an important purpose for the recreational enjoyment of a great many people. The national forests also offer much water-based recreation and incomparable hiking.

There are also increasing opportunities for recreation as a source of income for private own-ers of forest land through the development of vacation farms, picnicking and sports centers, fishing waters, camping, and hunting.

However, it must be remembered that the most important results of forest recreation can-not be estimated in terms of money. The parks, wilderness areas, and wildlife refuges were created to preserve natural, scientific, or histori-cal features for the enjoyment, education, and inspiration of all the people, and forests are an indispensable part of the scene. For obvious reasons, cutting of timber is prohibited or greatly restricted in such areas. Representative wild areas must be preserved.

References

Anderson, Henry W. and Clark H. Gleason, "Effects of Logging and Brush Removal on Snow Water Runoff," *International Assoc. Sci. Hydrol. Pub. 51*, 1960, pp. 478–489.

Barach, Arnold B., and Rudolph Modley, *U.S.A. and Its Economic Future*, A Twentieth Century Fund Survey, The Macmillan Co., New York, 1964.

Black, Peter B., "Timber and Water Resource Management," *Forest Service*, Vol. 9, 1963, pp. 137–145.

Boerker, Richard H. D., *Behold Our Green Mansions*, University of North Carolina Press, Chapel Hill, North Carolina, 1945.

"Conservation—a Key to World Progress," *Proceedings*, Seventeenth Annual Meeting, Soil Conservation Society of America, Washington, D.C., August, 1962.

Dewhurst, J. Frederic, and Associates, *America's Needs and Resources—A New Survey*, The Twentieth Century Fund, New York, 1955.

Forest Land Resources, Requirements, Problems, and Policy, Part VIII of the *Supplementary Report of the Land Planning Committee to the National Resources Board,* Government Printing Office, Washington, D.C., 1935.

Gauging the Timber Resources of the United States, Report I from a Reappraisal of the Forest Situation, U.S. Forest Service, Washington, D.C., 1946.

Problems and Progress of Forestry in the U.S., Report of the Joint Committee on Forestry of the National Research Council, and the Society of American Foresters, Washington, D.C., 1947.

Reinhart, K. G., A. R. Eschner, and G. R. Trimble, Jr., *Effect on Streamflow of Four Forest Practices in the Mountains of West Virginia,* U.S. Forest Service Research Paper NE-1, Northeast Forest Experiment Station, 1963, 79 pp.

"Report of the Forest Resource Appraisal," *Am. Forests,* Vol. 52, 1946, pp. 413–428.

Shantz, H. L., and Raphael Zon, *Grassland and Desert Shrub, Forests,* Section E, Natural Vegetation, *Atlas of American Agriculture,* Washington, D.C., 1924.

Some Plain Facts about the Forests, Misc. Pub. 543, U.S. Department of Agriculture, Washington, D.C., 1944.

U.S. Forest Service, *Timber Resource Review,* Washington, D.C., 1955.

Van Dersal, William R., *The American Land: Its History and Its Uses,* Oxford University Press, New York, 1943.

"Wood, Water, and People," *Proceedings of the Society of the American Foresters Meeting,* Washington, D.C., 1963.

OLIVER D. DILLER

The Ohio Agricultural Experiment Station

CHAPTER 11

The Practice of Forest Conservation

As was indicated in Chapter 10, the fact that one-fourth of the area of the nation is commercial forest land does not mean that there will always be an abundance of timber. The crucial factors are the age and state of depletion of forest growing stocks. These have been adversely affected by forest fires, insects, diseases, overgrazing, and destructive cutting. Prevention of further reduction of our forest capital or growing stock is imperative if adequate future supplies of forest products are to be available to meet the long-term needs of the nation.

A good illustration of this need is the history of forestry in the State of Michigan. The pioneers who settled in Michigan in the early 1800's were interested in farming, and since the State was almost entirely forested, they faced a formidable land-clearing job. Sawmills not only converted trees into lumber for building, but much of the original forest cover was windrowed and burned to make way for agricultural production.

The original forests in Michigan contained more than fifteen times their present sawtimber volume. Early loggers harvested timber as if the supply were unlimited. Michigan led the nation in lumber production for thirty years, but by 1925 it ranked twenty-fifth among the states in lumber production.[1]

The following tabulation from the Bureau of the Census records shows that the expansion of Michigan's lumber industry was relatively short-lived.

Year	Billion Board Feet of Lumber Produced	Year	Billion Board Feet of Lumber Produced
1870	2.4	1920	0.8
1880	4.3	1930	0.5
1890	5.2	1940	0.4
1900	2.8	1950	0.5
1910	1.8	1960	0.3

A similar land-use trend took place in Ohio during the past century. This is clearly shown by comparing the forest cover by counties for the years 1853 and 1953.[2]

[1] Con H. Schallau, *Forest Owners and Timber Management in Michigan.* U.S. Forest Service Research Paper LS-9, Lake States Forest Expt. Station, 1964.

[2] O. D. Diller, "More Land in Trees—This May Be a Profitable Use for Some Land Not Needed to Grow Field Crops," *The Ohio Farmer,* May 5, 1962.

Improved conservation practices not only are necessary for the production of more wood but also are a great reservoir for employment. A managed forest, with its continuous production of wood and its recurring needs for silvicultural treatment, can provide profitable employment to many more people than a forest that is abused or not managed at all. In Denmark 750,000 acres of forest furnish employment for about 6000 people, or one worker to 125 acres. In Switzerland the public forests give employment to one full-time worker for every 100 acres. The forests of the United States, if put under management, would give employment to over 6,000,000 people and would approximately double our annual growth of wood.[3]

As shown in Fig. 1, in 1958 one out of every twenty workers in the United States was engaged in some kind of timber-based economic activity. About 3 percent of the employment

[3] *Third Report of the Governments of the United Nations,* The Interim Commission on Food and Agriculture, F.A.O., Washington, D.C., 1945.

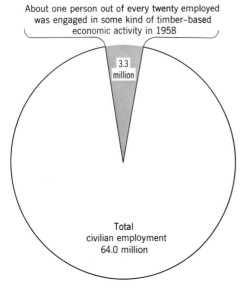

Fig. 1 One out of every 20 workers in the United States is employed in timber-based economic activities. (Misc. Publ. 941, U.S. Forest Service, 1963.)

was attributed to forest management, 10 percent to harvesting, 15 percent to primary manufacturing, 24 percent to secondary manufacturing, 25 percent to construction, and 23 percent to transportation and marketing.[4]

FOREST PROTECTION

The most significant fact about forests is their extraordinary capacity to reproduce themselves. Under modern forest management the forest crop is harvested while the forest is kept in a productive condition.

In spite of proper cutting methods, huge timber losses result from insects, disease, fire, and other destructive agents. Were it not for their ravages, saw-timber growth probably would exceed timber cut by 25 percent. The magnitude of timber destruction indicates that a combination of better prevention, control, and utilization of this loss would go far in contributing toward our future timber requirements.[5]

Protection from Fire. Fire is the greatest enemy of the forest. It destroys more forest growth and keeps more young trees from becoming established than any other single factor. That fire is a widespread national problem is indicated by the fact that over 14,711,000 acres of unprotected forest land were burned by 128,000 fires in 1952.[6]

One of the most serious forest fires on record occurred in Maine during October, 1947. Some 3500 people fled Bar Harbor, the famous Maine resort, when flames raced in from surrounding woodlands. Nearly 400 homes, including sixty large estates, were destroyed in this summer resort center. Forest officials estimate that October fires burned more than 240,000 acres in

[4] Hair, Dwight, *The Economic Importance of Timber in the United States,* Misc. Publ. 941, Forest Service, U.S. Dept. of Agriculture, Washington, D.C., 1963.

[5] *Timber Resources Review,* Chapter IV A. "Forest Protection against Destructive Agencies," U.S. Forest Service, Washington, D.C., 1955.

[6] *Ibid.*

Maine, with the timber loss and property damage amounting to millions of dollars.

American forests in every region show the effects of past forest fires. Repeated fires have converted some valuable conifer stands into brush fields and hardwood stands into ragged forests of unmerchantable trees. In addition to direct damage to timber, such fires result in the impaired condition of watersheds and the destruction of wildlife. The damage that fire does to standing timber is well illustrated in Fig. 2.

Causes of Fires. Careless smokers who toss lighted cigarettes out of automobile windows or drop them in the dry leaves in the woods cause about one-fourth of our forest fires. "Firebugs," or incendiaries, cause as many more. Lightning and careless campers who fail to make sure that their campfires are out before they leave are the other principal causes of forest fires. These factors account for over 75 percent of the fires each year in the United States. Of the 1962 total of 115,345 fires, 91 percent were man-caused and only 9 percent were due to lightning.

Methods of Fire Control. Fifty years' experience with the forest fire problem has shown that, since most of the fires are man-caused, the best approach to their control is through adequate forest protection laws, efficient forest protection organizations with a system of fire wardens and fire-fighting equipment, and intensive education.

Planes and parachutes to deliver men and equipment to forest fires are the most spectacular of the new methods of combating forest fires in the United States. They have proved especially successful with fires in inaccessible places and at the same time have caught the public fancy and made people conscious of the need for protection.

Holbrook describes an example of the suc-

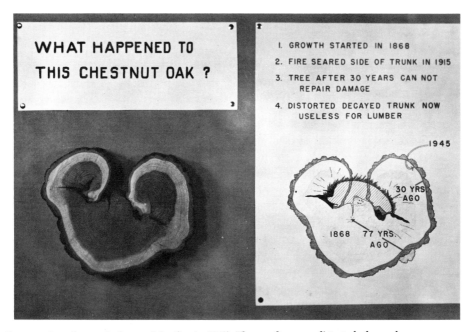

Fig. 2   Cross section of an oak damaged by fire in 1915. The result was a distorted, decayed trunk, useless for timber. The annual growth rings on the tree reveal: (1) growth started in 1868; (2) fire-seared side of trunk in 1915; (3) tree after 30 years had not repaired the damage. (Ohio Agricultural Experiment Station.)

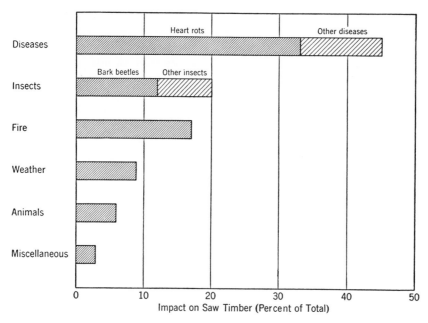

Fig. 3 Impact on saw timber by destructive agencies as a percent of total impact in contiguous United States and coastal Alaska. (*Timber Resource Review*, U.S. Forest Service.)

cessful use of planes at a big fire in the Siskiyou National Forest in Oregon and California.[7] The fire was in such remote and difficult country that, if plane service had not been available, supplies and equipment would have had to be trucked 31 miles over steep mountain roads, then packed on the backs of mules 22 miles more, or a total of 53 miles. One such trip would have consumed 24 hours. A Forest Service plane took off from the nearest airport, at Medford, Oregon, and 15 minutes later a ton of food and supplies was parachuted safely down to the firemen.

One of the newest methods in fire control is to drop bombs containing chemicals; as these bombs crash they release a fire-killing vapor which is three times as effective as an equal weight of water. Dry ice has also been used with success on certain types of fires.

There is no one cure-all for the fire-control problem. Research on methods of control should be continued, but, at the same time, an intensive educational program must be carried on so that

[7] Stewart H. Holbrook, *Burning an Empire*, The Macmillan Co., New York, 1944, Chapter 19.

a subconscious will to prevent forest fires will be created in the people who are going to the forest in increasing numbers.

CONTROL OF INSECTS AND DISEASES

Even though fire is considered the greatest enemy of the forest because of its effect on values other than timber, insects and diseases are causing even greater losses in standing saw timber than fire. Figure 3 shows that of the total impact on saw-timber growth, 45 percent is estimated as due to disease, largely heart rots, whereas fire and insects contribute 17 and 20 percent of the total, respectively.

In addition to our native pests, the situation has been complicated still further through the accidental introduction of several highly destructive pests from foreign countries.

The major insect enemies affecting our commercial forest stands are the white-pine weevil, the spruce bud worm, larch sawfly, pine-bark beetle, nut weevil, the gypsy moth, and the Pandora moth.

Considerable progress has been made in

methods of controlling insect pests. Airplane dusting and spraying with insecticides have been successful in combating a number of leaf-eating insects.

Several fungus diseases have made serious inroads on our forest resources. To date, no satisfactory controls have been developed for chestnut blight, oak wilt, Dutch elm disease, and elm phloem necrosis. However, treatment of western white pine with phytoactin, an antibiotic, has successfully controlled blister rust in white-pine stands in the northern Rocky Mountain region (Fig. 4).[8]

The greatest loss from fungus action in merchantable stands is the destruction of heartwood of living trees by decay fungi. The amount of

material that has to be discarded because of rot when timber is cut often runs as high as 10 percent of the total volume of the mature stand and occasionally amounts to more than one-third of the volume.

Although increased research and better organization of detection and control are needed, the best possible insurance against insect and disease losses is intensive forest management. Furthermore, since so many of our most destructive pests have been imported, it would seem that quarantine regulations should be made more stringent than ever before.

RANGE MANAGEMENT AND WOODLAND GRAZING

The forage produced by herbaceous and shrubby plants under the trees and in openings in the forest is an important forest resource. This

[8] Henry J. Viche, Virgil D. Moss, and Homer J. Hartman, "Developments in Aerial Application of Antibiotics to Control Blister Rust on Western White Pine," *Journal of Forestry,* Vol. 60, No. 11, 1962, pp. 782–784.

Fig. 4 Large stands of western white pine in the Rocky Mountains are now sprayed with aerial applications of antibiotics to control blister rust. (U.S. Forest Service.)

is particularly true of the forest ranges of the West and South, but much less of the central and northern forests.

Western Forest Ranges. The national forests administered by the U.S. Forest Service include approximately 61,000,000 acres of land used for livestock grazing. In the West the forest-land grazing problem centers around the utilization of large areas of public land by many private owners of ranch property and livestock. Before these areas came into public ownership, much of this land was overgrazed and the forage so seriously depleted that fertile topsoils were washed away, slopes were cut by gullies, and irrigation works and other improvements in the valleys were seriously damaged by floods and silt.

Four major principles are employed in the administration of western forest ranges to bring about the proper coordination of grazing with other forest uses: (1) use of the range by the class of livestock best suited to it; (2) adjusting the number of livestock to what the range can support on a permanent basis; (3) adjusting the season of use to the most satisfactory period from the standpoint of correlating maintained feed production with greatest value from the use of the feed; (4) distributing the grazing over the range to ensure even utilization of all parts and to protect parts of the range needing special attention.[9]

In spite of the obvious importance of keeping grazing in balance with sustained range capacity, a small segment of the livestock industry has proposed various measures to restrict the Forest Service in its administration of the forest ranges and to put greater control of grazing in the hands of private individuals. Since much of the land being grazed is important watershed and some of the area is important for commercial timber production also, it would seem that the public good would best be served by permitting the Forest Service to continue to administer the national forest ranges under a system of multiple use in which all the forest resources and values would be coordinated.

Forest Ranges in the South. The forests of the South furnish considerable feed for livestock, particularly for cattle during spring and summer. It is estimated that nearly 150,000,000 acres of the 217,000,000 acres classed as forest land are grazed to some extent.

Since 91 percent of the forest land in the South is held in private ownership, the grazing problem is quite different from that in the West. Among the more important problems in the grazing of southern forest lands are: the widespread practice of uncontrolled burning to remove unused grass, the serious damage by hogs in rooting out longleaf pine seedlings, and the grazing of sprouts of valuable timber species in the southern Appalachian hardwoods. Another important problem is the adequate coordination of forest-range grazing with improved pastures and supplemental winter feeding.[10]

Forest Grazing in the Central and Northern Forests. On the forest lands of the central and northern states grazing is confined almost entirely to the farm woodlands. The most intensive use of forest lands by livestock occurs in the central states, where livestock population is high and most of the open land is under cultivation. In most of the forest lands, timber production should be the objective and livestock grazing should be kept at the minimum in order to protect forest reproduction and ensure further timber crops (Fig. 5). If the land is more valuable for crops other than trees, the land should be cleared. If it is best suited to timber production, it should be protected from grazing to assure perpetuation of the forest.

PROPER CUTTING PRACTICES

The goal of forestry is to keep in continuous production all potentially productive forest lands not used or needed for other purposes. In

[9] *A National Plan for American Forests*, Senate Document 12, 73rd Congress, 1st Session, Government Printing Office, Washington, D.C., 1933, p. 539.

[10] *Ibid.*, p. 550.

Fig. 5   Woodlands can be perpetuated only when there is an abundance of young growth coming on. The woodland on the left has been protected since 1932. The results are vigorous natural reproduction and improved forest soil conditions. (Ohio Agricultural Experiment Station.)

a virgin forest that is not disturbed, trees die and the wood rots, but young trees come in, and the two processes, growth and decay, are roughly in balance. Complete utilization of increment is approached most closely under intensive forest management in which the selective-cutting method is usually the most desirable.

Continuous Production through Selective Timber Management. In general, until the 1930's timber owners and operators thought mainly in terms of the immediate returns, and the idea of continuously productive forests was given little consideration. Through judicious cutting, the growing stock can be improved, and at the same time a considerable harvest of wood

products can be obtained. Selective cutting can be applied to one acre, one stand, or to a whole forest property.

Under the selective-cutting method the merchantable timber stand is never cut all at once, but, instead, single trees or small groups of trees are removed. Under this system, timber can be harvested from the stand continuously, without the long waiting periods that are required after stands have been clear-cut. Also, light and frequent cutting will build up the volume and quality of the merchantable timber if the proper trees are removed. The volume can be increased by currently removing less volume than is added by growth, and the quality can be improved by removing trees of poor form and vigor and reserving the better trees until they are ready to be harvested.

Growth studies in well-managed hardwood stands indicate that such tracts having 10,000 board feet per acre grow at the rate of about three percent per year or 300 board feet per acre per year. At this rate, less than 4 years will be required for growth to replace the timber that was harvested.

In certain exceptional stands selective cutting may not be successfully employed. In the Pacific Northwest a major problem is the transition from a timber economy based on virgin Douglas fir to one based on second growth. Here a better method seems to be clear-cutting in strips or

Fig. 6   An example of selective cutting. Under this method of management mature saw timber is removed every few years along with crooked, defective, and other less desirable trees. (Ohio Agricultural Experiment Station.)

patches with provision for natural seeding-in from uncut stands bordering clear-cut areas.[11]

Another example in which tree selection loses some of its usefulness is the area where pulpwood is the major product. Here fully mature, high-quality trees for saw logs are not an objective of management, and a system of clearcutting in strips would permit the growing in short rotations of a greater volume of wood at a smaller cost.

In second-growth timber throughout the country, however, the selective cutting method based on frequent, light cuts appears to be the most desirable because it produces high yields of high-quality timber on a continuous basis (Fig. 6).

Other Values of the Selective Cutting Method. It is apparent that any management procedure that preserves a heavy growing stock and generally excludes extensive clear-cutting will promote esthetic values, provide protection to the soil, prevent excessive water runoff, and maintain a suitable environment for wildlife.

PLANTING

Artificial reforestation through planting is a necessary adjunct to forest management because it is a means of getting barren lands back into production. Once a forest has become established, however, planting of nursery-grown trees is not a feasible method of providing successive forest harvests on a broad commercial scale. Natural reproduction is by far the cheapest and most successful method of reproducing a forest.

According to estimates made by a recent survey,[12] the total planting on commercial forest land in the United States had reached 6.9 million acres by 1952. Of this total, 5.2 million acres were considered acceptable. The total plantable area in the nation has been estimated to be 51.9

[11] *Report of the Chief of the Forest Service*, U.S. Department of Agriculture, 1947, p. 37.

[12] *Timber Resource Review*, Chapter IV C, "Forest Tree Planting," U.S. Forest Service, Washington, D.C., 1955.

million acres, indicating that the rate of annual planting will have to be greatly accelerated if these unproductive lands are to be reforested within a reasonable length of time.

Fortunately, the planting trend is upward. The annual rate of planting increased from 68,000 acres in 1926–1929 to 388,000 in 1950–1952, and it is expected to go higher. From the 1952 total of nearly 400,000 acres planted acceptably, the rate may rise to a maximum of more than 800,000 acres during the period, 1965–1974.[13]

Before World War II, the labor cost for hand planting was prohibitive to many private owners. More recently tree-planting machines have been developed which are well adapted to level or gently rolling lands (Fig. 7), but on steep slopes hand planting or seeding from the air will be necessary.

In certain areas fire-ravaged forests are reseeded by air. During the spring of 1948 some 800 pounds of white pine seed from the Champlain Valley of New York state were sown across 2200 acres of the Massabesic Forest in Maine. The former Navy trainer biplane that was used flew 50 feet above surviving tree tops, seeding a 50-foot swath with each pass. A similar experiment was conducted in Oregon, where a mixture of Noble and silver fir and Sitka spruce seeds was sown by airplane.

Air seeding or seeding from aircraft is much more rapid than transplanting seedlings by hand. This method of reforestation is still in the experimental stage, and its success will, of course, depend on germination and survival.

Reforestation of Strip-Mined Areas. Strip mining or open-pit mining has created a new problem in the broad field of returning unproductive lands to useful crops. Strip mining is largely concentrated in the central states, where more than 500,000 acres have been disturbed.[14]

Fig. 7 A mechanical tree planter with fertilizer and herbicide spray attachments. Two men can plant 1000 trees per hour under favorable conditions. Fertilizer is placed in the furrow near the tree roots and the herbicide is sprayed on each side of the tree row to reduce vegetative competition. (Ohio Agricultural Experiment Station.)

Studies made in the Central States show that spoil banks can be afforested and that the future use of such areas will be chiefly for forestry purposes.[15] The data show that past failures have more often been due to unskillful planting than to conditions in the spoil banks themselves.

Recent legislation in Ohio, Pennsylvania, and West Virginia calls for grading and revegetating of spoil banks. This has created a strong trend toward the use of legumes and grasses in revegetating the more alkaline spoils for livestock grazing. The acid shale areas are best suited to tree growth.

EFFICIENT MILLING AND WOOD UTILIZATION

The process of converting round logs into square timbers is essentially a crude, uneconomic process, for the actual amount that emerges as the finished product is only a small fraction of the whole (Fig. 8).

It is estimated that at present only 40 percent

[13] *Timber Resources for America's Future.* Forest Resource Report No. 14, Forest Service, U.S. Department of Agriculture, Washington, D.C., 1958.

[14] *An Appraisal of Coal Strip Mining,* Tennessee Valley Authority, Knoxville, Tenn., 1963.

[15] "A Symposium on Strip-Mine Reclamation," *The Ohio Journal of Science,* Vol. 64, 1964, pp. 65–175.

Fig. 8 Chain saws have made it possible to mechanize operations in the woods, thereby reducing labor costs.

resents approximately 13 percent of a saw log. New processes have been developed that make it possible to use bark as an ingredient in plywood glues, plastics, insecticides, and soil conditioners. Shredded bark is also showing promise as a poultry litter which, when mixed with lime, makes a concentrated fertilizer high in nitrogen, calcium, and organic matter. The tannin industry is also using increasing amounts of bark from hemlock and oak trees.

More knowledge on how to reduce waste is available than it has been possible to apply, but we need to develop still better ways of utilizing what is now wasted.[16]

Chemical Utilization of Wood. In addition to finding improved methods of using wood in its natural state or treating it with certain materials to change its properties, scientific research has made an outstanding contribution in the conversion of wood into a multitude of products that bear little or no resemblance to its original state. Most people think of lumber as the chief forest product, but sawn lumber now accounts for less than one-half of the forest harvest in cubic feet.

The most important form of wood conversion in the United States is wood pulp for the manufacture of paper, paperboard, derived products of wood pulp (rayon, cellophane, etc.), and wood-fiber products such as hardboard and roofing felt. The use of wood in this field has more than quadrupled in a period of 33 years, having increased from 8.1 million cords in 1920 to 37.8 million cords in 1953.[17]

The items enumerated above are only a few of the many materials that are made from mechanically or chemically converted wood. Knowledge in this field has advanced to such an extent that the immediate problems of application are, to a considerable degree, economic rather than technological.

of the merchantable timber in the forest is converted into rough lumber. Of the 60 percent that is lost, 25 to 30 percent is logging waste in the form of defective trees, tops, stumps, and limbs. The remaining 30 to 35 percent consists of waste at the sawmill where the logs are converted into lumber. This waste can be broken down as follows:

Items of Loss	Log Volume Wasted (Percent of Total)
Bark	13
Sawdust	13
Edgings and trimmings	12
Slabs	6
Seasoning	6
Total	50

Utilization of Wood Waste. Many technological and industrial advances have made it possible to utilize a great deal more of the tree substance than was used in the past.

Bark, long considered almost worthless, rep-

[16] *Wood Waste in the United States,* Report 4 from A Reappraisal of the Forest Situation, Forest Service, U.S. Department of Agriculture, Washington, D.C., 1947.

[17] *Timber Resource Review,* Chapter VI, "Future Domestic Requirements for Timber," U.S. Forest Service, Washington, D.C., 1955.

Chemical Treatment of Wood. Pressure treatment of railroad ties with creosote has long been an accepted practice by railroads, but the initial cost of treatment has prevented the general use of chemically treated wood. Chemicals such as pentachlorphenol and copper naphthenate have been found to penetrate satisfactorily by cold soaking and in some instances by brush application. Wood preservatives have not only extended the service life of wood but also made available species of wood that were formerly avoided.

Considerable progress was also made during World War II in the development of fire-resistant treatment of wood. The chemicals and methods, however, are costly and preclude the widespread use of such treated material for general construction purposes.

An entirely new group of products classified as "modified wood" has been developed through the application of synthetic resins and urea to wood. Such products as impreg, compreg, staypak, and uralloy have greater hardness, compressive strength, and abrasion resistance than untreated wood.

It is significant that many of the new and improved developments in wood utilization, particularly structural plywood, laminated wood, timber connectors, and wood preservatives, have wide application in construction and other major fields and will therefore be important in filling civilian needs in the future.

New Developments in Forest Products. As indicated above, research in wood utilization is bringing to the American public new uses of wood in many forms. One of the most dramatic and significant chapters in the history of the use of wood is the develpment of modern plywood. In the 1920's plywood was largely an experimental material with a narrow range of specialty uses. Today it is a standard material for wide and increasing ranges of construction and industrial uses. Its advantages lie chiefly in its nonsplitting qualities, its dimensional stability, and its availability in relatively large sizes. Furthermore, synthetic resin glues which are not affected by sun and water have made possible the bonding of boards or other relatively small pieces of wood to form great laminated arches and timbers. This is a revolutionary development because large timbers are no longer restricted to the dimensions of logs from which solid timbers can be cut.

Another development in the utilization of wood is the invention of metal timber connectors which hold pieces of wood together as firmly as if they were one piece. Their efficiency is well exemplified in the construction of radio towers to a height of 400 feet and in the construction of airplane hangars with clear roof spans of more than 200 feet.

The modern approach regards wood as a raw material that can be used in an ever-increasing number of products. Sweden in 1947 made 25 percent of its pulp from sawmill waste. Over 90 percent of the Swedish lumber industry's solid waste, excluding bark and sawdust, was utilized in pulp mills.

The production of tall oil is a new thriving industry based on a paper mill by-product. Tall oil is made from the "black liquor skimmings" left over when southern pine wood is made into kraft pulp. Formerly, the liquor waste was dumped into rivers where it became a pollution nuisance, or it was burned.

Since wood is about three-fourths carbohydrate, it is possible to convert wood waste, exclusive of bark, into sugar through wood hydrolysis. Industrial alcohol, high-protein stock and poultry feed, furfural, methanol, wood molasses, and acetic acid are products that may be obtained by this process. The chemical utilization of wood waste and inferior timber species has been receiving much attention. For example, a process has been developed for the conversion of the cellulose in sawdust into sugar, which may be used either as food or to make industrial products. In this process, containers holding several tons of sawdust are subjected to repeated percolations of dilute sulfuric acid under heat, and the filtrate is neutralized with lime. The result is a solution of glucose and pentose sugars which are the basic raw materials for ethyl alcohol and feeding yeasts. In the Northwest a single commercial plant can process 200 to 300 tons of wood waste a day.[18]

Trends in Utilization. Although proper forest management is basic to building up and maintaining our forest resources in a productive condition, good markets for forest products provide the incentive for good management.

Better and more complete utilization in the

[18] *Trees, The Yearbook of Agriculture,* U.S. Department of Agriculture, Washington, D.C., 1949, p. 642.

woods and mill is largely a matter of economics and ingenuity. Steady improvement in equipment and methods have lowered production costs which have in turn contributed to better utilization by making more of the raw material profitable to handle. Tractors are now used to a great extent for skidding logs and motor trucks are becoming increasingly important in transporting logs and pulpwood from the woods to the mill. In 1950, considering both distance and volume transported, it was estimated that about two-thirds of the total job of handling saw logs, 70 percent of the total for veneer logs and bolts,

Fig. 9 Georgia-Pacific's sprawling complex of manufacturing plants at Crossett, Arkansas, is geared to the complete utilization of the timber grown on the surrounding Tree Farms. In the foreground the paper mills make household tissues, bleached foodboard, and kraft paper. To the right is shown a chemical plant where charcoal briquets and a wide range of industrial chemicals are made. In the center background is the huge lumber plant where quality pine lumber is produced at the rate of 100 million board feet each year. (Georgia-Pacific Corporation.)

and 40 percent of the total job of hauling pulpwood, was done by truck.[19]

An increased demand for pulp in recent years has resulted in a strong trend toward utilization of mill waste such as slabs, edgings, and trim. Since only a limited amount of bark can be tolerated, mechanical and hydraulic barkers that remove the bark from the logs as they enter the mills have been developed. The recent development of the chemiground process for the manufacture of pulp from hardwoods such as beech, maple, oak, and many others has provided a new outlet for many species.

Need for Integrated Timber Use. One major need in attacking the waste problem is greater integration of the timber products industries. One-product operations tend to be wasteful.

Crossett, Arkansas, is a good example of a prosperous forest community based on properly managed forests which are coordinated with the manufacture of wood products (Fig. 9). A permanent sawmill, wood-distillation plant, and paper mill are wood-using industries in this community that are integrated in such a way that almost complete utilization of the forest crop is possible. Management of forests for sustained yield will be an incentive to such integration. Operators who adopt the policy of combining recurring timber growth with the manufacture of forest products can develop their plants and plan to stay in business permanently, because they have some assurance of a continuing supply of raw material.

PUBLIC ACTION IN ADVANCING FORESTRY

Although it seems certain that private owners will continue to hold the largest portion of our forest land, the public, as represented by the organized forestry agencies of state and federal governments, will have an increasingly important part to play in a nationwide forest conservation program (Fig. 10).

[19] *Timber Resource Review*, Chapter III, "Growth and Utilization of Domestic Timber," U.S. Forest Service, Washington, D.C., 1955.

Fig. 10 A stand of government-owned, virgin, mixed hardwood timber consisting of maple, elm, and black ash in the Nicolet National Forest in Wisconsin. (U.S. Forest Service.)

Practice of Forestry on Publicly Owned Lands. It is the policy of the Forest Service and state forestery agencies to utilize timber and other forest products for the benefit of consumers, to support industries on a continuous basis, and otherwise to contribute to stable local and national economy.

Cutting operations on public forests are of great significance in determining and demonstrating methods of silvicultural practice. Great progress has been made in our knowledge of forest management procedures in publicly owned forests through research and experimentation. In addition to assuming the responsibility of ownership and rehabilitation of idle lands that are not attractive to private capital, our public forests have an important place in demonstrating better forest practices.

Public Regulation of Cutting on Private Lands. Public regulation of cutting on private forest lands has been recommended as an essential step in continued forest production. Individual owners are handicapped in adopting good forestry practices if other owners continue their "cut-out-and-get-out" policy of exploitation. Many economic obstacles disappear when all owners handle their forests under the principles of continuous forest production.

However, many owners and operators oppose the idea of public regulation on the ground that it would be an unwarranted encroachment on private enterprise.[20] It would be extremely difficult to regulate the 3.4 million farmers and 1.1 million other private owners who own less than 100 acres each. Many people feel that the American way to improve the situation is to provide increased assistance through education, technical guidance, tree distribution, conservation payments, protection, and research rather than legislation.

Federal versus State Regulation. Although the idea that some regulation is desirable and necessary is accepted by many people, they believe it can and should be imposed and administered by the states and that it is a state responsibility and function. These individuals feel that for the federal government to take on itself such a responsibility is to deprive a state of opportunity to develop initiative and resourcefulness and that a strong nation can rest only on a foundation of strong states.

Since 1941 thirteen states have enacted regulatory laws, but most of them have been in effect too short a time for their effectiveness to be judged. Legislation in Maryland and California[21] sets forth the need and objective of regulation, defines in broad terms the provisions for woods practice designed to ensure the constructive use of forest lands and to prevent injurious exploitation, and provides authority for enforcement of the law. In these laws the

[20] *Problems and Progress of Forestry in the U.S.*, Report of the Joint Committee on Forestry of the National Research Council and the Society of American Foresters, Washington, D.C., 1947.

[21] *The Forest Situation in California*, Report to the Legislature by California Forestry Study Committee, 1945.

details of the proposed cutting practices are formulated by local forest committees of timber owners and operators with the result that the rules come up from the bottom, rather than being imposed at the top and passed down. With the maximum of local rule and a higher agency determining the adequacy of the rules, the operation of public regulation on private lands to a large degree reflects industry regulating itself in the interest of preserving its own basic resource.

Taxation of Forest Lands. Forestry is inseparably linked with taxation. The burden of taxation is often given as the reason for failure to practice forestry. In individual instances this is undoubtedly true. Under limited selective management with regular returns annually or at short intervals, taxes are not a serious obstacle to forest management.

Several states have enacted special tax legislation designed to encourage the building up of the growing stock in immature stands. Such legislation has usually taken the form of abolishing the ad valorem system of taxation and imposing a yield tax at the time of harvest.

For young growth, a combination of a low, fixed annual fee, in lieu of a tax, and a yield tax collectible at the time of harvest, has been tried and has been the law in Oregon for several years. Indiana, a hardwood state, assesses classified forest lands at $1.00 per acre and collects a yield tax at time of cutting equal to the tax rate times the difference between assessed value at time of classification and assessed value at time of harvest.

In those sections of the country where chronic tax delinquency is a serious problem, the best solution seems to be absorption of such lands into public ownership, federal, state, or county.

There is need, however, for continued research in forest taxation. The guiding principle should be that forest land must contribute its share in support of public activities and institutions. Where woodlands are managed properly, taxes are seldom a serious obstacle.

Public Assistance to Private Owners. Public

officials, generally, consider it sound policy to make good forest practice attractive to private owners. This attitude has been reflected in public assistance to private operators in cooperative fire protection, forest research, assistance to the states in the production and distribution of forest planting stock, in the educational program of the Extension Service, in woodland demonstration projects, and in farm-forest marketing projects. The federal government is also giving aid directly to individuals through federal land banks and through complete farm plans furnished by the Soil Conservation Service.

An important development in public assistance to private woodland owners was started during World War II as the Timber Production War Project. In order to stimulate increased output of timber products, several federal and state agencies besides the Forest Service provided foresters to assist sawmill and logging operators and timberland owners in meeting production problems.

Since 1950 the state and federal agencies have expanded technical assistance in forest management to farmers and other timberland owners through the Cooperative Forest Management Act. In providing such technical assistance the states employ technically trained foresters who are commonly called service or farm foresters. Approximately two-thirds of the cost of this assistance program is paid by the states and one-third by the federal government.

Fig. 11   This stand of towering pine timber near Crossett, Arkansas, is a prime example of some 720,000 acres of forestland owned and managed by the Georgia-Pacific Corporation in southern Arkansas and northern Louisiana. These timberlands are managed on a sustained-yield basis under a policy of dynamic conservation. This policy means the growing of more trees per acre on a perpetual basis and the production of more wood products from each tree harvested. (Georgia-Pacific Corporation.)

PROGRESS IN PRIVATE FORESTRY

Since approximately 75 percent of the nation's forest land is in private ownership, the importance of good forest practice on privately owned land is self-evident (Fig. 11).

The great demand for wood products has shown that forests can be grown for profit, and many private owners, particularly the lumber, paper, and pulp industries, have come to realize that their own best interests will be served by maintaining their forests in a productive condition.

Industrial Forestry. Only recently have profit possibilities in the growing of timber crops, and the need to hold timberlands for protection of permanent plant investments, become generally recognized throughout the forest industries. Consequently, many pulp and certain other primary wood manufactures have adopted aggressive land acquisition programs. During the eight-year period 1945–1953 the acreage owned by pulp and lumber manufacturers combined increased by 13 percent.

The recent survey of forest management practices for the entire country which was part of the *Timber Resource Review* of the U.S. Forest Service[22] indicated that productivity of recently cut lands on industrial holdings rated high. Ratings of productivity of recently cut lands on larger forest industry properties averaged higher than on the limited areas of small industrial ownerships.

Within the past few years industry has initiated such movements as "Tree Farms" and "Trees for Tomorrow" in which the major emphasis is on growing more trees. These programs call for continuous growing of trees on every acre of land best suited for that purpose and bringing the widest possible area under permanent forest management.

Industry deserves much credit for having practiced sound forest management on so much land under private ownership during recent years. This has done much to counteract the need for public regulation of cutting practices on privately owned timberland.

Farm Forestry. As was indicated in Chapter 10, 60 percent of the commercial forest land in the United States is in small private holdings,

and about one-half of this is in farm woodlands averaging slightly over 40 acres each. Where farm tenure is reasonably stable, the resident farm owner is usually interested in managing his woodland properly, but, as a group, farmers owning small areas are not handling their forests to the best advantage. As a rule, farmers having a substantial amount of merchantable timber have sold their timber "lump sum" without provision for proper cutting. After such liquidation of the growing stock, there follows a long waiting period before another sale can be made.

In view of the economic difficulties that small woodland owners have in practicing forestry, it is apparent that added education and technical assistance in forest management and marketing are needed.

There is no one answer to the problem of making sound forest conservation a reality on a nationwide scale. The solution lies in a positive, aggressive attack on the problem from many angles, including proper cutting practices, restoring forest cover on barren lands through planting, more efficient utilization of wood, public assistance in the control of destructive fires, insects, and diseases, in education and on-the-ground technical assistance, in continued research and demonstration, and the adoption by private industry of practices that will result in continuous production. Public regulation can be justified only when the forest resource is not being protected and managed in the interests of the public.

---

[22] *Timber Resource Review*, Chapter IV, "Factors Affecting Future Supply and Quality of Domestic Timber." U.S. Forest Service, Washington, D.C., 1955.

References

Cope, J. A., *Farm Forestry in the Eastern United States*, Charles Lathrop Pack Forestry Foundation, Washington, D.C., 1943.

Diller, O. D., "Managing Hardwood Forests for Continuous Production," *The Chemurgic Digest*, Vol. 6, 1947, pp. 341–345.

Fifth World Forestry Congress, *Multiple Use of Forest Lands, Proceedings*, 3 vols., Seattle, Washington, 1960.

Greeley, W. B., "Industrial Forest Management in the Pacific Northwest as Influenced by Public Policies," *Duke University School of Forestry Lectures*, No. 7, Durham, N.C., 1948.

Hair, Dwight, and Alice H. Ulrich, *The Demand and Price Situation for Forest Products—1964*, Misc. Publ. No. 983, Forest Service, United States Department of Agriculture, Government Printing Office, Washington, D.C. 1964.

Hall, A. G., "Four Flaming Days," *American Forests,* Vol. 53, 1947, pp. 540–544.

Hawley, Ralph C., *Forest Protection,* John Wiley and Sons, New York, 1948.

Koroleff, A., and J. A. Fitzwater, *Managing Small Woodlands, a Guide to Good and Profitable Use of Forest Land,* American Forestry Association, Washington, D.C., 1947.

Managing the Small Forest, Farmers' Bull. 1989, U.S. Department of Agriculture, Washington, D.C., 1947.

Reynolds, R. R., W. E. Bond, and B. P. Kirkland, *Financial Aspects of Selective Cutting in the Management of Second-Growth Pine-Hardwood Forests West of the Mississippi River,* Tech. Bull. 861, U.S. Department of Agriculture, Washington, D.C., 1944.

Society of American Foresters, *Wood, Water, and People, Proceedings,* Boston Meeting, 1963, Soc. of Am. Foresters, Washington, D.C., 1964.

Timber Resources Review, U.S. Forest Service, Washington, D.C., 1955.

Timber Resources for America's Future, Forest Resource Dept. No. 14, Forest Service, United States Department of Agriculture, Washington, D.C., 1958.

Timber Trends in the United States, Forest Service, United States Department of Agriculture, Government Printing Office, Washington, D.C., 1965.

Trees, The Yearbook of Agriculture, 1949, U.S. Department of Agriculture, Washington, D.C.

United Nations, *World Forest Inventory, 1958,* Forestry and Forest Products Division, Food and Agriculture Organization, Rome, 1960.

Von Eckardt, Wolf, *The Challenge of Megalopolis, a Graphic Presentation of the Urbanized Northeastern Seaboard of the U.S.,* The Macmillan Co., New York, 1964.

Part 4

JOHN H. GARLAND
University of Illinois

CHAPTER 12

Water Supply for Domestic and Industrial Uses

The words of an old adage which, although often quoted, have seldom if ever been taken literally are: "Waste not! Want not! We never miss the water until the well goes dry." No doubt the universal need for water, its worldwide distribution, and apparent inexhaustibility have led to various human attitudes towards its utilization. It is indeed an anomaly that a resource that not infrequently creates a deluge of extremely destructive proportions needs on occasion to be conserved. Both too little and too much water are, in part, the result of the unwise use of all natural resources. The universal importance of water as a basic necessity of all forms of life makes its utilization a most complicated problem of conservation.

DOMESTIC AND INDUSTRIAL USES OF WATER RESOURCES

The various ways in which water is utilized are such that interests conflict and numerous problems arise. All life is completely dependent on water, which includes drinking water for man and beast, soil water for vegetation, and surface water for the habitat of all types of aquatic life. On the other hand, water is a source of power, an industrial ingredient, a medium of transportation, a waste removal and purification agent, as well as a recreational asset and a marker of boundaries. Of this array, domestic and industrial uses are but a small part, and even these vary widely from place to place. Domestic uses consist of at least two major groups which can be designated as primary and secondary uses. These become manifest in areas of permanent or temporary water shortage.

Primary Domestic Uses. By far of greatest importance is water for human consumption, drinking water, cooking, and the like, without which mankind would perish. Under most dire conditions of water shortage this usage is given first consideration. Closely akin is the use of water for sanitary purposes. The demands of modern civilization for water for personal cleanliness, laundry, and other hygienic needs within the home and within public and private institutions are enormous. In continental United States in 1960, 164,600 million gallons per day were withdrawn from ground and surface water supplies for industrial, public, and rural usage (Fig. 1). Public water systems supplied about 21,000 million gallons daily to approximately 136,000,000 people with a variation from 100

235

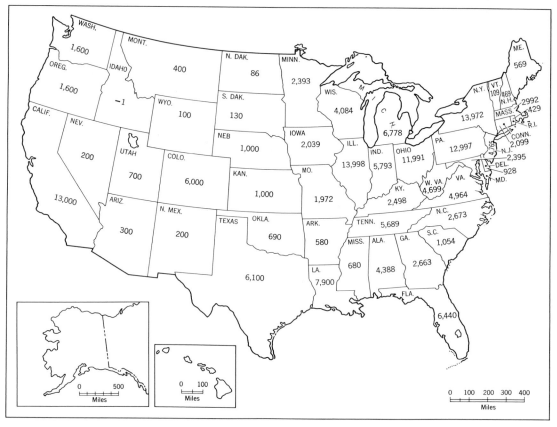

Fig. 1 Million gallons withdrawn daily by states from ground and surface water supplies for industrial, public, and rural uses. (*Water Atlas of the United States*, Water Information Center.)

to 250 gallons per person per day. The average for the nation was about 147 gallons per person per day. Regardless of area or population five states withdrew more than 10,000 million gallons daily, seven withdrew between 5,000 and 10,000, and eighteen withdrew between 1000 and 5000 million gallons daily. Only the state of Idaho withdrew less than 1000 million gallons daily.

Secondary Domestic Uses. The distinction between primary and secondary domestic uses of water, in some instances, is difficult to determine. It is obvious that great quantities of water are utilized in the sanitary sewage systems of all towns and cities, most of which has already been utilized as a primary domestic supply. Addi-

tional water is necessary to dilute and treat sewage or in many cases to carry the treated sewage away.

Water for fire protection is of greatest importance to towns and cities. Periods of water shortage are always threatened with the danger of a severe fire. Innumerable villages and towns as well as portions of many large cities in this country have been destroyed by fire because their supply of water was insufficient to meet the emergency. The volume of water consumed is not a crucial factor, since it is very small; it is the necessity of having a large flow of water available when needed that is the important factor for fire protection.

Closely associated is the utilization of water

to lay dust and wash debris from city streets as well as to flush accumulations from the catch basins of the storm sewers in periods of dry weather. In the humid portion of the country, the sprinkling of lawns and gardens and the forcing of vegetables by overhead irrigation constitute a domestic type of water utilization.

The air conditioning of stores, offices, and public buildings, as well as apartment buildings and private residences, by water cooling systems has placed an extra demand upon water for secondary domestic purposes. Some systems pump groundwater into the air conditioner and then return the water to a dry well; thus the water becomes groundwater again.

One of the lesser secondary domestic uses of water is for recreational purposes. In the present discussion utilization refers to the direct consumption of water for that purpose rather than the recreational uses made of streams, lakes, and the like. It includes the consumption of water for fountains, public and private swimming pools, and other types of ornamental and recreational uses of water that must come from the water supply. Both indoor and outdoor swimming pools have become users of the domestic water supply.

Industrial Uses. Numerous types of manufactures require large quantities of water in their industrial processes other than the water consumed by the employees of the plants. Thus the amount, the quality, and the cost of water are important factors of industrial localization for some types of manufacturing.

The industrial uses of water fall into three broad but somewhat interrelated categories: (1) water is an important ingredient of the finished product; (2) it is used as an agent for cooling, removing impurities, preparing solutions, and the like; and (3) it is important in the diluting and removal of industrial waste.

The several industries using water directly as an ingredient of the finished product include the food canning and preserving industries, the beverage and bottling manufactures, the distilleries, and commercial ice plants. It is also obvious that these industries will require large quantities of water for cleansing, for raw materials, for cooling, and for the removal of waste. The stockyards and meatpacking industries, where water is not important as a direct ingredient, consume millions of gallons of water per day, whereas a modern distillery consumes millions of gallons of water per day for steam, for cooling, and as an ingredient. In the making of one barrel of beer 300 gallons of water are required.

Many other industries, especially paper and pulp making, leather tanning, textile manufacturing, bleaching, dyeing, and printing of cotton textiles, oil refineries, electrical generating plants, coke plants, steel mills, and related types of industries, use enormous quantities of water both as cleansing, cooling, or solution media, and to flush away industrial waste. The paper and pulp industries utilize water to wash away impurities as well as to reduce the wood to pulp. In the mechanical grinding process, which produces most of the coarse paper and newsprint, about 15,000 gallons of water are utilized for every ton of paper produced, and in the sulfide and the soda processes as much as 100,000 gallons of water per ton of paper are utilized. A large paper mill uses more water per day than a city of 50,000. To refine 1 barrel of oil 18 barrels of water are consumed, and 10 gallons of water are utilized in producing 1 gallon of gasoline.

The steel industries are tremendous users of water. Twenty-six of the largest integrated steel mills each withdrew an average of 252 million gallons of water daily. This water, drawn mostly from surface sources is enough to supply a city of almost 2,000,000. About 7.9 percent of the total volume withdrawn is consumed chiefly by evaporation. The consumptive use of water by industry as a whole is about 6 percent; the rest returns to the source and is reused. Cooling, washing scale, reducing dust and gas, and quenching and granulating slag are the basic uses of water. In general, 94 percent of the industrial uses is for cooling.

The associated coke and gas plants also utilize enormous volumes of water to cool gas washers and to clean the gases as well as to quench the coke. As much as 50,000,000 gallons of water are used daily by an individual coke plant. Electrical generating plants are also great consumers of water for cooling and for steam power. For each ton of coal consumed in a steam power plant, 600 to 1000 tons of water are utilized. The estimated daily requirements of fuel-electric power generating plants are about 100,000 million gallons, about one-fourth of which is saline.

The utilization of water to flush away industrial waste is usually associated with the pollution of streams and rivers. The type of waste varies with the industry, some being more harmful than others. An important operation in the making of rolled and sheet steel, tin plate, wire, and galvanized pipe is the removal of flakes produced by the rolling process. The best method of removing the scale is to treat the steel in an acid bath, usually sulfuric acid. The removal of the oxide scale by the acid reduces the bath to an aqueous solution of free acid and metal salt. The problem of the disposal of industrial waste is enormous, and the amount of water used directly and indirectly probably cannot be estimated.

Numerous other industrial demands are made upon the water supply, especially to operate hydraulic mechanisms. The so-called hydraulic water under a pressure of 750 pounds is used in steel mills for the removal of scale as well as for operating hydraulic mechanisms that open and close furnace doors and move other heavy pieces of equipment. Large quantities of water are also used in connection with the pumping of salt, sulfur, and some oil wells, as well as in petroleum refining.

SOURCES OF WATER SUPPLY

The amount of water utilized each day for both domestic and industrial purposes immediately raises the question of the supply, its amount, and its quality as well as the probability of an adequate and continuous supply.

With the exception of the connate and magmatic waters our water supply falls as some form of precipitation. Thus in general the supply is related to distribution of precipitation. The map (Fig. 2) indicates the unequal distribution of precipitation over the United States. In general, east of the 100th meridian the precipitation is adequate, increasing from 20 inches per year on the Great Plains to 50 to 60 inches on the East coast and 60 to 80 inches on the Gulf Coast. Westward, except on the Pacific Northwest coast where the rainfall is very heavy, precipitation decreases to desert proportions over much of the intermontane region. Of the precipitation that falls, 71 percent is evaporated from the surface to the ground. The amount thus lost depends on the temperature of the air, the nature of the surface, and the vegetational cover on which it falls. A portion is absorbed by the surface materials of the earth, and a portion drains off to the sea. The water that enters the surface of the earth, and the water that flows off or remains on the surface, are the two sources of water for domestic and industrial uses.

Surface Water. Surface water or runoff is available in three forms: streams and rivers, lakes, and reservoirs and tanks. The larger the area drained and the heavier the precipitation the larger is the volume of the master stream. Although streams and rivers are an important supply of domestic and industrial water in the humid part of the United States, most of the large reclamation projects, which furnish water for irrigation and hydroelectric power as well as domestic water, are in the semiarid and arid portion of the country.

Inland fresh-water lakes, especially the Great Lakes, are outstanding sources of water for the many towns and cities along their shores, as are many of the smaller lakes in the glaciated portion of the United States.

The impounding of water of a tributary stream is a common practice of ensuring a water supply; reservoirs and tanks are used to store

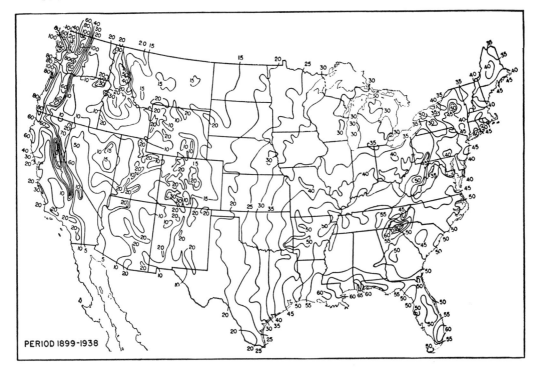

Fig. 2 Average annual precipitation in the United States. With the exception of the Pacific Northwest the average annual precipitation of western United States is inadequate. (*The Yearbook of Agriculture*, 1941, U.S. Department of Agriculture.)

runoff, usually referred to as "rain or storm water" to supplement the water supply. These range in size from the cistern and rain barrel of humid lands to the large reservoirs designed to impound melting snow and storm water to provide a domestic supply as well as water for stock and irrigation in the semiarid lands of the West. In the rural areas of the United States, the "drinking" water well and the cistern or soft-water pump are conspicuous features of the water supply of each home (Fig. 3).

Groundwater. The precipitation that soaks into the earth percolates downward through the unconsolidated soil and mantle rock and into the crevices and interstices of the underlying bedrock until a depth is reached where the density of the rock and the lack of crevices prohibit any further penetration. The greater portion of rock porous enough to contain water is within

a few hundred feet of the surface. The groundwater is maintained by the portion of precipitation that seeps into the earth. If the water is not of sufficient volume to fill all the interstices, the upper portions of the mantle rock may be damp while the areas below are saturated. The upper limit of the saturated zone is known as the "groundwater table."

The groundwater table or groundwater level is not a horizontal surface, nor is it at a constant depth below the earth's surface. The water table tends to assume a position between true surface configuration and a horizontal surface. Thus the water table is close to or at the surface of the ground in the valleys and at greater depths from the surface beneath the hills. Likewise the water table is at greater depths in subhumid and dry regions or after lengthy periods of drought in humid regions; whereas in humid regions,

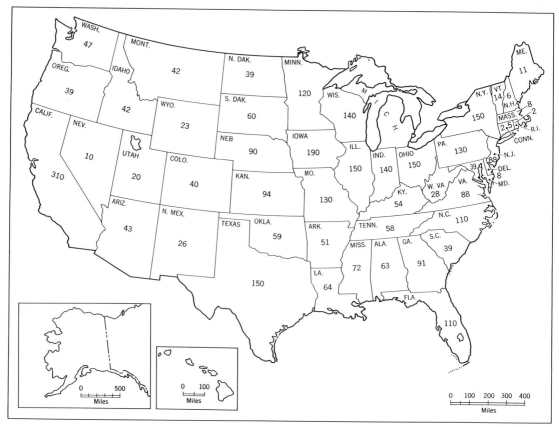

Fig. 3   Million gallons withdrawn per day for rural use. Water from both ground and surface sources not served by public water supply companies. (*Water Atlas of the United States*, Water Information Center.)

especially after periods of heavy precipitation, it may be near the surface.

SPRINGS. The location of springs depends on terrain and rock structure in relation to the position of the water table. In its simplest form a valley eroded below the water table is the locus of a series of springs which will cease to flow if drought or other causes lower the water table below the valley floor. A horizontal layer of impervious material, if exposed on a hillside, would allow the water to escape in a series of springs along the hillside. Fault and joint planes are also important features in permitting groundwater to rise to the surface, some of which may have been in contact with igneous

rocks of sufficient temperature to produce hot springs and geysers.

Many springs are of such limited volume or of intermittent nature that they are of value as a source of water supply only for individual houses, especially isolated farmsteads, and small villages. There are, however, in the United States several areas of springs of enormous volume. The U.S. Geological Survey[1] has located sixty springs each with a flow sufficient to supply completely a city of 500,000 inhabitants and at least six others any one of which would sup-

[1] O. E. Meinzer, *Large Springs in the United States*, Water Supply Paper 557, U.S. Geological Survey, Washington, D.C., 1927.

ply a city of 2,000,000 with all its water requirements. Large springs develop in regions of cavernous limestone and in porous lavas where groundwater from relatively large areas drains into subterranean channels of large capacity. The areas of large springs in the United States are northern Florida, the Ozark region of Missouri, central Texas, the Upper Snake Plains of Idaho, western Oregon and northern California, and central Montana. The springs of the northwestern portion of the country are largely in the porous lavas, whereas the rest of the large springs are associated mainly with cavernous limestone.

WELLS. A supply of water may be obtained by digging or drilling from the surface of the water table. Dug wells of necessity are shallow and are constructed in glacial drift or other unconsolidated material. The well, although curbed, is open and thus is subject to contamination from the surface. The water is lifted by a windlass, or sweep, or a simple lift pump. Supplies of this type, although numerous, are suitable only for isolated homes in rural areas, and even there, a summer's drought may lower the water table sufficiently to cause the well to go dry.

Dependable supplies of water for towns and cities, and even individual homes, are obtained by drilling deep wells, cased against pollution from surface seepage, into the drift or underlying bedrock. Water from most deep wells must be brought to the surface by force pumps.

ARTESIAN WELLS. Under special conditions large supplies of water are obtained from deep, flowing artesian wells. Hydrostatic pressures develop only under special conditions of terrain, underlying bedrock, and climate. The conditions consist of a porous formation, generally sandstone, exposed to sufficient precipitation to fill it and gently dipping below a layer of impervious material. If the water-bearing formation is closed off at its lower elevation the water is entrapped and is therefore under pressure. A well drilled into the water-bearing layer from any point on the surface lower than the exposed portion of the porous formation will flow, or at least will rise in the well as a result of the weight of the water in the higher portion of the porous strata.

In the United States artesian wells have been drilled on the Gulf Coastal Plain and on the Great Plains and Central Lowlands to depths of 3000 and some to almost 5000 feet.[2]

SETTLEMENTS AND WATER SUPPLY

It is convenient to think of the population of the United States as being composed of three settlement groups each of which contains about one-third of the total population. The first group is metropolitan and is made up of cities with populations of 100,000 and over; the second is composed of small cities, towns, and villages; and the third is composed of the rural population. The last two groups depend largely on groundwater, whereas the metropolitan group depends on surface supplies supplemented for secondary domestic and some industrial uses by groundwater.

Metropolitan Group. By far the greatest consumers of water are the metropolitan areas, for it is there that great concentrations of people make a tremendous demand on the domestic supply. Likewise the presence of industry within the cities places an industrial demand on the water supply that in most districts greatly exceeds the domestic use.

Although a variety of systems both private and municipal have been developed to supply the water needs of metropolitan areas, the volume required is so large that most urban areas depend on surface water supplemented for certain uses with groundwater. For some large urban districts it has been necessary to transport water long distances at great cost. Interstate conflicts over water rights have arisen in connection with the water supply of some of our large metropolitan areas.

[2] The deepest well in the world was drilled to a depth of 5,638 feet near Portland, Australia, in southern Victoria in 1959.

The relationship of population density and distribution to humid climate conditions in the United States is clear. Most of the cities of the metropolitan group are located on rivers or lakes that may be utilized as a source of domestic and industrial water.

Conspicuous among the city groups are those associated with the Great Lakes and with the Mississippi drainage system. Less conspicuous are the associations of the cities with the streams of the Gulf and Atlantic Coastal Plain, and those of the Pacific Northwest and the mountains. Thus only a few of the cities, those in the semiarid portion of the country such as Los Angeles, San Diego, and Salt Lake City, and those on bays and estuaries along the seacoast, such as Boston and New York City, have insufficient surface water supplies in their immediate environs. Although all urban groups have innumerable problems concerning the conservation of their water supply, these cities have the added problem of ensuring an adequate supply.

Los Angeles, the only city of over 1,000,000 outside of the humid section of the United States, is entirely dependent on a water supply from beyond its local area, in part beyond the limit of the state. The Los Angeles River was the original source of water for the first 125 years of the city's existence. By 1908 efforts were being made to increase the water supply since the growth of the city was limited by the local water supply. In 1914 the Los Angeles aqueduct was completed to the Owens River east of the Sierra Nevadas 238 miles away. At a cost of $25,000,-000 the water was brought by canal, siphon, and tunnel across the desert and under the mountains into the Los Angeles basin. Since one of the conditions by which the water of Owens Lake was obtained was the requirement that all the water be used within the city, Los Angeles enlarged by incorporating 50,000 acres of the San Fernando valley immediately north of the city. The population of the city increased to more than 500,000 by 1920. Additional water was secured from Mono Lake north of Owens Valley. By 1930 the population of Los Angeles

had passed 1,000,000 with another million people in the metropolitan district of the basin.

In 1934 the Colorado Compact was arranged to secure an additional supply from the Colorado River at a cost of $220,000,000 to the Metropolitan Water District of Southern California, which includes fourteen other communities including San Diego, and supplies a population greater than 6,500,000. The water from Lake Havasu above Parker Dam, 155 miles below Hoover Dam, is conducted through 241 miles of aqueduct. There are 92 miles of tunnels, and the water must be raised 1617 feet by five pumping stations operated by electric power generated at Hoover Dam. Several new lines, pumping stations, and reservoirs have been added to distribute the water.

The water table has been lowered to more than 75 feet below sea level. Desalted sea water has been offered as a supply and distant sources have been suggested. No doubt supply will be exceeded by demand by the end of the century.

Within the humid portion of the United States the New York metropolitan district is the largest that must reach out for a sufficient domestic and industrial water supply. The Ringewood system supplies groundwater from an elaborate system of infiltration galleries laid 10 to 15 feet below the water table for 6 miles in the glacial sands of Long Island.

Wells on Staten Island produce about 10 million gallons per day as compared with 100 million gallons from the Ringewood system. The other systems, which are the main sources, supply surface water impounded in reservoirs. The oldest is the Croton River watershed with twelve storage reservoirs and six impounded lakes with a total capacity of 103 billion gallons, the largest of which is Croton Lake with 34 billion gallons capacity. In Westchester County south of the Croton watershed are the Bronx and Byram rivers, Byram and Wampus ponds, and the 30-billion-gallon Kensico Reservoir. In the Catskill system, the Schoharie Reservoir with a capacity of 20 billion gallons is connected to the Ashokan Reservoir by the Shandaken Tunnel.

The Ashokan Reservoir has a capacity of 130 billion gallons and was in use in 1915. The Catskill Aqueduct connects it with the Kensico Reservoir 17 miles north of the city from which the water comes to the city.

In 1930 the State of New Jersey attempted unsuccessfully to enjoin the State of New York from diverting the water of the Delaware River for an additional water supply for New York City. In 1945 the Delaware-Rondout and Delaware Aqueduct system was developed in the watershed of the East Branch and Neversink, tributaries of the Delaware, and the Rondout, tributary of the Hudson. Because of the water shortage in New York City in 1950, an emergency station with a capacity of 100 million gallons per day was set up to pump water from the Hudson River into the Delaware River Aqueduct. In 1963 drought reduced reservoirs to about one-third their normal supply. Metered water to the three-fourths of the water users now on estimated consumption basis might help conserve the supply.

Boston, having outgrown the supplies of the Framingham and Wachusett reservoirs, receives an additional water supply from the Quabbin Reservoir in the Connecticut valley. Likewise the State of Connecticut filed a bill of complaint with the Supreme Court against the Commonwealth of Massachusetts for planning to divert the waters of the tributaries of the Connecticut from their natural flow into that river.

Other cities on secondary streams have ensured themselves a supply of surface water by impounding the rivers. Those cities on the major rivers and on the Great Lakes pump their water directly from the source with less danger of the supply diminishing acutely. Chicago and Milwaukee draw their water directly from Lake Michigan; Duluth, from Lake Superior; Detroit, from Lake St. Clair; and Toledo, Cleveland, and Buffalo, from Lake Erie, whereas Syracuse takes its water from Skaneateles Lake and Rochester from Hemlock and Canadice lakes.

Wells supply all the water for 150 cities with populations of 25,000, a dozen or more cities including Houston, San Antonio, Miami, Dayton, and Wichita are in the metropolitan group.

The surface supply of New York City, Los Angeles, San Francisco, Indianapolis, Columbus, Ohio, Louisville, Kentucky, Pittsburgh, Pennsylvania, and St. Louis, Missouri, are supplemented by wells.

Second and Third Groups. The remaining population of the United States lives in towns and cities with less than 100,000 population and on individual farm steads. The water supply for this portion of the population is obtained chiefly from groundwater. On the farms and in the villages individual wells are pumped by hand, windmill, gasoline engine, or electric motor.

In the larger towns and small cities the individual wells have given way to water companies or municipal water systems. As the demand for domestic and industrial water has increased, groundwater has not been adequate and many small cities have added surface supplies by pumping directly, if they were located on large rivers or lakes, by impounding small streams, or by purchasing water from nearby large cities that already had established an adequate surface supply. Mountain towns depend on the melting snow and rain to keep open reservoirs filled.

Although more than 75 percent of the municipal water systems in the Midwest, lower Mississippi Valley, Gulf Coast, Southwest, and New Jersey and Delaware on the Atlantic coast depend upon groundwater for their source of supply, about 53 percent of the communities with populations of 10,000 or more depend on surface supplies only, 28 percent on groundwater only, and 12 percent on a combination of both. Less than 25 percent of the nation's population supply their own water, with about one-fourth without running water. About 2000 million gallons are for domestic uses and the rest for livestock.

CONSERVATION PROBLEMS

The two major conservation problems affecting water for domestic and industrial purposes are the quantity of water available and its quality for the purpose for which it is to be used. It is upon these two conditions that the entire program of water conservation rests.

As cities have grown and running water for domestic purposes has been made available, the per capita consumption has risen. With urbanization came tremendously increased utilization of water for industrial purposes. Likewise the greater number of people and especially their concentration in urban groupings have caused a problem of sewage disposal which together with industrial waste has helped to pollute many of the existing sources of water supply. The conditions of deforestation, erosion, floods, and declining water tables are also contributing factors in the complete conservation problem.

Pollution. The disposal of sewage and industrial waste is an important problem of water conservation especially in the metropolitan districts. Great Lakes cities draw domestic water from the lakes and return sewage to them; Chicago discharges sewage into the Sanitary Canal, dilutes it by water diverted from Lake Michigan, and then the Illinois River delivers the city's waste to the Mississippi. River cities draw their domestic supply from the river above the town and return the sewage, partially or entirely untreated, into the river below the city. Industries likewise withdraw water for numerous industrial uses and return various types of industrial waste. The Ohio, the largest of the interior rivers flowing through the populated, industrial portion of the United States, is our most utilized river. From Pittsburgh at its source to Cairo at the Mississippi confluence, it is lined with industrial and commercial cities and towns, all of which draw their water supplies from the river and return domestic sewage and industrial waste. The tributaries of the Ohio are likewise utilized. The Mahoning River, which flows through the Youngstown, Ohio, steel district, is so extensively used and reused that the hot, rusty liquid has little resemblance to a river.

THE OHIO RIVER VALLEY SANITATION COMPACT. With the industrial and commercial develop-

ment of the Ohio River Valley, like that of many other valleys in the United States, has come increased utilization of the water in the streams. The Ohio is used for commerce, particularly for a heavy barge traffic in coal, sand and gravel, and iron and steel products. Many industries require enormous quantities of water in their industrial processes or for cooling.

The Ohio is the source of water for culinary purposes of the people who live in cities that are located on the river. These same cities dispose of their wastes by discharging them directly into the river. In times of drought when the river is low the condition of the river becomes a menace to health.

Although an average of more than two bills per year concerning water pollution was introduced in Congress in the past century, the Water Pollution Act was adopted in 1948, and on June 30, 1948, the Ohio River Valley Water Sanitation Compact was ratified by Ohio, Indiana, West Virginia, New York, Illinois, Kentucky, Pennsylvania, and Virginia. The cooperation of the several states can do much to reduce the pollution of the Ohio and its tributaries.

Although flowing water exposed to the sunlight and air tends to purify itself, the problem of pollution has become more complex as domestic and industrial uses have placed an ever-increasing drain on the volume of water. Sewage and industrial wastes have increased enormously; aquatic life has been partially destroyed; silting due to increased erosion has been accelerated; and floods and droughts have become more acute, produced in part by deforestation and improper utilization of the watersheds.

It has long been known that polluted water resources were among the most dangerous of disease carriers. Typhoid fever is one of the epidemic diseases that has been traced directly to the domestic water supply.

THE WATER FACILITIES ACT. A Cabinet Committee was appointed by President Eisenhower on May 26, 1954, to review all water policies and programs, to assist in the coordination of activities of the various government agencies concerned with water, and to consider national legislation on water. Nearly three months later the Water Facilities Act was signed by the President on August 17, 1954. Every state has set up some agency or division to work on water pollution problems, and research organizations have been established in many types of industries to find ways to treat waste, purify waste water, and reclaim usable materials.

At the National conference on Water Pollution in December, 1960, it was pointed out that cities were having great difficulties in keeping abreast of the ever-increasing amounts of sewage while trying to cut the backlog of untreated sewage from existing sewers. Industry was having an even greater problem keeping up with ever-increasing production. In the United States untreated sewage from 22 million people is discharged yearly, over 60 percent of which occurs in the river basins of the Northeast, North Atlantic, Ohio, and the Southeast.

Purification of water and the processing of sewage and industrial waste are two of the important steps in the program of conservation of surface water, since sewage and industrial waste in the rivers and lakes are among the major causes of pollution. Beginnings have been made to process sewage and industrial waste, returning only harmless residues to the streams and lakes. If these processes are carried to their logical ends, reclaiming usable materials from industrial waste and producing fertilizers from sewage, only pure water would be returned to the streams and lakes, and one of the conservation problems would be solved.

Because most surface water is polluted, domestic supplies taken from streams and lakes are purified according to the nature of the pollution. Because the water of the Great Lakes is potable in its natural state, the cities drawing their water supply from the lakes have placed their intakes far out in the lake in deep water to overcome in part the pollution from sewage and industrial plants along the lake shore. Most rivers have a much higher degree of pollution, and more extensive purification and sterilization processes must be followed than are necessary in the lake cities to ensure clean, tasteless, pure water for domestic use.

Among the numerous processes that have been developed to remove the various undesirable and dangerous substances from water of polluted sources that are intended for domestic consumption are sedimentation, coagulation, filtration, aeration, chlorination, and coppering.

River water is usually turbid or muddy from the amount of material carried in suspension by the flowing water. The more excessive erosion becomes, the greater is the problem of dealing with turbidity, the silting of reservoirs, and the like. Turbidity ranges all the way from 100 to 5000 parts of suspended material in a million in the various rivers of the United States.

Much of the suspended material is removed from turbid water in settling basins, after which sulfate of alumina is introduced to coagulate organic matter and entangle bacteria. Turbidity is further reduced and harmful bacteria are removed by both mechanical and bacterial filtration. Odor and taste due to the destroyed bacteria are removed by aeration. Coppering prevents the growth of algae, which tend to cause taste and odor in the water. Especially in water that has not been subjected to other processes of purification chlorination serves as a germicide and effective safeguard.

The water supply for both domestic and industrial purposes of almost all communities must be treated in some way before it is used. Of the communities of 25,000 or more in the United States served by organized water supply systems, all use chlorination processes. Chlorination alone is used in only 26 percent of the communities, filtration is added to chlorination in 29 percent, softening is included in 17 percent, and various combinations with chlorination are used in 28 percent.

Fluoridation has been a source of great controversy in recent years. It is not a problem of destroying impurities in the water but in adding fluorides to the human body.

Mineral Content. Groundwater supplies, especially from deep wells, are less likely to be polluted but usually present two equally perplexing problems. One is the presence of minerals in solution in the water; the other is a diminished supply due to falling water tables. Much of the groundwater, as well as some surface water that has been in contact with calcareous material, contains magnesium and calcium salts and other soluble material in solution in sufficient quantities to cause the water to be hard and therefore less desirable for many purposes. Hardness is a measure of the calcium and magnesium salts in solution in the water. Soft water contains less than 60 parts of salt per million; temporarily hard water contains from 60 to 120 ppm, and permanently hard water contains more than 120 ppm (Fig. 4).

Temporary hardness may be removed by simple softening processes, but permanent hardness cannot be removed without extensive and likewise expensive permutate operations. Municipal or water company softeners are sometimes employed, but in most towns and cities depending on hard groundwater the softening is at the discretion and expense of the user. Soft-water services have been established in hard-water communities, both the softener and the regenerating service being conducted on a rental basis. Since hard water does not permit the proper detergent action of soap, it is not desirable for household purposes or for laun-

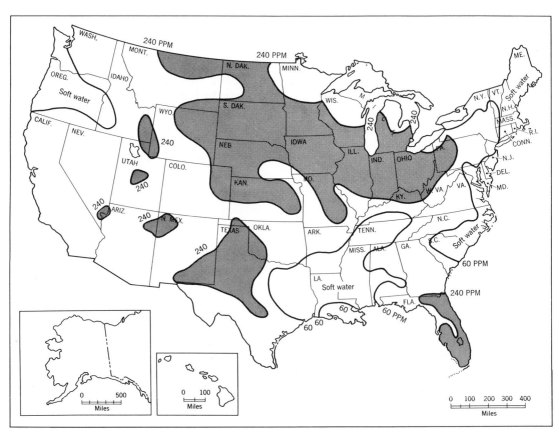

Fig. 4 Hard groundwater. The groundwater of the shaded areas contain more than 240 ppm of $CaCO_3$ in solution. (*Water Atlas of the United States.* Water Information Center.)

dries. Likewise various types of textile mills, breweries, photographic establishments, and steam boilers, require large quantities of soft water.

Since the development of the atomic energy, fallout, especially strontium-90, has become a contamination problem. In excess it is considered harmful to people and detrimental to certain industrial activities. More than 1 ppm exists in the streams of western Texas and Oklahoma and southeastern New Mexico and Arizona. The lowest concentration, less than 0.1 ppm, is in the Pacific Northwest, Central Valley of California, and Southeastern United States. The rest has a concentration between 0.5 and 0.1 ppm. The presence of nonradioactive natural strontium complicates the removal of strontium-90 from surface water.

Manganese, iron, sulfur, and sodium chloride are other harmful or undesirable mineral properties of groundwater that affect the taste or odor of the water. Sulfur water and salt water from deep wells are not potable but are suitable for cooling. If the salt water is dense enough, the brine is usable in the chemical industry. Sulfur water is suitable for air-conditioning plants. The spent water, however, is or should be returned to a dry well rather than the sewer.

The substitution of chemical detergents for soap has caused problems in water supplies. Since the detergents do not break down as soap does in sewage treatment, great quantities of suds create problems in surface water into which treated or untreated sewage charged with chemical detergents have been discharged. However, the detergent may have certain beneficial effects at the sewage disposal works.

Declining Water Table. One of the conservation problems confronting towns and cities that depend on groundwater as a source of supply is the declining level of the water table. Especially in the dry regions where numerous wells tap the groundwater for both domestic and irrigation water, the level of the water table has fallen a number of feet, making it necessary to deepen many of the wells. In humid areas likewise groundwater is being removed faster than it is being replaced by precipitation. Similarly, the hydrostatic pressure of artesian wells has been reduced until some of them have ceased to flow above the level of the ground.

Any well drilled into the groundwater and pumped continuously lowers the water table in a great cone in the vicinity of the well into which the water must percolate from the surrounding area. If the water-bearing formation is composed of coarse, porous material the water will flow in rapidly, but if it is fine-grained material the replacement will be slow and it will be relatively easy to pump the well dry temporarily. Thus it is necessary to drill a series of wells at rather widely spaced intervals to ensure an adequate water supply for a town or city entirely dependent on wells. More and deeper wells are drilled as the demand for water increases, and many communities turn to surface water for their supply.

About 70 percent of the population of the United States depends on public water-supply systems that utilize both groundwater and surface water to supply about 21,000 million gallons per day (Fig. 5). Of this group 58 percent of the systems furnishes an adequate supply of water at all times for 51 percent of the people. About 32 percent receives an inadequate supply all the time or must expect periodic shortages and restrictions in water use, and 17 percent depends on an uncertain supply. With the rapid increase of population and the rising industrial demand, adequate water for domestic and industrial uses will be a continuing problem.

CONSERVATION ATTITUDES

The problem of water conservation is not one that can be solved independently of the conservation of the other natural resources. It is possible to restrict the use of water by various devices of metering, checking leaks, and raising the price. Although desirable and necessary at times and in various places restricted use is not a solution.

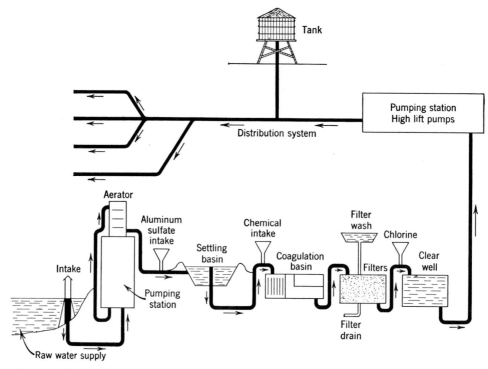

Fig. 5 Generalized diagram of the numerous processes that have been devised to remove undesirable and dangerous substances from water that is unsafe in the untreated state.

The total volume of water will always depend on the amount that falls as precipitation, whereas the available surface and groundwater will depend on the nature of the earth's surface materials. Sufficient forest and grass cover will retard runoff and floods, reduce erosion, and raise the level of the groundwater. With a proper balance of evaporation, runoff, and groundwater maintained by adequate reforestation and soil conservation programs an enduring source of water for everything but the most fantastic demands can be ensured.

To complete the conservation program the problem of pollution must be solved by disposing of domestic sewage and industrial waste in a manner that will not contaminate water supplies. The best conservation program to ensure a water supply for domestic and industrial purposes is a good reforestation and natural vegetation program, an intelligent soil conservation program, an adequate flood control program, as well as an enlightened wildlife conservation program, for they are all the same—the intelligent and continuous utilization of our natural resources.

References

Blake, Nelson M., *Water for the Cities*, Syracuse University Press, Syracuse, New York, 1956.

Fair, Gordon M., and John C. Geyer, *Water Supply and Waste-Water Disposal*, John Wiley and Sons, New York, 1954.

Journal of the American Water Work Association, American Water Work Association, New York.

Miller, D. W., J. J. Geraghty, and R. S. Collins, *Water Atlas of the United States,* Water Information Center, Port Washington, N.Y., 1962.

Murphy, Earl Finbar, *Water Purity, A Study in Legal Control of Natural Resources,* The University of Wisconsin Press, Madison, 1961.

Proceedings, The National Conference on Water Pollution, U.S. Department of Health, Education and Welfare, Public Health Service, Washington, D.C., 1961.

Public Water Supply, Business Report, U.S. Department of Commerce, Government Printing Office, Washington, D.C., 1955.

Thomas, Harold E., *The Conservation of Ground Water,* McGraw-Hill Book Co., New York, 1951.

Water, The Yearbook of Agriculture, U.S. Department of Agriculture, Government Printing Office, Washington, D.C., 1955.

Water and Sewage Works, Vols. 93–103, Chicago, Ill., 1946–1956.

Water Newsletter, Water Supply, Waste Disposal, Conservation, Water Information Center, Port Washington, New York.

Water Supply Papers, U.S. Geological Survey, Government Printing Office, Washington, D.C.

GUY-HAROLD SMITH

The Ohio State University

CHAPTER 13

Water Power and Its Conservation

In the cultural evolution of man he has striven to gain mastery over his environment, and in a large measure his achievements reflect an increasing use of mechanical power. In primitive societies man was limited to the strength of his own muscles. But in due time the domestication of animals gave him greater power and, as a consequence, increased control over his environment. The wheel, the lever, and other simple but fundamental inventions made possible the mechanical revolution which was to come. In a period of human slavery the man power available in a community or in the possession of a slaveholder was a measure of economic strength. It may be significant that the liberation of human slaves came when mechanical power was multiplying man's control over nature. Gradually and inevitably the work of the world was shifted from the muscles of man to the untiring machine driven by mechanical power. No longer was man power, particularly slave power, at a premium; hence the slaves could be given their freedom.

Water Power and the Hydrologic Cycle. In the operation of the hydrologic cycle, water that falls upon the land returns to the sea from which it was derived originally. In its return it fulfills its destiny, and man in his understanding of the ways of water may make full use of this essential resource. Wherever precipitation falls upon elevated areas potential power is available along the streams, depending on the quantity of water and the declivities along the watercourses. As long as the energy of the sun continues to evaporate the waters from the seas, and the vapor-laden winds penetrate the continents deeply, the precipitation that falls in elevated areas will flow back to the sea. This perennially renewable power resource should be developed wherever it is economically feasible, so that the nonrenewable fuels may be conserved for future generations.

Frontier America and the Early Development of Water Power. The aboriginal Americans who lived along the watercourses used the streams for their personal needs and for transportation, but they were unmindful of the power available in the rushing waters. The establishment of the colonies along the Atlantic seaboard preceded the great mechanical revolution. The early settlers, although they were compelled to live under relatively primitive conditions, brought to America a greater understanding of the value of resources than that possessed by the

251

Indians. From New England to the Piedmont, farms were being cleared, homes built, and at favorable locations water wheels were installed to utilize the local power resources. Many of these first-used power sites proved to be of temporary usefulness; others helped to localize settlements and to develop them into important mill towns.

Frontier America and the Water Wheel. Almost as soon as the colonists set foot on American soil they turned not only to the land for the production of food but also to the watercourses as a source of power. As people moved from the seaboard westward across America to settle along the moving frontier, they developed the power sites to turn the wheels of pioneer industry. These little water wheels at numerous power sites ground meal and sawed the timber into lumber. These were the important industrial products of the frontier. Larger wheels at the more important power sites, often requiring the construction of dams, replaced the little water wheels. Here was a division of labor and, thus, a division of responsibility. The farmers with their greater concern about food production were clearing the land and cultivating the fields and generally were changing the character of the headwater area so important in maintaining a regular supply of water power. Dams were built to provide the necessary head to turn the water wheels, but the reservoirs were soon silted up with the fertile soil from the farms in the upstream areas.

Eventually many of the old mills were abandoned. It was cheaper to use the more reliable steam engine which burned coal. The development of transportation made coal relatively easy to secure, and the local water wheels declined in importance. But the moving frontier, as it progressed westward across America, gave the water wheel a temporary place in the economy of the pioneers.

Evolution of the Water Wheel. The manner in which water power was first utilized is unknown to us, but available evidence indicates that the first water wheels were crude devices.

Probably the first was simply a paddle wheel which turned slowly in the current. The efficiency of such a water wheel was only 3 or 5 percent of the total available power, and in time the undershot wheel which had an efficiency of 25 to 30 percent was developed. The moving water was confined to a flume or channel constructed so that the paddles received the full impact of the moving water. The efficiency was further increased to 50 or even 70 percent when the flume was deepened so that the full surface of the paddles received the impact of the moving water. This is known as the "breast wheel."

A more efficient use of falling water was made possible by the development of the overshot wheel which utilized a system of buckets so that little energy was lost. The best wheels of this type were 80 to 85 percent efficient and were widely used in the early part of the nineteenth century.

Gradually the overshot wheel was replaced by the water turbine, which, after a number of improvements were made, utilized the energy of falling water more efficiently, particularly at the large power plants. The old overshot water wheel used a head of no more than 40 feet, but the turbine made possible the use of a head up to 1000 feet. Many of the old water wheels are still turning the wheels of industry and give some indication of their efficiency and their usefulness in certain power situations. But the modern turbine is more satisfactory for the utilization of the power available at large dams.

The Steam Engine. With the invention and development of the steam engine, the stage was set for coal-generated steam power to dwarf the power generated from falling water. The wheels of industry still were turned by water power, but steam power became increasingly important during the nineteenth century. By 1900, 70 percent of the total mechanical energy produced in the United States was derived from bituminous coal, 20 percent from anthracite, 5 percent from petroleum, and 3 percent from water. The remaining 2 percent was contributed chiefly by wind and animals. This gives some indication of the relative position of water power among the other power resources. In the more than 60 years since the turn of the century the proportion of the power developed from coal has declined to less than 25 percent; petroleum has risen to approximately 35 percent; natural gas supplies 35 percent; and water power yields only 4 percent of the total power developed (see Chapter 17).

THE ECONOMICS OF WATER-POWER DEVELOPMENT

Considered from a purely physical point of view the total amount of water power available along a watercourse or in a particular region is related to the quantity of water available in the streams, the vertical fall of the water, and the efficiency of the water wheels or turbines used in the development of the power resource. The gradient of a stream may be so gentle that power sites are limited and the necessary head difficult to obtain without the construction of expensive reservoirs. Another stream discharging a similar quantity of water may have a gradient characterized by long reaches of low fall interrupted by rapids and falls where power development is economically and physically feasible. The seasonal irregularity of precipitation may set definite limits to the utilization of a stream for power purposes. The dams and other engineering works necessary for the full utilization of a stream for power may affect adversely the use of the stream for navigation and other purposes. The physical characteristics of a stream should be thoroughly examined in terms of the several purposes for which water may be used immediately and prospectively when the stream is fully developed.

Water Power and the Localization of Industry. Before the invention of the steam engine or the development of electric generators and motors, power from falling water led to the location of many manufacturing establishments at the power sites. Many of the older industrial cities of the United States were founded at the river's edge and at the falls or rapids where the power could be used directly in manufacturing. Throughout New England and in many other sections of the country the power-located cities have continued to grow, although today little or none of the power is used directly.

Although the invention and development of the steam engine resulted in the abandonment of many water-power installations, riverside location was still important, for it was easy to obtain water for the boilers or for manufacturing processes. In some areas, such as the Ohio Valley, important quantities of coal are still transported by water. The steam engine produced power for direct use in industry and eventually became relatively more important than water power. Where water power continued to be used the supply was too restricted to meet the needs of the flourishing industrial cities. Many cities in the older sections of eastern United States were founded at a water-power site, developed and expanded under steam power, and now are making use of both and of other sources of power.

Electricity and Water Power. The electrification of industry and transportation in the latter part of the nineteenth century and the first quarter of the present century permitted a revaluation of the localization factors. No longer was it necessary to locate the mill at the water wheel or adjacent to the boiler which generated the steam. Within limits, which have been gradually extended, electrical power could be generated in one place and transported by high tension lines to the power-consuming centers.

The generation of electric energy from falling water makes possible the utilization of the power several hundred miles from the place where it is needed. Many of the most important power sites are located in or near mountain areas, but the places where the power is needed may be many miles away.

Transmission of Electrical Power. In the early stages of electrical power development the distribution of current was confined to the local areas where it was generated. Many small and large communities were served by power plants located at the waterfalls of a through-flowing stream. In others the electric current was steam generated. In either event the distribution was usually confined to the local municipality or to some industrial or private consumer. Localization of use was related to technical limitations, to long distance transmission, and to excessive costs of the lines in terms of anticipated returns.

Progressively through the years the transmission distance increased until power generated at a central station could be distributed to a consuming market 200 or 300 or, in particular situations more than 500 miles away. Transmission distance has increased with technological improvements in the electrical field, the development of major blocks of power in remote areas, and the necessity of delivering electric current to a distant market, as in the case of surplus power produced at the Hoover Dam, at Grand Coulee, at Chief Joseph, at The Dalles, at Bonneville, and at other large public projects in the West. The local market can utilize only a small proportion of the power generated. As a consequence large blocks of power are available for delivery to the major populated areas in Washington, Oregon, California, and in other power-deficient areas in the West.

Interconnection of Electric Power Facilities. The expansion of certain electrical facilities resulted in the absorption of smaller and financially weaker systems. These consolidations generally improved electrical service by providing greater diversity of load, a reduction of costs, and greater flexibility within the system. The integration of local units into major power systems leads inevitably to interconnection within the major systems. In spite of certain charges of monopoly and the concentration of financial control in a few hands, interconnection operates in the best interests of consumers.

The Federal Power Commission has encouraged interconnection. During the war years, and particularly in the postwar period, the demands for electric power have tended to expand faster than could be met by the utilities. In certain areas the supply and demand have been essentially out of balance, so that interconnection became a virtual necessity. The national welfare is dependent upon the willingness of the private and the public power interests to cooperate in order to secure the benefits of interconnection.

The interconnection of power-producing systems is not a new concept in the transmission of electric energy from a producing area to a power-consuming area. Extra high voltage transmission now makes it possible and economically feasible to carry the power up to distances as much as 3000 miles. Long-distance transmission makes it possible to locate the generating facilities at or near the mine mouth in the coal areas or at a distant water-power site, generate the electricity, transmit it over hundreds of miles at high voltages, and deliver it to the power-consuming centers.

In the not too distant future the hydroelectric resources of eastern Canada may be developed and by interconnection the power may be delivered into the Middle West and the Northeast. Also the considerable water-power resources of the mountainous section of western Canada may be developed and by interconnection and high-voltage transmission lines be delivered to the Pacific Coast section of the United States. This will give Canada and the United States additional opportunities for international cooperation.

POTENTIAL WATER POWER IN THE UNITED STATES

Water-Power Resources. The total hydroelectric power resources of the United States, both developed and undeveloped, were estimated to be approximately 148,893,000 kilowatts on January 1, 1963. A report by the Federal Power Commission places the developed hydroelectric power at 36,193,000 kilowatts, or just under 25 percent of the total. Slightly over 116,000,000 kilowatts remain to be developed in the future. The total power available is related to the construction of reservoirs

Table 1. Water-Power Resources, 1939–1962, by Geographic Divisions

(Thousands of Kilowatts)

Division	1939	1950	1960	1961	Undeveloped Water Power, 1962
New England	1,115	1,239	1,520	1,518	2,800
Middle Atlantic	1,633	1,678	2,472	3,852	5,700
East North Central	790	901	929	924	3,000
West North Central	537	629	1,594	1,694	6,000
South Atlantic	2,234	2,767	3,773	3,795	8,900
East South Central	1,270	2,729	3,750	3,953	4,300
West South Central	140	466	944	944	3,800
Mountain	1,583	2,286	4,621	4,821	24,100
Pacific	2,783	5,979	13,490	14,694	54,000
United States	12,075	18,675	33,092	36,193	112,700

[Source: *Statistical Abstract of the United States*, 1963.]

and the installation of power-generating equipment at the various sites as demand increases and as economic feasibility justifies development. It is possible therefore that the undeveloped resources in the future may prove to be somewhat greater than the 1963 estimates. But the inclusion of the relatively small powers will not greatly increase the total (Table 1).

Storage of water within a drainage basin is not everywhere related simply to the need for sufficient head and a regular flow to meet power needs. The same storage facilities may serve other useful purposes also, such as providing water for irrigation, the maintenance of an adequate minimum depth for navigation, flood control, and recreation. Water control for all purposes in a river basin is an ultimate objective of water-resource planning, but it may be necessary in certain drainage basins to achieve these several objectives in an orderly sequence instead of simultaneously.

WATER-POWER DEVELOPMENT IN THE UNITED STATES

The electric plants of the United States have nearly one-third of the producing capacity of the installed generators in all parts of the world. Progressively, and in spite of some wartime destruction of generators, the installations have increased steadily. The capacity of electric power plants in the United States in 1962 was 209,774,000 kilowatts. The capacity in the Soviet Union was 82,600,000 kilowatts, in the United Kingdom 42,242,000, in West Germany 31,826,000, and in Japan 29,142,000. These five countries, on the basis of installed capacity, produced in 1962 two-thirds of the world's electric power. Other important producing countries include Canada, France, Italy, China (Mainland), and Sweden. Consumption on a per capita basis is highest in Norway with 10,346 kilowatt-hours, in Canada with 6290, in Sweden with 5268, and in the United States with 5075.

Of the 209,774,000 kilowatts of electric generator capacity in the United States 36,193,000 kilowatts were hydrogenerators in 1962. Power from falling water is relatively more important than fuel-generated power in the Rocky Mountain and Pacific Coast states where competition from coal and other fuels is reduced. Generally in the West electricity is hydrogenerated, whereas in the East coal is the principal source of energy in the generation of electricity.

At the end of the year 1962 electric energy production by source of energy was 53.1 percent from coal, 5.5 percent from petroleum, 21.6 percent from gas, and 19.7 from hydrogenerators. The proportion generated from coal has remained essentially unchanged since 1940. Production from oil rose to 10.3 percent in 1950, but declined to 5.5 percent in 1962. Gas as a source of energy in the generation of electricity rose from 7.7 percent in 1940 to 21.6 percent in 1962. In spite of the fact that hydrogenerated capacity increased from 12,075,000 kilowatts in 1939 to 36,193,000 kilowatts in 1961 the share of the electric energy produced from hydrogenerators declined from 33.4 percent in 1940 to 19.7 percent in 1962.[1]

Nuclear Energy. The place of nuclear energy among the other sources of energy is difficult to forecast with accuracy. A report from the Atomic Energy Commission predicts that atomic energy will be competitive with other sources of energy in the 1970's and by 1980 10 percent of the electricity generated in the United States will be produced by the use of atomic energy.[2] It may be assumed that the increased use of nuclear fuels will reduce the demand for electrical power from the conventional sources. The development of some of the

more costly hydrogenerators may be delayed.

President Lyndon B. Johnson, in a commencement address delivered in early June 1964 at Holy Cross University, indicated that nuclear fuels probably would become increasingly important in the generation of electricity. It is expected that in a few years the cost of atomic-fueled power will be low enough to be competitive with power generated by fossil fuels or from falling water. The President's forecast was anticipated by Meyerhoff who estimated that in 1975 the total energy consumed in the United States will be produced from the following sources: coal 32.7 percent, oil 38.4 percent, natural gas 24.2 percent, water power 2.9 percent, and nuclear energy 1.8 percent.[3]

Hydroelectric Power in the United States. The capacity of hydroelectric generators in the United States has continued to increase year after year with one or two exceptions. The construction of new dams and the installation of new turbines and generators has gone forward in peace and war, in good times and bad, and bids fair to continue until the water-power resources are more fully developed and utilized (Table 2).

The electricity produced by steam generators and by internal-combustion engines required

[1] *Statistical Abstract of the United States,* Government Printing Office, Washington, D.C., 1963.

[2] Sam H. Schurr, "Energy," *Scientific American,* Vol. 209, 1963, pp. 111–126; Reference on page 124.

[3] Howard A. Meyerhoff, "Energy in the United States," *Focus,* Vol. 13, April 1963, p. 3.

Table 2. Production of Electric Energy in the United States, 1925–1962

Year	Total, 1000 Kilowatt Hours	Hydro, 1000 Kilowatt Hours	Steam, 1000 Kilowatt Hours	Internal Combustion, 1000 Kilowatt Hours
1925	61,451,091	21,797,874	39,367,118	286,099
1930	91,111,548	31,189,554	59,293,363	628,631
1935	95,287,390	38,372,154	56,141,412	770,824
1940	141,837,010	47,321,278	93,001,738	1,531,997
1945	222,486,283	79,970,312	140,435,268	2,080,703
1950	329,141,343	95,938,317	229,543,366	3,659,660
1955	547,037,985	112,975,069	430,119,086	3,943,830
1960	753,037,271	145,516,253	603,341,840	4,692,178
1961	792,038,586	151,849,873	635,563,762	4,624,951
1962	891,919,989	168,135,050	683,978,226	4,806,713

[Source: The Federal Power Commission.]

the use of fossil fuels which are diminished by use. To the extent that electricity is produced by hydrogenerators a renewable resource is used and its reuse can go on indefinitely. In the United States where the fossil fuels are relatively abundant the saving resulting from the use of water power may not be important, but in Norway, Sweden, Italy, and Japan where coal and oil must be imported the savings may be significant in the national economy.

THE GEOGRAPHICAL DISTRIBUTION OF WATER POWER

The pattern of water-power distribution in the forty-eight contiguous states of the United States reflects chiefly the terrain conditions and the amount of precipitation. Where the land is elevated and the precipitation heavy the potential water power is great. In areas that are low with streams of slight gradient the available power is also low. In dry areas the water power is generally restricted. Maps of annual precipitation and relief are basic to an understanding of the geographical distribution of water-power resources.

New England. New England which contains slightly more than 1 percent of the total area of the United States and has between 6 and 7 percent of the population has slightly under 4 percent of the potential water power in the United States. However, the development and utilization of water power are well advanced in New England which has approximately 4 percent of the capacity of water wheels in the United States. As one of the oldest industrial areas in the nation, New England originally used her water power directly in manufacturing processes. With the coming of electricity an important proportion of the available water power was used in the generation of electricity. And by 1963 the proportion derived from water was further reduced to less than 20 percent. The industrialization of New England makes heavy demands on other sources of power, such as coal, petroleum, and gas.

Water power in New England both before and after the development of electrically driven equipment has been extensively used in the woodworking and in the textile mills. With the growth of the larger urban centers the domestic use of electricity has increased and water-wheel capacity has increased also.

The industrial readjustments consequent upon the transformation of the United States from a major agricultural to the greatest industrial nation in the world have wrought changes in the economic character of New England. This does not mean a decline in manufacturing or a reduced demand for hydroelectric power. It is expected that further use will be made of the power resources of New England as greater control of the rivers becomes urgent and economically feasible. Extensive development of the power resources of the major rivers provides New England with hydroelectric power, and the reservoirs supply water for industrial and municipal purposes and in a measure alleviate the danger of floods. The great floods of August 19–21, 1955, stimulated the construction of many new reservoirs to hold back the flood waters and at the same time contribute to the waterpower capacity of New England.

The chief rivers that supply power to New England, and can be developed further, include the Connecticut, the Kennebec, the Merrimack, the Penobscot, the Androscoggin, and the Housatonic. On many of the smaller streams the power resources are restricted, but the recurring floods are a major economic hazard. Waterpower development in this area therefore may be secondary to the solution of a more urgent water problem (Fig. 1).

The Passamaquoddy Bay project intended to utilize the power of the high tides of the Bay of Fundy and adjacent waters was started in the mid-1930's and then abandoned. In July 1963 President Kennedy ordered that the project be revived with the thought that the completed system of dams would demonstrate the feasibility of installations intended to utilize the power of the tides.

Fig. 1   The Samuel C. Moore hydroelectric installation on the Upper Connecticut River has a capacity of 190,000 kilowatts. This plant is located at Littleton, New Hampshire, and began operation near the end of 1956. The dam is 175 feet high and water in the reservoir covers 3500 acres. The installation generates electricity in its power plant, helps to regulate the flow of the Connecticut River, and provides recreational opportunities along the shores of the reservoir. (New England Electric System.)

The Middle Atlantic. New York, Pennsylvania, and New Jersey together make up the Middle Atlantic division. This area is economically one of the most important sections of the country because of the density of the population and the high development of the power resources for industrial and commercial purposes.

In the United States as a whole less than 20 percent of the electricity produced for public use is generated by hydroelectric plants. In the Middle Atlantic division the percentage is under 10, which means that access to coal results in steam-generated electricity for the public utilities.

Most of the water power is developed along the Niagara, the St. Lawrence, and the Susquehanna rivers. Important power sites have been developed at the northern edge of the Appalachian Plateau and along the margin of the Adirondacks.

Important supplies of undeveloped power are still available along the Niagara and St. Lawrence rivers. The completion of the St. Lawrence Seaway and the construction of the

necessary dams and power plants, a large quantity of hydroelectric energy became available. Between Ogdensburg and Massena there is a 92-foot drop in a distance of only 46 miles. Three dams, the Iroquis, the Long Sault, and the Barnhart Island powerhouse, help to regulate the flow of the river and provide the head necessary for the generation of the estimated 13 billion kilowatt-hours divided equally between Canada and the United States. The New York State Power Authority receives the power for distribution to public utility companies in the market area. Under the terms of a 50-year license granted by the Federal Power Commission, a share of the power must be made available to users in nearby states as well as in the State of New York.[4]

One of the most notable developments in the Niagara area was the completion of the Robert Moses Niagara Power Plant which houses thirteen 150,000 kilowatt hydrogenerators. This plant is a 2,190,000 kilowatt installation and in-

[4] "St. Lawrence Power and Seaway Projects," *New York State Commerce Review,* Vol. 8, November 1954, pp. 1-13.

cludes not only the Robert Moses Power Plant but the Lewiston Pump Generating Plant. The reservoir above the Lewiston plant is used for water storage when the demand for power is low and when the diversion of water above Niagara Falls will not affect their scenic value. The water can then be used to generate power at both the Lewiston plant and at the Robert Moses power plant (Fig. 2). The power from this major installation is distributed by the Power Authority of the State of New York.

The chief hydroelectric plants in Pennsylvania are in the southeastern part of the state.

These hydroplants interconnected with fuel generators provide most of the electrical energy for the municipal, industrial, and commercial users. The relative accessibility of coal in western Pennsylvania has retarded somewhat the full utilization of water power, but in the future, multiple-purpose water-control projects will result in an increased use of hydrogenerated electricity.

East North Central. The division that consists of Ohio, Indiana, Illinois, Michigan, and Wisconsin is an area of relatively low relief and moderate rainfall; hence the power resources of

Fig. 2 The Robert Moses Niagara Power Plant houses thirteen, 150,000-kilowatt hydrogenerators. The installation is 1840 feet long and features a power vista at the right designed to accommodate tourists and others who will visit this plant. In the background is the Lewiston Pump-Generating Plant which operates alternately to pump water into the reservoir during the night and to generate electricity when the water flows toward a downgrade to the Robert Moses Power Plant. (Power Authority of the State of New York.)

these East North Central states are not great. In Ohio, Indiana, and Illinois the unglaciated and the older drift areas have limited water-power resources. Michigan and Wisconsin are somewhat more elevated and glaciation disorganized the drainage so that numerous sites are available. This in effect is an area of little powers which collectively total only 2½ percent of the potential water power of the country.

In the Upper Lakes Region the high percentage of the land in forests, the extensive swamp areas, and the numerous lakes regulate the discharge of the streams. In Wisconsin and Michigan the potential resources will permit a substantial increase in the capacity of water turbines.

South Atlantic. The South Atlantic division consists of the District of Columbia and the eight states of Delaware, Maryland, Virginia, West Virginia, North Carolina, South Carolina, Georgia, and Florida. This area embraces slightly more than 9 percent of the land area of the United States, has approximately 14 percent of the population, and has slightly over 5 percent of the potential water power.

The low-lying Coastal Plain with its through-flowing streams of low gradient has little available water power. But inland along the Piedmont and at the margin of the Southern Appalachians several major streams provide numerous sites for the development of power.

A major part of this area was for a long time largely agricultural. As a consequence, rapid or full utilization of the water resources lagged behind industrial New England. But with the shift of many of the textile mills to the Piedmont and with the growing demands for power in other industries, particularly woodworking, tobacco, and chemicals, the installed capacity of the water wheels increased.

It is estimated that the available undeveloped energy resources will permit doubling the present output of power without exhausting the potential water power available in the area. Full development cannot come at once, for power generation is related to other water problems

such as municipal and industrial supplies of water, stream pollution, navigation, and flood control.

On the east slope of the southern Appalachians the chief power rivers include the Savannah, the Santee, Roanoke, Potomac, Saluda, Warrior and Tombigbee, Yadkin-Pee Dee, the Chattahoochee, and many smaller streams. One of the largest reservoirs in this area is the Saluda, on the Saluda River in South Carolina.

In the South Atlantic area the power produced from projects under the control of the Corps of Engineers is marketed by the Southeastern Power Administration. Under the terms of 136 contracts involving more than a dozen installations blocks of electric energy are delivered to the local utilities for sale to the ultimate consumers.

Full development of the water-power resources must take into account the occasional dry years which greatly reduce the discharge of the streams. Reservoirs to provide storage of great quantities of water in periods or seasons of abundance and interconnection with fuel-generator systems are necessary to assure the consumer that adequate power will be available at all times.

East South Central. The four states of Kentucky, Tennessee, Mississippi, and Alabama which lie south of the Ohio and east of the Mississippi comprise the East South Central division. Mississippi, which is largely in the Coastal Plain, is least important in respect to water-power resources. A high percentage of the area is in the drainage basin of the Tennessee River and as a result has experienced, since 1933, a rapid development of the water-power resources under the jurisdiction of the Tennessee Valley Authority.

The Tennessee River, largely an uncontrolled stream before the initiation of the TVA program, had a number of small reservoirs in the headstream area and the great Wilson Dam at Muscle Shoals. A program of acquisition of dams already built and the construction of new dams has brought the Tennessee largely under control.

The impounded waters make the Tennessee a navigable stream at all times; the power developed at the several dams is available within the Valley and to the tributary areas; the floodwaters resulting from excessive precipitation are held back and contained within the reservoirs and the stream channel; and as a byproduct the impounded waters provide fishing and recreational opportunities for great numbers of people (Fig. 3).

By 1963 after the Tennessee Valley Authority had been in operation for 30 years the twenty-first dam, the Melton Hill, was nearing completion. The Authority controlled a total of 32 reservoirs and virtually regulated the flow of the Tennessee River. The generator capacity of the power-producing facilities reached an installed capacity of 12,711,000 kilowatts compared with 800,000 kilowatts in 1933. Nearly two-thirds of the power-generating capacity or 8,724,000 kilowatts was in relatively new and efficient steam-electric plants.[5]

[5] Tennessee Valley Authority, *Annual Report*, 1963, p. 8.

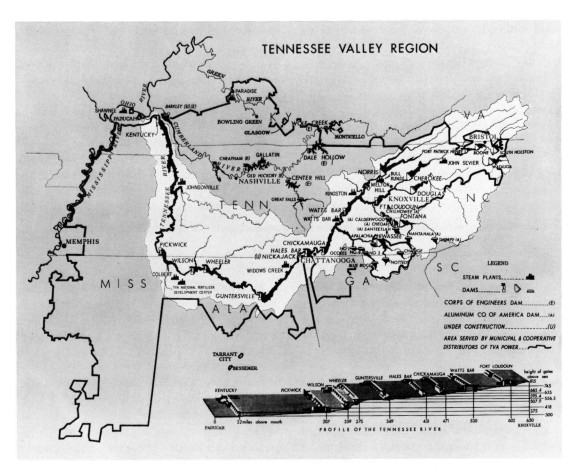

Fig. 3 Map of the Tennessee Valley, showing the location of the dams, the steam plants, and boundary of the area served by the municipal and cooperative distributors of TVA power. Five of the dams are privately owned, but control or release of the water is a responsibility of the Authority. Note the location of the steam plants which collectively generate approximately two-thirds of the electric power produced in the TVA. (Tennessee Valley Authority.)

Interconnection with nearby electric utilities permits the TVA to supply power in the summer to the power-deficient areas to the south and southwest. In the winter season the TVA purchases power from other producers to meet the needs of the area, chiefly for heating.[6] In the TVA the per capita consumption of electric energy is 10,406 kilowatt-hours annually or more than double the consumption of 4353 kilowatt-hours for the country as a whole.

West North Central. The seven states of Minnesota, Iowa, Missouri, North and South Dakota, Nebraska, and Kansas make up the West North Central division. Contained within these states is 17 percent of the total area of the United States and 8 percent of the population but only 5 percent of the potential water power.

Inadequate hydroelectric power is available in this area for industrial purposes, municipal users, and the rural electrification program. Much of the electrical energy will have to be fuel-generated. Coal and petroleum are available in the southern part of the area and are used extensively in the generation of electricity. Multiple-purpose water-control projects in the eastern part of the area are under development chiefly to control the floods and to permit the development of hydroelectric power.

The through-flowing rivers such as the Missouri have important power resources in the sparsely populated headstream area. It is not economically feasible to transport the power to the Dakotas, Nebraska, and Kansas. These areas will probably continue to meet their power needs chiefly from the local or nearby fuel resources although the completion of several authorized projects has increased greatly the power derived from water. In Nebraska and in the Black Hills area of South Dakota small water-power installations can contribute a limited supply of hydroelectric energy in an area of scant water resources.

The largest power installations now in operation in the West North Central area include the

Keokuk on the Mississippi in southeastern Iowa, Lake-of-the-Ozarks on the Osage in Missouri, and the Oahe, the Garrison, Fort Randall, and Gavins Point all on the Missouri. The Fort Randall Dam was constructed by the Army Engineers under the Flood Control Act of 1944 and required 10 years for completion. It has a capacity of 320,000 kilowatts and began the generation of electricity in January 1956 (Fig. 4).

West South Central. The West South Central division consisting of the four states of Arkansas, Louisiana, Oklahoma, and Texas contains less than 15 percent of the area of the United States, slightly over 3 percent of the potential water power, and slightly under 10 percent of the population. This is one of the least important water-power areas in the United States. A small fraction of the resources has been developed. Here as in many other sections of the country the movement to bring the great rivers and the little waters under control has resulted in the installation of generators at some of the dams built partly for flood control and navigation.

The Southwestern Power Administration markets the power generated by nine hydroelectric installations in this area. These plants have a total capacity of just under 800,000 kilowatts. Ten plants now under construction will double the capacity of the hydrogenerators in this area.

Mountain. Geographically this is the largest census division and includes Montana, Idaho, Wyoming, Colorado, New Mexico, Utah, Arizona, and Nevada. This large area contains approximately 20 percent of the water-power resources of the United States. Here the generation of water power is closely associated with other water uses, particularly irrigation. Generally these two major uses are not in conflict, for the melt water of the winter snows can be impounded during the spring and early summer. The water can first be utilized for power and then distributed to the thirsty land.

The major centers of power development are in the Northern Rockies or the adjacent plains where mining and mineral processing require

[6] *Ibid.*, p. 40.

Fig. 4   An aerial view, looking northwest, of Fort Randall Dam on the Missouri River in southeastern South Dakota showing the main structures, the intake facilities, the surge tanks, the power house where eight generators have an installed capacity of 320,000 kilowatts, the spillway, and the reservoir covering 102,000 acres at maximum height. (Corps of Engineers, U.S. Army.)

a large amount of electrical power. The headwaters of the Missouri, particularly at Great Falls, at Hungry Horse, and at Cabinet Gorge now provide power for western Montana. In Idaho the Snake River generates power for the southern part of the state and adjacent areas. The largest installation in this division is at the Hoover Dam on the Colorado River below the Grand Canyon. Downstream below the dam the generator capacity installed at Davis Dam and at Parker Dam is 225,000 and 120,000 kilowatts, respectively. Along the western margin of the Colorado Plateau and along the Wasatch Mountains, many small hydrogenerators provide power for the populated areas in Utah.

After a long controversy over the development of the water resources of the Upper Colorado basin, the 84th Congress in 1956 authorized

federal financing of this multiple-purpose project. It is estimated that the Upper Colorado project when fully developed will have a capacity of over a million kilowatts.

The Flaming Gorge and the Glen Canyon units of the Colorado River Storage Project have been completed. The generator capacity of the two units is 108,000 kilowatts, and 910,000 kilowatts, respectively (Fig. 5).

Pacific. Washington, Oregon, and California include within their boundaries only 10.7 percent of the area of the United States but contain approximately 46 percent of the potential water power. Approximately one-half of the available power is in Washington, and the other half is divided almost equally between Oregon and California. The availability of water power and the relative scarcity of competing fuels, except

Fig. 5   The Glen Canyon Dam on the Colorado River is one of the major units in the water storage and power projects in the headwater section of the river. Each of the eight units will generate 112,500 kilowatts, or together the capacity is 910,000 kilowatts. (U.S. Bureau of Reclamation. Photo by Stan Rasmussen.)

in southern California where petroleum is abundant, have been conducive to the development and use of hydroelectric energy. Coal produced in Oregon and Washington, although economically important, is not competitive to the extent that water-power development is seriously retarded. In view of the scant supplies of high-grade coal the development of perennially renewable water-power resources will prolong or extend the life of the limited reserves.

Great reserves of undeveloped power remain in the Pacific Northwest where the relatively high mountains and the heavy precipitation, particularly in the form of snow during the winter, are favorable conditions. This seasonality of the precipitation will require many relatively large reservoirs to even out the discharge of the streams and to provide a contin-

uous and uniform delivery of electric current to the consumers. East of the Cascades and in the agricultural valleys of California water is also needed for irrigation. Economic development of the Pacific area will require both the expansion of irrigation agriculture and the utilization of the water-power resources.

Before 1930 most of the power development was along the west slope of the Cascades and the Sierra Nevada, but the Columbia, one of the great power rivers of America, is now contributing its power to the consumers of the tributary area. The construction of the Bonneville Dam where the Columbia breaches the Cascades and the Grand Coulee Dam more than 400 miles upstream has made available power which served well the wartime industries (Fig. 6).

Between the Bonneville and Grand Coulee dams, other structures such as The Dalles, the McNary, Priest Rapids, Wanapum, Rock Island, and Chief Joseph and the power installations have together a capacity in excess of 5,000,000 kilowatts. These and other power facilities on the main stem of the Columbia and the Snake River can provide a large block of hydroelectric power for use in the Pacific Northwest.

Along the Columbia River and its major tributaries twenty-seven federal multipurpose projects have been completed or are nearing completion. The larger hydroelectric plants include the Grand Coulee, The Dalles, Chief

Joseph, McNary, Priest Rapids, Rocky Reach, and Bonneville. The power from these major installations and the many projects of lesser capacity is marketed through the Bonneville Power Administration. Blocks of power from these several sources are delivered to local electric utilities in Washington and Oregon and by interconnection can be distributed to more remote markets in adjacent states, particularly in California where population growth since World War II has created a need for increased amounts of electrical energy.

In addition to the numerous reservoirs that have been constructed on the west slope of the

Fig. 6   When the Grand Coulee Dam was completed in 1941 it was the largest concrete structure of its kind in the world. Since that time five dams in the Soviet Union (three completed), one in Canada, the John Day in the United States, and the Aswan dam in Egypt will have an ultimate installed capacity greater than Grand Coulee with a capacity of 1,974,000 kilowatts. (U.S. Bureau of Reclamation.)

Cascade–Sierra Nevada Mountains, some of which rank among the highest in the world, the Shasta Dam on the Sacramento was completed in 1945. This great dam serves the multiple purposes of supplying water for the dry plains of the Sacramento Valley, of holding back the floodwaters which in times past have been so destructive, and of generating power for the tributary area.

The developed water power in the Pacific division is slightly more than 21 percent of the total feasible undeveloped resources. Rapid development is largely dependent on the expansion of the market and the ability of the power-producing companies or agencies to deliver cheap electrical energy to the consumer.

THE FEDERAL CONTROL OVER WATER POWER

From the foundation of the federal government it was generally understood that the Constitution gave the government jurisdiction over the navigable waters of the United States. There existed some doubt in respect to the extent of this jurisdiction. However, in 1824 the issue was settled by a decision of the Supreme Court which declared that the commerce clause embraced navigation. The River and Harbors Act of 1884 gave the United States Government control of structures on navigable waters. In 1901 Congress passed a bill giving the Secretary of the Interior the power to grant rights of way over public lands for water-power plants, dams, reservoirs, and transmission lines. After large areas of public land had been set aside as national forests, the Secretary of Agriculture gave easements for rights of way across forest lands. The interest of the Forest Service was related to the important relationship between the flow of streams and the forest cover. Under the leadership of Gifford Pinchot the Forest Service was much interested in protecting the watershed areas and controlling the streams in the national forests. Since the jurisdiction of the navigable waters came under the Department of War, the

national forests under the Department of Agriculture, and large areas of public land were still administered by the General Land Office of the Department of the Interior, these three departments were most concerned with the problem of government control over water resources, particularly power and water-power sites.

The National Conservation Congress of 1913 urged Congress to provide the necessary legislation to permit the utilization of navigable streams for power. At a conference in 1914 governors of the states of Utah, Colorado, Nevada, Washington, Oregon, Idaho, Wyoming, New Mexico, and North Dakota claimed the waters in their respective states as state waters and therefore under their jurisdiction. Here was a conflict between the interests of the several states and the federal government. In 1912 the Commissioner of Corporations had recognized the futility of divided authority and had recommended either public ownership or public control of the power sites. In this period of experimentation several bills related to the problem of power development and control of the water resources were introduced in the Congress.

The Federal Power Commission. During the first two decades of the present century it had become evident that federal jurisdiction over the power resources, or at least public control, was a necessity. A bill, introduced in the House by Congressman John J. Esch in the special session of the 66th Congress, was passed by the House on May 4, 1920, was passed by the Senate on May 27, and was signed by the President thus becoming the Water Power Act of June 10, 1920. This act created the Federal Power Commission giving it ". . . general administrative control over all water-power sites and kindred establishments that are located on the navigable waters on the public lands and on the reservations of the United States." [7] The Federal Power Commission became an investi-

[7] Milton Conover, *The Federal Power Commission*, Service Monograph 17, Institute for Government Research, Baltimore, 1923, p. 1.

gative and judicial agency of the federal government. Its activities include cooperation with state agencies concerned with water control. It can investigate water-power resources, issue permits and licenses, evaluate properties, and fix rates. From this beginning in 1920 when the basic legislation became a part of the law, the Federal Power Commission has continued to function very effectively in the development and control of the water-power resources of the nation.

Although the original Federal Power Act prescribed the jurisdiction of the Federal Power Commission as applying to the power resources on navigable rivers and on public lands, it was evident that, in time, its function would be extended.

During the first 10 years from 1920 to 1930 it became evident that the commission required reorganization. The cabinet members who had previously served on the commission were aware that their duties should be transferred to full-time commissioners. They would be relieved of this responsibility which would give them more time to handle the other affairs of their respective departments.

Reorganization of the Federal Power Commission. An act passed by the Congress reorganizing the commission was signed by President Hoover on June 23, 1930. A five-man commission was appointed by the President and promptly took over the duties of the commission. The first chairman was George Otis Smith, formerly Director of the U.S. Geological Survey. At the time of reorganization the capacity of water-power installations on public lands or on navigable waters had reached 3,000,000 horsepower. This was 24 percent of the total hydroelectric generating capacity of the United States. In 10 years from 1920 to 1930 there had been a 100 percent increase in capacity. In this interval the rates for electric current had declined from 7.52 cents to 6.06 cents per kilowatt hour. There still remained much to be done in the field of electrification. The commission reported in 1929 that 90 percent of the farms were without electrical service and only 2 percent of the railroad

mileage was electrified. In 1960 only about 3 percent of the farms were without electricity.[8]

When President Roosevelt was inaugurated in 1933, he realized the need for further investigations in the fields of power utilization and in the regulation of the power industry. He issued an executive order on August 19 of that year calling for a power survey. The President called upon the commission not only to survey the water resources of the country, but to consider also the problem of rates and to formulate a program of public works. The power survey ordered by President Roosevelt was one of the most comprehensive investigations of the power situation in the United States made either by a private or federal agency.[9] The problem of appropriate rates became a major concern of the commission which has cooperated with state agencies in determining fair rates to the consumer of electric current.[10]

The passage of the Public Utility Act of 1935 extended the jurisdiction of the commission to electrical energy regardless of the method of generation if the electric current was involved in interstate commerce. The commission then had power to facilitate interconnection and coordination of power facilities where the two were geographically and economically feasible.

By 1938 the Federal Power Commission was operating under six major acts of Congress: the act that created the commission in 1920, the amendatory act of 1930, the Public Utility Act of 1935, the Natural Gas Act of 1938, the Flood Control Act of 1936 as amended in 1938, and the act that created and authorized the TVA.

During World War II the Federal Power Commission was able to facilitate the allocation of power to a great variety of war industries. Between 1940 and 1945 the installed capacity of the electric power industry increased from approximately 51,000,000 kilowatts to nearly

---

[8] *Power to Produce, The Yearbook of Agriculture, 1960,* Government Printing Office, Washington, D.C., p. 71.

[9] Federal Power Commission, National Power Survey, *Interim Report, Power Series* 1, Washington, D.C., 1935.

[10] *Ibid.*

63,000,000 kilowatts. By 1953 the capacity had been further increased to more than 107,000,000 kilowatts.

The need for multiple-purpose projects on many of the great streams and the little waters of the United States requires that the commission make comprehensive surveys of the drainage basins requiring engineering works to control stream flow. Both the River and Harbors Act and the Flood Control Act of 1946 provided for the installation of penstocks in the dams when approved by the Secretary of War upon the recommendation of the Chief of Engineers and the Federal Power Commission.

The jurisdiction of the Federal Power Commission was greatly expanded when the Natural Gas Act of June 21, 1938 (and as later amended) and an Executive Order 10485, September 3, 1953, when the Commission was given responsibility and authority to regulate the interstate distribution of natural gas and to fix and adjust rates in the natural gas industry.

At last the Federal Power Commission can participate fully in the multiple-purpose projects as well as those devoted exclusively to the generation of power.

Rural Electrification. The federal government is actively engaged in the promotion of consumption of electric power in rural areas. Under the jurisdiction of the Rural Electrification Administration the government has facilitated the organization of power-distribution systems. The REA has made few loans for the development of hydroelectric power projects, but has been more concerned with the distribution of low-cost electric current to people in rural areas, so that the farmers can have power for home lighting, the electric appliances in the home, and power-driven equipment on the farm.

Public Control of Water Power. Most of the economic activities of this country are carried on by private enterprise. This is an American tradition, and there is every indication that this essential feature of our economy will be continued. However, the public interest is vitally important in those enterprises where the welfare of the people is directly involved. In the

development and distribution of power derived from falling water the public interest is evident. Development of a major water-power site under private auspices confers upon the company a quasi monopoly, and to protect the interests of the public some kind of control or regulation either by the state or by the federal government is essential.

One generation which uses the power is under some obligation to pass it on to the next in such a manner that the public welfare will be served. The use of exhaustible and diminishing resources does not imply the necessity for public control except for fair rates to the ultimate consumer of the power generated. The great size of some of the water-power projects has required public financing, for private capital could not be expected to undertake development with the necessary long-term amortization of the cost at the low rates determined by the regulatory commissions. Venture capital has been reluctant to invade this field of power development.

Numerous arguments can be advanced for public control of water-power resources. It is important that the people of the country have available at all times adequate power at reasonable rates. The facilities may be privately owned, but reasonable rates must be subject to determination by a state or federal agency, thus guaranteeing to the consumer the best electrical service for the least cost. This does not mean that private interests and the public welfare are seriously in conflict. A fair-minded state utility commission will see to it that a privately owned power company gets a reasonable return upon its investment and at the same time will be mindful of the need of the people for adequate and cheap electric service.

The monopolistic character of water-power development and particularly the generation and distribution of electric current eliminates competition as an effective force in the determination of fair and equitable rates. It would be very uneconomical and unwise to try to achieve fair rates by competition between two or more companies. Competition would require duplication of facilities which probably would result in higher costs for electrical service than would be obtained from a publicly owned utility or from a privately owned company whose rates were established by the state utility commission.

The impounding of waters in reservoirs and the discharge of the waters downstream calls for an agency whose jurisdiction transcends the local interests of a power company developing the power resources at a single site. Over-all basin control by a government agency is necessary to see that all interests, both private and public, are served.

State Commissions. In the various states there are commissions, or other agencies, that exercise jurisdiction over the intrastate power resources. These several agencies may not have the necessary personnel and financial resources to carry out all the investigations, and generally they are dependent on the fact-finding agencies of the federal government, particularly the Federal Power Commission and the United States Geological Survey.

Generally most of these state commissions are concerned with the determination of rates based on the fair appraisal of the assets of the power companies or in the determination of actual cost. The fixing of a fair rate for electric current in the market areas is a neccessary and useful function. However, in the development and distribution of power, which are interstate in character, the state agencies must cooperate with the Federal Power Commission.

In this matter, as in a number of others, individual states have been jealous of their respective rights. On occasion there has been objection to federal participation. In those cases involving the interstate commerce in power, and where the federal government has corresponding jurisdiction, as with power developed on navigable waters and on the public lands, cooperation of the state water-control agencies and the Federal Power Commission has usually been achieved without serious difficulty.

Private versus the Public Interest. In the United States to permit individuals and private companies and corporations to develop resources has been a long-standing tradition, based largely on the principle that the public lands should be distributed to relatively small landowners. Thus the development of a strong economy for the nation and personal security for the individual has been possible. The same tradition or principle has been applied also to minerals, to forests, and to waters. Great abundance has permitted the wide distribution of resources to many people, but as scarcity has developed there has tended to be a reversal of this trend, and great areas of land have been held in perpetuity by the federal government in national forests, national parks, and national monuments. The reservation of certain mineral lands to protect the public interests also has come about.

The situation in respect to water power has been a little different from that of farmlands and mineral deposits on public lands. Water power is derived from precipitation which falls widely on the land. The water then is concentrated in a watercourse, and because of fortuitous or other circumstances the water power can be developed only in a limited number of favorable locations. Water power, therefore, is a right that belongs to all the people, and, if the privilege of developing the power resources is granted to an individual or to a private company, it seems logical that a license and an appropriate fee should be required. This is the logic behind the idea that water-power resources are invested with a public interest which requires either public ownership and consequent development or private development under governmental regulation.

THE FEDERAL GOVERNMENT IN THE POWER BUSINESS

The federal government is the largest single producer of electric energy in the United States. The development of power by the federal government began with the sale of power generated at the Roosevelt Dam built on the Salt River in Arizona and at the Minidoka Dam on the Snake River, both built for irrigation purposes. Then by a succession of acts, such as the Boulder

Canyon Project Act, the act that created the Tennessee Valley Authority in 1933, the Flood Control Act of 1936, and several others, the federal government was firmly established as a producer of power for its own use and for sale.

When President Eisenhower assumed office in 1953, a reaction set in against the continued expansion of power development by the federal government. It became evident that new power projects proposed by the thirteen federal agencies involved in power activities would be closely scrutinized before they were presented to Congress for approval.

The Commission on Organization of the Executive Branch of the Government, commonly known as the Hoover Commission, made an extended study of the power industry particularly with reference to the participation of the federal government. In addition to specific recommendations that apply to particular power projects, such as the Tennessee Valley Authority, the Central Valley Project in California, the Southeastern Power Administration, the Rural Electrification Administration, and many other projects, the Commission implied, if not directly recommended, that the federal government discontinue or slow down the development of power resources in competition with private power companies. It could hardly be expected that a policy that had gained considerable momentum over a period of 20 years could be immediately reversed. Most of the recommendations of the Commission were concerned with improvements in the federal government's operation in the field of power development and distribution. Implicit in the report was the recommendation that the government discontinue activities in a field where private industry is able to finance the power developments.[11]

Interstate Compacts. Most water-control projects transcend the state boundaries and require joint or multiple state agreements for their

development. Water power in all its aspects is not limited to the site where the generator is located but extends to the headstream area where the water begins its flow to the sea. This is the area of water storage, either natural or man made, which regulates, as far as possible, the supply of power where the turbines and generators are installed. A proper and full development of the power resources of a drainage basin would require an interstate compact as a means of securing the cooperation of the several states and the Federal Power Commission. The development of such interstate compacts requires a number of stages before the compacts can be given final effect.

1. They must be authorized by Congress which provides the enabling legislation.

2. State legislatures must also authorize the project and provide the personnel and agencies that are to carry out the negotiations.

3. The commissioners of the several states must draw up the compact.

4. The compact must now be submitted to the legislatures of the several states for approval and ratification.

5. Congress must also ratify the compact.

Any break in this series of five steps may mean the ultimate failure of a project applicable to a drainage basin. However, the defection of a single state, depending somewhat on its location in the drainage basin, may or may not affect the proposed project.

The Partnership Idea. President Eisenhower in his first State of the Union message to Congress in January 1953 expressed himself in favor of the development of natural resources not by federal bureaucracy but by a partnership involving the cooperation of the several states, local communities, private citizens, and the federal government.[12] In the power field the President intended this to mean that the federal government would not pre-empt all power sites in a drainage basin but would encourage local

[11] Commission on Organization of the Executive Branch of the Government, *Water Resources and Power*, Vol. 2, Washington, D.C., 1955, pp. 275–716. Many of the specific recommendations of the Commission in respect to power and other water-resource problems are presented in Vol. 1 of this three-volume report.

[12] Commission on Organization of the Executive Branch of the Government, *Water Resources and Power*, Vol. 3, Washington, D.C., 1955, p. 1585.

governments and private industry to undertake power developments. The partnership idea is not new, but one of its chief effects will be " ... to limit new starts on Federal power projects." [13] It was clearly the policy of the Eisenhower administration to give private industry greater opportunities in the development of the power resources of the nation.

In spite of the efforts of private power interests and the attitudes of some public officials the participation of the federal government in the development of the water-power resources of the nation is an established policy. Not uncommonly the development of power is tied in with multipurpose projects including flood control, irrigation, navigation, and recreation. It would be unwise to neglect the development of the water-power resources simply because of the objections to the development of water power by the use of public funds. The schedule for the completion of dams over the next few years by the Bureau of Reclamation and by the Corps of Engineers is convincing evidence that the development of water power is an on-going concern of the national government.

CONSERVATION OF WATER POWER

Water power is a renewable resource. Unlike the fuels, it is not depleted by use and once used can be reused time and time again. The fuel minerals are extractable and expendable, but water power is perennially renewable. It must be used as the water seeks its lowest level, or the power is lost forever. This distinguishing feature of water power has led many people to believe that we should make every effort to make immediate and full use of water-power resources. Unhappily, this is hardly possible when con-

[13] Ben Moreell, *Our Nation's Water Resources—Policies and Politics*, Chicago, Illinois, 1956, p. 45.

sidered in the light of both the physical characteristics of the streams and the economic conditions under which the power must be developed and utilized.

The irregular discharge or flow of the streams introduces a serious limitation to the development and use of water power. Storage may achieve reasonable regularity, but the dams may be very expensive and add greatly to the cost of the power. Since full use of the power is economically unwise, it may be possible, however, to utilize a high percentage of the power available and use stand-by steam plants to maintain a satisfactory flow of electric current to the consumers. Where competing fuels are not available it may be economically feasible to develop the water power to the fullest. In other areas, such as the upper Ohio Valley where enormous quantities of coal are available, the development of the water resources for the production of power may be quite uneconomical. Only where control of the rivers for multiple purposes and where the cost can be distributed among several beneficiaries would it be wise to develop to the fullest the power resources. The conservation of water-power resources therefore is not a simple engineering problem of bringing a river completely under control and utilizing the total power available. Development must take place in a context of the local and national economy: at a particular time it may be inadvisable to install water wheels to utilize the power of falling water; in a later period is may be entirely possible and economically very desirable to make partial, if not a full, use of the water-power resources. Conservation is therefore both an engineering and an economic problem and may require the solution of the several water problems *seriatim* instead of simultaneously according to a grandiose plan.

References

Ackerman, Edward A., and George O. G. Löf, *Technology in America's Water Development*, Resources for the Future, The Johns Hopkins Press, Baltimore, 1959.

Ayres, E., and C. A. Scarlott, *Energy Sources—The Wealth of the World*, McGraw-Hill Book Co., New York, 1952.

Commission on Organization of the Executive Branch of the Government, *Water Resources and Power*, 3 Vols., Government Printing Office, Washington, D.C., 1955.

Conover, Milton, *The Federal Power Commission*, Service Monograph 17, Institute for Government Research, Baltimore, 1923.

Daugherty, C. R., A. H. Horton, and R. W. Davenport, *Power Capacity and Production in the United States*, Water Supply Paper 579, U.S. Geological Survey, Washington, D.C., 1928.

Federal Power Commission, *Annual Reports*, Washington, D.C.

Federal Power Commission, *Estimated Future Power Requirements of the United States by Regions, 1953–1975*, Washington, D.C., 1954.

Federal Power Commission, *Hydroelectric Power Resources of the United States, Developed and Undeveloped, 1960*, P-33, Washington, D.C.

Federal Power Commission, *Natural Power Survey, Interim Report*, Washington, D.C., 1935.

Krutilla, John V., and Otto Eckstein, *Multiple Purpose River Development*, Resources for the Future, The Johns Hopkins Press, Baltimore, 1958. Reprinted 1961.

Kuenen, Philip Henry, *Realms of Water*, translated by May Hollander, John Wiley and Sons, New York, 1955.

Langbein, Walter, *Topographic Characteristics of Drainage Basins*, Water Supply Paper 968-C, U.S. Geological Survey, Washington, D.C., 1947.

Moreell, Ben, *Our Nation's Water Resources—Policies and Politics*, The Law School, The University of Chicago, Chicago, 1956. See particularly Lecture IV, "Federal Power Developments," pp. 149–188.

National Resources Committee, *Our Energy Resources*, Washington, D.C., 1939.

The President's Materials Policy Commission, *Resources for Freedom*, Volume III: *The Outlook for Energy Resources*, Government Printing Office, Washington, D.C., 1952.

Rayhawk, Arthur L., *The Energy Resources of the United States in Relation to Future Population Developments*, Chapter II: "Water Power," Washington, D.C., 1932, pp. 33–67.

Schurr, Sam H., Bruce C. Netschert, et al., *Energy in the American Economy, 1850–1975*, Resources for the Future, The John Hopkins Press, Baltimore, 1960.

United Nations Department of Economic Affairs, UNSCCUR, Vol. IV, *Water Resources*, New York, 1951.

United States Department of Agriculture, *Power to Produce*, The Yearbook of Agriculture, *1960*, Government Printing Office, Washington, D.C.

Voskuil, Walter H., *The Economics of Water Power Development*. A. W. Shaw Co. New York, 1928.

EDWIN J. FOSCUE
Southern Methodist University

GUY-HAROLD SMITH
The Ohio State University

CHAPTER 14

Waterways and Their Utilization

Bodies of water—oceans, seas, gulfs, sounds, lakes, and rivers—provide the cheapest form of transportation for man if they are used in their natural form and under the most favorable conditions; man-made waterways may also provide cheap transportation, if these canals are dug in areas requiring them. Unfortunately, many canals have been constructed without due consideration of their costs and relative values when completed, and this has caused an apprehensive attitude in the mind of the general public toward inland waterway transportation that is not always justified.

Other than the digging of canals, the chief improvement that has been made in water transportation is in the carrier itself. The dugout canoe and the raft were some of the earliest improvements on the floating log. The development of the power-driven boat or raft, whether propelled by man power, wind, steam, or diesel engine, was perhaps the greatest improvement in the carrier in that it allowed man to ascend a stream against a current.

Improvements in the carriers of commerce, however, were not all that was needed to make waterways useful to man. Some streams flowed in the wrong direction, or had circuitous courses which had to be straightened and widened, or

contained obstructions such as rapids and falls which had to be by-passed by canals or other means of transportation, or were blocked by ice during the winter. In attempting to overcome the natural handicaps so as to make the waterway more serviceable as a carrier of commerce, man has built portage trails, railways, and canals and has spent money lavishly on many projects that never should have been attempted. However, these mistakes should not cause one to condemn all waterway projects nor overlook those that have been successful in the past or those that may be desirable in the future. In making improvements, either in the carriers or the navigated waters, man must adapt his work to:

1. The physical condition of the water bodies.
2. The types of commodities to be carried.
3. The ever-increasing commercial demands resulting from an increasing population and a changing economic order.
4. The mechanical developments and improvements that are continually being made under the spur of competition.

Large sums have been spent by the United States government for improvements in harbors and rivers and in constructing canals. To-

273

day, improvements in navigation are linked so closely with the development of water power and flood control on streams, as in the case of the Tennessee Valley Authority, that it is perhaps unreasonable to charge the large appropriations to navigation alone. The various valley authorities should be analyzed from all points of view before they are either approved or condemned. It is true that the ultimate consumer pays the transportation bill, but, when certain parts are charged off to national defense, perhaps this cost is not too great. In the future, all forms of transportation by land and water should be studied so that the available facilities may be fully utilized by the people of the United States both in time of war and in time of peace. Waterways, railroads, motor-truck lines, and airlines, all have a place in the development and growth of a modern nation. The combined arteries of transportation should be able to withstand the shock of any commercial or military demand.

WATER-BORNE COMMERCE

Approximately 17 percent of the commerce of the United States is water borne. The railroads carry 43 percent, motor trucks 22 percent, pipelines under 20 percent, and aircraft less than 1 percent. Over many years the railroad and the waterways carried most of the commerce, but in recent decades the motor truck using the public highways and the pipelines have become competitors for cargoes appropriate to the carriers.

Commodities in bulk make up the commerce along the coast, on the riverways, and on the Great Lakes. These bulky products move in quantity at slow speed and at freight rates that give the water carriers a competitive advantage in the movement of such cargoes. The combination of major commodities differs with the waterway. Coastwise commerce is characterized by the movement of great quantities of petroleum in fleets of tankers. Other raw materials include minerals such as iron ore, bauxite,

sulfur, and a number of food products including coffee and sugar. On the inland waterways not including the Great Lakes the principal products carried include petroleum and petroleum products, bituminous coal and lignite, sand, gravel and crushed stone, logs, sea shells, grain, and grain products.

On the Great Lakes the trade from the Upper Lakes area consists chiefly of wheat and other grains, iron ore, limestone, and timber products. Upbound cargoes are dominated by bituminous coal for the Upper Lakes area. With the completion of the St. Lawrence Seaway and the entrance of ocean-going freighters into the Great Lakes the commodities have become more diversified.

OUR WATERWAY RESOURCES

The United States ranks high among the nations of the world in its navigation resources. The types of "waters" used for the movement of commodities are:

1. Ocean waters.
2. Seacoast harbors (the deeper intracoastal waters).
3. Intracoastal waters, other than harbors.
4. Lakes.
5. Rivers.
6. Canals.

Ocean Waters. The total length of the "general" coastline of the contiguous states of the United States is 4883 miles, subdivided as follows: Atlantic Coast, 1888 miles; Gulf Coast, 1629 miles; and Pacific Coast, 1366 miles. The tidal shoreline (reaching into harbors to points where such waters narrow to a width of 3 statute miles) is 7314 miles. With the exception of the Gulf Coast of Texas and Florida, jurisdiction over coastal waters extends only to the 3-mile limit. Improvements for ocean and coastal navigation—lighthouses and lightships, lifesaving stations, and coast guard patrol boats and airplanes—are for the safety of vessels and men. These, although contributed by the federal government, are international in their benefits.

Multiple-Purpose Water-Control Projects and Navigation. Rivers in their natural state are not entirely satisfactory for the several purposes they are called upon to serve. Navigation may be hazardous in time of flood and impossible at the low-water stage. The long-time efforts to maintain forests or water-retaining vegetation in the upper sections of a drainage are intended primarily to prevent rapid runoff, soil erosion, and floods along the down-stream sections of the main stream. The longer water can be held on the land the greater is the probability that the groundwater reserves can be built up. The building of dams along the tributaries of a major stream may provide water for municipal and industrial purposes, for recreation, for power development, for irrigation, and at the same time help to reduce floods and provide water for the benefit of navigation in times of minimum flow. It may be necessary also to build dams along the main stream chiefly for navigation as along the Ohio, the Upper Mississippi, and several other navigable riverways. In drainage basins where the benefits are widely distributed among different groups of people it becomes very difficult to assign costs among the beneficiaries of the public works required to bring a river and its tributaries under control.

Seacoast Harbors (the Deeper Intracoastal Waters). The effectiveness of a coastline is measured more by the number and usableness of the harbors than by length (Fig. 1). Those north of and including Chesapeake Bay are spacious. From Sandy Hook northeastward they are largely the result of glacial action and drowning.

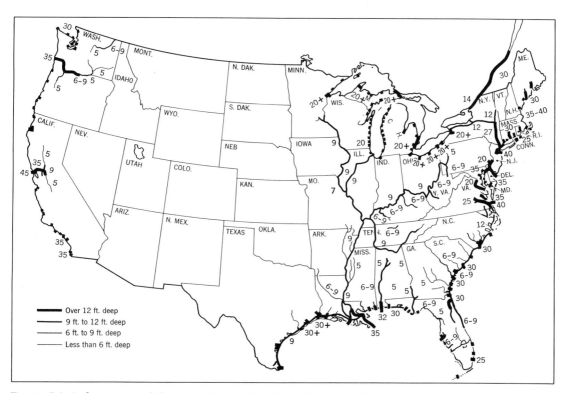

Fig. 1 Principal waterways of the United States, 1957. (After Office of the Chief of Engineers, U.S. Army.)

Boston Harbor is separated from the ocean by drumlins. New York Harbor is largely the drowned lower Hudson Valley.

Along the southern Atlantic and Gulf coasts, from Sandy Hook to the mouth of the Rio Grande, harbors for the most part are estuaries, the result of drowning of valleys carved in the Coastal Plain. At Philadelphia, Baltimore, and Richmond the estuaries cut completely across the Coastal Plain to the Fall Line. Most estuaries are shallow and thus require much dredging to provide navigable channels for modern vessels. Moreover, they call for continual attention because of the tidal shifting of sediments.

The Pacific coast harbors, although excellent in general, are few in number. The harbor at Los Angeles is largely man-made. Two shallow, marsh-bordered water areas have been dredged into a very serviceable harbor. San Francisco Bay and Puget Sound are excellent natural water bodies, requiring only the minimum of improvement. San Francisco Bay is a drowned mountain valley; Golden Gate which leads out to the ocean is a drowned mountain pass. Puget Sound besides being drowned has been glaciated. The lower Columbia River Valley is also drowned. There are shifting bars at the mouth that require constant attention even with fairly permanent improvements. It was the shallow water of these bars that deterred Admiral Vancouver from claiming the Columbia as a British river; shortly afterwards, Gray, a New England clipper ship captain, sailed up the Columbia River and laid claim to the lands it drained for the United States of America.

With the admission of Alaska and Hawaii as the forty-ninth and fiftieth states, respectively, the shoreline of the United States was greatly increased and the natural harbor areas were enlarged. In Alaska the island-guarded inner passage and bays provide anchorage areas and docking facilities for a number of towns such as Ketchikan, Juneau, and Skagway. Prince William Sound, protected from the wind and waves of the Gulf of Alaska, gives access to Valdez and Cordova. Anchorage fronts on Cook Inlet which

extends inland between Kenai Peninsula and mainland Alaska. The port of Seward on the south side of the Peninsula was badly damaged in the Good Friday (1964) earthquake. It is the Pacific terminus of the Alaskan railway, an important access route to the interior. All the coastal waters have very high tides which make freight handling difficult and require high piers to permit loading and unloading at times of low or high tides.

The several islands that make up Hawaii are not deeply indented, but fortunately on the Island of Oahu a large protected anchorage area serves the port city of Honolulu and Pearl Harbor, and adjacent land areas provide anchorage and space for on-shore facilities adequate for a major military installation.

A harbor to be serviceable should be spacious enough to provide anchorage space and freedom of movement for vessels visiting the harbor. Since anchored vessels shift their position with changes in the wind and the tide, each vessel must have a space allotment greater in radius than the length of the vessel. The additional space demanded is proportional to the length of anchor chain used. Deep harbors are not essential, but they should be from 5 to 10 feet deeper than the draft of ships being served at lowest tide.

Until well into the nineteenth century the depth demands of ocean vessels were modest and little dredging of channels and anchorage space was needed. The large harbors today have 25- to 30- and even 40-foot channels with a width of 300 to 600 feet. Harbor improvements that have to do with serviceable channels, anchorage space, and turning basins are, as a rule, provided by the federal government. State, city, and private companies ordinarily provide the freight piers and channels to state, city, or private wharves or to dry docks and ferry slips (Fig. 2).

Harbors with broad mouths on low coasts require artificial breakwaters or piers for protection. Harbors on northern rivers or lakes which are subject to freezing in winter also require breakwaters. In Delaware Bay, both types of protection are needed.

Lagoon harbors, such as the one at Miami, require constant dredging to secure the requisite depth of the channel across the bar at the mouth of the lagoon. At Baltimore, at the head of the Patapsco estuary, a channel 20 miles long has been excavated from the city harbor to the 35-foot isobath in Chesapeake Bay. Near the mouth of York River another channel 4.5 miles long has had to be dredged in Chesapeake Bay to provide a 35-foot depth for large ocean vessels bound to or from Baltimore. As cities such as New York, Philadelphia, Baltimore, and others expand their overseas commerce, additional wharf space, anchorage basins, and channels are called for.

The silt-laden Mississippi makes the maintenance of a deep channel for ocean vessels from the Gulf to New Orleans a costly project. Silting at both the head and the mouths (passes) of the channels of "bird-foot" deltas, presents a problem which calls for constant supervision and frequent dredging. Jetties[1] have not entirely solved the problems of providing a usable channel.

An interesting harbor development on the Gulf Coast is the Houston Ship Channel that extends 50 miles northwesterly from the ocean across Galveston Bay, and thence along San Jacinto River and Buffalo Bayou. This channel, with a depth of 36 feet and a width varying from 300 to 400 feet, ends in a turning basin at Houston (Fig. 3).

Even San Francisco Bay has required aid in deepening and widening its main ship channel, and the State of California has given generous contributions to enable the bay ports to handle large volumes of commerce.

[1] This device was designed by James B. Eads for South Pass in 1879. He and his associates contracted to maintain the channel 26 feet deep and 200 feet wide at the bottom for a term of 20 years. The total sum paid them by the government was $8,000,000. Although the jetties are probably more effective than any other method known, other devices are needed to control the silt (400,000,000 tons a year) that is deposited where river currents meet tidal waters of the Gulf.

Fig. 2 Sea trial of the *Marine Texan*, a ship designed to transport molten sulfur in coastwise commerce. Insulated barges also carry molten sulfur along the Intracoastal Canal and up the Mississippi River. (Texas Gulf Sulphur Company.)

The entrance to the Columbia River is protected by jetties, and frequent dredging is required to maintain a 35-foot channel across the bar at the mouth of the river at mean low tide. The lower Willamette and lower Columbia are here considered intracoastal. From Portland to the ocean is 110 miles. In its original condition this section of the Columbia had controlling depths of only 10 to 15 feet at low water, but it now has a 30-foot channel from Portland to the head of the estuary.

Harbors and Waterways and the National Interest. After America was discovered the interior was explored along its watercourses. Until other means of transportation became available the waterways were used to settle and develop the country. All major means of transportation, waterways, railways, highways, and airways have received financial aid in one form or an-

Fig. 3 The turning basin and upper harbor of the Port of Houston. This man-made harbor has a depth of 36 feet at mean low tide and is capable of docking a large number of ships. It is located 50 miles from the Gulf of Mexico and is connected with it by the Houston Ship Channel. (Houston Chamber of Commerce.)

other from the federal government. Harbor development and maintenance, waterways and their special needs and long-tern maintenance, and the size of the dams, power houses, and other facilities necessary in the development of water resources are beyond the means of private financing and require heavy contributions by the federal government.

Members of Congress and other political leaders have often been accused of favoring economy in government as long as public works projects were in their particular state or district

approved for construction. Considering the number of steps a project concerned with navigation must go through, only the most worthy proposals are likely to receive financial support and be constructed. A project may be proposed by an individual, by any one of a number of private organizations, or by an agency of the local, state, or federal government. A senator or member of the House may be asked to submit the project to the appropriate Public Works Committee for consideration. By the time the proposal meets all the tests imposed by the Congressional Committees, the Corps of Engineers, the Director of the Budget, and all interested parties the proposal will be ready for the final steps in its development. After the appropriation bill providing for the financing of a particular project passes both houses of Congress and is signed by the President, the Corps of Engineers may call for bids on the project, or structures may be built, or some other work such as dredging be done by the Corps itself. In time, usually several years after an improvement was first suggested, the project is completed and becomes a functioning facility in the economy of the nation.

Intracoastal Waters, Other Than Harbors. In addition to the major harbors, several other large intracoastal water bodies have required but little improvement to enable them to handle both ocean and coastal traffic. These include Narragansett Bay, Long Island Sound, Delaware Bay, Chesapeake Bay, Albemarle and Pamlico sounds, Tampa Bay, Mobile Bay, Galveston Bay, San Francisco Bay, and Puget Sound. Lagoon waters are almost continuous from New York Harbor southward to the tip of Florida and also border almost the entire Gulf Coast. Most of these shallow intracoastal waters and several deep intracoastal water bodies have been connected by short canals to form the great Intracoastal Waterway that extends from Cape Cod Bay to Key West, and from Apalachee Bay in Florida to the mouth of the Rio Grande.

Lakes. In area of water surface, in depth, and in volume of commerce, the five Great Lakes of North America form the most important inland body of navigable waters in the world. This great waterway, in its original condition, had two distinct barriers to continuous navigation, one between lakes Superior and Huron and the other between lakes Erie and Ontario.

At the rapids in the St. Marys River, which connects Lake Superior with Lake Huron, the water is only 2 or 3 feet deep where it plunges over the resistant red sandstone ledges. The first American ship canal (with one lock) at the St.

Marys rapids was completed in 1855. A canoe and bateau canal, however, had been constructed on the Canadian side of the river in 1798. It was destroyed by the Americans in 1814. There are now four chambers on the American side of the St. Marys River at Sault Ste. Marie, in two canals. The depths of water at the locks are 12.6 feet, 18 feet, 34.5 feet, and 24.5 feet, respectively. A sum of $600,000 for the construction of a new lock in the St. Marys River at Sault Ste. Marie was included in the appropriation bill for $31,600,000 for water-related projects in the Great Lakes signed by President Johnson on December 31, 1963. The new lock will be 1200 feet long and 110 feet wide.

The Canadians have a ship canal (and one lock) that accommodates the largest lake vessels. All the locks are free to the vessels of either country. The St. Marys River has been improved, and two channels have been provided for upstream and downstream navigation.

On December 4, 1963, the Canadian House of Commons authorized the borrowing of $180,000,000 for twinning four locks on the Welland Canal.[2] When completed the delays occasioned by more ships than the locks could accommodate will be avoided.

In the St. Clair and Detroit rivers, the connecting waters between lakes Huron, St. Clair, and Erie, much dredging and blasting of hard rock have been necessary to provide a 27-foot channel that would accommodate the large lake carriers and ocean-going freighters which now serve the major ports on the Great Lakes.

The greatest obstacle to navigation of the Great Lakes in the beginning was Niagara Falls. Between 1824 and 1833 the original Welland Canal was constructed connecting Lake Erie and Lake Ontario. The chambers were deepened to 14 feet and lengthened to 270 feet. By 1931 the canal had been enlarged and the locks rebuilt so that vessels drawing 27 feet could use this section of the Great Lakes system.

[2]*The Great Lakes News Letter,* Vol. VIII, 1963, p. 4.

There are few natural harbors on the Great Lakes. Every harbor has had some improvements, which, in general, are similar to those of ocean harbors.

Navigation improvements of the Great Lakes in comparison with those of the Mississippi and ocean harbors are permanent features. Tides are scarcely discernible even with a tide gauge. The lake levels are fairly constant, varying not more than 1 or 2 feet during the year and 3 or 4 feet in a decade or two. The changes in the level are correlated closely with the relative amount of rainfall of the Lakes Region. The velocity of the currents in the connecting waters varies but little from season to season, but river harbors, like those at Cleveland and Toledo, require close attention to maintain a uniform channel depth.

The total length of the shoreline of the Great Lakes is 8345 miles. As a result of navigation improvements in the channels connecting the lakes and the numerous harbors, large vessels (many 600 feet long drawing 17 to 18 feet of water) can sail 1000 miles from Buffalo to Duluth-Superior, and about the same distance to Chicago, carrying loads larger, in tons of cargo, than those in most ocean carriers. Some of our largest cargo carriers can transport 18,000 to 20,000 tons of iron ore or an equal volume of coal or grain.

With the vast expanses of water, hundreds of traffic routes could be developed instead of the few that now exist, if the demand for them were sufficient.

Rivers. The navigable rivers of the United States drain into (1) the Atlantic Ocean, (2) the Gulf of Mexico, (3) the Pacific Ocean, and (4) the Great Lakes. All of these, other than the Mississippi and its tributaries, are relatively short, but length alone does not determine the importance of a waterway.

In their original condition, most of the Atlantic-slope rivers were navigable for only short distances upstream from their mouths. The navigable sections of New England rivers measure but a few miles, for the rock of the upland comes nearly to the ocean's edge. The only exception is the Connecticut which has a 12-foot channel to Hartford, 52 miles from the mouth. Southward from New York Harbor the navigable sections lie between the Fall Line and the intracoastal waters, and it is largely in these sections that improvements have been or are being made under "existing projects."

Several rivers of the west Gulf coast have been used to transport commercial products, but because of insufficient water in these streams, they have not been satisfactory. At recurring intervals agitation is revived for making the Trinity River navigable from the Gulf to Dallas and Fort Worth, but it is questionable that this is economically feasible, even though physically possible.

Only a few rivers on the Pacific slope are navigable. When existing projects are completed the Sacramento River will be navigable for shallow-draft vessels to Red Bluff, nearly 250 miles from Suisan Bay; and the San Joaquin will have a shallow channel to Hills Ferry about 126 miles upstream. Since the region was settled river craft have used the Columbia from Portland to the Cascade Water Gap about 160 miles from the mouth, or 50 miles above Portland. Canals and locks at the water gap of the Cascades open up long stretches for navigation (Fig. 1). The Willamette has long been available for shallow-draft river craft.

In certain respects the greatest of all river systems of the world is the Mississippi. The Missouri-Mississippi from the Rockies to the Gulf is 4200 miles long, the longest river in the world. The Missouri is 2945 miles long, the Arkansas 1460 miles, the Ohio (including its longest headwater tributary) 1283, the Tennessee nearly 1000, and the Cumberland more than 700.

Some 15,000 miles of riverways have been navigated within the Mississippi River basin, but the mileage of existing projects is far less than this (Fig. 1). It is more than a thousand miles from Cairo, near the mouth of the Ohio, to the Gulf, and nearly a thousand miles from Pittsburgh to Cairo. St. Paul, at the head of navigation on the Mississippi, is 874 miles by river from the mouth of the Ohio. Fort Benton in Montana, once the head of navigation on the Missouri, is 2285 miles by water from the mouth of the Missouri.

The navigable lengths of the rivers were once far longer than now—not that there is less water but the present standards of efficiency, and even necessity, are higher. Many rivers listed as navigable in the past were navigable only during seasons of high water, 3 to 7 months of the year. The Ohio, for example, in low-water periods had only 1 to 2 feet of water in portions of the navigable channel. The first locks and dams were provided for by Congress in 1879. The first navigation dam and lock at Davis Island, 4 miles below Pittsburgh, was opened to river traffic on October 7, 1885. Other dams were constructed at later dates by special appropriations. On September 28, 1929 President Herbert Hoover dedicated the New Cumberland Dam and Lock, the first of 46 low-lift facilities designed to maintain navigation even at times of low water on the Ohio. These dams are now being replaced by nineteen new structures which will create pools 80 to 90 miles in length. The project now underway will require 20 years to complete at an estimated $10,000,000.

MAN'S USE OF THE WATERWAYS

Use of the Riverways. Explorers, fur traders, colonizers, and farmer-settlers have found our waterways almost indispensible. Our ocean harbors welcomed the first explorers and colonizers. On some of them were founded the first settlements from which began the conquest of the land now included in the United States. Fur traders, the advance guard of civilization, used the Hudson, the Connecticut, several of the Maine rivers, and the St. Lawrence for their operations. British and Dutch traders ascended the Hudson and Mohawk valleys to the Great Lakes, and the French came by way of the St. Lawrence and Ottawa valleys to the same inland

sea whose drainage basin was once the greatest fur-producing region of the continent.

The low divide between the Mississippi tributaries and the Great Lakes favored the wide wanderings of the French voyageurs in their trading operations with the Indians. After them into the heart of the continent went the British and British-American trader along the same routes. Navigable waterways to them meant rivers and creeks of a foot or more in depth. The birch-bark canoe was the carrying agent, particularly in the Great Lakes region. It could be carried over portages and even pushed through marshes in wet seasons. As commerce expanded on the Great Lakes, bateaux which were pushed, cordoned, or sailed, carried European commodities to the French trading posts at Detroit, Mackinac, and elsewhere and returned ladened with furs. Both the canoe and the bateau were used on the Ohio, Mississippi, and Missouri by fur traders. When pioneer farmers began to settle in the Mississippi basin, they used larger craft to transport themselves and their household goods to their new homes on or near the rivers and to ship their produce downstream to markets. These primitive craft were the raft, the flatboat, and the keelboat (Fig. 4). Some flatboats, suitable only for downstream navigation, were 50 to 60 feet long, and 20 feet wide. They could carry 250 to 300 barrels of flour or an equal weight of other products. The journey from the Ohio to Natchez or New Orleans took 25 to 30 days. The flatboat used the cheapest form of propulsion—the river currents.

The keelboat, although smaller than the flatboat and therefore not an efficient carrier in downstream traffic, could nevertheless be poled, "bushwhacked," or cordoned upstream and hence it remained important until the advent of steam power.

All forms of river carriers were eclipsed by the steamboat when it appeared in the early part of the nineteenth century. The *New Orleans*, the first steamboat to appear on the Mississippi River, made its initial trip from Pittsburgh, where it was built, to the city of New

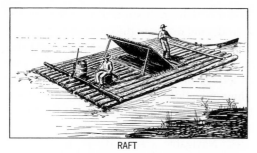
RAFT

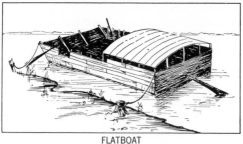
FLATBOAT

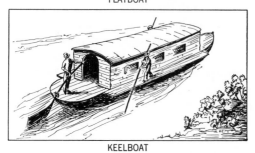
KEELBOAT

Fig. 4 Early means of transportation on the rivers of the United States. (From *A History of Navigation on the Tennessee River*, House Document 254, 75th Congress, 1st Session, pp. 18–19.)

Orleans in 1811. But it never returned, for its boiler and engine were not powerful enough to cope with the strong currents of the Mississippi and Ohio. Effective steamboat navigation on the Mississippi and its larger tributaries dates from about 1815. The first river steamboats had hulls like the *Clermont* on the Hudson. In time the designers of river steamers found that the hulls of their vessels must be patterned after the flatboat—long and broad, with a shallow draft. In reality the river steamers were flatboats with engines added. As time went on engines and boilers of steamboats were improved and the

speed increased. In 1815 the *Enterprise* steamed from New Orleans to Louisville in 25 days and 2 hours. In 1828 the *Tecumseh* ran the same distance in 8 days and 4 hours, and in 1852 the *Eclipse* in 4 days and 18 hours. The fastest time ever made—even to date—on the Mississippi was by the *Robert E. Lee* in 1870. This steamer made the 1200 miles between New Orleans and St. Louis in 3 days, 18 hours, and 14 minutes.

Most steamers on the interior rivers between 1840 and 1870 were excellent passenger and packet boats—veritable floating palaces. No wonder, then, that the steamboat in its maturity was treated with respect, for it greatly reduced the costs of transportation. Besides, it was the only comfortable and speedy means of travel for long distances. It served, except in low-water seasons, a large part of the Mississippi basin within 50 or so miles of the navigable rivers. Ice gave no trouble south of the Ohio and very little on that river. The steamboat hastened the settlement of the basin. It carried settlers westward and afterward kept them in touch with friends, relatives, and markets that they had left behind. The increasing population in turn called for more steamboats.

In 1820 there were seventy-two registered steamers on the Mississippi, by 1842 the number had reached 400, and 5 years later there were 1200. It was estimated that in 1840 some 40,000 men were employed in river transportation and that more than 7,000,000 people were dependent on the rivers for transportation. The steamboat brought many economic advantages to the people that it served. The Mississippi basin for the first time was brought into connection with national and international channels of trade.

The Decline of the Steamboat and Riverway Transportation. By 1850 a new form of transportation began to dispute the supremacy of the steamboat. Railways using steam locomotives were introduced in the United States about 1830. In the early days of steamboat traffic, railroads were not considered as competitors since most lines were built to supplement water transportation—to fill in the gaps around rapids or to connect rivers and lakes with tidal waters.

In the late 1830's railways became a subject of such importance that many state governments and private corporations projected lines to connect navigable rivers or to extend from seaports to navigable rivers in the interior. At first all lines were short and in few instances competed with steamboats. When the numerous short lines were consolidated into through trunk lines many of them were parallel to the rivers, and the struggle for supremacy between steamboats and railroads became active.

Not always did the railroads fight honorably. They often cut freight rates to starve out the boat lines. The Interstate Commerce Commission, empowered to supervise railway rates and finances, was the public's reaction to such unfair activities. The practice of lowering rates on railroad lines that were competing with river transportation and raising rates on noncompeting lines to offset the loss in revenue, became common. Even though these unfair practices can no longer exist, public sentiment still condemns the railroad for its former policy.

Undoubtedly the greatest factor, however, in the decline of river transportation from the 1860's to recent decades was the changing conception on the part of the public of what constitutes efficient transportation. Railways continued to improve their services to meet the more exacting demands of the public, while steamboats made little or no attempt to modernize their equipment. The old generalized passenger-packet boat had reached its highest stage of development in speed, carrying capacity, efficiency in loading and unloading, and operation. The river steamer of 1920 differed but little from that of 1840. But many improvements were made in the transportation equipment of the railways during the period.

Many adverse natural conditions existed on the waterways of the United States, particularly on the Mississippi and its tributaries, which caused a decline in river transportation, and practically none of these affected the railroad.

Some of the major natural handicaps of rivers are: (1) wrong general direction, (2) meandering courses, (3) falls, rapids, and snags in the streams, (4) swift currents, (5) ice, (6) fluctuating volume, and (7) relatively small tributary area. In addition to these natural handicaps, the rivers also suffered in competition with the railroads because:

1. The flow of commodities was variable. The steamboat for the most part served agricultural regions whose marketable products were highly seasonal.

2. At best river steamers were slow in comparison to railroads.

3. Terminal facilities were usually inadequate.

These adverse conditions and many others brought about the near extinction of the old-time passenger-packet steamboat on our rivers. Only a few are now engaged in the transportation of freight. Many river cities have one or more that are in the excursion business.

After World War II several palatial river steamers designed to carry vacation passengers have appeared on the Ohio, Tennessee, and Mississippi rivers. The most important company operating this type of service is the Greene Line Steamers with headquarters in Cincinnati. The type vessel used (Fig. 5) is similar in external appearance to the old river steamer but the interior accommodations have been completely modernized to provide for every comfort of its passengers. The lounges, public rooms, and staterooms are newly decorated and completely air-conditioned. Other attractions for tourists include sun-decks, cocktail lounges, southern-style cooking, and a dance orchestra. Cruises operate from Cincinnati to New Orleans or St. Paul on the Ohio-Mississippi, and to Muscle Shoals on the Ohio-Tennessee. Even with this modernization, however, steamboats cannot compete with railways, highways, or airways for passenger traffic, except for pleasure trips.

Again the adverse conditions have had to be recognized and avoided or eliminated in the new

Fig. 5 The *S. S. Delta Queen* on the Ohio River. This luxury river steamer provides regular pleasure cruises on the Ohio, Mississippi, and Tennessee rivers. (Greene Line Steamers, Inc., Cincinnati.)

era in river transportation that is now upon us before river transportation can hope for success. The railways which were so successful in the struggle of the nineteenth century are still with us, and moreover are improved. Auto-trucks and good roads, which in certain types of traffic are more serviceable, are offering keen competition to both railroads and waterways, and the freight-carrying airplane is surpassing all of them for high-value, small-bulk commodities, because of its greater speed and its ability to go in any direction.

Riverway transportation on the Mississippi was at a high level in 1859, just before the hostilities between the North and the South severed commercial relations and the trade of the upper Mississippi basin turned eastward.

Use of the Great Lakes. The Great Lakes have never experienced the decline that characterized the history of navigation on the rivers. Railways act as feeders from the farming and mining regions to the west of the lakes and connect the lakes with the Atlantic. Even if the cost of navigation improvements are considered in determining "real" rates, railways can hardly compete with the large lake vessels. The great

size and specialized character of the carriers, their speed and lack of interruption en route, and the numerous labor-saving devices used in loading and unloading at the lake terminals make for efficiency in modern transportation equivalent or superior to that of ocean transportation (Fig. 6).

Steam navigation on the lakes began in 1818 when the steamer *Walk-in-the-Water* made its first trip between Buffalo and Detroit. Travel between the two cities was reduced from 5 days to 48 hours, and the journey was accomplished with much greater comfort. By 1826 there were six steamers on Lake Erie. From Lake Erie, steamers entered the commerce of Lake Huron and Lake Michigan, though sailing vessels long continued to carry a large part of the commodities on these lakes where the services of tugs were scarcely needed. Sailing vessels found some difficulty in navigating the St. Clair and Detroit rivers unassisted, but a large percentage did use these waters. In 1852 there are eighty steamboats, fifty barges, and 270 schooners on the Great Lakes. The completion of the "Soo" Canal in 1855 extended the active traffic lines into Lake Superior, and soon iron ore became important in lake commerce.

The increase in the size of lake vessels has kept pace with the increase in the depth of navigable channels. The first waterway improvements were made in the harbor at Erie, Pennsylvania, in 1825. By 1851 nearly $3,000,000 had been spent on harbor and river channel improvements. A 20-foot channel project was adopted by Congress in July, 1892. In 1905 Congress authorized a preliminary examination and survey with a view to enlarging the channel to 22 or 25 feet. Subsequently, appropriations have been made to deepen channels to 25 or 26 feet. In certain channels where the currents are strong, and especially where fogs are frequent, as in the St. Marys River, two channels are provided, one for upbound and one for downbound vessels.

Today the greatest physical obstacle to navigation on the Great Lakes is ice. The season

Fig. 6   At the Bethlehem Steel Corporation's plant at Lackawanna, New York, a 4000-ft.-long ship canal harbors ore boats from the Great Lakes, and huge unloaders lift the ore from the carriers in 17-ton bites. A 20,000-ton capacity ore vessel can be emptied in eight hours. (Bethlehem Steel Corporation.)

of navigation varies from 225 to 240 days. For about a third of the time each year all movement must cease except for the ice breakers that operate across Lake Michigan and Lake Erie. The long period of inactivity is not so serious to the continued success of water transportation as such a period would be on the lower Mississippi, for the great bulk of the commodities carried are iron ore, grain, and lumber. The grain can be transported to eastern markets in the fall before the navigation season closes. Iron ore, coal, and lumber can be stored readily.

The importance of the Great Lakes in domestic and foreign commerce lies in (1) the width and depth of the channels, (2) the large size of the lake carriers, (3) the efficiency of the loading and unloading devices, (4) the completion of the St. Lawrence Seaway, and (5) the location of the lakes between areas producing basic raw materials and a densely settled industrial region.

In the adjacent industrial region are produced large quantities of coal. The blast furnaces of the region consume most of the iron ore produced in our country, and the demands for the grain of the western part of the region are great. In no other region of the world is man utilizing navigation resources as in the Great Lakes region.

RECENT DEVELOPMENTS IN RIVER TRANSPORTATION

Transportation on the Mississippi reached its lowest point between 1900 and 1920. There had been roughly a half century or more of rise followed by a period of decline in riverway transportation.

Harbors, the deeper coastal waters, and the Great Lakes show a steady rise in traffic movement. There has been a gradual and profound advance in the capacity and efficiency of the carriers and freight and passenger terminals. The growth of railways aided overseas commerce and also, to a certain degree, coastal and lake commerce. Deep-water transportation like that of our Great Lakes or coastal waters has little to fear from railway or motor truck competition.

The Federal Barge Line. The new era in river transportation was ushered in about 1918 when the federal government took over the railways and the director general of transportation appointed a committee to study the possibilities of reviving or increasing commerce on the rivers, canals, and deep waterways. The committee in 1918 recommended that a fleet of modern river carriers be created on the lower Mississippi River and another on the Warrior-Tombigbee-Mobile riverway. Congress that year authorized the War Department to proceed with the development, and thus the Mississippi-Warrior River Barge Line was created. Large appropriations were made to develop efficient water carriers, and the work in channel improvement was speeded up. By 1920 the beginning of a fleet of modern tugboats and efficient barges was in operation on the Mississippi and on the Warrior-Tombigbee riverways. The Inland and Coastwise Waterways Service, under

the direct control of the War Department, was created to operate the steadily increasing fleet. This venture was far from successful. The federal government lost on the average $1,000,000 a year between 1920 and 1924. To give the experiment further trial Congress in 1924 created the Inland Waterways Corporation, a quasi-independent organization. The federal government purchased capital stock in the corporation from time to time and made donations or special appropriations.

The major function of the Inland Waterways Corporation was, as the articles of its creation stated, to demonstrate to private companies the feasibility of inland water transportation. When success had been demonstrated and private corporations showed a willingness to utilize the waterways, the federal government was to retire from the field. The IWC's engineers exhibited much enterprise and intelligence in developing efficient carriers. The larger barges have a cargo capacity of from 2000 to 3000 tons, but there are many smaller ones which vary from 400 to 1500 tons. The towboats are among the most powerful ever constructed on inland rivers. The largest are of steel, twin-screw tunnel type, powered by diesel engines. The corporation also owned several car floats, oil tankers, derricks, and terminal and landing barges (Fig. 7). The federal government through the IWC maintained federal barge lines on the lower Mississippi (New Orleans to St. Louis), the Warrior-Tombigbee (New Orleans to Port Birmingham), the Illinois River (St. Louis to Chicago), the upper Mississippi (St. Louis to Minneapolis), and the Missouri (St. Louis to Kansas City).

In 1927 the federal investment in the Inland Waterways Corporation, which paid no interest on the loans from the federal government, was 24 million dollars. It paid no taxes except indirectly in the rents to municipalities for the use of their terminals; it paid no corporation taxes, no insurance, and no office rent. Private operators would be called upon to meet these costs. The "way" over which the Federal Barge Lines boats traveled was also a federal contribution.

Fig. 7   A dry-cargo barge for use on the Mississippi River and connecting waterways. (Federal Barge Lines.)

The competing railroads, however, had no such advantage.

In 1929 the IWC achieved what it had been attempting—the coordination of river and rail transportation. The Interstate Commerce Commission ordered the railways connecting with the barge lines "to establish a sweeping system of barge-rail and rail-barge-rail rates and routes" for shippers who desired to combine water and rail facilities.

During 1952 the Inland Waterways Corporation made a profit of more than 1 million dollars, and in the summer of 1953 the government finally sold the Federal Barge Lines to the St. Louis Shipbuilding and Steel Company, for the sum of 9 million dollars. In transferring this government barge line to private capital after 33 years of operation at public expense, certain terms were stipulated, such as (1) that a certain number of trips must be maintained on the Mississippi, Missouri, Illinois, and Warrior rivers, and (2) that no dividends be declared until the entire purchase price, plus interest, has been paid to the government. With total river tonnage much greater today than during the so-called golden age of river transportation,

Federal Waterways expects to develop this into a successful business.[3]

In 1963 the enabling act that created the Inland Waterways Corporation was repealed. The function of the Corporation as the creditor of the St. Louis Shipbuilding-Federal Barge (successor to the St. Luis Shipbuilding and Steel Company) was assumed by the Secretary of Commerce. The new owners, up to the end of 1962, had invested $16,427,077 in new equipment and the rehabilitation of old equipment. The schedule of annual payments to the federal government was renegotiated in 1958 and the final payment to the Secretary of Commerce is to be made by June 30, 1969.[4]

Waterway Improvements. Since about 1875, desultory improvements have been made in various rivers of our country. Often improvements in one part of a river bore no relation to those in another. Even moderate federal appropriations were not requested until a decade or two after the decline in river transportation set

[3] "Betting on Federal Barge," *Business Week*, August 15, 1953, pp. 166–167.

[4] Personal communication, from A. C. Ingersoll, Jr., President, Federal Barge Lines, August 18, 1964.

in. The lower the traffic figures sank on the river-ways the more insistent became the demands. At the same time the railways were extending their lines and improving their service. The development of good roads and autotrucks have given both the waterways and railways serious competition.

Existing River Projects. Nearly every river that has been navigated in recent decades, if by nothing more than motorboats, is included in the list of rivers receiving federal funds. The waterways map (Fig. 1) shows most of the larger existing projects.

Early improvements in our waterways consisted of (1) building dams of loose rock from the bank to the edge of the deep channel, (2) removing rocks and snags from the main channel, and (3) constructing devices to prevent the caving of banks. These did not require large appropriations. Substantial dams and locks were constructed and channels were dredged when large appropriations were made available.

The phenomenal growth of postwar river traffic has been due in part to the increase in traffic on the Ohio River. This has been the result of four factors: (1) marked improvement in new types of barges (Fig. 8), (2) improvements in terminal facilities at Pittsburgh, Cincinnati, and other river ports, (3) a de-emphasis on speed in transit for certain classes of goods, and (4) rapid growth of industry along the river. Since the close of World War II, more than 2500 new industrial plants have been built along the Ohio River, representing an investment of billions of dollars. Of the variety of commodities carried, four groups, coal and coke, oil and gasoline, chemicals, and iron and steel, account for most of the tonnage.[5]

This heavy increase in traffic on the Ohio has greatly overtaxed the capacity of the old locks and other structures, and the United States Corps of Engineers now have a plan for ultimately replacing the forty-six outmoded, and in some cases dangerous, locks with nineteen new structures. When this is done and when other improvements are made, the Ohio River will be one of the most modern as well as the most used of our inland waterways, other than the Great Lakes.

[5] "Resurgence of the River Boat," *Monthly Business Review*, Federal Reserve Bank of Cleveland, February 1955, pp. 4–10.

Fig. 8 A multiple tow of both loaded and empty barges on the Ohio River. Note the several types of barges that make up the tow. (Dravo Corporation.)

THE ADVISABILITY OF RIVER AND HARBOR IMPROVEMENTS

The question of the advisability of waterways involves a consideration of (1) the total cost of improvements, (2) the financial returns, and (3) a comparison of the relative costs of providing water and rail transportation, where such comparison is possible.

There seems to be little question about the advisability of the improvements that the federal government has made in most of the ocean and lake harbors. Expenditure of large sums of money on improvements of ocean harbors and channels to make them serviceable for a long time in the future is certainly good business, although there are, no doubt, many ports at which the expenditures can hardly be justified. One must agree also that the amount used on the harbors and the channels connecting the Great Lakes is money well spent.

Costs of Transportation, Riverway versus Railway. Advocates of riverways claim that riverways give shippers much lower rates than do the railways. This is true, but river carrier rates are not based on the same complex of items as railway rates. Railways must purchase the right-of-way, construct roadbeds and tracks, and provide depots and terminals. They must provide traffic equipment, a large part of which is idle many weeks each year because of the seasonal variation in the flow of traffic; pay immense sums in taxes on their tangible properties; and hire a veritable army of employees to keep the right-of-way in perfect condition, to man the traction equipment, and to keep the proper records demanded by efficient operation and by the Interstate Commerce Commission.

In contrast, waterway rates are based only on the cost of operating the power boats and barges. With privately owned common carriers the shipper pays for the craft. The way is provided and maintained, the locks (if any) are operated, and the channel lighted to make navigation safe and reduce insurance rates by the federal government at no cost to the carrier. Cities usually furnish terminals. Only the traffic equipment is taxed. The very expensive "way" pays no taxes. If the shipper does not recompense the federal government the general public must. The taxpayers of the United States pay the entire cost of transportation, directly or indirectly, whether by rail, water, highway, or air. They have the right to demand the cheapest form of transportation available, consistent with adequate service. If the common carriers on the Ohio, for example, were operated on the same basis as the railways, that is, if they were called upon to meet these hidden costs and amortize the capital investment through a 50-year period, their actual rate would have to be considerably higher than that of the railroads.

In this discussion of relative costs, no consideration has been given to the possible allocation of some of the costs of navigation dams to flood control, power development, and recreation. The reason for not considering these other uses is that, so far, federal appropriations on the Ohio, Illinois, upper Mississippi, and the Missouri have been made specifically for navigation.

The Intracoastal Waterway or Canal. The location and depth of the various parts of this waterway are shown on Fig. 1. Cape Cod Canal, Long Island Sound, and Chesapeake Bay belong, in our classification, to the deeper intracoastal waters. It is on these that most of the commerce of the Intracoastal Waterway is carried. The deeper sections, as previously stated, represent proper investments. The Chesapeake-Delaware Canal carries a fair commerce, mainly between Baltimore and Philadelphia. Its cost is far less than the value of the commodities moved annually. The channel from Norfolk to Beaufort, North Carolina, has much less traffic. Commerce on the shallower channels to the South is largely local. The chief beneficiaries of the shallow Atlantic Intracoastal Waterway as a "through-route" are owners of private yachts and other pleasure craft who migrate between northern ports and Florida resorts. The Gulf Intracoastal Waterway between Apalachee Bay, Florida, and the Mexican border carries considerable barge traffic, although the tonnage is largely in petroleum and heavy chemicals. That part of the waterway between the Mississippi River at New Orleans and the port of Corpus Christi on the southwest Texas coast carries by far the greater part of the tonnage.

CANALS OF THE UNITED STATES

In the first half of the nineteenth century the United States was in a canal-building boom. The Middlesex Canal in Massachusetts was opened for service in 1808, the Erie in 1825, the Pennsylvania in 1840, and the Chesapeake and Ohio after 1840.

By the time the railway mesh had become well developed over the American landscape east of the Mississippi, many states and private corporations had constructed about 4000 miles of canals. Figure 9 shows the location of the more important canals about 1840. New York and Pennsylvania, Maryland, and Virginia, each projected canals in the latter part of the eighteenth century from the Atlantic seaboard cities westward to the Great Lakes and toward Ohio. New York's canal is the only one that has

survived, and that only after two expensive enlargements. Topographic conditions were more favorable than in most states, and the New York canal occupied a natural and strategic traffic route. Pennsylvania had to use portage railways to connect east-flowing and west-flowing canalized rivers. Neither Maryland nor Virginia got its canal over the bold Allegheny Front and the Appalachian Plateau.

The Pennsylvania Canal ceased to operate in the 1860's; and the Chesapeake and Ohio Canal carried little traffic after 1890, although some coal was shipped by barge to tidewater until the great flood on the Potomac in the 1930's destroyed most of the locks. Today, a 5-mile stretch of this canal in the edge of Washington, D.C., used entirely for pleasure craft, is all that is in operation. Since the 1870's more than 4000 miles of canals, that probably cost 200 million dollars, have been abandoned.

In the early part of this century the State of New York greatly enlarged the Erie Canal and some of its branches at a cost of more than $120,000,000. Being toll free, it was estimated that the enlargement would enable the canal to transport 20,000,000 tons of freight a year. The 1936 volume of 5,014,206 tons declined steadily,

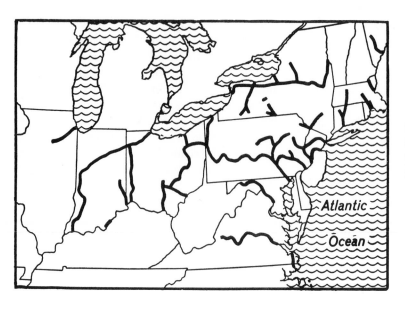

Fig. 9 Barge canals about 1840. (Data from R. S. Tanner, *Canals and Railways of the United States, 1840,* and Coulton's *Atlas of the World,* Vol. I, 1856.)

**Table 1. Traffic on the New York State
Barge Canal System, 1940–1963**

Year	Tons	Year	Tons
1940	4,768,160	1960	3,415,095
1945	2,968,682	1961	3,223,558
1950	4,615,613	1962	3,279,944
1955	4,616,399	1963	3,225,526

[Source: U.S. Dept. of the Army, Corps of Engineers, *Waterborne Commerce of the United States*, Part I Waterways and Harbors, Atlantic Coast, Calendar Year 1963 and earlier years.]

however, throughout the boom period of World War II to a low of 2,820,541 tons[6] in 1946, showing that, in spite of many supposed benefits and much publicity, the New York shippers still prefer to use railroads and motor trucks to haul their commodities. Although there has been a slight increase in traffic in the past few years (Table 1), it never has approached the goal set for the canal.

In 1890, Congress authorized the construction of the Hennepin Canal between the Illinois River near La Salle and the Mississippi River at Rock Island. The canal had a controlling depth of 3.5 feet at low water and was designed to handle barge traffic between Chicago and the Upper Mississippi. Over the years, traffic decreased practically to the vanishing point, and on July 1, 1951, the canal was closed to through traffic.

Ship canals, such as the one in St. Marys River, that accommodate large carriers, are in an entirely different category from the almost extinct barge canals.

The Cross-Florida Barge Canal was one of the most controversial projects ever planned in the United States. The proposed canal was designed to extend from the Atlantic Ocean via the St. Johns River across the divide and down the valley of the Withlacoochee River to the Gulf of Mexico, about 95 miles north of Tampa. The project, authorized by Public Law 675 of the 77th Congress, was approved July 23, 1942.

Some construction work had been done as early as 1935, and to June 1950, more than $1.4 million was spent on the project.[7]

After 1950 construction was suspended until 1964 when the project was revived. President Johnson participated in a ceremony marking the resumption of work on the canal. During World War II German submarines sank enough oil tankers off the Florida peninsula to have paid the cost of construction. The canal's practical usefulness is related in part to its function as a connection between the Atlantic and Gulf sections of the Intracoastal Canal and to its strategic value.

In the middle of last century men thought of wheeled vehicles as supplementary to the river steamer and the canal boat. In this modern age of speed, river and canal traffic is too slow except for bulky commodities. Man and goods now move by modern means of land transportation as far in an hour as they did a century ago in a long day. The river was dominant when there was no other form of "rapid transit." It was dominant when speed and efficiency were measured by the oxcart and the Conestoga wagon. The railway brought about the decline of river transportation because it was more efficient. Today on short hauls, and under certain conditions even on long hauls, the truck and the bus are more efficient than the railways, and a large part of our population is turning to them. The river boat now has to compete with modern means of transportation that are more efficient than even the new type of river carrier.

Speed is a dominant condition of our age. The speed of railroad trains has been materially increased in recent years, through the use of diesel-powered locomotives, in the face of competition offered by fast-moving automobiles, auto buses, auto trucks, and airplanes. The rate of movement of freight has been increased materially. Fast freight express trains that handle package freight have been placed in operation

[6] *Annual Report of the Chief of Engineers, U.S. Army,* 1946, p. 283.

[7] *Report of the Chief of Engineers, U.S. Army,* 1951, Part 1, Vol. I, Government Printing Office, Washington, D.C., 1952, pp. 587–589.

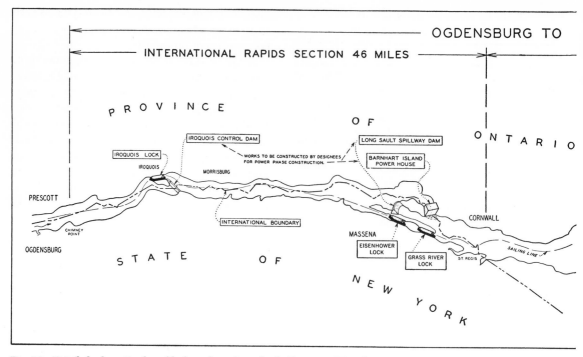

Fig. 10 Detailed schematic plan of locks and canals on the St. Lawrence River between Ogdensburg and Montreal.

on many railways leading out of the great distributing centers. Streamlining is an aid. Since water is 800 times as dense as air, an increase of the speed of freight carriers on riverways can be obtained only at a tremendous increase in the consumption of power.

THE ST. LAWRENCE SEAWAY[8]

The five Great Lakes constitute the finest inland waterway in the world, but for many years the rapids in the St. Marys River between Lake Superior and Lake Huron, the Niagara escarpment between Lake Erie and Lake Ontario, and the series of rapids on the St. Lawrence limited through traffic. The possibility of a deep-water route from the Great Lakes to the sea had been the dream of commerce-minded people since the beginning of settlement in the New World. When Jacques Cartier reached the turbulent

waters of the St. Lawrence above Montreal in 1535 he called them La Chine Rapids.

The Canadian government built a 14-foot canal around the rapids that permitted shallow-draft boats to negotiate the St. Lawrence between Lake Ontario and the sea. After the Welland Canal and its eight locks were completed in 1931 interest in the Great Lakes-St. Lawrence Seaway was renewed.

After many years of discussion in Canada and in the United States and extended negotiations between the two countries the construction of the seaway became a possibility. Opposition to the project came from (1) the Great Lakes carriers, (2) the coal-mining industry, (3) the ports along the eastern shores of the Great Lakes and on the Atlantic and Gulf coasts, and (4) the railroads. In time their opposition, sometimes exaggerated, was overcome and the seaway became a possibility.[9]

[8] See *The St. Lawrence Survey,* U.S. Department of Commerce, Washington, D.C., 1941, particularly Part IV.

[9] *Questions and Answers on the St. Lawrence Seaway,* 83rd Congress, 2nd Session, Government Printing Office, Washington, D.C., 1954.

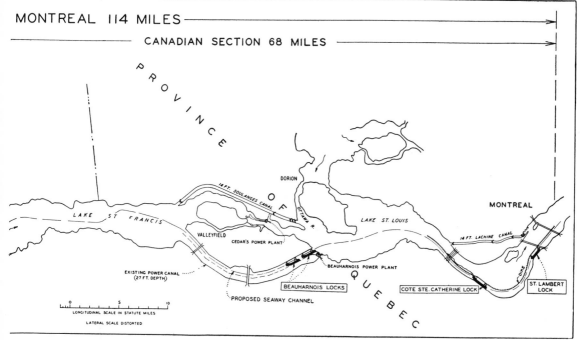

MONTREAL 114 MILES

CANADIAN SECTION 68 MILES

(Office, Chief of Engineers, U.S. Department of the Army.)

World War II demonstrated the need for the St. Lawrence Seaway in the defense of Anglo-America. The availability of the hydroelectric energy was an incentive to improve navigation and develop the power resources simultaneously.

The active and official cooperation of the United States and Canada began when the St. Lawrence agreement was signed on March 19, 1941. Involvement in World War II and a succession of difficulties in the postwar period delayed for more than 10 years the passage of the legislation necessary for the construction of the seaway. Much of the delay was failure of the United States Congress to pass the necessary legislation to authorize and finance the project.

The Canadian Parliament enacted legislation in the fall session, 1951, to borrow 300 million dollars to construct the waterway entirely on the Canadian side. President Truman supported the Canadian proposal but expressed the hope that the project might be a joint undertaking of the two countries. In his January 28, 1952 message to Congress he urged that the St. Lawrence Seaway and Power Project receive support. In urging Congress to enact the necessary legislation to permit cooperation with Canada he mentioned the following.

1. Iron ores of the Upper Lakes Region were being depleted and the high-grade ores of the Labrador-Quebec area would soon be needed by the steel industry of the United States.

2. If Canada built the canals, the tolls necessary to finance the project would be set by Canada. Since much of the commerce along the waterway would originate in or be destined for the United States, it should have some authority in establishing the tolls.

3. On the basis of a long-term friendship between the two countries the project should be a joint undertaking.

It was not until May 6, 1954 that the 83rd Congress in Public Law 385 passed the necessary legislation. A week later, on May 13, the

Fig. 11 The completion of the St. Lawrence Seaway in 1959 permitted ocean-going ships drawing less than 27 feet to reach the Great Lakes. In this view the *Mormacpride* out of New York is tied up at dockside at Detroit. The Ambassador bridge between Detroit and Canada is shown in the background. (Photograph by Albert G. Ballert.)

measure was signed by President Eisenhower, 2 years after President Truman's message to Congress urging enactment of a bill authorizing the project (Fig. 10).

The cost of the project was $471,000,000, of which $131,000,000 was borne by the United States and $340,000,000 by Canada. The project was completed and formally dedicated on June 26, 1959 by Queen Elizabeth II and President Dwight D. Eisenhower in an appropriate ceremony (Fig. 11).

In the first 5 years of operation revenues exceeded expenses but were not adequate to meet the schedule of payments necessary to amortize the project over the prescribed period of 50 years. It may be necessary to increase tolls or it may be that revenues may increase in the future as fuller use is made of the Seaway.

References

Annual Reports of the Inland Waterways Corporation, Government Printing Office, Washington, D.C.
"Army Engineers Decry Precarious State of Ohio River Navigation Facilities," *Engineering News*, Vol. 152, 1954, p. 26.

Barton, Thomas F., "Twenty-five Years' Use of the Nine-Foot Ohio River Channel," *Annals, Association of American Geographers,* Vol. 45, 1955, pp. 166–167. Abstract.

Becht, J. Edwin, "The Chemical Industry and the Midwestern Rivers and Intracoastal Canal," *Annals, Association of American Geographers,* Vol. 45, 1955, p. 167. Abstract.

Boardman, Fon Wyman, *Canals,* H. Z. Walck, New York, 1959.

Foscue, Edwin J., "The Industrial Port of Corpus Christi," *Proceedings, Seventeenth International Geographical Congress,* 1957, pp. 151–157.

Foscue, Edwin J., "The Ports of Texas and Their Hinterlands," *Tijdschrift Voor Economische en Sociale Geografie,* Vol. 48, January, 1957, pp. 1–14.

Glaeser, M. G., "The St. Lawrence Seaway and Power Project," *Land Economics,* Vol. 30, 1954, pp. 289–300.

Great Lakes Commission, *Great Lakes News Letter,* Ann Arbor, Michigan. Bimonthly.

Great Lakes Commission, *Proceedings of the Institute on the St. Lawrence Seaway,* Cleveland, Ohio, March 6, 1964, 44 pp.

"Gulf Intracoastal Waterways Needs New Look to Handle Oil Volume," *National Petroleum News,* Vol. 45, 1953, pp. 63–64.

Inland Water-Borne Commerce Statistics for the Calendar Year, 1962, Prepared and distributed by The American Waterways Operators, Washington, D.C., December 1963 (Processed).

"Inland Waterways is Sold," *Railway Age News,* Vol. 135, 1953, pp. 9–10.

Locher, Harry O., editor, *Waterways of the United States,* The National Association of River and Harbor Contractors, New York, 1961.

Lounsbury, John F., "Industrial Development in the Ohio Valley," *The Journal of Geography,* Vol. LX, 1961, pp. 253–262.

Mississippi River Navigation, Mississippi River Commission and U.S. Army Engineer Division, Lower Mississippi Valley, Corps of Engineers, Vicksburg, Miss., November 1963 (Processed).

"Oil Hauls on Inland Waterways Grow as Efficiency and Speed Increase," *National Petroleum News,* Vol. 45, 1953, pp. 43–45.

Port Series, prepared by the U.S. Army Engineers.

"Quebec's Head Start on St. Lawrence Seaway," *Engineering News,* Vol. 154, 1955, pp. 34–36.

Questions and Answers on the St. Lawrence Seaway, Subcommittee on the St. Lawrence Seaway, 83rd Congress, 2nd Session, Government Printing Office, Washington, D.C., 1954.

Report of the Chief of Engineers, U.S. Army. Government Printing Office, Washington, D.C. Annual.

"Resurgence of the River Boat," *Monthly Business Review,* Federal Reserve Bank of Cleveland, February 1955, pp. 4–10.

St. Lawrence Seaway and Power Project, Message from the President of the United States Relative to the Construction of the St. Lawrence Seaway and Power Project, 82nd Congress, 2nd Session, House Document 337, Government Printing Office, Washington, D.C., 1952.

St. Lawrence Seaway and Power Project, Communication from the President of the United States Transmitting Application to the International Joint Commission, 82nd Congress, 2nd Session, House Document 528, Government Printing Office, Washington, D.C., 1952.

St. Lawrence Seaway, Report of the Committee on Public Works, 83rd Congress, 2nd Session, House Report 1215, Government Printing Office, Washington, D.C., 1954.

St. Lawrence Seaway Manual: A Compilation of Documents on the Great Lakes Seaway Project and Correlated Power Development, 83rd Congress, 2nd Session, Senate Document 165, Government Printing Office, Washington, D.C., 1955.

The St. Lawrence Seaway, Report of the Committee on Foreign Relations, 83rd Congress, 1st Session, Senate Report 441, Government Printing Office, Washington, D.C., 1953.

The St. Lawrence Seaway and Power Project, Department of External Affairs, Ottawa, Canada, November 1954.

U.S. Army, Corps of Engineers, *Future Needs for Navigation; the Inland Waterways of the United States,* Government Printing Office, Washington, D.C., 1960.

U.S. Army, Corps of Engineers, *The Intracoastal Waterway,* Government Printing Office, Washington, D.C., 1951 [i.e. 1962].

United States Department of the Army, Corps of Engineers, *Waterborne Commerce of the United States,* Part 5, National Summaries, Calendar Year, 1962.

"Tomorrow's Inland Seaports," *Fortune,* August 1955, pp. 92–101.

Wattenberg, Ben, *Busy Waterways, The Story of America's Inland Water Transportation,* The John Day Co., New York, 1964.

Wood, Harold A., "The St. Lawrence Seaway in the Cornwall-Cardinal Area, Ontario," *Geographical Review,* Vol. 45, 1955, pp. 509–530.

GUY-HAROLD SMITH
The Ohio State University

CHAPTER 15

Floods and Flood Control

The control and useful development of water in our streams constitutes an important segment of the larger problem of water conservation. In the operation of the hydrologic cycle the return of the water to the sea from which it was originally derived provides an opportunity to use the water beneficially and as far as possible to prevent destructive floods. Rivers come into existence as the result of precipitation falling on the land and have as their ultimate destiny the return of the waters to the sea. Because the lands receive their precipitation at irregular intervals and because the amount varies from place to place, the streams resulting from the runoff are markedly irregular in their discharge. In fact, a stream with a uniform flow does not exist.

If all of the precipitation that falls could be absorbed into the earth and then discharged more or less steadily or uniformly, most streams could be confined to their channels. But an important proportion of the precipitation that falls never becomes a part of the reservoir of underground waters but flows quickly to the watercourses, swelling the streams beyond their constraining banks. The placid stream which between rainstorms is so attractive and useful becomes in times of flood a raging torrent. With its carrying capacity and its competency greatly

increased, a river in flood becomes a powerful agent of destruction.

The fertile alluvial lands of the Nile, the Tigris-Euphrates, the Hwang Ho, and the Mississippi, the creation of their respective rivers, have been repeatedly inundated. These and other great rivers are, at the same time, the givers and the destroyers of life and property. The flood problem may be said to have its beginning when the excessive waters derived from runoff and from underground sources spread beyond the banks of the stream channel. On occasion, torrential rains may produce flooding of local areas by the runoff from highland areas to the adjacent lowlands, the water not having reached the channels of either the permanent or intermittent streams. Usually such floods produced by sheet-wash are of short duration and cause little water damage. The principal damage is done by rill erosion and sheet erosion on the slope lands and by burial of the adjacent lowland areas under a layer of sediment.

FLOOD DESTRUCTION

It is difficult to determine exactly the extent of flood damage and to compare in a satisfactory manner one great flood with another (Fig. 1).

297

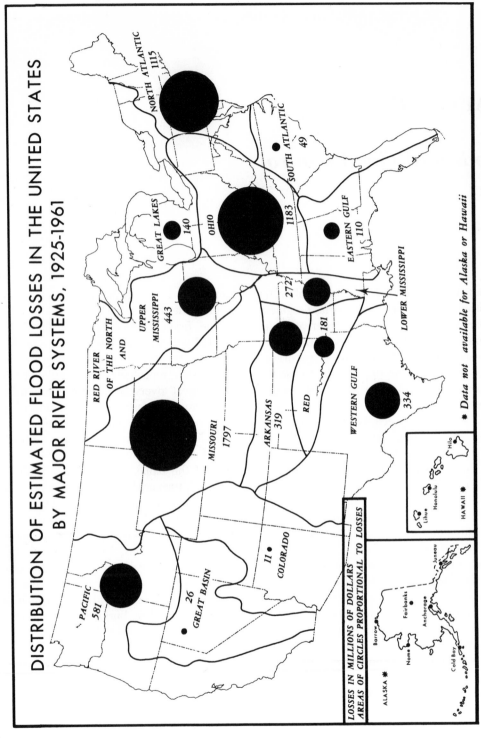

Fig. 1 Distribution of estimated flood losses in the United States by major river systems, 1925-1961. (U.S. Weather Bureau.)

This is due in part to the tendency to overestimate flood damage, particularly at the time of the flood. In 1913 the damage from floods along the Mississippi and Ohio rivers was computed to be in excess of $162,000,000. The great flood of 1927 caused a total loss of more than $284,000,000 within the Mississippi drainage basin. The unprecedented flood of 1937 along the Ohio caused damage estimated at $417,000,000, not including soil losses. The "duck drownder" flood along the Mississippi and the tributaries in the St. Louis area in the summer of 1947 caused an estimated damage of $160,000,000 to agriculture alone. The long-continued flooding of the lowlands of the Columbia during the early summer of 1948 caused an estimated damage in excess of $100,000,000.[1]

In 1936 New England suffered from a dis-

[1] Douglas W. Polivka, Chief, Technical Information Branch, Office of the District Engineer, Portland District. Personal communication.

astrous flood, the result of heavy rains falling on frozen ground in northeastern United States. The Atlantic slope from New England to Florida is subject to occasional floods which damage riverine property amounting to millions of dollars. Along the coast of Florida flooding also results from the hurricanes which are accompanied by heavy precipitation and high winds. These strong onshore winds drive the tidal waters inland causing inundation of low-lying areas.

In mid-August 1955, Hurricane Diane moved northward across North Carolina, Virginia, Maryland, and Pennsylvania and then turned northeastward across northern New Jersey, southern New York, and southern New England. This storm, coming closely behind Hurricane Connie, dumped an enormous quantity of water into the river basins, and as a result southern New England suffered on August 19–20 and the following few days a major disaster (Fig. 2). The

Fig. 2   Flood damage in Putnam, Connecticut, caused by hurricane Diane on August 20, 1955. (Corps of Engineers.)

damage from Hurricane Diane was estimated by the Army Corps of Engineers to be $1,677,000,-000.

Late in 1955, northern and central California was subjected to serious flooding which resulted from continued heavy rains in the mountain areas (Fig. 3). Immediately after the flood waters receded, there were pleas for flood-control projects, which, if approved by Congress and the President, would cost approximately $2,000,-000,000.[2]

Flood Damage to Transportation Facilities. The predisposition of the people to pre-empt the rich riverine lands for agricultural, indus-

[2] *New York Times,* January 15, 1956.

trial, and commercial purposes subjects them to the hazards of recurring floods. Railroad builders found the land adjacent to watercourses nicely graded and therefore well suited for the railway lines, and as a consequence the flood damage to railway property has been high. However, the damage is lessened by the studied relocation of the tracks and the redesign of bridges. As data on floods have become available, the railways in order to protect their large investment have spent millions on the relocation of tracks and bridges.

Flood Damage in Urban Areas. Many of our large cities, such as New Orleans, Cincinnati, St. Louis, Pittsburgh, and Nashville, were located on rivers when the watercourses were

Fig. 3   Break in the levee along the Feather River near Yuba City, California, December 24, 1955. (Division of Highways, California.)

Fig. 4   Flooding of Jasper, Indiana, on March 11, 1964 when the Ohio River and many of its tributaries inundated the bordering lowlands. Note the box cars along the submerged railway line.
(Corps of Engineers.)

the principal highways of commerce. The utilization of the low-lying lands adjacent to the
rivers for industrial and commercial purposes
has resulted in heavy damage in times of flood,
owing both to the destruction of property and
to the suspension of business for periods varying
from a few days to several weeks (Fig. 4). Urban
areas subject to floods are abandoned only with
great difficulty, for industries seeking low land
values and people in the low income group seeking low rentals are likely to locate on these
cheaper lands along the river. Usually protection against floods is sought before abandonment is considered. If protective levees, gen-

erally built at public expense, prove adequate,
property values increase and the utilization of
the land is intensified. Then an unprecedented
flood overtops or breaks through the levees and
causes enormous damage. The increased property damage reported from many cities is due
to man's encroachment upon the rivers.

Flood Damage to Agricultural Lands. In
agricultural areas the amount of damage depends on the season and whether intensive economic use is made of the land. A winter flood
may cause little damage to farmlands, but in
southern California where the intensive cultivation of vegetables is an important winter indus-

try, the occasional winter floods may be very destructive. The floods of spring may inundate newly planted fields and delay replanting until it is too late to secure a fully matured crop. The immediate losses in a single season may be offset somewhat by the enrichment of the lowland by the deposition of silts.

PHYSICAL CONDITIONS AFFECTING FLOODS

Causes of Floods. Floods are the result of many conditions working singly or in combination. Usually no single cause can be assigned the whole responsibility. The immediate cause of most floods, however, is the excessive runoff from precipitation of high intensity, although many other conditions may be necessary to cause a great flood. Although most floods are related directly to heavy precipitation and the immediate surface runoff, floods are also caused by dam failures, ice obstructions, high tides, and gales.

Precipitation Features. Rainfall is not a continuous but a recurrent phenomenon. In the United States the results of the occasional rains can be combined into several distinct types. The long-time averages give the normal annual rainfall regimes for the several sections of the United States. Ward[3] resolved the thousands of individual rainfall records into fourteen major types, but these may be further reduced in number.

In northeastern United States the annual precipitation of 40 to 45 inches is quite evenly distributed throughout the year. During each month sufficient precipitation is received to maintain a continuous flow of water in the streams, although occasional droughts may reduce some to insignificant trickles. This is the "New England type" and is characteristic of much of the northeastern part of the country.

Farther west the quantity of precipitation is reduced and the regime becomes characterized

[3] Robert De C. Ward, *The Climates of the United States*, New York, 1925.

by a late spring–early summer maximum. Since this distinguishing feature is common to extensive areas within the Missouri basin it is known as the "Missouri type." Toward the Rocky Mountains the quantity of precipitation is reduced to 10 to 15 inches annually, but the regime remains essentially the same.

Along the Gulf coast the annual precipitation of 55 to 60 inches is so distributed as to produce a monsoon-like maximum in the summer with two periods of minimum rainfall in May and October. This is the "north Gulf coast type," which is modified along the south Atlantic coast by the late summer–early autumn hurricanes which produce a secondary maximum in the early autumn.

In much of the semiarid and arid interior of North America the seasonal regime of the precipitation is of little significance as a flood factor. The floods are due chiefly to melting snows or to torrential downpours falling on barren ground or on steep slopes.

Along the Pacific slope of western United States the numerous rainfall records may be resolved into the "north Pacific type" and the "south Pacific type." Both are characterized by a winter maximum and a summer minimum. In the south Pacific area the winter precipitation is much less than in the north and the summer becomes an extended dry season. The limited moisture is inadequate for agricultural needs, and most crops require irrigation. Floods are generally confined to the rainy season or to the spring and early summer (Fig. 5).

THE INTENSITY OF PRECIPITATION. The surface runoff which is the chief source of floodwaters is dependent not only on long-continued precipitation but also on heavy storms of short duration. A 2-inch fall of rain would hardly produce a flood if it fell in a drizzle extending over several days, but if it were concentrated within an hour or two the resulting runoff would in areas of steep slopes produce local flooding. In a large section of eastern United States a 10-minute rain of more than an inch may be ex-

Fig. 5   In late December, 1964, northern California and southern Oregon were drenched by a succession of storms that resulted in extensive flooding and severe damage to highways and other structures. The new turnpike under construction has been engineered to escape damage except in the once-in-a-century floods. (Division of Highways, Sacramento, California.)

pected once in 25 years.[4] Such heavy rains of short duration are the cause of considerable flood damage in limited areas (Fig. 6).

The great floods of the Ohio River, such as the disastrous inundation of 1937, are generally related to the conjunction of two major air masses.

The flow of warm moist air from the Gulf of Mexico northward over the edge of a stationary cool air mass results in heavy frontal rains, which, if long continued, cause excessive runoff and destructive floods.[5]

[4] David L. Yarnell, *Rainfall Intensity—Frequency Data,* Misc. Pub. 204, U.S. Department of Agriculture, 1935, p. 33.

[5] Charles F. Brooks and Alfred H. Thiessen, "The Meteorology of Great Floods in the Eastern United States," *Geographical Review,* Vol. 27, 1937, pp. 269–290.

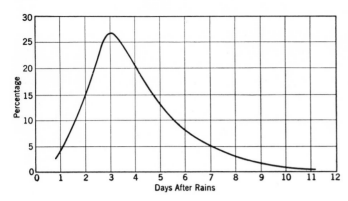

Fig. 6 A composite distribution graph for eight streams in the Muskingum River basin above Dresden, Ohio. The surface runoff, as shown by the graph, produced the greatest rise in the river on the third day following the precipitation in the tributary area and then gradually declined to normal on the twelfth day. (Data from W. G. Hoyt and others, *Studies of Relations of Rainfall and Runoff in the United States*, Water Supply Paper 772, U.S. Geological Survey, Washington, D.C., 1936, p. 141.)

In the Rocky Mountains the floods are of two principal types: those which are due to heavy general rains, and those due to the so-called cloudburst type of rainstorm. Rains of the first type are infrequent, and the resulting floods are confined to the principal streams that receive the waters of large drainage areas. The long-continued rains accompanied by rapidly melting snows cause a steady rise in the streams until the flood stage is reached, and then gradual retreat to the watercourse follows (Fig. 7). The cloudburst type seems to localize principally in the open basins along the front of the Rocky Mountains and along the valleys within the mountain mass. The high intensity of the rainfall results in rapid runoff, swelling the local streams to flood proportions. Such floods quickly subside, but their suddenness usually causes heavy damage particularly to roads, railroads, and reclamation projects. Occasionally the two types are combined into a single flood, for there is no sharp distinction between the two.

FORMS OF PRECIPITATION. When precipitation falls as rain, the streams reflect in their discharge the increased supply of water. But when the precipitation comes in the form of snow, there will be no immediate response in the runoff unless the snow melts quickly. A heavy snow cover lying upon deeply frozen ground or upon well-saturated ground is a potential flood hazard particularly if the melting is rapid and accompanied by a heavy rain.

The impending floods from a dangerously heavy snow cover may be prevented by recurring cold periods which check the runoff. If the night temperatures fall well below freezing, the runoff may be so delayed as to give ample time for the flood crest to flatten out. Also short cold periods may be very effective in delaying the runoff set in motion during the warm periods.

In northern United States and in the higher areas in the West, where a cold winter season holds temperatures well below freezing for long periods, spring floods may be expected annually. In New England the winter snows are particularly heavy and yield upon melting sufficient runoff to cause devastating spring floods. Since the precipitation of northeastern United States is quite evenly distributed throughout the year, it is evident that the floods are caused chiefly by heavy spring rains falling on the snow-covered highlands.

The increased discharge of the Columbia River in late spring and early summer is due very largely to the progressive melting of the snow in the mountain sections of the drainage basin. The great flood of June, 1948, was related to the rapid melting of the heavy snow cover in the headstream area.

Runoff Characteristics. Every drainage basin has a characteristic runoff pattern, but from year to year there is considerable variation due to the amount and the seasonal irregularities in precipitation, the rate of melting of the snow cover,

Fig. 7 Flooding along the Sun River west of Great Falls, Montana, on June 10, 1964 when the flood waters inundated large areas and caused considerable damage in Glacier National Park. (Montana Highway Department.)

and many other conditions. In much of eastern United States the maximum runoff comes in the spring months, chiefly because the winter snows upon melting add their contribution to the spring rains and the frozen condition of the ground prevents sink-in. The runoff is usually least in late summer when occasional droughts and high evaporation reduce the amount of water that reaches the streams, and in the midwinter when subfreezing temperatures maintain a snow cover, thus delaying runoff until spring. The winter minimum is quite characteristic of the more northern states because of the severity of the winter season. In the interior of the country where the late spring–early summer maximum is a characteristic feature of the rain-

fall the maximum discharge of the streams becomes more sympathetic with the rainfall regime (Fig. 8).

In New England the runoff shows both a spring and an autumn maximum. The most disastrous floods are associated with the melting snows of spring, as illustrated by the floods of early March 1936, and with the occasional but heavy rains of late summer and autumn.

In the western part of the United States the maximum runoff comes chiefly in the early summer. Along the Pacific coast the winter precipitation may produce floods immediately, as was true within the Sacramento basin during the winter of 1936 and along the Willamette in the winter of 1948, but usually the precipitation

Fig. 8 In June 1964 a flood on the West Papillion Creek near Millard, Nebraska, seriously damaged this trailer court. Many trailers were too seriously damaged to be salvaged. Water damage was considerable in trailers that were not moved off their foundations. (Corps of Engineers, U.S. Army.)

falls as snow in the mountains and is not released until spring and early summer. As the snow fields are reduced the discharge of the streams is greatly diminished by late summer and early autumn.

Shape of the Watershed. It is evident that a circular watershed with the several tributaries joining the main stream at or near a common point would be conducive to flood at times of widespread and heavy rains. Regardless of the shape of the drainage basin, heavy rains in the tributary areas may occur in such a manner as to produce a serious flood along the bottomlands of the main stream. Distribution of the heavy rains locally and timing are significant elements in the development of a great flood.

Floods on such major streams as the Mississippi, the Missouri, the Ohio, the Columbia, and the Susquehanna may be caused by a number of storms so distributed within the watershed and spaced at the proper time intervals that coincidence of crests in the lower course of the master stream results.

Configuration of the Terrain within the Watershed. On relatively flat lands each field becomes to a limited extent a catchment basin retarding the discharge of water to the watercourses. Water drains slowly from the lands of low relief, giving time for the stream to discharge its waters continuously within its confining channel, unless successive storms fall upon saturated ground. In areas of low relief and gentle slopes runoff may be delayed sufficiently to permit infiltration, but in regions of steep slopes there is a rapid streamward movement of the surface water unless precipitation is light and spread out sufficiently to give time for infiltration to the reservoir of underground waters. In rugged areas with steep slopes torrential rains are accompanied usually by rapid runoff and flooding of the lowlands along the watercourses. A heavy protecting cover of vegetation may reduce somewhat the runoff and consequently the flood damage, but forested areas are not free from floods. Slope, stream density, and other terrain conditions are important factors in determining the flow or discharge of a river.[6]

In the basin of the Red River of the North the annual precipitation averages approximately 21 inches and the surface runoff is only 1.25 inches. For the Mississippi basin above Koekuk, Iowa, the precipitation averages 29.51 inches, of which 6.98 inches, or approximately 23 percent, are lost by surface runoff. Here the slightly more rugged terrain and the increased precipitation are conducive to a greater runoff than is characteristic of the nearly level Red River plain. As illustrated by the Tennessee River, the steeper slopes of the southern Appalachians cause even greater runoff. The proportion escaping to the streams without having become a part of the groundwater reaches nearly half of the average annual precipitation of 50.36 inches.

Orientation of Rivers. The orientation of streams is a significant factor in the flooding of the adjacent floodplains. In Siberia the northward courses of the Ob, the Yenisei, and the Lena are favorable to flooding because spring comes to the headstream areas while the northern and downstream sections are still frozen. To a limited extent the Red River of the North is affected in a similar manner because of its south to north orientation.

In much of continental United States the

general rains of cyclonic origin and the local thunderstorms move from the west toward the east. The Ohio drainage basin is so oriented that frontal rains may occur simultaneously and repeatedly over the full length of the watershed. Fortunately, most of the storms move upstream, and precipitation falls first in the lower section of the watershed and a part of the runoff is discharged downstream before the waters from the headstream area reach the lower course of the river. Along sections of the Missouri and other western tributaries of the Mississippi storm movement is downstream. Generally the storms move more rapidly than the flood crests. Watercourses that are oriented transverse to the paths of local thunderstorms may escape serious damage, for the flooded area is likely to be restricted.

Soil and Rock Conditions. Floods occur in part because the soil and the soil material are unable to absorb the precipitation as fast as it falls or before it escapes as sheet wash. Where the surface soil consists of coarse sands and gravels which permit a high proportion of the precipitation to infiltrate to the underground reservoir, floods seldom occur unless the ground is saturated or frozen, or the intensity is so great that excessive runoff results. In the Coastal Plain of the Atlantic and Gulf coasts where the underlying formations are particularly porous, there is little danger from floods of local origin.

In the Great Lakes states where the glacial drift consists of sand and gravel the danger from floods is not great. Here also the slight relief of the glacial landscape is conducive to infiltration. These sandy and gravelly areas are particularly characteristic of Michigan, central and northern Wisconsin, and northeastern Minnesota.

Where the surface soil is clayey and more or less impervious to infiltration, the runoff will be heavy in all storms of great intensity. In the Piedmont and the Southern Appalachians both the surface soil and the underlying crystalline rocks have limited storage capacity, and, as a result, the many rivers are subject to flood. At times of heavy storms destructive floods may spread beyond the protecting channels and

[6] Walter Langbein and others, *Topographic Characteristics of Drainage Basins*, Water Supply Paper 968-C, U.S. Geological Survey, Washington, D.C., 1947.

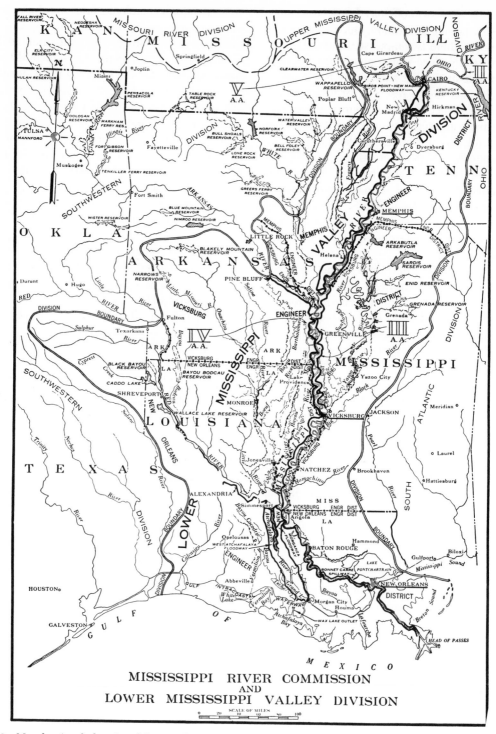

Fig. 9 Map showing the location of the major levees, floodways, spillways, and other flood-control works in the lowland of the lower Mississippi basin. (Mississippi River Commission.)

progress seaward causing damage in the Coastal Plain, where floods of local origin are rather uncommon. The most disastrous floods are inherited from the Appalachians and are confined to the major streams that rise in the crystalline areas to the west and north.

Physiographic Aspects of Floods. Streams that are lowering their courses into bedrock are bordered usually by rather steep slopes and the floodwaters do not inundate extensive areas. And many streams that flow on more gentle gradients are commonly bordered by narrow alluvium-covered flats which are subject to limited flooding when the rivers rise above the protecting banks. Along such streams little damage results from inundation, but bridges, roads, and other structures that lie close upon the rivers suffer from the rush of the floodwaters.

Rivers such as the Mississippi, Missouri, Red, Illinois, and many others flow seaward on a broad alluvial plain. Where the gradient is very low the stream follows a meandering course. The most notable example of such a stream in the United States is the lower Mississippi, although streams of all sizes may be characterized by meanders.

The large streams that flow along broad alluvial plains are commonly bordered by important natural levees of their own creation. By repeated floodings this riverside strip is built up into a protecting natural levee. The river is then confined, except for the major floods, between the protecting levees. The land slopes away from the river to low-lying back swamps partially drained by smaller rivers which flow more or less parallel to the master stream. Such streams are known as the Yazoo type, the name being derived from the stream of that name in the alluvial plain of the Mississippi above Vicksburg (Fig. 9).

Since the natural levees that border the streams are made by the rivers, it may be expected that in times of great floods the water will rise above the levees and inundate extensive areas beyond the levees. Where the levees are low or weak the floodwaters may break through to the back swamp areas by way of crevasses. In time of high water there is always the danger

that crevasses will be formed. By this process of levee building and silting of the back swamp areas the alluvial plain is built up.

The seaward extension of the delta of the Mississippi results in a gradual lengthening of the stream. As a consequence the river bottom is built up slightly to maintain the necessary gradient. Later floods will build up the adjacent levees, confining all but the greatest floods to the levee-bordered channel. A great river flowing seaward is a powerful physiographic agent, ever changing the configuration of its alluvial plain.

FLOOD CONTROL

To escape the danger of floods various control measures either singly or in combination have been utilized to provide the necessary protection. Probably one of the earliest methods was to evacuate the area at the first warnings of impending danger. This method is still used when there is a failure of other protective measures. Throughout the history of civilized man the fertile alluvial lowlands have been preferred areas of habitation; and, as high water menaced periodically the homes of the people, the protecting dike or levee became one of the first methods of defense against floods.

Channel Improvements. One of the simplest and most individual methods of flood protection is channel improvement. Along relatively small streams riparian owners may without a great deal of expense improve a stream channel by clearing out obstructions such as brush and trees. Accumulated débris from previous floods may be removed, facilitating the discharge of floodwaters, thus preventing the stream from overspreading its banks and inundating adjacent lands. This simple method is usually accompanied by a straightening of the channel by cutting across meanders and other sharp bends in the river.

Such local flood-prevention methods are effective unless the stream is aggrading its channel and building up its floodplain. Then the puny efforts of man may be wasted in a futile attempt to prevent flood damage. The control of such a stream will require preventive works in the headstream areas and perhaps along the lower course as well. Channel straightening has the effect of steepening the gradient, thus increasing the velocity. Unless the stream is loaded to capacity, it will deepen and perhaps widen its channel sufficiently to carry the water of subsequent floods if the course is not allowed to become clogged with débris.

Local improvements in the channel planned to protect only the adjacent property may actually increase the flood hazard downstream. Improvements designed to facilitate the rapid downstream movement of water along the tributaries may heighten the flood crests along the master stream. It is because of the conflicts of interests within a drainage basin that all flood-control works should be coordinated, so that preventive measures applied in one area may not nullify the works in another.

Protection by Levees. Levees are very commonly associated with other local preventive measures used along the smaller streams as well as along such major streams as the Mississippi and the Missouri. Short levees are usually constructed where the banks are low in order to maintain a uniform channel height. Channel straightening will require fill-ins and protecting levees to make sure that the stream in time of flood is confined to its new channel. The levees or dikes should not be placed too close to the river's edge, but set back somewhat, leaving room for other preventive works along the stream and providing a safety margin in anticipation of unprecedented floods. Such a system of protecting dikes will require a correlated system along the tributaries and a series of gates to provide for the drainage of the lowlands outside the dikes in time of low water. In times of flood the gates will have to be closed, preventing drainage of the lowlands. To avoid local inundation it may be necessary to install pumping equipment to lift the water over the levee to the main stream.

The confinement of a river between closely spaced levees creates a dangerous situation because the floodwaters, no longer having access to the floodplain, rise above former levels and increase the danger of breaks or crevasses. This danger may be lessened somewhat by a scouring and a deepening of the channel which becomes a restricted floodway in time of high water. Temporarily, at least, levees give protection to riverine property, but there is no general agreement as to the effectiveness of the method.

Levees as a protective device have been most extensively used along the lower Mississippi, but they are necessary along many of the major tributaries such as the Red, the Arkansas, and the Illinois. Many of our principal cities are located upon the larger rivers, and wherever there is likely to be extensive damage to valuable urban property by inundation protecting levees have been constructed.

It is estimated that the flood damage along the Illinois River averages more than $2,000,000 annually. The watercourse is bordered by expensive levees which in many places are located too close to the river, resulting in disastrous breaks and extensive inundation. Because of the high cost involved in the maintenance of the system of levees, limited areas once used for farms have reverted to their former condition and now are used for floodways and game refuges.

Along the Red, the Arkansas, the White, and the Ouachita rivers the construction of levees has given inadequate protection to more than 2,000,000 acres of alluvial lands. The system of levees needs to be reorganized and coordinated into a unified project not only for the sake of the 2,000,000 acres now receiving partial protection but also to give increased security to the 7,000,000 acres subject to inundation in times of high floods.

Levees along the Mississippi River. Levee construction along the Mississippi was begun at New Orleans in 1717. The first single mile of levee was gradually extended upstream, the individual planters assuming responsibility for their respective sections along the river.[7] Since the early settlers along the Mississippi were interested in navigation as well as flood protection, the levees were so placed as to serve the dual function of facilitating commerce and giving protection to the rich alluvial lands.

Recurring floods along the river called for additional levees constructed chiefly by riparian landholders, by counties, parishes, levee boards, and the several states. Many areas were unable to assume their full share of the responsibility, and as a result floodwaters overtopping the natural levees spread downstream inundating farmlands locally well protected. As a result of the lack of coordination of the levee systems and the absence of protective works in the sections still remaining in the public domain, there developed very early a movement for flood control by the federal government.

The ever-growing levee system was severely tested by the disastrous flood of 1859, which destroyed important sections of the system. Before adequate repairs could be made the Civil War, like a series of destructive floods, had as one of its unfortunate consequences a deterioration of the levees. And during the reconstruction period recurring floods, culminating in the great flood of 1882, aroused the nation to the need for adequate protection. In 1879 Congress created the Mississippi River Commission which was charged with the responsibility of drawing up plans for preventing flood damage and supervising expenditures for flood-control works.

The commission established the standards for levee construction and otherwise cooperated with local agencies, such as levee boards, in providing the necessary protection. Specifications for levees and other control works have been revised from time to time, but continual efforts toward standardization and coordination

[7] Andrew A. Humphreys and Henry L. Abbot, *Report upon the Physics and Hydraulics of the Mississippi River*, War Department, Washington, D.C., 1874, p. 150.

of systems have resulted in constructive although inadequate protective works, as was demonstrated by the great floods of 1922, 1927, and 1937.

Congress by a succession of acts from 1917 to 1954 has provided funds for the control of floods on the Mississippi and at the same time authorized the use of methods other than levee building to protect the alluvial bottomlands. The federal government also assumed a larger share of the costs. The use of floodways, created by the set-back of major levees, indicated recognition of the need of the river for a larger share of the bottomland. The Flood Control Act of 1936 authorized the construction also of retarding basins in the upper reaches of the alluvial basin.

Spillways and Floodways. The natural history of a river confined to a levee-protected course includes not only an overtopping of the levees in time of flood but also the breaking of wide gaps in the levees permitting the floodwaters to escape to the back swamp areas. Because a large river may at times need more of the floodplain than is available between the levees, an additional floodway may be provided in the lower backswamp areas. Such floodways should be protected by dikes and coordinated with the levee system of the master stream and its major tributaries (Fig. 10). Old crevasses may be used for the spillways through which the waters may be diverted to the floodways.

In the lower section of the Mississippi the water that seeps through or overtops the levee does not return to the river but flows to the Gulf of Mexico by way of the Atchafalaya River and the Bayou Lafourche. The latter is a levee-guarded channel extending from Donaldsonville, Louisiana, almost to the Gulf. This condition along the lower Mississippi illustrates how the diversion of waters from the main stream may lower flood crests in the downstream section of the river and for a limited distance upstream.

The Mississippi River Commission from its

Fig. 10 Lower Auxiliary Channel, Yazoo Basin, Mississippi, looking downstream from the upper end of the channel at the confluence of the Yazoo River. This is the biggest ditch ever dug in the State of Mississippi. This auxiliary channel will provide an additional outlet for floodwater which accumulates in the central area of the basin. At the highest flood stages half of the flow of the Yazoo River will use this channel. (Mississippi River Commission.)

inception in 1879 to the disastrous flood of 1927 when 23,573 square miles[8] were inundated stood rather firmly for flood control largely by levees. After the 1927 flood, the commission's policy was broadened to include a more comprehensive scheme of levees as a first line of defense supplemented by spillways, floodways, and other protective measures.

In 1928 Congress recognized the validity of the floodway method of alleviating the flood

[8] *Monthly Weather Review*, Supplement 29, 1927, p. 34.

danger and provided for a system of floodways to supplement the levees along the Mississippi. By the time of the 1937 flood, levees, floodways, upstream reservoirs, and other protective measures were accepted as essential in the over-all control of the river.

Above New Orleans the Bonnet Carré floodway can be used to discharge the floodwaters of the Mississippi into Lake Pontchartrain and thus provide a measure of protection to the downstream communities. The Morganza floodway above Baton Rouge can be used in time of emergency to divert floodwaters to the Gulf of Mexico by way of the levee-guarded Atchafalaya basin (Fig. 11).

Retarding Basins. Along the larger rivers that have broad natural levees and expansive back-swamp areas, retarding basins may be developed as a means of reducing the flood crests. Water discharged from the constricted channel of a major river in flood may raise the level of the water in the swamp area very slightly and at the same time may reduce the flood crest sufficiently to prevent serious flooding or damage to other protective works. The retarding dams are usually constructed of earth except for the spillways or the gateways and so designed that local floodwaters accumulate behind the dams and are discharged automatically, maintaining a bank-full condition along the watercourse. If such retarding basins are equipped with outlet structures and control gates, the normal emptying progress may be arrested.

After the Dayton flood of 1913 the Miami Conservancy District of Ohio was organized to protect the valley from such disastrous floods.

Five retarding dams across the Great Miami River and its tributaries were constructed. This flood project with its retarding dams, levees, and channel improvements has been regarded as one of the most successful flood-control methods, although there has been no flood equal to the 1913 inundation to test its effectiveness.

Flood Control Moves Upstream. The construction of storage reservoirs for flood prevention alone is a costly method of control unless the reservoirs may be used for other purposes, such as water supply, power, recreation, and the regulation of the low-water level of the master stream. Multiple-purpose reservoirs are recommended unless there are conflicts that cannot be easily resolved. For example, a reservoir to be useful for water power must be kept as nearly full as possible, but the same reservoir to be effective in the prevention of floods must be kept empty so that the floodgates can be closed in time of emergency. This conflict may be resolved by a series of dams, some of which are built primarily for flood control and others designed for the generation of power. A large dam, which in effect is two dams in one, may

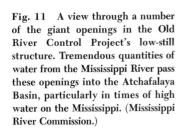

Fig. 11 A view through a number of the giant openings in the Old River Control Project's low-still structure. Tremendous quantities of water from the Mississippi River pass these openings into the Atchafalaya Basin, particularly in times of high water on the Mississippi. (Mississippi River Commission.)

serve both purposes. The lower section of the dam may be used for power and be kept as nearly full as possible while the upper section may be available for water storage if a flood threatened.

Many of the reservoirs that now serve as flood-prevention works were constructed for other purposes, and flood control was a secondary, although important, consideration. For example, the Wilson Dam on the Tennessee was constructed for power purposes, but it also helps to regulate the flow of the lower course of the river. This dam is now a part of the Tennessee Valley Authority which includes several multiple-purpose reservoirs.

In the Cascades and the Sierras the many dams constructed for power purposes and for the storage of irrigation water minimize the flood hazards resulting from melting snows. Such dams not only reduce the flood crests but also may improve the low-water stage of the rivers. The great dams such as the Hoover Dam on the Colorado, the Bonneville and the Grand Coulee dams on the Columbia, and the reservoirs on the Missouri are all part of a long-range water-conservation program.

The construction of many small dams in the headstream area of certain major streams not only will serve in flood prevention but also will provide recreational opportunities. If the stored water is not needed for culinary purposes these numerous reservoirs may be used by a large number of persons if they are easily accessible to the public.

The flood problem has its origin where the rain falls upon the land, and if there is to be effective downstream control of floods, there must be flood prevention at the sources. The Flood Control Act of 1936 committed the federal government to a program of reservoir construction in the upstream areas of rivers subject to floods.

In order that reservoirs may have a long life and serve the function of flood prevention, efforts should be made to prevent their silting up. The drainage basin above a reservoir should be so protected from erosion that maximum capacity of the reservoir can be maintained. If the runoff carries great quantities of sediment into the ponded waters of the reservoir, the capacity may be greatly reduced. Not all sedimentation can be prevented, but if the watershed is forested or grass covered, the load of silt carried by the stream is reduced to the minimum.

To be most effective reservoirs should not be placed too far upstream, for such placement will require more dams and will intercept only a small proportion of the runoff. A downstream location as near as possible to the area to be protected is to be preferred. One major dam across the master stream just above the area subjected to floods will give greater protection probably than ten smaller dams in the headstream area. It is not recommended, however, that the large dams be substituted for small dams in the tributary areas but that a coordinated system of reservoirs be considered not only for flood prevention but for other water needs as well.

The Flood-Control Controversy. In essence there are two principal locations where flood control can be carried out. In the headstream areas where the excess precipitation occurs, runoff can be reduced by maintaining an effective vegetal cover or by agricultural practices that tend to hold the water on the land. Small dams constructed on the numerous tributaries of the master streams are presumed to be adequate to prevent or at least reduce flooding downstream. The other approach to the problem of flooding is to construct levees, dams, floodways, and other protective structures in the areas where the floods occur. In many drainage basins because of the need for agricultural land, it is hardly feasible to maintain a forest cover that normally is most effective in reducing immediate runoff. Since much of the land in many river basins is under cultivation to meet the needs of the people for food and fiber, it is impracticable to maintain a luxuriant cover of grass which like forests tends to reduce rapid runoff.

Because of the basic differences between

these two concepts of flood control, the proponents have tended to organize themselves into opposed camps, and as a consequence certain agencies of the government have become identified or allied with one camp or the other. For example, the Corps of Engineers, because of its long concern with navigation in the lower courses of the major coastal streams and because flood control on the lower Mississippi and on other streams was carried out more or less incidental to the improvement of navigation, is generally favorable to the use of downstream structures.

Those who believe in a solution based on land management and the use of numerous small dams in the upstream areas are allied with the Department of Agriculture in its bid for Congressional support of its erosion-control program and land-management plans that are designed to conserve the soil resource so essential to high productivity of the land. By strip cropping, contour cultivation, the reduction of over pasturing, and by other measures, the soil, water, and forest resources are to be conserved in the headstream areas.[9]

This conflict has been specifically labeled the "big dam—little dam controversy" and implies that the Corps of Engineers is the strong proponent of big dams on the main stem of the principal rivers and that the Department of Agriculture and its supporters are in favor of small detention dams in the headstream areas. It may be observed, however, that the differences expressed are not entirely irreconcilable. Many engineers recognize that certain dams well placed on important tributaries may be very effective in reducing if not in preventing floods. Such well-placed reservoirs may serve other purposes as well, such as municipal water supply and recreation, but they will not satisfy the land-management people who may have been denied adequate funds to carry out their programs. The conflict has brought forth some

very strong statements by the proponents of both points of view.

In Mid-March 1964 the Ohio River, repeatedly subject to floods, overflowed its banks and inundated extended sections of the bottomland. In press releases dated March 13 and 21, Brigadier General W. P. Leber, Ohio River Division Army Engineer, reported that 30 of the projected 39 flood-control reservoirs and 62 flood walls and levees saved approximately $290,-000 in flood damage. He also estimated that flood crests were reduced from 2.0 feet at Cincinnati to 10.5 feet at Parkersburg by the operation of these flood-control projects.[10] Currently the Corps of Engineers is trying to cope with the hazard of floods by the construction of new reservoirs in the headwater areas and levees and flood walls along the downstream sections of the Ohio and its principal tributaries.

Forests and Floods. It has been often stated that a forest cover in a drainage basin materially reduces floods, but forested areas are not free from the hazard of flood damage. There is conclusive evidence that the eastern tributaries of the Mississippi and the lower section of the master stream suffered from great floods before the land was settled and the forest was largely removed.

Adequate flood protection is dependent on engineering structures, but the forest cover should be considered as a supplementary protective measure. A closely forested area with its absorptive leaf-litter delays runoff somewhat and gives greater seasonal uniformity to the discharge of the streams.

This slight retardation of runoff may serve to reduce floods provided that the subsequent rains are delayed a sufficient length of time to permit the lowering of the water table and a drying out of the litter. If the absorptive capacity of both the litter and the soil is reduced because of saturation, heavy recurrent storms will cause floods even in forested areas.

[9] For an extended discussion of this controversy see Luna B. Leopold and Thomas Maddock, Jr., *The Flood Control Controversy*, New York, 1954, pp. 83–92.

[10] Press releases, U.S. Army Engineers District, Louisville, Kentucky, March 13 and 21, 1964.

THE RESPONSIBILITY FOR
FLOOD CONTROL

Introduction. The control of floods is a responsibility that extends beyond the limits of the inundated areas. The calamitous floods of the Mississippi and other major streams of the United States always arouse widespread public interest in the causes of floods and their control. To charge the whole cost of protective works to the immediate beneficiaries would burden them with taxes beyond their capacity to pay. Conversely, to charge the cost to people who in no way receive any of the benefits directly from flood control is to misplace the responsibility for control. These two conflicting concepts can be harmonized by expecting the local beneficiaries to accept a share of the costs in proportion to their capacity to pay and charging the remaining costs to the general public by means of federal and state taxation.

Floods have no respect for political jurisdictions, just as political boundaries show little relation to hydrographic boundaries. Since flooded areas seldom coincide precisely with political areas the existing minor civil divisions such as townships and counties are unable individually to cope with the flood problem. This inadequacy of the political units as originally delimited has led to the organization of levee boards, conservancy districts, water-control boards, reclamation districts, and other legally constituted bodies for the practical solution of many water problems including the control of floods. The magnitude of the problem of the lower Mississippi transcends the local jurisdictions and consequently becomes invested with a public interest national in scope.

Individual Responsibility. The flood problem begins with the formation of a tiny rivulet in the farmer's field. Its control is both a personal and a social responsibility. His personal interest is not confined to the hazard of floods on his farm but to the associated loss of soil as the run-off gathers into rivulets that converge into larger and more devastating streams, producing both water and soil damage.

The individual interest may be inimical to the public interest, however, in the matter of flood control. The farmer who hastens the downstream movement of water across his farm may be contributing to floods in the lower section of the river. With an understanding of his individual responsibility the farmer may by altering his farm practice so delay runoff as to contribute to the solution of the flood problem, and all farmers working collectively may materially reduce flood crests in downstream areas.

The personal responsibility of many individuals enlarges to a regional responsibility co-extensive with each important drainage basin. If the whole watershed lies within a single state the flood-control agency or conservancy district may be organized under the laws of the state and, if the problem is of sufficient moment, may deserve the blessing of the state in the form of financial aid.

Regional Aspects of Flood Control. Planning for the best use of water resources is essentially a regional responsibility, the region being coincident with the drainage basin of the streams concerned. This concept of the planning region cannot be adhered to rigidly, for the transmission of water power in the form of electricity and the distribution of water for irrigation and municipal purposes extend far beyond the limits of the drainage basin, and require a modification of the hydrographic region to include adjacent areas that constitute the peripheral sections of an economic region (Fig. 12).

The problem of flood control, however, is rather strictly confined to the drainage basin. So long as control measures involve only riverine works, the plan would require the cooperation of riverside communities, but as control is extended to include preventive measures, the whole drainage basin should be organized into a unit. Levee boards, conservancy districts, and other water-control organizations may serve as the legally constituted agencies to deal with local, state, and federal authorities.

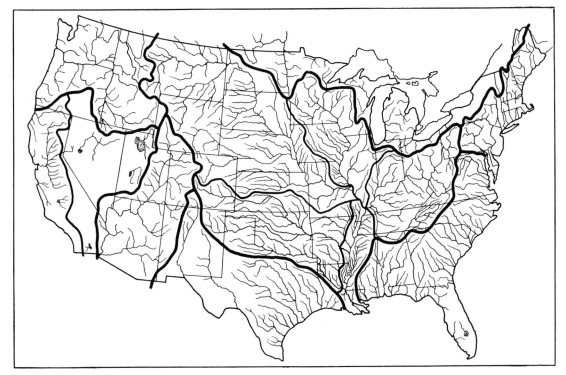

Fig. 12   Major drainage areas of the United States. (National Resources Board, Part III, Report of the Water Planning Committee.)

One of the most notable experiments in regional planning in the United States is the Tennessee Valley Authority authorized in 1933. Flood control is only one of the objectives of the multiple-purpose plan for the Tennessee River basin. The Columbia River basin with its several water conditions should have a plan that embraces and integrates all aspects of the water problem. In a similar manner the waters of the Colorado and the Missouri whether used for power, recreation, or irrigation should be made to serve as many people as possible.

The Pick-Sloan Plan. President Franklin D. Roosevelt believed that regional authorities were suitable agencies for an attack upon the many problems identified or associated with a drainage basin. This was demonstrated in the 1930's by the creation of the Tennessee Valley Authority. He displayed great interest in the

early years of World War II in a similar authority for the Missouri Valley. During the discussion of this proposal two separate reports on the development and control of the water resources were prepared. One report was prepared by William G. Sloan and represented the plan of the Bureau of Reclamation. The other was prepared by Colonel, later General, Lewis A. Pick for the Corps of Engineers.

These two reports were published in 1944 and immediately attracted the attention of the Congress and other government agencies as well as the general public. During the summer of 1944 the two reports were examined very carefully, certain differences were reconciled, and a workable division of authority was agreed to by the Corps of Engineers and the Bureau of Reclamation. This joint plan known as the Pick-Sloan plan was submitted to Congress on

November 21, 1944.[11] The several water problems of the Missouri will involve a succession of
projects requiring many years or decades for
their development before the river will be
brought under control.

The Missouri River valley has never been
organized into a regional authority such as the
TVA, but the construction of multiple-purpose
dams has gone forward decade after decade.
Constructed in the 1950's and 1960's or scheduled for completion in the current decade are
the Oahe, the Big Bend, Fort Peck, Fort Randall,
Canyon Ferry, Yellowtail, Boysen, Fremont
Canyon, Gendo, Kortes, Fontelle, and others.
Some of the early dams such as Shoshone (1922)
were built chiefly for power and irrigation, but
in recent years the several functions of flood-
control, power, water supply, irrigation, navigation, and recreation have been served.

Floodplain Zoning. One neglected but very
important aspect of water control is the authority of planning commissions and similar agencies
to regulate the use of land along watercourses. It
may be trite but very truthful to say that the
floodplain belongs to the river, and people, individually or collectively, who pre-empt the bottomlands may expect on occasion extensive flood
damage. Effective zoning of bottomlands may
result in dedicating large areas to use by the
river in times of flood. Only the higher and easily
protected lands should be approved for residential and industrial purposes.

The flood-hazard zones in the bottomlands
may be delineated and a series of regulations
developed to guide prospective users of the
lowlands. Where the damage from floods is
repeated year after year with the risk of severe
floods every few years use of the land for structures such as homes and factories should be
prohibited. In a higher belt with less danger
use may be restricted. And in still higher areas
where the land is likely to be inundated only in
the rare once-in-a-lifetime flood the planners,

developers, and users should be warned about
the possibility of floods.[12]

Flood Insurance. After every great flood
there is a clamor for some kind of insurance plan
which will provide protection from the heavy
losses commonly suffered in a flooded area. The
enormous property damage caused by Hurricane Diane in August 1955 revived interest in
some kind of insurance plan. In a report for 1952
the National Association of Insurance Agents
stated that sound flood insurance policies could
not be written. Another report based on a study
of the 1955 floods in northeastern United States
confirmed the insurance industry's long-time
position that it is impracticable to write flood
insurance on a sound economic basis. This traditional resistance of the insurance companies
to writing policies is related basically to the fact
that the premium would have to be excessively
high to provide adequate reimbursement for the
heavy damage often sustained by industry,
transportation, utilities, residential property,
and agricultural land. Only the owners of property that is subject to flood would be interested
in carrying flood insurance. In the case of minor
flood damage, the risk would be distributed
sufficiently widely to make payments possible
to the limited number of claimants. But in the
case of a great flood, the damage would be so
great and the claims so large that a flood insurance plan would become ineffective and might
be wiped out completely.[13]

There has been the suggestion that the federal
government undertake to do what the private
stock companies feel they cannot do, by authorizing the establishment of a governmental in-

[11] William G. Hoyt and Walter B. Langbein, *Floods,*
Princeton, N.J., 1955, p. 280.

[12] For a discussion of this problem see Robert W. Kates and
Gilbert F. White, "Flood Hazard Evaluation," in Gilbert F.
White, editor, *Papers on Flood Problems,* Research Paper
No. 70, Department of Geography, University of Chicago,
Illinois, 1961, pp. 135-147.

[13] For a discussion of the flood insurance problem see the
task force report of the Commission on Organization of the
Executive Branch of the Government, Vol. III, *Water Resources and Power,* Washington, D.C., pp. 1261-1267. See
also William G. Hoyt and Walter B. Langbein, *Floods,* Princeton, N.J., 1955, pp. 104-113.

surance corporation to provide protection.

The flood insurance question was referred to Congress, and during the second session of the 84th Congress in 1956, the problem received careful consideration. Opinion inevitably was divided on how to provide adequate insurance coverage for areas subject to recurrent flood damage. Many people believe that flood insurance on a sound economic basis is basically unattainable by private means and, therefore, some kind of government aid will be required to give any flood insurance plan the large reserves required to meet the emergency of a great flood. The 84th Congress passed a flood-insurance bill which President Eisenhower signed in the week of August 11, 1956. The bill put the federal government in the business of flood insurance. The maximum coverage was set at $250,000 for each business and $10,000 on each residence. The premium on the insurance was to be divided unequally between the government and the insured, 40 percent by the government and 60 percent by the insured. In 1957 the 85th Congress failed to support the flood-insurance measure before it.

The Responsibility of the State.

Where a drainage basin lies entirely within a single state, a conservancy district or flood-control board may be authorized by the legislature or by a conservation board charged with the responsibility of handling the many water problems of the state.

Flood problems that involve two or more states may require interstate cooperation in order that a flood-control program may be extended to all parts of the drainage basin. The cooperation should include not only an interstate agreement but also a uniformity of laws to facilitate the work of the organization charged with the responsibility of flood control. An interstate compact that provides an acceptable distribution of costs is difficult to attain. In addition to the economic difficulties the legal requirement of authorization and ratification of interstate compacts by Congress and the legislatures of the states concerned practically precludes

their wide use. One of the most notable interstate agreements is the Colorado River Compact involving the interests of seven states. Flood control was, however, a minor consideration in the negotiations of this interstate compact.

Only those flood-control projects that are self-liquidating or in which there is an important public interest should be authorized. It may be necessary to appropriate what appear to be unduly large sums to protect such utilities as water-supply plants in order that there be no interruption of the service. For such purposes excessive expenditures may be justified, but there should be a careful scrutiny of all flood-control plans to make certain that the benefits to be gained equal or exceed the cost of the protective works.

Federal Responsibility.

During the early history of the United States the many functions of the federal government did not extend to the construction of flood-control projects, partly because such works were not considered within the jurisdiction of the government. But as recurring floods inundated an increasing acreage of valuable farmlands along the lower Mississippi, there developed a strong sentiment in favor of the federal government assuming a share of the financial burden.

Where state boundaries transect a watershed, interstate cooperation becomes necessary to control floods. Federal responsibility begins first with the government's control of legally navigable streams where state and national cooperation is essential to an effective control program. The navigation needs and the flood-control requirements should be welded into a common program.

It required many years for the concept of national responsibility to develop, but the magnitude and recurrence of the Mississippi floods kept the question before the public. After each great flood the people of the lower Mississippi appealed to Congress for aid. Among many people there was some doubt as to the constitutional authority for the federal government to undertake the building of levees for the protection of private property. The federal government began to participate actively in the program of flood control, although the first moneys expended were primarily for the improvement of navigation and flood protection was an incidental consideration. Therefore the federal government entered upon a program of flood control under the guise of the constitutional authority to promote navigation.[14] With the settlement of the rich alluvial lands along such rivers as the Mississippi, the Sacramento, and other major streams, and the development of our complex system of railroads, highways, and postal system, the federal government became empowered under the commerce clause to build flood-control works to maintain and facilitate interstate commerce. The early doubts on the constitutional authority have largely been removed and the government has extended its jurisdiction to include flood-prevention projects in the headstream areas.

After the great Mississippi flood of 1927, the people of the United States were awakened to the need for a comprehensive plan of protection against the recurrence of such a disaster. The limited participation of the federal government in the period immediately after the establishment of the Mississippi River Commission has been extended. From this limited participation responsibility has been expanded to an assumption of 100 percent of the costs of labor and materials in the construction of levees and other protective works.

As the question of constitutional authority has been settled and as engineers have come to recognize that flood control involves also flood prevention, government participation has moved upstream from flooded areas to the headstream areas. Every great flood on the lower Mississippi is related to a flood of major proportions on the Ohio, although a flood on the Ohio does not always cause a flood on the lower Mississippi.[15]

The Tennessee Valley Authority, by its system of reservoirs, controls the flow of the Tennessee River. In a similar manner the Muskingum Watershed Conservancy District in Ohio is primarily a flood-control project, although other water uses are included in the plan. The Tennessee Valley Authority is chiefly a federal project, but the Muskingum Watershed Conservancy District was financed by the federal government, the State of Ohio, and the District.

In order to circumvent the extravagant use of federal money for flood-control works the Water Planning Committee of the National Resources Board recommended

". . . the policy of requiring appropriate contributions from localities benefited as a most satisfactory general test whether a particular project is meritorious." [16]

The Flood Control Act of 1936 and the amendatory act of 1938 made possible the waiving of local contributions as previously required. After 1938 the federal responsibility for flood-control projects was acknowledged as a government obligation. Local participation was not entirely abandoned, but more than a century of levee construction, channel improvement, and the development of multiple-purpose projects reflect a broadening of federal authority in the control of the nation's water resources.[17]

Benefit-Cost Ratio. It is generally recognized that many of the great water conservation projects developed by the federal government should be self-liquidating or at least return a high proportion of the original cost. The total benefits, both recoverable and intangible, should equal or approximate the cost of the projects. This principle has not been, and perhaps cannot be, rigidly adhered to because the long-range and intangible benefits cannot be exactly determined. Many of the large multiple-purpose projects permit a partial recovery of the costs by making appropriate charges for the power generated and for the water used for irrigation

[14] National Resources Board, Part III, *Report of the Water Planning Committee*, Washington, D.C., 1934, p. 378.
[15] *Monthly Weather Review*, Supplement 29, 1927, p. 7.

[16] National Resources Board, Part III, *op. cit.*, p. 273.
[17] Gilbert Fowler White, *Human Adjustments to Floods*, Chicago, 1945, pp. 5–24.

and for municipal and industrial purposes. The revenues derived can be applied toward the amortization of the original cost. It is much more difficult to determine the benefits which should be assigned to flood control, improved navigation, and recreation. As a consequence, an important share of the costs are borne by the taxpayers who may be indirectly the beneficiaries.

International Control of Floods. Fortunately, the boundaries of the United States are so located that floods of international character are not beyond the control of man. An important section of the Canadian boundary lies within the Great Lakes–St. Lawrence system which is relatively free from floods. Our conflicts with Canada have involved the low-water stages of the Great Lakes rather than high levels. The diversion of water from Lake Michigan for the purpose of sewage disposal at Chicago has at times of low-water stages on the Great Lakes drawn vigorous protests from Canada.

Another section of the Canadian boundary, from Lake of the Woods to the Rocky Mountains, lies across a region of slight rainfall where the problem of floods is very local and minor. Also a long section of the boundary from the Red River of the North to the Rockies lies very near the water parting between the Missouri River and the Assiniboine River which joins the Red River of the North at Winnipeg.

The Red River of the North rises within the United States and flows northward across the Canadian boundary to Lake Winnipeg. Spring advancing from the south sometimes opens the headstream area while the northern and lower course is still blocked by ice. These occasional spring floods overspread the flat alluvial plain across which the river flows, damaging the adjacent farmlands and a number of small urban centers. The drought conditions of the period between 1930 and 1936 turned the attention of people to the problem of water deficiency, although floods, such as the inundations of 1882, 1897, 1916, and 1950, may recur when the wet phase of the climatic cycle returns. In 1912 a treaty between the United States and Canada created the International Joint Commission which serves for the adjudication of the many water problems of interest to the two countries, and if the problem of floods becomes critical the commission stands ready to facilitate negotiation and arbitration.

Along the boundary between the United States and Mexico there are two areas requiring international cooperation for the control of floods and the apportioning of the water resources. The lower course and the delta of the Colorado were long subject to recurring floods, but the construction of the Roosevelt reservoir on the Salt River and the Coolidge reservoir on the Gila River somewhat reduced the flood hazard, and the completion of the Hoover and Parker-Davis dams has greatly reduced the danger of inundation in the delta. The apportionment of water remains as the critical unsolved water problem of the Colorado.

More than 800 miles of the Mexico–United States boundary lies along the Rio Grande. The water of the upper course is derived exclusively within the territorial limits of the United States. Above El Paso the control of the river is essentially an American problem, although Mexico is vitally concerned with the quantity and the quality of the water that enters Mexican territory. Below El Paso additions to the Rio Grande are drawn chiefly from the Sierra Madre of Mexico. Floods in the lower course so far as they are the result of increments from the south can be controlled only by the cooperation of the Mexican government. The construction of the Elephant Butte Dam across the Rio Grande at Hot Springs, New Mexico, practically prevents the danger of floods in the 125-mile section above El Paso.

The Falcon Reservoir on the Rio Grande was completed in 1954 and stores 4,054,000 acre-feet of water. It functions to provide water for the generation of power and for irrigation and at the same time permits the storage of water when floods threaten the down-river sections of the lowland.

The water problems of Mexico and of the United States are not so susceptible of arbitration as the Canadian-American problems. In the dry regions of southwestern United States the shortage of water has often precipitated disputes under the doctrine of prior right, and an equitable distribution of the limited water resources is very difficult to obtain.

The International Boundary and Water Commission, United States and Mexico, functions under the jurisdiction of the Department of State, and over a period of more than 25 years has actively sought solutions to the numerous water problems along the Mexican border.[18]

[18] Ben Moreel, *Our Nation's Water Resources—Policies and Politics*, Chicago, 1956, p. 81.

References

Barrows, H. K., *Floods, Their Hydrology and Control*, McGraw-Hill Co., New York, 1948.

Bock, Carl A., *History of the Miami Flood Control Project*, Dayton, Ohio, 1918.

Dunham, Allison, "Flood Control Via the Police Power," *University of Pennsylvania Law Review*, Vol. 107, June 1959, pp. 1098–1132.

Eckstein, Otto, *Water Resource Development*, Harvard University Press, Cambridge, 1958.

Frank, Arthur DeWitt, *The Development of the Federal Program of Flood Control on the Mississippi River*, Columbia University Press, New York, 1930.

Goddard, James E., *Changing Concepts in Flood Plain Management*, Tennessee Valley Authority, Knoxville, 1960.

Goddard, James E., *Flood-Plain Regulation to Avoid Flood Damage*, Tennessee Valley Authority, Knoxville, 1960.

Holzman, Benjamin, et al., "Flood Hazards and Flood Control," *Climate and Man, The Yearbook of Agriculture*, Washington, D.C., 1941, pp. 531–578.

Hoyt, William G., and Walter B. Langbein, *Floods*, Princeton University Press, Princeton, New Jersey, 1955.

Hoyt, W. G., et al., *Studies of the Relation of Rainfall and Run-off in the United States*, Water Supply Paper 772, U.S. Geological Survey, Washington, D.C., 1936.

Humphreys, Andrew A., and Henry L. Abbott, *Report upon the Physics and Hydraulics of the Mississippi River*, War Department, Washington, D.C., 1861.

Jarvis, Clarence S., et al., *Floods in the United States*, Water Supply Paper 771, U.S. Geological Survey, Washington, D.C., 1936.

Kilpatrick, F. A., and H. H. Barnes, Jr., *Channel Geometry of Piedmont Streams as Related to Frequency of Floods*, Professional Paper 422-E, U.S. Geological Survey, Government Printing Office, Washington, D.C., 1964.

Langbein, Walter B., and William G. Hoyt, *Water Facts for the Nation's Future*, The Ronald Press Co., New York, 1959.

Leopold, Luna B., and Thomas Maddock, Jr., *The Flood Control Controversy*, The Ronald Press Co., New York, 1954.

Mississippi River Commission, *Annual Reports*.

Moreel, Ben, *Our Nation's Water Resources—Policies and Politics*, The Law School, The University of Chicago, Chicago, 1956.

Murphy, Francis C., *Regulating Flood-Plain Development*, Department of Geography Research No. 56, The University of Chicago, Chicago, 1958.

Peterson, Elmer T., *Big Dam Foolishness*, The Devin–Adair Co., New York, 1954.

Renshaw, Edward F., *Toward Responsible Government: An Economic Appraisal of Federal Investment in Water Resource Programs*, Idyia Press, Chicago, 1957.

Report of the Mississippi Valley Committee of the Public Works Administraton, Washington, D.C., 1934, 234 pp.

Sheaffer, John R., *Flood Proofing: An Approach to Flood Damage Reduction*, Department of Geography Research Paper No. 65, The University of Chicago, Chicago, 1960.

Silcox, F. A., W. C. Lowdermilk, and Morris L. Cooke, *The Scientific Aspects of Flood Control,* Ecological Society of America and the American Association for the Advancement of Science, 1936.

Tennessee Valley Authority, *A Program for Reducing the National Flood Damage Potential,* Tennessee Valley Authority, Knoxville, 1958.

United Nations Department of Economic Affairs, "Flood Control and Navigation," *UNSCCUR,* Vol. IV: *Water Resources,* New York, 1951, pp. 325–349.

United States Department of the Army, Chief of Engineers, *Annual Reports.*

United States, 87th Congress, 1st Session, *Report of the Select Committee on National Water Resources,* Senate, Report No. 29, Government Printing Office, Washington, D.C., 1961.

United States National Resources Board, *Report of the Water Planning Committee,* Part III, Washington, D.C., 1934, pp. 253–388.

United States National Resources Committee, *Drainage Basin Problems and Programs,* Washington, D.C., 1937.

United States Senate, Select Committee of National Water Resources, *Flood Problems and Management in the Tennessee River Basin,* Committee Print No. 16, 86th Congress, 1st Session, Government Printing Office, Washington, D.C., 1960.

United States 75th Congress, 3rd Session, *Comprehensive Flood-Control Plans,* Hearings before the House Committee on Flood Control on Report of the Chief of Engineers, April 6, 1937, and subsequent Reports of the Chief of Engineers, and Amendments to the Flood Control Acts of June 15, 1936, June 22, 1936, and August 28, 1937, Washington, D.C., 1938.

United States 76th Congress, 1st Session, *Comprehensive Flood Control Plans,* Hearings before House Committee on Flood Control, Washington, D.C., 1941.

United States 77th Congress, 1st Session, *Flood-Control Plans and New Projects,* Hearings before House Committee on Flood Control on H. R. 4911, Washington, D.C., 1941.

United States 82nd Congress, 2nd Session, Committee on Public Works, *The Flood Control Program of the Department of Agriculture,* Government Printing Office, Washington, D.C., 1952.

White, Gilbert F., and others, *Changes in the Urban Occupance of Flood Plains in the United States,* Department of Geography Research Paper No. 57, The University of Chicago, Chicago, 1958.

White, Gilbert Fowler, *Human Adjustments to Floods, a Geographic Approach to the Flood Problem of the United States,* University of Chicago Press, Chicago, 1945, 225 pp.

White, Gilbert F., editor, *Papers on Flood Problems,* Department of Geography Research Paper No. 70, The University of Chicago, Chicago, 1961.

Part 5

GUY-HAROLD SMITH
The Ohio State University

CHAPTER 16

Conservation of Mineral Resources

The mineral materials which make up the accessible portions of the earth's crust are unlike most of the other natural resources. Their concentration in the earth's crust in sufficient quantity and richness to form ores is the result of geological processes operating over a very long period of time. In terms of human history, or when considered in relation to man's occupancy of the earth and his use of earthly materials, the natural resources such as plants and animals can be so managed that production can be maintained and even improved over a long period. Even a soil seriously eroded and depleted can be restored by proper management. By reforestation and protective measures, a forest can be restored in quality comparable with the virgin forest, although the association of species may be altered. By restrictions on hunting and fishing and by improving and protecting the habitat, many game animals and fishes may become as abundant as under primitive conditions. But minerals once mined, processed, and put to beneficial use, cannot be restored, though a fraction may be recovered. They cannot be replaced or accumulated again at any foreseeable time in the future. The resource has been diminished by use, and the deposit may be completely exhausted.

The situation in respect to minerals is not as gloomy as it may appear from the previous statement. The combustible materials, once they are used, are gone forever. But many minerals, particularly the metals, can be used over and over again, and, as a consequence, metals-in-use become a resource which can be tapped in time of emergency and made to supply important quantities of reusable metal. Conservation of these diminishing resources can be achieved also by the use of mining and processing methods that result in the least waste and the maximum protection of the unmined portion of the mineral deposits. This may be a means of leaving to future generations their share of the resources. With improved technology, a low-grade deposit of one generation may become a workable ore of the next. It becomes the duty of people now living to use the irreplaceable resources of the earth's crust so that generations yet unborn will get their share of the mineral wealth.

THE HISTORICAL DEVELOPMENT OF MINERAL PRODUCTION

The progressive development of man and his cultural and technological attainments are manifestations of man's mastery over his physical

327

environment. As men advanced culturally, their use of materials about them increased. The use of metals in weapons and tools by the more advanced groups gave them greater mastery over the earth and over the other peoples who had not made similar advances. But when men were able to tap the energy contained in the great fuel resources of the earth and to manufacture the complex power-driven machinery, they were possessed of a powerful mechanism which could be used to bring great wealth and comfort to millions of people. The development and expansion of the modern mineral-using civilization have made enormous demands upon the earth to supply fuels, metals, and nonmetallic substances in ever-increasing quantities.

Metals in Primitive Societies. Early man, as he took on the cultural characteristics which distinguished him from the lower animals, used whatever was at hand in the way of tools and implements. In time he learned to chip stone, shape bone, and work wood into useful tools or weapons. He had little or no knowledge of metals in the early stages of his cultural evolution. It is believed that gold was the first metal used by man. Copper, like gold, occurs in nature as a native metal and very early became a useful and prized possession of the cultures that were making material progress. Gold, because of its rarity, its softness, its rich brilliant color, and its untarnishable quality, was particularly well suited for jewelry and as a standard of value. Copper was more abundant, and although it was used for decorative purposes, it had great value to early man as an implement or tool and as a weapon. The value of copper to early man greatly increased when by accident or intention tin was alloyed with it to produce bronze. Neither tin nor copper is particularly hard, but when the two metals are combined in an alloy, the resulting bronze is hard and strong. When the Roman Empire extended its frontiers westward to the shores of Britain, the tin of Cornwall was carried back along with copper from southern Iberica to make bronze; the use of bronze strengthened the legions of Rome.

Primitive man was largely dependent on the metals that occurred in nature in the native or metallic form. Those that are easily smelted, such as tin, were obtained by the application of the metallurgical skills that had been developed. The ores that were more difficult to smelt had to wait until man's knowledge was equal to the task. The great achievement of early man was the smelting of iron ore. When he was able to produce metallic iron in quantity, he was on the threshold of a great technological revolution.

Pure or metallic iron occurs in nature in small quantities, usually in meteorites. In a few places in the world, meteoric iron had been picked up before rust had destroyed it. Primitive man had acquired some knowledge of metallic iron, and small quantities had been accumulated. By repeated experimentation iron was eventually separated from its ore. It is known that the recovery of metallic iron from iron ore dates back to the fourteenth century B.C., but production in quantity had to wait many centuries. The full importance of iron in the cultural history of man had to wait upon other important developments, particularly the invention of the steam engine.

The Industrial Revolution and the Use of Minerals. James Watt invented the steam engine in 1768, only a few years before the United States won its independence. It was the practical use of the steam engine that ushered in the Industrial Revolution. The United States was still in the pioneer stage of its economy. The farms still had to be won from the forests and the prairies. In England the use of steam power had sounded the death knell of the handicrafts and the household industries.

In the United States agriculture continued to dominate the economy, but with the invention of the cotton gin in 1793 and the increased use of machinery in the North, the country began to take on some of the characteristics of an industrial nation.

The abundant resources of coal made it possible for the United States to make rapid progress in the development of the metal-using industries. Late in the nineteenth century the production and use of electrical power marked a notable achievement in the industrial transformation. By 1900 the great mineral resources of the United States were being developed to satisfy the ever-increasing demands for machines, which in turn required increasing quantities of fuel to keep them going.

Rapid Rise in the Use of Mineral Resources. Between 1900 and 1950 the population of the United States doubled. In the same period the consumption of agricultural products including food increased two and one-quarter times. "By 1950—in comparison with the year 1900—we were taking from the earth:

Two and one-half times more bituminous coal
Three times more copper
Three and one-half times more iron ore
Four times more zinc
Twenty-six times more natural gas
Thirty times more crude oil

Indeed, there is scarcely a metal or a mineral fuel of which the quantity used in the United States since the outbreak of the First World War did not exceed the total used throughout the world in all centuries preceding." [1]

The great increase in the use of minerals as compared with agricultural and forest products is related in part to mechanization. Not only in industry and transportation, but in the home as well, power-driven machines and appliances require both metals and fuels in large quantities to maintain our way of life. These are the so-called fund resources, and once they are used they are gone forever. This is particularly true in the case of the fuels such as coal, petroleum, and natural gas. By secondary recovery many of the metals, at least fractionally, can be recycled back into essential uses.

The Future Demand for Earth Materials. To project the curves of production for most of

[1] The President's Materials Policy Commission, *Resources for Freedom*, Vol. I: *Foundations for Growth and Security*, Washington, D.C., 1952, p. 5.

the minerals to 1975 raises some very disturbing questions. It is clear that the demands for materials drawn from the earth will rise unevenly. Because of the inadequate reserves available to us both from domestic sources and from foreign areas, it may be necessary to shift the demand to more readily available substitutes. It is expected that the demand and use of tin, zinc, and copper will rise less than 50 percent by 1975. In the same period a 100 percent increase in the demand for nickel and petroleum and even greater increase for such metals as tungsten and aluminum can be expected. [2]

The changing character of the resource base results from the depletion of once abundant resources, the discovery and development of new resources, and the changes in technology which bring into use materials that previously had not been available, at least economically. A combination of factors, both physical and economic, affects the availability of materials for economic use in modern society. The physical conditions are generally unchanging in character, but changes in technological and economic conditions may determine whether a mineral deposit can be worked or left untouched (Fig. 1).

The Extravagant Use of Materials. The American people have long been accustomed to

[2] *Ibid.*, p. 9.

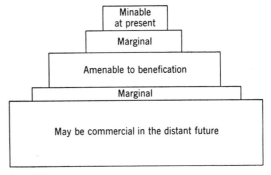

Fig. 1   Mineral deposits and mineral reserves. As costs are reduced and technological advances make possible the mining of leaner ores, the ultimate reserves may be very large.

great abundance of many materials and as a consequence have been extravagant with the bounty of nature. The per capita use of metals, power, fibers, and foods is so high that many other peoples of the world are poor by comparison. The great abundance has made a high standard of living possible for a high proportion of the population. For example, Americans are very extravagant in the use of metals in automobiles. The size, weight, and beauty of our automobiles are not a reflection of need but an expression of abundant materials, high purchasing power, and a desire for an automobile that not only has utility but also gives prestige as well.

If it became a national necessity because of a great emergency, the power and the size of passenger automobiles could be reduced. The decorative trim which requires chromium, nickel, aluminum, and other strategic metals could be eliminated or greatly reduced, thus producing great savings. The extravagant use of many metals that are recoverable may have the effect of creating a valuable reserve of metals-in-use which can be recycled into essential uses in case of emergency.

Reserves for Posterity. Among the students of mineral resources there are some who believe that a proportion of the known reserves of many minerals should be set aside for future generations. This assumes that discovery and other means of increasing the reserves will not be able to keep pace with the rising rate of use. There are others who believe that each generation through the development of science and technology will be able to discover and process the ores required. There may be important minerals in short supply, and others may be relatively abundant. This condition could be expected to exist indefinitely. An ever-expanding economy which seems to be the hope of many people will require larger and larger quantities of minerals. It seems clear that the readily accessible ores of high value will be depleted or will be increasingly difficult to mine. But in the earth's crust there is a variety of minerals that can be made

available by the genius of the technologist and the resourcefulness of the businessman. This is the view of the optimist who believes that the future will take care of itself and the present generation need be concerned only with its own problems of supply.

Among geologists and mineral conservationists there are many who have a genuine concern about the problem of supplying the needs of the country with minerals, particularly the metals required to maintain the high standard of living and our national defenses. The realization that mineral deposits contain a fixed quantity of usable metal or material has prompted some conservationists to accept the viewpoint that a reserve of workable ores should be set aside for the future.

The future supplies of minerals or the volumetric dimensions of the reserves are related to the price we can afford to pay for the mineral materials and the metals we need. A substantial increase in the price of ores and in the metals extracted therefrom increases the quantity of ores available to the economy. At a new high price the mining operation can be extended to greater depths and leaner ores can be worked economically. There is no assurance that every advance in price, which in effect increases the reserves of mineral resources, can be absorbed by the metal-using industries. If the latter can absorb the increased cost of the metallic raw materials they use by greater efficiencies in fabrication, the high level of use of metals in our economy can be maintained. If the increased costs must be passed on to the ultimate consumer and if the purchasing power will not permit him to pay for the metal products and structures necessary to maintain our high standard of living, the process may be reversed, so that a lower price for ore may actually diminish the reserves.

If an important mineral is in short supply, the rising price may have the effect of limiting its use to absolutely essential purposes. Or, an important rise in price might have the effect of causing a shift to metals of the more abundant minerals in the common rocks. Such metals as iron, aluminum, silicon, and magnesium are available in unlimited quantities. Under such conditions it would not be necessary to set aside important reserves for the future. Perhaps in the more distant future, the metals in the common rocks and in sea water and ceramic materials can be used in place of such metals as tin, lead, zinc, copper, and the ferroalloys which are relatively less abundant.

Prospecting and Exploration. The search for minerals must continue. The prospector of a past age is being replaced by a modern mineral explorer who brings to his task a knowledge of the basic science of geology including paleontology, stratigraphy, and petrology. The geologist does not work alone but brings to the task of finding new deposits other scientists who are qualified to utilize the most sophisticated techniques of exploration. The sciences of geophysics and geochemistry have been enlisted to press the search for mineral resources.

Exploration transcends its physical aspects and becomes involved with the economic and legal problems related to the addition of newly discovered deposits which, when proved, can be added to the known reserves. The application of new techniques in mining and processing may save an industry from failure, but the economic gains may be offset by an antiquated system of taxation.[3] Further exploration requires the application of modern techniques and an enlightened approach to the economic and legal aspects of the mineral problem.

THE EARTH MATERIALS

Composition of the Earth's Crust. The common materials and the rarer substances of the earth's crust vary greatly in their relative abundance and the degree to which they are concentrated in valuable minerals and ores (see Table 1). The eight most abundant elements—

[3] See John D. Ridge, "The Problem of Mineral Exploration," *Mineral Industries*, Pennsylvania State University, University Park, Pa., Vol. 32, November 1962, pp. 1, 3–7.

Table 1. Composition of the Earth's Crust

Element	Weight Percent
1. Oxygen	46.60
2. Silicon	27.72
3. Aluminum	8.13
4. Iron	5.00
5. Calcium	3.63
6. Sodium	2.83
7. Potassium	2.59
8. Magnesium	2.09
9. Titanium	0.44
10. Hydrogen	0.14
Total	99.17

[Source: Brian, Mason, *Principles of Geochemistry*, New York, 1952, p. 41.]

oxygen, silicon, aluminum, iron, calcium, sodium, potassium, and magnesium—make up 98.58 percent of the earth's crust. All of the other elements make up less than 1½ percent of the earth's crust. Because of the very unequal quantities of the minerals, composed of common and rare elements, it is more or less obvious that over a long period of time the commonest and most abundant elements and minerals will be used increasingly in a maturing industrial society. In the modern economy, the widely used metals, such as copper, lead, zinc, and the ferroalloys, are in reality relatively rare, and it is only because of their concentration in localized deposits that they can be used at all. If they were uniformly dispersed within the earth's crust, it would be impossible or at least economically unfeasible to process the great quantities of material necessary to recover adequate quantities of these metals.

The precious metals, such as gold, silver, platinum, and the rare metals, such as antimony, tin, mercury, and tantalum, occur in such small quantities that ordinarily their relative abundance cannot be determined with accuracy. They are relatively rare, and again it is only because of their concentration in localized ore bodies that they can be profitably developed and used for a number of specialized purposes.

The Metalliferous Ores. An ore is a mineral

deposit that can be mined and processed at a profit. A mineral deposit may contain important quantities of an essential metal, but unless it is economically feasible to work, the deposit may be regarded as rock or at best as a marginal or submarginal ore. An advance in technology, an increase in price, or both may have the effect of making a low-grade ore into a mineral resource of great value. It may be that the success of a mining operation may be related to the scale of operations. If great quantities of the ore can be mined and processed, the unit cost may be so low that the operation shows a profit. Conversely, to reduce the scale of operations might make the mining operation uneconomical.

Aluminum, iron, and the less abundant metals, while widely distributed in the earth's crust, do occur in important ore bodies which have resulted from the operation of long-continued geological process. It is clear, therefore, that the modern economy must rest upon geologic processes of the past; in almost every case, the geologic processes that form ore bodies are not rapid enough to meet the needs of an industrial society requiring large quantities of materials. In effect, at present man is drawing on capital resources accumulated in the past, and in the interests of conservation it is necessary that he understand the nature and dimensions of this great reserve and the rate at which he is using it.

In many cases the ore-forming processes operate at great depth and the evidences of the existence of ore bodies are not revealed at the surface. Fortunately, many ore bodies formed in the remote geologic past and at great depth have been laid bare or have been revealed near the surface by uplift and long-continued erosion. In the Laurentian Upland of Canada and the Upper Lakes section of the United States the rich iron ores, believed to be of sedimentary origin, have been down folded in great linear formations and largely covered by a veneer of glacial drift. Continued mining and exploration have revealed the true dimensions of these rich iron deposits.

It is because of the prospect that there remain many undiscovered ore deposits, particularly in areas that have not been thoroughly explored, that many people believe that new deposits will be found when the need arises. When the conservationist expresses the fear that known resources of some important mineral will be exhausted there is the optimist who has an enduring faith in the ability of the prospector and the geologist to find new deposits to take the place of the depleted ores.

The Minerals in the Sea and in the Atmosphere. Both the sea and the atmosphere contain great quantities of certain elements and compounds that can be recovered and used in connection with the mineral materials taken from the earth's crust. (See Table 2.)

The sea is known to contain a great variety of elements, but the quantity of each is very small. By processing a large volume of sea water, sodium chloride, magnesium salts, magnesium, potassium, iodine, and bromine are recovered commercially. Calcium carbonate and calcium sulfate also occur in the sea, but calcium salts and the metal, calcium, are usually obtained from limestone and gypsum formations in the earth's crust.

The atmosphere contains such valuable gases as nitrogen, oxygen, and the rarer gases of helium, neon, and argon that are recovered, purified, and prepared to serve the needs of industry. The great reservoir of nitrogen constitutes an inexhaustible source of a vital element used in the manufacture of synthetic ammonia and other nitrogen-containing fertilizers. (See Table 3.)

Table 2. Composition of the Ocean

	Percent		Percent
Oxygen	85.79	Calcium	0.05
Hydrogen	10.67	Potassium	0.04
Chlorine	2.07	Sulfur	0.09
Sodium	1.14	Bromine	0.008
Magnesium	0.14	Carbon	0.002

[Source: Professional Paper 127, U.S. Geological Survey.]

Table 3. Composition of the Atmosphere

	Percent		Percent
Nitrogen	78.03	Hydrogen	0.01
Oxygen	20.99	Neon	0.00123
Argon	0.94	Helium	0.0004
Carbon		Krypton	0.00005
dioxide	0.03	Xenon	0.000006

[Source: Professional Paper 127, U.S. Geological Survey.]

THE MINERAL SITUATION

Iron. In the period between 1953 and 1957 the production of iron ore in the United States averaged over 100,000,000 tons annually. In 1962 production was under 72,000,000 tons. Imports of iron ore averaged 22,880,000 tons annually between 1953 and 1957 and rose to 33,431,000 tons in 1962. Ores from foreign sources have become increasingly competitive in the United States market and domestic producers have turned to the beneficiation of the taconite ores to hold on to a major share of the market.

Domestic production is centered in the Lake Superior area where Minnesota, Michigan, and Wisconsin mine 78 percent of the output. The northeastern states of New York, New Jersey, and Pennsylvania and the southeastern states of Alabama and Georgia both produce 11 percent, and 10 western states, chiefly Utah and Wyoming, also produce 11 percent.

In 1950 imported iron ore represented only 5 percent of the ores consumed in the iron and steel industry. By 1955 the percentage of imported ores was 28 percent and by 1962 it was 32 percent. Imported ores came chiefly from Canada, Venezuela, Chile, and Brazil with smaller quantities being imported from Mexico and Peru in the western hemisphere and from Liberia (Fig. 2).

Beneficiation continues apace. In the Upper Lakes area, in Wyoming, in Pennsylvania, and in Missouri taconite and other low grade ores are processed by concentration and pelletizing before they are shipped to the blast furnaces. In

Fig. 2 The *Ore-Meridian,* a giant ore-carrier shown at the Canton dock area, Baltimore, Maryland. Such ocean-going ore-carriers transport iron ore from Venezuela and other overseas sources to Sparrows Point and other shipping and smelting centers in the Middle Atlantic area. (Curtis Bay Towing Service, Photo by Hans Marx.)

1962 only 15 percent of the ore was shipped directly to the consuming market in the crude form, "whereas 85 percent was treated at some type of beneficiating plant before shipment." [4]

In looking forward to 1975 the Bureau of Mines estimated that the need for steel would increase about 80 percent in the 20-year period from 1955 to 1975. This estimate was later reduced to 60 percent. Steel-making capacity in the United States has been built up to a level just under 150,000,000 tons annually. Production reached 117,000,000 tons in 1955 and then dropped below 100,000,000 in 1958 and by

[4] United States Bureau of Mines, *Minerals Yearbook, 1962,* Vol. I, Metals and Minerals, Government Printing Office, Washington, D.C., 1963, p. 659.

1963 had not exceeded this level.[5] Steel is feeling the competition from aluminum, magnesium, structural concrete, titanium, plastics, and resin-bonded wood. Common steel is being replaced by alloy steels that provide great strength with less weight.[6]

The Ferroalloys. The manufacture of specialty steels requires the addition of small quantities of metals or their compounds to impart to the steel the qualities desired. These are the ferroalloys and include manganese, chromium, cobalt, molybdenum, nickel, tungsten, and vanadium, and a number of others such as boron, columbium, titanium, and zirconium. Of the principal ferroalloys only molybdenum and vanadium are genuinely abundant in terms of the needs of the nation. The United States is a major producer of molybdenum. Vanadium supplies are adequate, but the metal is recovered as a by-product in the processing of uranium ores.

The supply situation is particularly unfavorable in the case of manganese, chromium, nickel, and cobalt. Domestic production of manganese represents only a relatively small fraction required to meet the needs of the iron and steel industry. In 1962 domestic production was only 25,000 tons, far below the output of 327,309 tons in 1958. Imports of manganese ore were 2,543,841 tons in 1960. In 1962 the quantity imported decreased to 1,971,232 tons. The chief suppliers were Brazil, Ghana, South Africa, and India contributing over 70 percent of the imports.

The relationship between domestic production and imported ore is particularly unfavorable with chromite. Domestic production totaled 53,358 tons in 1953, rose to 143,795 tons in 1958, and then declined to 82,000 tons in 1961. Imports in 1961 reached 1,329,000 tons well below the 2,226,610 tons imported in 1953. The principal sources of chromite to meet the metallurgical and chemical needs of the country include South Africa, the Philippines, Rhodesia (now

[5] Julian W. Feiss, "Minerals," *Scientific American,* Vol. 209, 1963, pp. 129–136. Reference on p. 129.
[6] *Ibid.*, p. 130.

Zambia) and Nyasaland (now Malawi), and Turkey.

The domestic production of tungsten concentrates was 8,280,000 pounds in 1962. Imports in the same year amounted to 3,709,000 pounds. In the period 1953–1957 production averaged 12,210,000 pounds and imports in the same period averaged 21,565,000 pounds well above recent production and importation of tungsten concentrates. The supply situation in relation to consumption improved significantly during the 1950's and early 1960's, but tungsten ores are still imported from Korea, Bolivia, Australia, and Peru.

The United States is dependent chiefly on Canada for nickel which produces 83 percent of the world's supply. New Caledonia ranks second as a producer of nickel ores with 11 percent, and the United States contributes 4 percent. Metallic nickel is also recovered by the processing of scrap metals that contain nickel.

Because of the variety of metals that make up the ferroalloy group and the remoteness of many of the source areas it has been necessary to build up stockpiles of these strategic metals or ores and to take other measures to assure the United States of adequate supplies in case of a national emergency.

The Nonferrous Metals. The metals commonly listed as nonferrous include copper, aluminum, lead, zinc, tin, mercury, antimony, magnesium, and a number of others. The degree of self-sufficiency varies greatly among the several metals. For example, the United States must import both bauxite and aluminum in order to meet the needs of industry and the national stockpile. Bauxite, totaling 10,585,000 tons in 1962, was imported chiefly from Jamaica, Surinam, Dominican Republic, British Guiana, and Haiti. Imports entered the United States chiefly through the ports of New Orleans, Galveston, and Mobile. In 1962 metallic aluminum in the crude or semicrude form to the extent of 373,000 tons was imported. Canada supplied 61 percent of the imported metal with Norway, France, and Belgium-Luxembourg contributing 13, 12, and 4 percent, respectively.

The United States was largely self-sufficient in copper, lead, and zinc until the late 1930's, or World War II, when demand for these and other strategic metals increased more rapidly than production from domestic mines could meet. In relation to a continuing high demand for copper "the return of the United States to a position of self-sufficiency is not likely under foreseeable conditions." [7] It is expected that the demand for copper in 1975 will be substantially above the consumption of the 1950's and the early years of the 1960's. In 1962 production of copper as reported by the smelters using domestic ores was 1,282,126 tons (Fig. 3). Consump-

tion for the same year including both primary and secondary metal was 1,769,000 tons. The United States is both an importer and exporter and in any year imports and shipments abroad may be nearly in balance, but the importation of ores, concentrates, and metallic copper are necessary so the United States can maintain its position as a supplier of copper and copper products in the international market. In 1962 imports of copper totaled 478,851 tons and exports for the same year amounted to 375,269 tons.

The domestic consumption of lead in the United States in 1962 was 1,110,000 tons derived from domestic production, secondary recovery, and importation. Production of only 237,000 tons of new lead in 1962 was the lowest since 1900. The availability of lead in the international market and the relatively low price of

[7] Helena M. Meyer, "Copper," *Mineral Facts and Problems*, Bulletin, 556, U.S. Bureau of Mines, Government Printing Office, Washington, D.C., 1956, pp. 219–245. Reference on p. 219.

Fig. 3   Mine water, containing copper sulfate in solution, flows over shredded detinned cans and by precipitation thousands of pounds of copper are recovered each month at Butte, Montana. (The Anaconda Company.)

the metal have depressed the mining and smelting of new lead. The leading producing mines are in Idaho, Missouri, Utah, and Colorado. Metallic lead is imported from Australia, Mexico, Canada, and Yugoslavia and ores are imported from the Republic of South Africa, Peru, Canada, Australia, and Bolivia.

The situation in respect to zinc is similar to that of lead. Domestic production has felt this competition of foreign producers. Stockpiling has given both metals some support in the domestic market. Secondary recovery returns large quantities of lead and zinc to the metal market. The domestic production of zinc was 505,491 tons in 1962 mined chiefly in Tennessee, Idaho, Illinois, Colorado, and several other states. Imports came chiefly from Mexico, Canada, and Peru. It is hoped that increased research in the use of zinc and zinc-containing products may bring more favorable economic conditions to the zinc industry.

The United States is an unimportant source of tin as measured by mine production. Domestic production averaged under 72 tons annually for the years 1953–1957. Consumption in 1962 was 79,085 tons, with slightly less than one-third being secondary tin. Most of the remainder in the form of concentrates or metal was imported from Indonesia, Bolivia, Burma, Netherlands, Belgium-Luxembourg, United Kingdom, and Nigeria. The government-owned smelter at Texas City, Texas, smelted tin ores from Bolivia and other sources for a number of years but was sold to private interests in 1956 and has since abandoned tin smelting. In order to meet the needs of industry and the national stockpile, importation and secondary recovery are currently employed.

Other nonferrous metals such as antimony and mercury must be imported. In the case of antimony only 5 percent is produced from domestic mines, 17 percent is derived by secondary recovery, and 78 percent must be imported chiefly from Mexico, Republic of South Africa, and Bolivia. The domestic production of mercury, supported through the Office of Mineral

Exploration, totaled 26,277 flasks in 1962. A somewhat larger quantity was imported chiefly from Italy, Spain, Mexico, and Yugoslavia. The supply situation in the case of magnesium is particularly favorable because the source materials and the productive facilities are adequate to meet domestic needs.

Metals of Special Importance. The platinum metals include platinum, palladium, iridium, rhodium, and ruthenium. Once used chiefly for jewelry these materials are of major importance in the chemical and electrical fields. Supplies of these metals are imported chiefly from Canada, United Kingdom, Switzerland, the Soviet Union, and the Netherlands. Domestic production of only 28,742 troy ounces in 1962 is derived chiefly as a by-product of copper refining.

The situation in respect to uranium is more favorable than for a number of strategic metals. Uranium ores are produced in quantity in New Mexico, Wyoming, Utah, Colorado, and Arizona. However, 41 percent of United States' needs were met in 1962 by the importation of ores from Canada, South Africa, Australia, and Portugal. Vanadium is a by-product of the uranium processing industry, and the cutback of uranium production in 1964 may affect adversely the production of vanadium.

Gold and silver, because of their monetary importance, received increased attention in the mid-1960's. Gold production has trended downward since 1947. Exploration is subsidized under the Office of Mineral Exploration. The leading producers of gold are South Dakota, Utah, Alaska, Arizona, California, Washington, and Nevada. The costs of mining and refining are jointly too high to expect a significant increase in production. The increased use of silver in industry and a renewed interest in coin collecting has made it difficult for the mints at Philadelphia and Denver to meet the domestic demand for silver coins. Large numbers of coins are fed into coin-operated vending machines and are not immediately returned to circulation. In the United States, 36,789,000 ounces of silver were produced in 1962. In the same year,

76,359,000 ounces were imported chiefly from Canada, Mexico, and Peru. Idaho, Arizona, Utah, and Montana mined 88 percent of the domestic production.

The Nonmetallic Minerals. The common earth materials such as stone, sand and gravel, and clay are available in relative abundance, hence there is little reason to be concerned about supplies. In the United States the fertilizer minerals and closely related materials are now adequate to meet the nation's requirements without importing. The United States is the leading producer of phosphates and sulfur, ranks second to the combined East and West German production of potash, and leads in the production of nitrogen for use in the production of ammonia.

A selected number of nonmetallic minerals essential to industry and to national defense must be imported and stockpiled. They include asbestos imported chiefly from Canada and the Republic of South Africa; quartz crystals, from Brazil; fluorospar, from Mexico and Spain; cryolite, from Greenland; mica, from India, Indonesia, and Brazil; and graphite, from Ceylon, Malagasy Republic, and Mexico. These and many other mineral products which the United States cannot produce in quantity and competitively must be imported. Many in one form or another are stockpiled so that a supply can be readily available in case of a national emergency.

CONSERVATION IN MINING AND PROCESSING

Open-Pit Mining. Certain mineral deposits occur at the surface or are covered with a thin overburden. If the material which covers an ore body is relatively thin and nonresistant, it can be readily and cheaply removed, making it possible to mine the ore by open-pit methods. In the Lake Superior area, open-pit mining of iron ore has made possible the recovery and shipment of great quantities of ore since the mines were opened. In Bingham Canyon in Utah, in

Nevada, and in other localities, copper ores have been mined by the open-pit method.

Under such conditions, the ores are readily accessible and mining may be carried on as a large-scale operation. In the more northern latitudes, the cold of winter may interrupt or halt operations. But in spite of obstacles to continuous operations the open-pit method of mining, wherever conditions will permit, is one of the cheapest methods of ore recovery.

More Complete Recovery of Mineral Resources. Important quantities of minerals are left in the ground because of the difficulties in achieving 100 percent recovery. In open-pit mining where the overburden can be completely removed, recovery approaches 100 percent. Underground operations, because of the necessity of providing supporting walls and pillars, may leave as much as half of the ore in a condition that prevents recovery. The recovery of minerals in underground workings may contribute substantially to the reserves by the improvement of mining methods. In the course of time, economic necessity may require that the mineral resources be so developed that a high percentage of the mineral or ore can be recovered.

Block-Caving Method of Mining. Where an ore body lies near the surface but too deeply buried to be mined by the open-pit method, undeground methods may be employed to reach and to recover the ore. If the ore occurs as a large mass of considerable thickness but of limited areal extent, the block-carving method may be used to recover a high percentage of the ore at a relatively low cost. In this method of mining, a vertical shaft is cut in the country rock to a level beneath the base of the ore body. Then a horizontal tunnel or drift is extended to a position directly under the ore body. Above this tunnel or haulage way, a system of vertical and inclined chutes are cut in the rock upward to the base of the ore body. Then after undercutting and blasting the ore loose, the broken ore moves downward by gravity so it can be loaded into the cars and hauled directly to the shaft to be lifted to the surface. This method permits the recovery of a very high percentage of the original ore if the caving is carried out so as to avoid the incorporation of the low-grade overburden.

Beneficiation. When commercially workable ores approach exhaustion, means will be sought to process profitably the low-grade or marginal ores. The richer ores are commonly associated with low-grade ores which because of depth beneath the surface, the inclusion of deleterious substances, or for some other reason cannot be worked profitably. These low-grade or marginal ores may become workable at a profit when costs can be reduced or when the price of the ore advances sufficiently to encourage development or exploitation.

The low-grade ores may become usable by the development of processing techniques which have the effect of enriching the ores or of increasing the metal content of the ore shipped to the smelter. In the Lake Superior Upland, from which the United States has been receiving the major share of its iron ore for more than a half century, the taconite and jasperite deposits are now becoming available to the iron and steel industry by the process of beneficiation. In the case of the magnetic iron minerals in the taconite deposits, the iron-bearing minerals can be separated from the gangue materials by the use of a powerful electromagnet. The low-grade ore after mining must be crushed and pulverized so that the finely divided magnetic minerals can be separated from the remainder of the material. By this means a relatively rich iron ore is produced from the abundant low-grade ores of the Lake Superior area.

This fine granular material cannot be used

Fig. 4 A pelletizing plant at the Empire mine in the northern Peninsula of Michigan. The iron ores that have been upgraded by benefication are finally pelletized to produce hard balls of concentrated ore suitable for delivery to the blast furnace where it will become one of the components of the charge. (The Cleveland-Cliffs Iron Company.)

Fig. 5 A sintering plant in Pennsylvania. The three circular structures in front of the large building are the coolers that are used to reduce the temperature of the sinter before it moves on to the
storage bins or to the smelters. (Dravo Corporation.)

directly but requires solidification into pellets
of such size that they can become a part of the
charge in the blast furnace. Pelletization is an
integral part of the beneficiation process and is
necessary for the proper functioning of the blast
furnace (Fig. 4).

The jasperite and other nonmagnetic iron
ores must be enriched by other mechanical
processes. By these means the very abundant
low-grade ores can and will replace the less
abundant high-grade ores which are subject to
early exhaustion. In the case of iron, which is the
fourth most abundant element in the earth's
crust, beneficiation has the effect of increasing
the relative abundance of iron ore to meet our
industrial needs.

In 1963, 72.6 million tons out of a total of

116.5 million tons of iron ore used by the iron
and steel industry were beneficiated.[8]

Sintering. Important tonnages of iron ore
occur as a soft powdery material which is not
well suited for charging the blast furnace. The
fines that result from the benefication process
also require treatment before they are satisfactory for a good furnace charge. The mix that is
fed into the sintering machines consists of ore
(approximately 70 percent), limestone, dolo-
mite, mill scale, flue dust, and coke (Fig. 5). As
the material moves forward a sheet of flame in
the sintering furnace plays on the material and
heats it to incipient fusion (Fig. 6). The hard,
resistant sinter as it leaves the machine is cooled

[8] *Steel Facts,* April 1964, No. 181, p. 3.

Fig. 6   A sintering machine used to prepare the fine ores for the blast furnace. The fine ore particles, fluxes, coal, and coke move slowly through the sintering machine in which the ore becomes a clinker-like mass as it moves forward to a breaker which prepares the material for the blast furnace. Remaining fines are recycled back to the sintering machine. (Dravo Corporation.)

and sized. The coarser fragments are ready for the blast furnace, but the fines are returned to the sintering machine. By this means, important quantities of powdery iron ore can be used in the iron and steel industry. In 1963, 36 percent of the iron consumed in the United States was sinter.[9]

CONSERVATION PROBLEMS

Corrosion. The destructive effects of corrosion, chiefly the rusting of iron and steel, are difficult to estimate or determine with accuracy. It has been estimated that the loss because of corrosion in the United States is five and a half billion dollars annually.[10] The large losses are sustained by the railroads, the Navy and the merchant fleet, automobiles, and metal struc-

[9]*Ibid.*
[10]*Business Week,* November 10, 1956, p. 136.

tures of all kinds. The losses can hardly be prevented, but they may be delayed. Each year three or more million automobiles are scrapped. Their deterioration in usefulness is related in part to corrosion. Whatever the average life of an automobile, it may be in the best interests of our economic society to scrap the cars as soon as genuine obsolescence sets in and return their metals to the steel furnace.

Corrosion Control. Most metals which have been freed from the ores with which they were associated in nature, unless specially protected, tend to corrode or combine with other elements or substances. Iron is more readily susceptible to rusting or corrosion than the nonferrous metals, such as aluminum, copper, lead, zinc, tin, and others. All are subject to corrosive action if the atmosphere is charged with gases or other substances that will combine with the native or pure metals. Without the use of protective coverings or alloys to prevent or reduce the loss by corrosion, the annual waste of metals would be much greater than it is. Steel structures, such as the great suspension bridges, exposed as they are to the weather, require almost continuous repainting and protection to save the metal from corrosion.

The use of enormous lengths of tubing and pipes to carry a great variety of gases and liquids exposes both the internal and the external surfaces to corrosion unless protected by some kind of covering to prevent or delay the rate of deterioration. The losses sustained by failure of metals in use may be many times the value of the pipe or tubing required as a replacement. The failure of a major water line may mean that an important section of a city is without fire protection and industries within the area affected may have to shut down for hours. A break or a perforation in the tubing in a chemical plant, a battleship, a petroleum refinery, or a pharmaceutical factory may result in great damage to a plant, but even greater losses may result from the shutdown required to make the necessary repairs. The failure of metals because of corrosion and the protective measures required to protect them against deterioration become a heavy charge upon the general economy.[11]

Protective Coatings on Metals. If a metal that is normally subject to rapid corrosion can be coated promptly by some substance resistant to weathering and alteration, the life of the metal may be greatly extended. Metal structures such as bridges and machinery are painted to prevent or at least delay the destructive consequences of corrosion. Most common metals, particularly iron and steel, cannot be protected against all forms of corrosive action, but regular and repeated painting of the surface can give many years of useful service to structures which would deteriorate rapidly if not so protected.

[11] W. H. J. Vernon, "The Cost of Corrosion and of Its Control," *Preceedings, Department of Economic Affairs, U. N. Scientific Conference on the Conservation and Utilization of Resources,* Vol. 11: *Mineral Resources,* New York, 1951, p. 219.

The availability of suitable pigments and high-quality drying oils such as linseed oil may be a factor affecting the conservation of metals by an overlay of paint. As new coating materials are produced by the chemical industry, it is expected that metals used in particular situations may be especially treated and coated to resist corrosion. The rubber-base paints, those made from synthetic resins, and others containing some of the new plastic materials may prove to be well suited as coatings for sheet metal and metal products and structures.

In addition to the paints, lacquers, and enamels which may be applied by brush or spray, metals may be used to coat other metals. Galvanizing which consists of coating a steel product with molten zinc is well known. Every hardware store carries a line of galvanized products consisting of watering cans, pails, wash tubs, screening, and many other utensils and products. The surface of metals subject to corrosion may be protected by plating with such metals as nickel, chromium, tin, and cadmium.

Certain chemical substances may function as rust inhibitors and may be used in the water that comes in contact with the metal tubing of boilers or the cooling system of an automobile. One effect of the inhibitor is to reduce the oxygen, thus preventing the rusting or oxidation of the iron which, in the presence of water and oxygen, tends to rust.

If a coating of paint or metal is to be used, it is very important that the surface be properly prepared or the coating will fail to serve its protective function. In the case of steel the mill scale should be removed so that the coating material can be applied to the clean surface of the metal. After large metal plates have been pickled in warm sulfuric acid to remove the mill scale, they may be dipped in other solutions to remove the acid and prepare the surface for painting or plating. It is known that the thin layer or residue of certain chemical washes which adhere to steel are effective in getting a good bond between the undermetal and the coating material.

Generally, for good results in plating one metal upon another, there should be no pinholes or breaks in the plating metal. In the process of coating a sheet of steel with a thin film of zinc or aluminum, an electrochemical condition exists in that the steel becomes the cathode and is covered by a protective film of the salts of zinc or aluminum. Even though there may be a break or thin area in the covering metal the steel does not rust or corrode easily.

Alloys. Corrosion of iron and steel may be greatly reduced or largely eliminated by combining small amounts of alloy metals with the metal to be protected. The best-known example is the manufacture of stainless steel by combining nickel and chromium with the molten steel. To give stainless steel certain qualities required for particular purposes, small quantities of other metals such as copper, silicon, titanium, columbium, molybdenum, and other elements may be added. The durability of steel may be increased manyfold by the addition, in the proper proportions, of these and other alloy metals.

The addition of alloying elements to steel may improve the resulting specialty steels in such a way that great savings are achieved by reducing the amount of steel required for certain purposes. If steel is given great strength and stiffness by the addition of alloying elements such as nickel or vanadium, there is a large initial saving. There is a further saving of fuels where these special steels are used in the manufacture of transportation equipment. The development of a great number of specialty steels for a variety of purposes reduces the quantity of steel required and at the same time permits the selection of exactly the right steel for a particular purpose.

Recovery of By-Products. In order that a mineral resource may make its fullest contribution in satisfying the needs of man, the associated minerals should be recovered. To develop a mineral deposit for a single metal or product may be uneconomical, but the recovery of a single by-product may mean the difference between failure and success of a mining venture.

The waste or tailings may contain small quantities of important minerals, but at one stage in the processing it might not be practical or feasible to recover the metal contained. Later, with improved methods of recovery and increased price of the metal contained in the waste material, it might be economically profitable to rework what was formerly regarded as waste.

Substitutes. In the event that metals are not available in adequate quantities to meet the nation's needs, other materials may be used as substitutes to a limited extent. It is not to be expected that all metals can be replaced. When there is not enough steel to meet all needs, wood and stone can be used for certain structural purposes. If and when the several ferroalloys are not available in the usual quantities and at fair prices, specialty steels may be made by using the alloys that are in good supply. During World War II it became necessary to reduce the number of specialty steels and concentrate on the production of a few standardized types.

In the United States molybdenum is relatively abundant, for nearly two-thirds of the world's supply is produced in this country. A major share of the world's nickel is produced in Canada, and we can assume that in a national emergency nickel produced by a friendly neighbor would be more readily obtainable than manganese, tungsten, and chromium which must come from more distant sources. Within certain technical limits the use of the ferroalloys may be adjusted in terms of their relative abundance. This may be in effect a substitution of one metal for another in lesser abundance.

When copper is not available in adequate quantities to meet the needs of industry, certain uses may be curtailed in order that the supply available may be adequate to meet urgent needs. Silver has been used in buss bars to free copper for more essential needs. In 1943 the one-cent piece was coined out of zinc-coated discs of steel. Copper for siding and roofing was replaced by cheaper materials which were relatively more abundant. By these and other means, the available supply of copper could be and was allocated to meet the critical needs of the wartime economy.

The ubiquitous tin can did not disappear completely from the grocer's shelves, but many changes or substitutes were necessary because of the critical shortage of tin in the United States. By research and improvements in tin-plating, the amount of tin used per can was decreased slightly. Many foods, cosmetics, and other materials were put up in glass containers, thus freeing great quantities of tin for more essential purposes. Lacquered cans were used where the contents did not require tin for protection from deterioration.

In order that substitutions may be made with little disturbance in the metal-using industries, research and technological developments should be carried out in advance of need so the new alloys or new materials can be quickly substituted for the scarce metal. If the nation waits until an emergency exists, it may be too late to be able to carry out easily and quickly a program of replacement and readjustment.

Shifting from Scarce to Abundant Materials. A change in the relative abundance of a mineral or metal, providing the price differential does not interfere with the change, is the essential first step in shifting use from a scarce to a relatively abundant material. For example, aluminum is a satisfactory replacement for copper in the electrical field, and it can be expected that the relative importance of these two metals in the electrical industry will result in the increased use of aluminum. It is also evident that plastic materials made out of air, water, and other abundant substances can be substituted for metals, thus diminishing the demand for copper, lead, zinc, and other metals which are in short supply.

Recycling of Metals in the Economy. It is fortunate indeed that many metals and other materials can be recovered and reused. Unlike the fuel minerals the metals can be used over and over again. In the case of the precious metals, such as gold, silver, and platinum, to-

day's supply includes metal which was first mined and refined decades if not centuries ago. The wedding circlet worn by the modern bride may at one time have been a part of the ceremonial jewelry of an ancient princess or the loot of priates. It is important in the conservation of many metals that the supply available for current use consists of both virgin metal produced from ores freshly mined and of secondary or scrap metal being prepared for new uses.

The nonferrous metals, such as copper, lead, zinc, aluminum, tin, and others which resist corrosion or deterioration in use, may be recovered and used again and again. Whenever a small amount of these metals is widely dispersed in connection with its use, it may be quite uneconomical to recover it, except in a national emergency. During World War II tin-can-collecting stations were set up to facilitate the accumulation of tin cans which were sent to the de-tinning plants. In the scrap-metal or junk business, machinery and other heavy scrap may be broken up, and the nonferrous metals recovered through a process of sorting or refining.

Great quantities of metals are lost each year because the form in which they are used makes recovery impossible. The pigments used in paint in the form of lead, zinc, and titanium oxides are so thinly spread on painted surfaces that they are lost forever. Other uses may permit reuse after varying intervals of time. The owner of an automobile generally exchanges his old battery for a new one, and the dealer returns the old battery to the manufacturer who recovers the lead and uses it in the manufacture of new batteries.

The metal that is recoverable in the great est quantities is iron commonly used in the form of steel. The iron and steel industry is an important producer of scrap. Wherever steel is a major raw material in the manufacture of machinery, new scrap becomes available for recycling back into the manufacture of steel. In densely populated areas particularly where heavy industry is concentrated, the amount of used scrap available is very large.

During World War II, the junk dealers of America were called upon to speed up the collection and delivery of scrap to the steel-makers. In remote and thinly populated areas the derelict auto, the abandoned mowing machine, and a section of oil pipe may never be recovered and reused because it is uneconomical to collect such isolated quantities of scrap.

The destruction of military equipment in wartime constitutes an enormous loss of valuable resources. On the battlefields and in matériel depots where bombing and military action converted weapons and vehicles into scrap, there can be and usually is some recovery of this spent material. However, the enormous tonnage of steel and other metals in ships sunk at sea is largely lost forever. The merchant ship and naval craft lost in World War II constitute not only a loss of the metals from the original supply, but for every ton of steel which was sunk in the open sea beyond the possibility of salvage, there was also a loss of manpower and other materials used in the production of the steel in the first place. The secondary recovery of steel and other metals for reuse in industry represents more than a saving of metals. There are also the recovery or the salvage of the power, the labor, and the capital used in the smelting of the ore and in the manufacture of steel and the other metal products.

Some Lessons from World War II. Over a long period of time the relatively abundant mineral resources of the United States had been conducive to an attitude of complacency. During World War I and during the 1920's, a limited number of shortages served as a warning to conservation-conscious Americans who realized the increased use of metals would eventually mean depletion of some relatively rich but small deposits.

The number of strategic minerals in short supply before World War II was about ten, or a dozen at the most. But during the war the number increased until more than sixty different minerals were imported from more than fifty different countries to satisfy the insatiable war

machine. Of the twenty most essential minerals in the wartime economy, eight were imported entirely from foreign sources. For another half dozen, 85 to 100 percent of the nation's needs had to be imported. A continuing high level of industrial activity and a defense program based on the use of large quantities of minerals make clear that shortages of vital mineral resources in continental United States are real and not imagined.[12]

Stockpiling. Late in the 1930's it became evident that the United States should have been stockpiling a large number of nonperishable but essential materials during the depression years when prices were low. In 1939 when Public Law 117, the Strategic Materials Act, was passed by the 76th Congress, prices had risen and many materials had become scarce. When the United States became involved in World War II, the nation was soon confronted with shortages among the metals and other strategic materials.

After the war was over new legislation in the form of the Strategic and Critical Materials Stockpiling Act was enacted in 1946. At the outset funds were inadequate to finance a comprehensive program of stockpiling. Furthermore, the international situation did not suggest urgency in the stockpiling program. However, the outbreak of hostilities in Korea in 1950 made it clear that supplies of a large number of strategic materials should be built up quickly. But it was impossible to meet the needs of the civilian economy, of the defense industries, and the stockpiling program all in the space of a few years after 1950.

Under the authority of Public Law 520 of the 79th Congress entitled "The Strategic and Critical Material Stock Piling Act," approved on July 23, 1956 the national stockpile acquired inventories accumulated under previous authorizations and was extended to include materials

[12] Alan M. Bateman, "Our Future Dependence on Foreign Minerals," *The Annals*, Vol. 281, 1952, pp. 25–32. Reference on p. 26.

deemed necessary to the national defense.[13] Public Law 480 of the 83rd Congress entitled "Agricultural Trade Development and Assistance Act of 1954," approved on July 10, 1954, authorized "the barter of surplus agricultural commodities produced in the United States for strategic and critical materials produced abroad."[14] A supplemental stockpile was authorized and material acquired under the "Agricultural Act of 1954" and Public Law 733 of the 84th Congress entitled, "Domestic Tungsten, Asbestos, Fluorspar, and Columbium-Tantalum Production and Purchase Act of 1956." The establishment of stockpiling policies and goals was chiefly the responsibility of the Office of Emergency Planning and its predecessor agencies. The General Services Administration was assigned the duty of implementing the policies of OEP.

On January 31, 1963, President Kennedy announced that the stockpile program would be reviewed and that the cloak of secrecy would be removed. Accordingly the information on stockpiling was declassified and Senator Symington and his subcommittee of the Committee on Armed Services, United States Senate, began an extended study of the stockpiling program. This report lists fifty-four categories of materials and ores, in the national stockpile on March 31, 1963, and that these materials cost the United States $8,096,850,000. They were valued at $7,150,940,000.[15] The committee recommended among other things that the objectives and goals of the stockpiling program to be re-examined and that Congress authorize the orderly disposal of surplus materials.

[13] For a brief review of the stockpiling operations, goals, and problems related to authorization, acquisition, execution of contracts, and disposals of surplus materials see the *Inquiry into the Strategic and Critical Materials Stockpiles of the United States*, Draft Report of the National Stockpile and Naval Petroleum Reserves Subcommittee of the Committee on Armed Services (Senator Stuart Symington, Chairman), United States Senate, on the National Stockpile, Government Printing Office, Washington, D.C., 1963, 126 pages.

[14] *Ibid.*, p. 11.

[15] *Ibid.*, pp. 123–125.

STOCKPILING FROM DOMESTIC SOURCES. If the capacity to produce minerals and mineral products from domestic sources cannot be expanded quickly to meet urgent defense needs, stockpiles should be built up to such levels as deemed necessary to meet the emergency. Conceivably productive capacity might be damaged or destroyed by sabotage or more direct enemy action. Under such circumstances large stockpiles of ores and other mineral products above ground would be an element of strength in conversion to a war economy when manpower and materials generally become scarce. A stockpile of ores and metals built up by the employment of domestic skills and local resources would have the effect of maintaining an operating facility which would be expanded quickly to meet a national emergency.

STOCKPILING FROM FOREIGN SOURCES. Building up the stockpile of strategic materials, particularly the metals, is absolutely essential in the case of those materials that are not available in economically accessible reserves. Certain of the ferroalloys such as manganese, chromium, tungsten, and nickel and the nonferrous metals such as tin, mercury, aluminum, and copper should be purchased abroad and added to the government-owned stockpile. A more or less continuing policy of purchasing supplies regularly would have the effect of maintaining continued production abroad. If the importation of minerals for the stockpile were reduced or abandoned, the economic consequences might be very great. For example, for a copper mining and smelting operation in an area where there is no alternate employment, a shutdown would cause great hardship through the loss of wages and purchasing power of a large number of people. The need of the United States for metals and other strategic materials that must be imported from foreign sources should not lead first to overdevelopment of a mineral resource and then abandonment of the operation. For the greatest security, based on continued accessibility to mineral resources beyond our national frontiers, the mining and processing operations must be maintained, and the routes of commerce kept open if at all possible.

STOCKPILING DIFFICULTIES. In addition to the major objective of establishing an adequate stockpile of the essential strategic materials, it is also important that stockpiling achieve other purposes as well. When federal funds are provided for the purchase of strategic materials, it is important that the funds be allocated and expended in a very businesslike manner. Priorities should be established so that the scarce and inaccessible materials can be promptly built up, deferring until some later time the stockpiling of materials that are less urgently needed. Appropriated funds set aside for the stockpiling program should be used in a manner that will assure the taxpayer that his government is making good use of his money and achieving the aims of the program.

Purchases for the stockpile should be carried out in such a manner that the government does not compete with private industry for the same materials at the same time. This would have as one consequence an increase in price which in turn would limit the quantity of material the available funds would purchase.

STOCKPILING OF LABOR AND POWER. Whenever strategic materials such as copper, aluminum, tin, and other metals are stockpiled, the labor, the power, and transportation used in their production are also stockpiled. For example, nearly 40 percent of the price of metallic aluminum represents the cost of the electrical energy required to separate the metal from the ore. To the extent that the electrical energy was produced from falling water, the stockpiling of aluminum is a means of stockpiling water power which otherwise might have gone to waste. When the stored materials are released from the stockpile, the other constituents are also released.

RESERVES IN THE GROUND. In the case of petroleum, copper, lead, and several other mineral resources, it is important that large proved reserves are known with some exactness. Dis-

covery of new resources or reserves should be well ahead of use so that the reserves will be large enough to permit the rapid expansion of production to meet an emergency. It is not enough to have adequate reserves in the ground. It is also essential that stand-by facilities for expanding mining and smelting be in readiness so that production of strategic metals can be increased promptly to meet the industrial and military needs after the stockpiles have absorbed the first shock of an enemy attack.

DANGER IN STOCKPILING. The stockpiling program of the federal government may have some inherent weaknesses which might be regarded as dangers to the national economy. The goals must be determined a few to several years in advance of achievement. To be genuinely effective the stockpiling program should be continually re-examined to make sure that the objectives are realistic in relation to the military and civilian needs of the nation.

The industries that require large quantities of strategic raw materials to carry on their manufacturing activities should be encouraged to build up and maintain substantial inventories so that it will not be necessary for them to draw upon the national stockpile. The inventories of the manufacturing companies and the stockpile of the federal government should jointly be adequate to meet a national emergency extending over a period of years.

There is also the danger that the stockpile may be conducive to the development of an attitude of complacency.[16] It is important that stockpiling be considered as only one of the means of meeting the material needs of the country in case of a national emergency. Exploration for new supplies of minerals must go on; the search for substitutes must not be relaxed; and technological advances must be sought at every opportunity. Stockpiling must be recognized as only one of the ways of preparing for an emergency.

[16] The President's Materials Policy Commission, *Resources for Freedom*, Vol. I, p. 163.

NATIONAL POLICIES AND INTERNATIONAL CONSIDERATIONS

The Prospect for Future Discovery. In the portions of the world such as northwestern Europe, the United States, and limited areas elsewhere, geological knowledge is reasonably complete. In these areas it is highly improbable new deposits of great value will be discovered. Further exploration, especially at great depth, may have the effect of increasing the known reserves and give the people and the nation a greater sense of security. The deposits that are known at great depth may not be readily accessible because of both engineering and economic limitations.

The greatest hope for new discoveries lies in the exploration of areas that have not been carefully examined geologically. These lesser known areas lie in Asia, Africa, South America, Australia, Antarctica, and limited sections in Europe and North America. Unless new and important discoveries are made in the United States or in areas easily accessible by trade, it is clear that the nation will become increasingly dependent on imported mineral products.

Removing the Barriers to International Trade. Tariffs and other devices have been used in the past to protect American industry from competition from abroad generally where labor costs are relatively low as compared with the wage scale in the United States. The advantages gained by the use of the protective tariff on minerals such as mica, mercury, graphite, manganese, tungsten, bauxite, and copper were matched by disadvantages of higher costs to the consumer which delayed or interfered with the development of the resources in foreign source areas. The lowering of a tariff or its abandonment altogether might not lower prices immediately especially in those situations where the domestic production is small and where production abroad is under the control of a monopoly

or international cartel. But in the long run there should be an effort to reduce tariffs or abandon them entirely.

TARIFFS VERSUS SECURITY. The tariff has been used to protect a domestic industry which as a going concern could give the nation a degree of self-sufficiency in case of a national emergency. But the argument in favor of a protective tariff for security can be challenged. There are other means of achieving national security, such as stockpiling and long-term contracts with domestic and accessible foreign producers of strategic minerals. The tariff on each mineral or metal product should be reviewed periodically to determine if the national interest might be better served by he reduction or elimination of the import duties.

EXPORT QUOTAS AND CONTROLS. By the use of embargos, restrictions, and quotas the free movement of materials in international trade can be controlled. The government in an emergency or in anticipation of an unfavorable situation may, by decree, put export controls into effect. When prices in the metal market tend to stimulate the outflow of essential metals to the extent that the supplies on hand are too low to meet domestic needs, it may be necessary that export controls be used in order to maintain adequate inventories to meet all domestic requirements.

Export controls may be used to restrict the movement of selected commodities to particular destinations. This is well illustrated by the ban on the shipment of strategic materials to communist countries. Generally there is strong public and official opinion against the shipment of metals, machine tools, and other materials that would add to the economic and military strength of the communist-bloc countries.

The Concept of Custodianship. Minerals are very irregularly distributed in the earth's crust and over the surface of the earth. The natural division of the earth into great continental land masses has resulted in dividing the mineral wealth unequally among the continents.

The further division of the continents among the nations has resulted in great inequality among the countries in material wealth.

Any nation that contains within its frontiers a high percentage of a mineral resource that is widely needed over the world should be under some compulsion to share this bounty of nature with other peoples. A spirit of custodianship should be promoted that would encourage development and exportation of minerals essential to the world economy. Strategic minerals such as nickel, mercury, molybdenum, and manganese may be in high demand when the nations are experiencing industrial expansion or building up their national defenses. To the extent that these and other strategic minerals might be used for carrying on war they may be denied to an aggressor and made available to nations defending their independence. Under wartime conditions the concept of custodianship can be modified to serve the ends of peace.

Foreign Trade—A Necessity. At the close of World War II is became clear that the United States was no longer self-sufficient in certain minerals. For many years some of these had been produced in excess of domestic requirements and limited quantities were available for export as native metals or in the form of products made from these metals. The change over from a surplus-producing country to an importer occurred at different dates depending upon the metal. By the middle 1930's the United States became a net importer of zinc and copper. It was near the end of World War II that imports of petroleum exceeded exports. It also became clear that increasing quantities of iron ore would have to be imported to satisfy the needs of American industry.

The importation of strategically important minerals may have other beneficial consequences besides supplying the nation with an essential resource. The money necessary to purchase the imports would become available in the country supplying the mineral for the further development of their resources and for the raising of the standard of living of the people. They would be able to make purchases of other materials produced in their own country and in other countries.

In those countries where the standard of living is relatively low and where their industry is in the extractive stage of development, there is a great need for capital, technological help, and managerial skills. The United States because of its great wealth and technical knowledge is in a position to provide the capital and skills to develop the resources of certain underdeveloped areas of the world. In return we might secure minerals essential to our national well-being. Trade in minerals becomes a virtual necessity, for no nation no matter how large or richly endowed can be entirely self-sufficient in essential minerals.

Trade Routes and the Accessibility of Mineral Resources. Strategic minerals which must be imported from distant sources make it necessary that the routes of commerce be kept open and in case of emergency strongly protected. The United States because of its enormous demand for a great variety of minerals which cannot be produced in adequate quantities from domestic resources must maintain a more or less continuous flow of minerals or metals to the American market. This is well illustrated by tin, the production of which from domestic resources is practically nil. This metal or its ores, in order to meet the needs of the country, must be imported from Bolivia or from the more distant, producing areas in the Malay Peninsula and the nearby islands in Indonesia. Minerals that are available in foreign areas which lie adjacent to the United States or in areas which are readily accessible may be utilized to meet the industrial and defense needs of the nation. Relatively short trade routes which lie within areas that can be defended or protected against enemy action are more dependable than the long trade routes that reach out to the more distant sources of strategic minerals. Over the longer trade routes it may be necessary to move essential minerals and other materials in convoys which necessarily move only as fast as the slowest ship and require many types of naval craft to provide adequate protection.

References

Adams, John A. S., James Boyd, and Paul W. McGann, "Exploring for Minerals," Chapter III in *Science and Resources*, edited by Henry Jarrett, Resources for the Future, The Johns Hopkins Press, Baltimore, 1959, pp. 75–112.

Bateman, Alan M., *Economic Mineral Deposits*, Second Edition, John Wiley and Sons, New York, 1950.

Blondel, F., and S. G. Laskey, "Mineral Reserves and Mineral Resources," *Economic Geology*, Vol. LI, 1956, pp. 686–697.

DeMille, J. B., *Strategic Minerals*, McGraw-Hill Book Co., New York, 1947.

Landsberg, Hans H., Leonard L. Fischman, and Joseph L. Fisher, "Metals," Chapter 16, and "Nonfuel Minerals," Chapter 21, in *Resources in America's Future*, Resources for the Future, The Johns Hopkins Press, Baltimore, 1963, pp. 293–316 and 422–496.

Leith, C. K., "Principles of Foreign Mineral Policy of the United States," *Mining and Metallurgy*, Vol. 27, 1946, pp. 6–17.

Leith, C. K., J. W. Furness, and Cleona Lewis, *World Minerals and World Peace*, Brookings Institution, Washington, D.C., 1943.

Lovering, Thomas S., *Minerals in World Affairs*, Prentice-Hall, Englewood Cliffs, New Jersey, 1944.

Marovelli, R. L., et. al., *Lake Superior Iron Resources*, U.S. Bureau of Mines Report of Investigations No. 5670, Governmental Printing Office, Washington, D.C., 1961.

Netschert, Bruce C., and Hans H. Landsberg, *The Future Supply of the Major Metals, A Reconnaissance Study*, Resources for the Future, The Johns Hopkins Press, Baltimore, 1961.

The President's Materials Policy Commission, *Resources for Freedom*, Vol. I: *Foundations for Growth and Security*, Vol. II: *The Outlook for Key Commodities*, Vol. III: *The Promise of Technology*, Government Printing Office, Washington, D.C., 1952.

Riley, Charles M., *Our Mineral Resources*, John Wiley and Sons, New York, 1959.

Staff of the Bureau of Mines and Geological Survey, *Mineral Position of the United States*, Appendix, Investigation of National Resources, Hearings Before a Subcommittee on Public Lands, United States Senate, 80th Congress, May 15, 16, and 20, 1947, Government Printing Office, Washington, D.C., 1947, pp. 165–310.

United Nations Department of Economic Affairs, Proceedings of the United Nations Scientific Conference on Conservation and Utilization of Resources, August 17—September 6, 1949, Vol. II, *Mineral Resources*, United Nations, New York, 1951.

United States Bureau of Mines, *Mineral Facts and Problems* (1960 edition), Government Printing Office, Washington, D.C., 1960.

United States Bureau of Mines, *Minerals Yearbook*, Government Printing Office, Washington, D.C., Annual.

Van Royen, W., and Oliver Bowles, "Atlas of the World's Resources," Vol. II, *Mineral Resources of the World*, Prentice-Hall, Englewood Cliffs, New Jersey, 1952.

Willard, F. W., "Some Aspects of Our Wasting Assets," *Mining and Metallurgy*, Vol. 27, 1946, pp. 583–584.

E. WILLARD MILLER
Pennsylvania State University

CHAPTER 17

The Mineral Fuels

The mineral fuels have been the catalysts that have motivated modern world industrialization. The United States, without its rich heritage in mineral fuels, could not be one of the leading nations today, nor could the citizens of our country have attained the highest standard of living in the world. The economic and military strength of our nation depends increasingly on the capacity to exploit these resources.

To meet the energy needs of the United States two broad groups of potential sources may be utilized. The first are continuous sources, such as solar, water, wind or tidal energy, and vegetation. At present, these furnish less than one-seventh of our energy requirements, primarily in the form of water power and vegetation.

The second group includes the irreplaceable energy sources, such as the fossil fuels and atomic energy. Of the irreplaceable energy sources, petroleum, coal, and natural gas currently furnish six-sevenths of our total requirements. Atomic energy developments are still in the initial stages, but basic industrial research promises a wide utilization of this energy to supplement the traditional fuels within a relatively few years.

At present the mineral fuel production represents more than two-thirds of our total value of minerals produced in the United States. The nation in 1962 produced nearly 15 percent of the world's coal, 30 percent of the petroleum, about 70 percent of the natural gas marketed, and had approximately 40 percent of the electric energy production.

The mineral fuel reserves are exceedingly unequally proportioned. A comparison on a uniform British thermal unit basis of reserves of coal and other fuels shows that coal constitutes 68 percent of the total estimated recoverable fuel reserves, and that petroleum and natural gas combined constitute about 16 percent. The remaining 16 percent is oil from oil shale which is not presently utilized. Information is not available on the national reserves of fissionable materials—uranium and thorium.

Relative Importance of Energy Resources 1800–1962. During the early days of our country, water and wind power, wood, and work animals provided the principal sources of power. However, between 1800 and 1870 there was a gradual shift from the predominance of nonfuel energy sources to mineral energy sources. About 1830 coal began to be increasingly important as a source of energy and reached its relative peak

351

of importance in 1899 when bituminous and anthracite accounted for 89.1 percent of the total energy contributed by both mineral fuels and water power in the United States. In that year oil and gas accounted for only 7.7 percent of the total (Fig. 1).

The relative importance of coal as a source of energy has been declining since the early 1900's. In 1918, the peak production year of World War I, coal supplied 82 percent of the energy resources, whereas petroleum and natural gas supplied 13.4 percent. The relative value of coal as a source of energy decreased rapidly after 1918 to 63 percent of the total in 1929 and to 26.1 percent in 1962. Oil and natural gas have largely replaced coal in domestic consumption and on the railroads. Since 1955 essentially all new locomotives have been powered with diesel engines.

With the coming of motor transportation, petroleum's share of the energy produced increased from 4.6 percent in 1899 to a peak of 38.0 percent in 1954. Since then the relative position of petroleum has declined slightly to 35.3 percent of the total energy consumed in 1962 primarily as a result of the rapid rise in the consumption of natural gas. Natural gas has followed the same general trend as petroleum, increasing from 3.3 percent of the total in 1899 to 13.7 percent in 1945 and to 34.2 percent in 1962. The production of water power has closely followed the total consumption of energy, increasing many times, but maintaining about the same relative position.

Trends in Energy Consumption. The consumption of energy in the United States has been continuously upward. It has risen from 2354 trillion Btu's in 1850 to 22,975 trillion Btu's

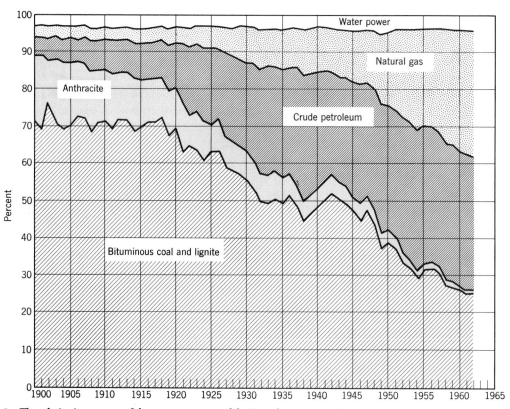

Fig. 1   The relative importance of the power resources of the United States. (U.S. Bureau of Mines.)

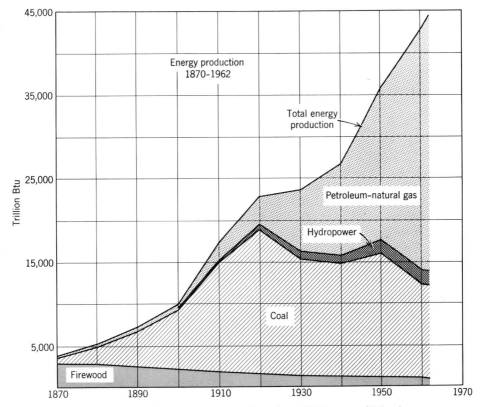

Fig. 2 Energy production in the United States, 1870-1962. (Data from U.S. Bureau of Mines.)

in 1922, to a peak of 47,882 trillion Btu's in 1962 (Fig. 2).[1] In recent years consumption has been rising at the rate of more than 1500 trillion Btu's annually. In the past century fuel wood was replaced by coal as the dominant source of energy, and in turn coal has been replaced by petroleum and natural gas. To maintain the present rate of increase in the future it is likely that another fuel must be found to replace petroleum and natural gas. At the present time the most promising future source of energy will be nuclear energy.

COAL RESOURCES

Importance of the Coal Industry. Coal was the wonder fuel of the nineteenth century and

[1] Btu, British thermal unit, is the quantity of heat required to raise the temperature of one pound of water one degree Fahrenheit at or near its point of maximum density.

is still of major importance in providing the comforts and necessities of life. It has been a vital factor in the growth of modern world power. The United States can attribute her rise to world leadership largely to this dynamic power resource.

Although the coal industry has been affected by competition from competing fuels, coal remains the major fuel for heat and process steam in thousands of industrial plants. The annual value of bituminous coal has been nearly $2,000,000,000 in recent years. The coal industry is the largest bulk-handling industry in the United States. About 200,000,000 tons of coal were transported by the railroads in 1962, and an additional 75,000,000 tons were shipped to market on river barges.

Coal is a major supporter of economic life in many regions and of great importance in others. In West Virginia the number of coal miners is nearly double that employed in the chemical and allied products industries, and the coal industry of Pennsylvania employs twice the number in the metalworking machinery industry.

Origin and Nature of Coals. Coal is a combustible earth material composed of fixed carbon, volatile matter, moisture, and ash originating from the alteration of plant life.[2] In every geologic age since the Pre-Cambrian period, great swamps have existed in which layer upon layer of vegetation accumulated to form peat bogs. Peat developed into coal in a number of stages. The vegetational material was first compressed under successive layers of vegetation. Later as marine or continental deposits covered the coal swamps the accumulated weight of sediments compressed further the plant materials and caused a progressive decrease in volatile matter and moisture. It is estimated that it takes 100 years to form 1 foot of peat and from 3 to 8 feet of peat to produce 1 foot of coal. Pressure, therefore, is one of the great factors in coal development. Lignites are characteristically found where burial is shallow and where there is little crustal distortion, whereas anthracite and high-carbon coals are formed by great compression related largely to crustal disturbances.

Fixed carbon gives the black color to coal and burns with a short flame giving almost no smoke. The volatile matter, consisting of compounds of carbon and hydrogen, is important because of its high heat content and the number of by-products that are obtained from it in the destructive distillation of coal in coke ovens.

Besides fixed carbon and volatile matter there are a number of waste materials in coal. The moisture content of coal varies from as little as less than 1 percent in anthracite to more than 40 percent in lignite. The ash in coals comes from foreign matter in the original plant material or from sediments washed into the swamps as the peat was formed. The ash content in some coals varies from less than 1 percent to as much as 55 percent. Ash and water are diluting substances, so that they are an economic waste factor in storage, handling, transportation, and consumption.

Ranks of Coal. Rank indicates the differences in the progressive evolution of coal from lignite to anthracite. The alteration is marked by a decrease of volatile matter and an increase in fixed carbon from the low-to high-rank coals. This change is a function of weight of original overburden, age, and local deformation. It does not refer to grade or quality which is primarily a function of the amount of ash and sulfur in the coal.

The standard classification of coal by rank in use in the United States was established by the American Society for Testing Materials.[3] (Fig. 3 and Table 1). The basic scheme of classification is according to fixed carbon and heat efficiency (expressed in Btu's) calculated on a mineral-matter-free basis. The higher-rank coals are classified according to fixed carbon on a dry basis, and the lower-rank coals according to Btu's on a moist basis. Agglomerating and slacking indices are used to differentiate between certain adjacent groups.

Lignite, frequently called brown coal, is the lowest rank. It is characterized by a moisture content of 30 to 43 percent and a fixed-carbon content of 30 to 55 percent. The structure is fibrous and woody. It disintegrates readily on exposure and must be stored carefully to prevent spontaneous combustion.

Subbituminous coal is black and may be dull or lustrous, but it still retains the woody appearance of lignite. Its moisture content also may be high, ranging from two to 40 percent. Fixed carbon varies from 35 to 60 percent. On weathering it slacks and has a tendency toward spontaneous combustion. Subbituminous coal has a fairly high-heat value and is mined locally in the United States.

Bituminous coal is the most important industrial and heating coal in the world. It may

[2] Wilfrid Francis, *Coal: Its Formation and Composition*, London, 1961, Chapters 2, 4, and 5.

[3] *Classification of Coal by Rank*, ASTM Standards, Part 8, American Society for Testing and Materials, Philadelphia, Pennsylvania, 1961, pp. 1227-1232.

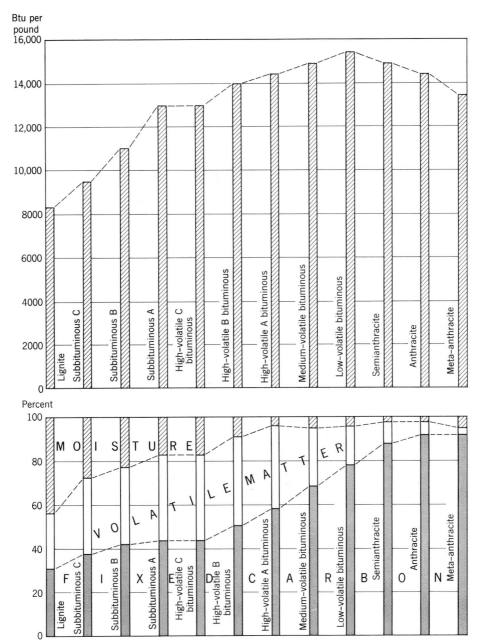

Fig. 3 Heat efficiency and the composition of different types of coal. (American Society for Testing and Materials.)

be dull black to highly lustrous. The moisture content is small, and the fixed-carbon content varies between 48 and 86 percent. This coal stores well and burns with a yellow flame, frequently giving off a penetrating odor. There are many varieties of bituminous coal of which the

Table 1. Classification of Coals by Rank

Legend: FC = Fixed Carbon   VM = Volatile Matter   Btu = British thermal units

Class	Group	Limits of Fixed Carbon or Btu Mineral-Matter-Free Basis	Requisite Physical Properties
I. Anthracitic	1. Meta-anthracite	Dry FC, 98 percent or more (dry VM, 2 percent or less)	Nonagglomerating
	2. Anthracite	Dry FC, 92 percent or more and less than 98 percent (dry VM, 8 percent or less and more than 2 percent)	
	3. Semianthracite	Dry FC, 86 percent or more and less than 92 percent (dry VM, 14 percent or less and more than 8 percent)	
II. Bituminous	1. Low volatile bituminous coal	Dry FC, 78 percent or more and less than 86 perecent (dry VM, 22 percent or less and more than 14 percent)	
	2. Medium volatile bituminous coal	Dry FC, 69 percent or more and less than 78 percent (dry VM, 31 percent or less and more than 22 percent)	
	3. High volatile A bituminous coal	Dry FC, less than 69 percent (dry VM, more than 31 percent); and moist Btu, 14,000 or more	
	4. High volatile B bituminous coal	Moist Btu, 13,000 or more and less than 14,000	
	5. High volatile C bituminous coal	Moist Btu, 11,000 or more and less than 13,000	Either agglomerating or nonweathering
III. Sub-bituminous	1. Sub-bituminous A coal	Moist Btu, 11,000 or more and less than 13,000	Both weathering and nonagglomerating
	2. Sub-bituminous B coal	Moist Btu, 9500 or more and less than 11,000	
	3. Sub-bituminous C coal	Moist Btu, 8300 or more and less than 9500	
IV. Lignitic	1. Lignite	Moist Btu, less than 8300	Consolidated
	2. Brown coal	Moist Btu, less than 8300	Unconsolidated

[Source: *Classification of Coals by Rank*, ASTM Standards, Part 8, American Society for Testing and Materials, Philadelphia, Pennsylvania.]

most common are coking, cannel, noncoking, torbanite, and boghead.

Semibituminous has a high fixed-carbon content and has the highest heating value of all ranks of coal. It is an excellent steam coal and is used for general manufacturing and utilities when a high degree of heat is required.

Semi-anthracite differs from anthracite only in that it is more friable. It has a fixed-carbon content of 86 to 92 percent and is thus a smokeless fuel with a high heat value, is free from soot, and burns slowly, making an excellent domestic fuel when used with a stoker system.

Anthracite is a hard dense coal with the highest fixed carbon and lowest hydrocarbon content of all coals. It is characterized by a jet black color, freedom from ash and moisture, excellent coherence, and burns with a short blue flame. It is an ideal domestic fuel because of its smokelessness and steadiness in burning.

Coal Reserves and Centers of Production. The nation's coal reserves are extensive but are unevenly distributed and highly variable in quality and accessibility. The coal areas, located in twenty-six coal-bearing states, have been classified into seven major provinces: Eastern, Interior, Gulf, Northern Great Plains, Rocky Mountain, Pacific, and Alaskan (Fig. 4).

The original reserves of coal in the United States, computed by the United States Geological Survey, are placed at 1719 billion tons, of which, on January 1, 1960, it was estimated that 830 billion tons still remain unmined (Table 2). These totals, which are considerably lower than the widely quoted estimates of M. R. Campbell in 1929 and the estimates of Paul Averitt and

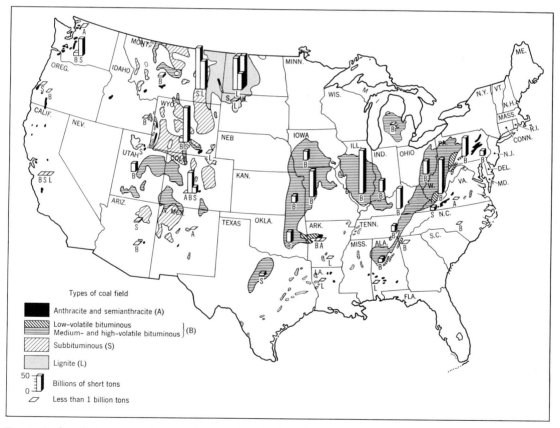

Fig. 4   Coal producing areas and reserves by states. (U.S. Geological Survey.)

Table 2. Estimated Coal Reserves of the United States

Rank	Estimated Original Reserves	Estimated Total Reserves Remaining in the Ground, January 1, 1960	Estimated Reserves, 50 Percent Recovery	Recoverable January 1, 1960
			Million of Short Tons	Quadrillions of Btu's
	Millions of Short Tons			
Bituminous	808,420	760,554	380,277	9,963
Sub-bituminous	437,742	436,812	218,406	4,150
Lignite	447,966	447,596	223,798	2,999
Anthracite and semi-anthracite	25,836	15,328	7,664	195
Total	1,719,964	1,660,290	830,145	17,307

[Source: U.S. Geological Survey.]

Louise R. Berryhill in 1950, are based on new appraisals of coal reserves.[4]

The estimates of reserves are based on a combination of factors. Detailed geologic maps showing the outcrops and correlations of the individual coal beds and geologic reports giving detailed measurements of the coal augmented locally by data from exploratory and development drilling and from operating mines are primary sources. Unfortunately, many coal-bearing areas in the United States have not been mapped geologically. As a result many areas which are known to have coal have been omitted from the estimates because of lack of information. For example, in Colorado 75 percent and in Wyoming 53.5 percent of the coal-bearing seams were not considered in the estimates of reserves. Progress toward full knowledge of the coal reserves of the United States depends on an active program of detailed geologic mapping and exploratory drilling by the United States Geological Survey and the states geological agencies. The present reserve figures are provisional and will change as additional information becomes available.

In estimating reserves the minimum thickness of coal that can be mined commercially was placed at 14 inches for bituminous, 30

[4] Paul Averitt, *Coal Reserves of the United States*, A Progress Report, January 1, 1960, Bulletin 1136, U.S. Geological Survey, Washington, D.C., 1961, pp. 10-11.

inches for subbituminous, and lignite under less than 3000 feet of overburden. All coals with an ash content to 30 percent are included. The average specific gravity of anthracite and semi-anthracite was estimated at 1.47, bituminous coal 1.32, subbituminous coal 1.30, and lignite 1.29, and tonnages were computed on this basis. Under present mining operations it was estimated that 50 percent of the coal in underground mines is recoverable. Using these criteria it was estimated that on January 1, 1960, the total recoverable reserves were 1442 times the recent average annual production. There can be no doubt that reserves of coal will last many generations under any conceivable rate of production.

Eastern Province. The Eastern province, containing the Atlantic coast, the Anthracite, and the large Appalachian regions, is the oldest mining area in the United States. The Atlantic coastal region in Virginia and North Carolina is of little importance. The Anthracite region of northeastern Pennsylvania is the most important in the country, producing 98 percent of our anthracite and containing 80 percent of our reserves.

The Appalachian region is one of the largest areas of high-grade bituminous coal in the world. An area of approximately 50,000 square miles is underlain with coal. West Virginia has led the nation in coal production since 1928, followed by Kentucky and Pennsylvania. The famous Pittsburgh coal seam of western Pennsylvania, eastern Ohio, and West Virginia is one of the world's largest single deposits of high-volatile bituminous coal. It supplied the coal for the beehive ovens of Connellsville which were the primary source of coke in the early development of the iron and steel industry of the Pittsburgh region.

Interior Province. This province consists of four regions: Eastern, Western, Northern, and Southern. The coal of the Interior province is largely bituminous, but the quality is not as good as in the Appalachian fields. The coal of the Eastern region, Illinois, Indiana, and western Kentucky, has been mined most extensively and has been one of the prime factors in the growth of manufacturing in the Central Lowlands. Illinois, with 77 percent of its area underlain by coal, has the greatest reserves of bituminous coal in the United States and because of low-cost mining and good-quality coal is now the fifth largest producer. The coal deposits of the western region, which extend from Iowa to Oklahoma, are large, but are mostly low-rank bituminous which consequently burns with considerable soot and smoke. It has little coking value, but it does have a high heat content and is therefore used locally for domestic heating and as a steam coal for industry. Only limited mining activity is carried on in the Northern region of Michigan and the Southwestern region of Texas.

Gulf Province. The Gulf province which extends along the coast from Texas to Louisiana has mostly lignite. The coal is in a region of young, undisturbed rocks so that it has remained of low rank. The lignite is of highest quality in northern Texas and southern Arkansas where some mining is practiced locally. Since the coal has a high volatile content it has a potential use in coal hydrogenation.

Northern Great Plains Province. This province includes all the coals of the Great Plains of the United States and extends into the Prairie Provinces of Canada. This province has tremendous quantities of lignite and subbituminous

coal. Montana and Wyoming, ranking first and second, respectively, in reserves of subbituminous coal, have nearly 55 percent of the United States total of 437 billion tons. North Dakota has 350 billion tons of lignite of the total United States reserves of 448 billion tons. Although the northern Great Plains states possess huge quantities of coal, these reserves are largely of low-rank coals with only about two-thirds of the heating value of bituminous, and the coals are essentially noncoking.

Rocky Mountain Province. This area is composed of a large number of noncontiguous fields extending from Montana to New Mexico. The province contains all ranks of coal from lignite to anthracite. The coal is found in great basins, and the rank depends largely on crustal disturbances. Coal production has been limited because of the small regional market.

Pacific Province. The coal of the Pacific province is found largely in Washington, with minor deposits in Oregon and California. Although Washington has a good supply of subbituminous and bituminous coal, mining is difficult because the rocks were folded and faulted in many places and subsequently were covered by thick deposits of glacial drift.

Alaskan Province. The coal deposits of Alaska are widely distributed and reserves may total more than 50 billion tons. Most of the reserves are subbituminous and lignite, but some bituminous and anthracite are present. There was little mining of coal in Alaska until the 1930's. Population increases in recent decades have spurred production. At the present time two fields are under exploitation. The Matanuska Valley coal field is a good grade bituminous. The Nenana field (or Healy River field) in the interior southwest of Fairbanks produces a high-grade lignite. Two-thirds of the state's production comes from the Nenana field. Strip mining produces between 85 and 90 percent of the Alaskan coal. The scattered deposits, lack of accessibility, complex geologic conditions, and small local markets have handicapped development. The United States Armed Forces are the principal consumers of Alaskan coal.

The coals of the Appalachian and Interior provinces were the foundation on which the great manufacturing districts of eastern United States were established. Approximately 85 percent of our bituminous production is in West Virginia, Kentucky, Pennsylvania, Illinois, Ohio, and Indiana. At present about 2.8 percent of the output consists of anthracite which makes up only 1.5 percent of the tonnage reserves. The fourteen northeastern states consume over 70 percent of the coal produced but have only 17 percent of the reserves. For the most part the nation's best coals are being depleted at a rapid rate. The famous Pittsburgh coal bed has an estimated life of less than 100 years. The reserves in beds thicker than 42 inches in the fields of southern West Virginia have an estimated life of less than 75 years at present extractive rates.

The industrial pattern of the United States is related directly to the location of the high-grade bituminous coal. Present production centers in the coal fields nearest the consuming markets where transportation changes are at the minimum. At present more than half the cost of bituminous coal, delivered at the purchaser's siding, consists of freight. Extensive transportation of coal would make the delivered price prohibitive for many users.

PRODUCTION TRENDS AND PROBLEMS OF THE AMERICAN COAL INDUSTRY

Coal in the United States was first mined in the early colonial period, but the modern coal-mining industry began only about 1820. Although the relative growth was rapid, the output remained small until after the Civil War. In 1840 production was 2,070,039 tons and by 1860 only 14,610,042 tons. Anthracite exceeded the production of bituminous until 1869, and until 1873 the United States imported more coal than it exported.

From 1850 to 1910, during the great industrial expansion of the United States, coal production virtually doubled every 8 to 9 years (Fig. 5). This rate of gain was maintained almost unabated

until 1910, but after that there was a tendency toward retardation. From 1890 to 1900 the gain was 91 percent, but from 1910 to 1920 only 36 percent. Production rose to a peak output of 579,385,820 tons in 1918. From 1850 to 1920 was the most rapidly growing industrial period of our country, and coal was the principal energy on which this growth was based.

Although there were annual fluctuations in production, the general trend from 1919 to 1938 was downward. World War II once again created tremendous demands for coal. In 1944 a total of 619,576,240 tons of bituminous coal were produced. Production declined temporarily at the close of the war, primarily as a result of prolonged strikes in the industry. However, in 1947 the bituminous production of 630,623,000 tons was an all-time peak. Since 1947 production has once again declined drastically. In 1962 bituminous coal output was only 422,149,000 tons.

Production trends in the anthracite industry have generally paralleled those of the bituminous industry. Anthracite production reached its peak in 1917 when 99,611,811 tons were produced. Although production declined gradually in the next quarter of a century, the drastic drop from 63,701,363 tons in 1944 to 16,015,366 tons in 1962 has placed this branch of mining in a particularly precarious position. The anthracite region of northeastern Pennsylvania has long been plagued by an economic depression, which indicates the region is undergoing economic changes to which it has been unable to adjust.

Although production of bituminous and anthracite coals has declined greatly, the decline in number of coal miners has been even more significant. In the bituminous industry the number of workers has been steadily declining since 1923 when 704,793 were employed to a low of 145,100 in 1962. This was a decline of 559,693 or 79.4 percent. A similar trend is evident in the anthracite industry with the number of workers declining from a peak of 165,386 in 1926 to 14,010 in 1962. This was a decrease of 151,376 workers, or about 91 percent.

The plight of the coal industry is due to a

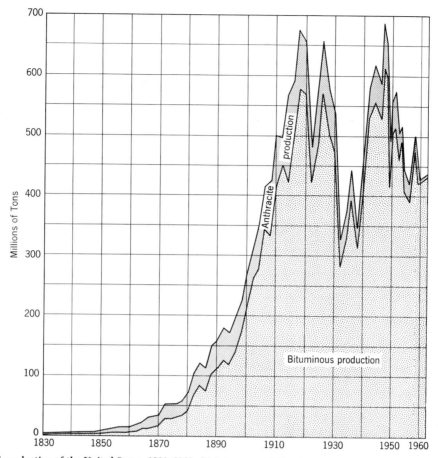

Fig. 5 Coal production of the United States, 1830–1962. (U.S. Bureau of Mines.)

number of causes. The encroachment of oil and gas is the basic reason for the decline in production of both bituminous and anthracite fuels. The decrease in employment is due not only to a decrease in total coal output but also to greater efficiency in mining coal. The mechanization of the underground mine and the growth of surface strip mining have been major factors in increasing productivity. The output of bituminous coal per man per day was 4.28 tons in 1923. At that time 68.3 percent of the coal was cut by machines, 31.7 percent was cut by hand, and underground mechanical loading was virtually unknown. In 1962 the average daily output per man in underground mines was 11.97 tons with 63.3 percent of the coal cut by machines,

32 percent was mined by continuous mining machines, and only 4.7 percent was cut by hand and shot from the solid seam. In strip mining the average daily output per man in 1962 was 26.76 tons.

Principal Uses of Coal. Most of the 35,000,-000 tons of bituminous coal produced monthly in the United States is consumed in the nation's electric power utility plants, factories, and for domestic heating. The consumption of coal in the electric power utilities has increased from 12 percent of the total in 1945 to 33 percent in 1955 and to 49 percent in 1962. The electric power utilities are now the largest single user of coal. Of the industrial users, the manufacturing industries take about 24 percent and the coke industries about 19 percent of the nation's coal output. Coal used for domestic heating has declined from 25 percent of the total in 1945 to about 15 percent in 1955 and only 6.6 percent in 1962. This same trend has occurred in coal used by railroads, with a decline from 22 percent of output in 1945 to 7 percent in 1955 and less than 1 percent in 1962. Other minor uses are for colliery fuel, bunker coal, and a small foreign trade.

COAL CONSERVATION PROBLEMS

Mining Practices and Losses. There are two principal methods of mining coal, underground workings and open pit or stripping. The loss of coal in underground mining is still a very serious problem. The percentage of total coal recovered in mining varies to a considereable extent. In individual mines as much as 80 to 90 percent of the coal in the area actually being mined may be recovered. From the total resource point of view, however, recoverability appears to be only about 50 percent of the coal in the ground.

A number of causes lead to underground mining losses. Present mining methods, utilizing only the best coals, leave millions of tons of coal untouched in the ground in a condition that makes future recovery unlikely, even at a markedly higher price. Coal left on the roof and floor, in rooms, in entries, and in panel pillars causes other losses. Formerly, the greatest loss in mining came from coal left in pillars to support the roof of the mine. Modern methods employing the long-wall or panel system avoid much of this loss, for the coal is mined in retreat and the roof allowed to fall as soon as the coal is recovered. Other wastes involve coal lost under buildings, transportation routes, in boundary pillars, in cemeteries, and around oil and gas wells. Coal may also be wasted in handling and in its preparation. Economic pressure and insufficient margin between the cost of mining and the selling price of coal are other reasons for leaving large areas of coal unmined. The suspension of mine operations at times of

strikes and shutdowns frequently results in great loss of coal, especially on pillar lines. A continuously operated mine will aid materially in the conservation of available coal still left in the ground.

Since the early 1930's open-pit mining has increased greatly in importance. Coal stripping began before World War I, but was relatively unimportant until large shovels were developed. Before 1926 the largest stripping shovels had a dipper capacity of only 1 to 3 cubic yards. The largest shovels now hold 75 cubic yards, and it is possible to dig with them to a depth of 120 feet. The amount of coal mined by stripping has risen rapidly from 1 percent of the total in 1917 to about 33 percent in 1962.

The advantages of strip mining are many. In 1962 the average surface miner produced more than twice as many tons per day as the subsurface worker. Although investment in stripping machinery is high, the salvage value of this equipment is much greater than that of subsurface equipment. The danger in open pit operations is minimal. The recovery of coal is from 75 to 95 percent of the original total.

The great problem of strip mining is the restoration of the land after the power shovels have worked to uncover the coal.[5] The great furrows of rocky materials, commonly called spoil banks, have often become major areas of desolation. A number of states and local communities has passed legislation requiring that the land be leveled and improved. However, restoration to the original contour is now questioned. Usually the cost of such operations is prohibitive. The leveling processes often pack the soil so firmly that seedling trees do not survive. In many situations it has been found that the best restoration is the planting of trees on the original spoil banks. In many mines the last open cut can be made into small lakes with excellent recreational facilities. In hill country the furrows, which are usually on the contour, hold the runoff water effectively and are thus highly

[5] D. Jackson, Jr., "Strip Mining, Reclamation and the Public," *Coal Age*, Vol. 68, May 1963, pp. 84–95.

beneficial to the growth of trees. Excellent timber stands have been developed in Illinois, Ohio, and Pennsylvania on the banks.[6] In some instances the income from the land is greater after such treatment than it was before the stripping operations.[7] However, no two spoil bank areas can be subjected to the same treatment. Some spoil banks have high lime content and can support various grasses and deciduous trees. Pasture and forage use is usually limited because the strip slopes prevent mowing. Other banks are highly acid and will support only conifer plantings at best. Because of its many advantages, strip mining will remain until the surface deposits are exhausted.

Production of Coke. The processing of coal into coke resulted in tremendous losses when the beehive oven was employed. With the introduction of the by-product coke oven in the early 1900's these losses have been largely eliminated. A ton of bituminous coal coked in a beehive oven will yield about 1300 pounds of metallurgical coke, whereas the same amount of coal, coked in a by-product oven, will yield 1500 pounds of coke as well as 22 pounds of ammonium sulfate, 9 gallons of tar, 2.5 gallons of light motor oil, and 10,000 cubic feet of gas. In 1905 less than 10 percent of the coke was produced in by-product ovens. Since then the growth has been rapid, and in 1962, 98.2 percent of the coke was produced in this way.

Conservation in Consumption. There has been a remarkable gain in efficiency of coal utilization by the principal consumers. This substantial reduction in consumption of coal per unit of work is an important form of conservation, for it increases the potential usefulness of our coal resources. These improvements have been due largely to the following advancements: (1) growth of knowledge of the composition and properties of coal; (2) improvement of

the physical processing of coal for specific uses; (3) introduction of economies in conversion of coal to heat energy; (4) introduction of economies in conversion of coal to mechanical energy; and (5) reduction of energy required for a given purpose.

Improved Knowledge of the Nature of Coal. Coal is a highly complex substances which is the source, in part, of thousands of products from aspirin to dyes. The first survey of the composition and properties of coal was made in this country in 1904. This work has been continued by such groups as the United States Geological Survey, the Bureau of the Mines, and the American Society for Testing. Special attention has been placed on such research as reactions involved in the utilization of coal, classification of coals as they occur in the ground, development of standard grades and specifications for most efficient utilization in marketing, and utilization of the coal as a raw material in the chemical industry.

Physical Processing of Coals for Specific Uses. Coal as it comes from the mines usually has impurities and is not the best size for efficient utilization. Nearly all the anthracite and nearly two-thirds of the bituminous in 1962 was sized and cleaned before it was marketed. Mechanical cleaning means cleaning raw coal with mechanical devices that separate out the impurities, usually by differences in specific gravity. In 1962, of the 339,407,841 tons of raw coal cleaned there were only 271,632,559 tons of cleaned coal. Refuse amounted to 67,775,282 tons or 20 percent of the total.

The washing of coal to reduce its ash and sulfur content developed about 1920. The keen competition with other fuels and introduction of mechanical methods of mining have encouraged this development. The percentage of coal washed has increased from 5.3 percent in 1927 to nearly two-thirds in 1962. The cleaning of coal is a conservation measure, for it permits the crushing of lumps of impure coal and recovering a considerable portion of the coal.

After the coal is washed, the problem of re-

[6] W. G. Jones, "Land Conservation in Pennsylvania's Open Pit Mines," *Mining Congress Journal*, Vol. 49, October 1963, pp. 52–56.

[7] "Reclaiming Land for Profit," *Coal Age*, Vol. 68, October 1963, pp. 94–101.

moving surface moisture is critical. The need to remove the moisture is necessary in order to avoid freezing difficulties and to facilitate handling the coal during shipment and transfer to the firebox, to reduce the heat wasted in evaporation of surface moisture of the coal, to decrease transportation costs, to improve the coal so that it may be used for specific purposes, such as producing coke and briquets, and to facilitate dry cleaning. The three principal methods of removing surface moisture from coal are gravity drainage, mechanical dewatering, and thermal drying. Thermal drying is generally used on coals that cannot be easily dried by gravity drainage or mechanical means. Thermal drying became important in the late 1950's and by 1962 thermally dried bituminous coal and lignite amounted to 47,000,000 tons, or about 11 percent of total production in the United States.

Conversion of Coal to Heat Energy. Most modern home furnaces are inefficient producers of heat energy. Efficiency tests by the Battelle Memorial Institute in Columbus, Ohio, have revealed wide variations in effective utilization, summarized as follows: 45 percent efficiency for hand-fired bituminous, 55 percent for stoker-fired bituminous, 50 percent for hand-fired semi-bituminous, 70 to 75 percent for natural gas, and 60 to 70 percent for oil. The largest losses are due to escape of heat in dry flue gases, ranging from one-third to two-thirds of the total. Other losses are from moisture, carbon monoxide gas, and unconsumed carbon in the ash.

Most of the prevailing losses can be prevented by improved firing methods. Stoker firing gives higher efficiency and eliminates a large percentage of the smoke. In hand firing, efficiencies depend to a large extent on the personal factor. The public needs to be educated in the handling of coal furnaces. The schools of the nation can contribute greatly to the saving of coal by educating the coming generations in the most economical and efficient manner of using the particular coal available in the different parts of the country. Maximum efficiency, as great as 90 to 92 percent, can be attained by proper firing of pulverized coal in stokers.

Conversion of Coal to Mechanical Energy. Efficiency when coal is converted to mechanical energy has been increasing steadily, but still needs improvement. By the end of World War I the most efficient steam engines consumed a little more than a pound of coal per horsepower hour, and by 1962 this figure had been reduced about 50 percent. The electric-utility power plants have made significant gains in fuel efficiency. From an average in 1902 of 6.4 pounds of coal per kilowatt hour the level was reduced to 0.86 pounds in 1962. The quantity of coking coal consumed per ton of pig iron was reduced from 3194 pounds in 1918 to about 1700 pounds in 1962, a decrease of over 45 percent.

Coal-burning steam turbine plants have been able to attain an efficiency of only 31 percent, and mercury-vapor plants have a maximum efficiency of 38 percent. Industrial boilers have an efficiency between 60 and 65 percent. One of the great needs is for more extensive and better utilization of insulation materials to eliminate these wastes.

The Future of Coal. The future of coal in the coming decades will depend on two important factors. The first, and more important, is the availability and utilization of petroleum, natural gas, water power, and atomic energy; the second is the development of technical improvements that will continue to raise the efficiency of coal-burning furnaces.

Industry has constantly carried on a research program in order to improve coal-burning equipment. Although more efficient stokers, boilers, and fire boxes will lessen the demand for coal per unit of work performed, these improvements will tend to overcome the competition with petroleum and natural gas and consequently increase the total coal consumption. Because of the limited supplies of petroleum and natural gas, the great consumption of these fuels carried long distances in pipelines for burning under stationary boilers may be, in one sense at least, considered anticonservational.

Super power plants located at the mine for the conversion of coal to electric energy are now in operation to eliminate the expensive charges for transporting the bulky coal. The production of synthetic rubber, plastics, nylon, explosives, and hundreds of other products in which coal can be a basic raw material has grown greatly in the past two decades. Coal may also become a major source of certain rare elements such as germanium. An increased number of by-products from the coking of coal could become of importance. The Germans are known to have produced edible fats and cooking oils from low-grade coal.

Coal remains one of the cheapest and most abundant fuels. It thus should continue to be used in such processing and manufacturing where it can compete successfully with other fuels. Most leaders in the coal industry believe that its problem would be eased if the United States adopted a national fuels policy. Such a policy would specify the chief uses to which each fuel would be best adapted with respect to economic and national security considerations. Coal would thus be assigned the primary responsibility of fueling heavy industry, especially electric power utilities. In this manner coal would be assured a strong competitive position among the mineral fuels.

PETROLEUM

Importance of the Petroleum Industry. Petroleum is probably our most indispensible and limited mineral fuel. It has been one of the most significant minerals in shaping our modern civilization. With petroleum products used for illumination, power, heating and lubrication, it has grown to be one of our largest industries. The value of crude oil produced from 1859 to January 1, 1963, was $142,451,163,000. The assets of the American petroleum industry are now valued at $47,000,000,000 in comparison to $30,000,000,000 for the chemical industry, $26,000,000,000 each for the motor vehicle and food industries, and $20,000,000,000 for the iron and steel industry. In 1962 the total value of crude oil, natural gas liquids and natural gas produced was $10,659,079,000. To produce its products the petroleum and natural gas indus-

tries employ 295,000 workers in drilling and production. Approximately 40,000 are engaged in transportation; 150,000 in petroleum refining; 125,000 are employed in wholesale marketing; 600,000 men attend to service stations and retail outlets; and more than 20,000 highly trained research personnel are engaged in developing new processes and products. More than 200 taxes have been imposed on various forms of petroleum products from which federal, state, and local tax collecting authorities receive an average of $2,500,000,000 in taxes each year.

Even though the use of petroleum has influenced many aspects of our economy, its most far-reaching effects have been in the field of transportation. Today approximately 70,000,000 passenger cars and 14,000,000 trucks and buses crowd the nation's highways. The effect on our economy of faster travel has been enormous.

The utilization of petroleum has also been important in other phases of our modern life. Its influence in changing agricultural practices has been striking. When the oil industry began over a century ago, about two-thirds of the gainfully employed were in agriculture. At present only about 8 percent are so employed, but agricultural output is many times greater than that of 100 years ago. The use of petroleum products in present-day mechanized farm machinery has been a major factor in the increased efficiency of agricultural operations. The farmer is one of the best customers of the oil industry. Many of the insecticide sprays are produced from petroleum. Substitution of tractors for horses and mules has released much farm land for growing crops for human consumption. This is a basic reason for the improved American diet.

While petroleum is important for peacetime endeavors, it is possibly even more important in war. Ever since World War I petroleum has played a major role in providing the fuel for our armed defenses. The demands for petroleum products have sometimes been overwhelming, but the industry has always met its obligations. During World War II, 5,000,000,000 barrels of oil were produced. New refineries with a capacity of a billion barrels were built in the United

States. The industry built, relaid, or reversed the flow of more than 10,000 miles of pipelines; the flow of oil to the east coast by land routes increased from the prewar level of 5000 barrels daily to over 1,000,000 a day at the peak. And the American tanker fleet, despite all losses, grew by more than four and one-half times.

The compelling demands of war have also encouraged rapid technical progress. The unprecedented needs for 100 octane aviation gasoline during World War II brought about rapid commercialization of new processes. At the start of the Korean War, the United States was threatened with a shortage of benzene which is a basic raw material for many kinds of plastics, synthetic rubber, nylon, detergents, and other products for both defense and civilian needs. Previously the entire production of benzene had come from coke ovens. Within a few months, the petroleum industry had become a large-scale producer of benzene, and the shortage had been alleviated.

The petroleum industry is an inherent part of the American economic system. Although our resources are limited, demands continue on a spiraling-upward trend. If our reserves are depleted within a few decades as predicted by some oil experts, America will face one of its most complex industrial problems in providing a substitute fuel.

The Nature of Petroleum. Crude petroleum is a complex mixture of oily hydrocarbons, which also frequently contains small quantities of oxygen, nitrogen, and sulfur, with varying amounts of natural gas, water, and inert materials.[8] A large number of different mixtures makes possible wide variations so that crude oils may range from gasoline to pitch or asphalt. Petroleums, in general, are divided into three classes—paraffin, asphaltic, and mixed base—according to their dominant chemicals composition.

Petroleum may be colored a light straw,

green, brown, or black. Usually the light-colored oils are high-grade crude, and the darker-colored oils produce the lower-quality products. The density of crudes is expressed in specific gravity, which is the ratio of the weight of a given volume of water under standard conditions. The specific gravity of crudes varies from 0.77 to 1.00. Since the specific gravity scale is expressed as a fraction and the numbers are read with difficulty, an arbitrary scale, known as the Baumé, is used. On the Baumé scale a specific gravity of 1.00 is read as 10°. Oils nearly as heavy as water have readings close to 10°, whereas those lighter than water have much higher readings. A crude is said to be heavy if it tests below 20° Baumé or light if the reading is above 30° Baumé. In general the value of crude rises as the Baumé reading increases, for light oils are usually rich in gasoline and light naphthas.

Occurrence of Petroleum. Petroleum is generally considerd to have originated from organic material, such as marine animal organisms and plant life, which was first deposited in sedimentary rocks. This material was then covered, and theories advanced for the change of organic matter into crude petroleum include the effects of heat and pressure over a long period of time, of bacterial action, of low-temperature catalysis, and of radioactivity. It has also been suggested that oil was not formed in the sediments, but was produced in living organisms and only released in the sediments. The process of origin is, however, an important key to exploration, for petroleum is found chiefly in sandstones and limestones.

Many geologic structures are favorable to the accumulation of petroleum. A common form of trap is the anticline with the typical arrangement of natural gas at the top of the anticline, oil beneath and on either side, and water at the base. Intrusions of deep-seated rocks may also provide a suitable medium for oil accumulation. This is particularly true of rock salt, which is highly plastic under pressure. The salt usually takes the form of a dome pushing up the surrounding rocks and forming a seal against their

---

[8] H. M. Smith, "Composition of United States Crude Oils," *Industrial and Engineering Chemistry*, Vol. 44, 1952, pp. 2577-85.

fractured edges, thereby preventing the escape of liquids or gases from those rocks. Another common trap is the stratigraphic trap. The accumulation of oil is due to the variation in permeability providing a closure to the reservoir. An example of this trap would be a layer of sand thinning out into an impermeable shale or a lens of sand enclosed entirely by clay or shale.

Products of Petroleum. The petroleum industry produces a wide variety of products. Each product performs a unique and distinctive function which has not been adequately met by any substitute or competitive material.

The earliest important product obtained from crude oil was kerosene, providing inexpensive artificial illumination which was superior to all illuminants of its day. Kerosene contributed greatly to the spread of information, for it gave the opportunity for more and more people to read and learn. Kerosene also became an illuminant in the field of transportation, contributing greatly to the world's safety. Although kerosene has been replaced by gas and electricity in most sections of our country, it is still an important illuminating and cooking agent in many rural areas and foreign countries.

Gasoline, which has replaced kerosene as the most important product, is the most fundamentally necessary fuel of the modern world. An outstanding achievement of the petroleum industry has been keeping pace with automobile manufacturing which uses a large percentage of the total oil output. The proportional yield of gasoline from crude has risen greatly as a result of improvements of refining technology, recovery of gasoline from natural gas, and cracking of heavy crudes.

The lubricating materials suitable for high-speed, high-temperature machinery are obtainable in sufficient quantities only from petroleum. To meet the needs of hundreds of different machines and engine designs, lubricating oils and greases are produced in infinite varieties. The power and production machine, which characterizes our civilization, has been made possible by petroleum lubricants.

After gasoline, kerosene, and light lubricating oils have been extracted from the crude, there still remains the heavy, less volatile oils in the form of gas oils and fuel oils. These oils may be used as raw material for cracking gasoline or directly as a fuel in industry, transportation, agriculture, and for domestic heating.

Besides the traditional petroleum products, petroleum has become one of the major raw materials for a mammoth petrochemical industry. This vast industry, which only became important about 1940, is now valued at more than $5,000,000,000. At present, petrochemicals account for one-third of the nation's total chemical production. Except for ammonia which is the largest volume single petrochemical, the greatest markets lie in the group of compounds used for plastics, synthetic rubber, and synthetic fibers. At present the petrochemical industry consumes only about 1 percent of our total petroleum production and less than 5 percent of our natural gas. Furthermore, the maximum requirements projected to 1975 can be met without utilizing more than 3 or 4 percent of anticipated oil and gas production.

Geographic Distribution of Petroleum. Petroleum is widely distributed in conterminous United States where nine major provinces cover thirty-two states (Fig. 6). Although the petroleum areas are widespread, the really large yields of oil are obtained from a few states.

THE APPALACHIAN PROVINCE. This region, which extends from southwestern New York through Pennsylvania and from southeastern Ohio to Tennessee, is the oldest producing region in the world. The first well was drilled in 1859 near Titusville, Pennsylvania, and with the discovery of oil on August 28, the modern oil industry was born. The first oil boom soon followed and has been repeated a hundred times in most of the new oil areas. Pennsylvania was the principal supplier of the world's oil until the Lima-Indiana province was discovered in 1884. The maximum for the Appalachian province was reached in 1891 when more than 33,000,000 barrels were produced. Production has declined slowly since that date and annual output now totals less than 13,000,000 barrels. Most of the

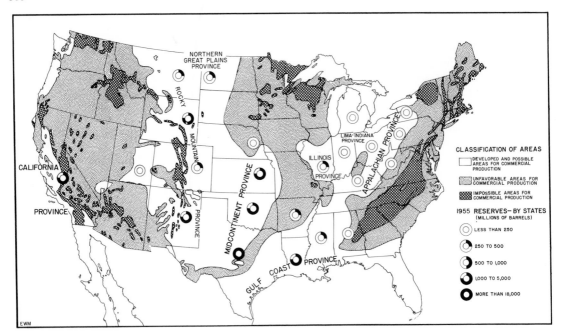

Fig. 6 Petroleum areas in the United States. (U.S. Geological Survey and American Petroleum Institute.)

wells of the province are now extremely small. Over 140,000 wells have been drilled in the province. Several fields have developed secondary recovery methods in order to secure a greater yield of petroleum. The Bradford field has applied water repressuring measures since the early 1900's and in the principal area of production. This was the first major experimental center for testing secondary recovery efforts in the United States. The oil is high grade, ranging from 35° to 50° Baumé. It is paraffin base with few impurities. Because of its quality and traditional reputation it commands the highest price of all petroleums. It is of particular value in the making of high-quality lubricants.

THE LIMA-INDIANA PROVINCE. This region extends from the northwestern corner of Ohio to Indianapolis, Indiana, It was discovered in 1884, and peak production was attained in Ohio in 1896 and in Indiana in 1906. The oil is paraffin base but contains sulfur and water which have lowered its value. The province was developed at a time when conservation principles

were disregarded so that production rose and declined rapidly. From 1884 to 1931, more than 60,000 wells were drilled. No doubt one-tenth of this number could have recovered more petroleum. Today the province is nearly exhausted.

THE MICHIGAN PROVINCE. This oil-producing area was discovered in 1925, and most of the production has come from the Saginaw and Muskegon fields. In 1939, the peak year, production was only 23,500,000 barrels. After a long decline to 9,308,000 barrels in 1958, production rose to 18,901,000 barrels in 1961 as a result of new discoveries. There is, however, little indication that the Michigan province will become a major producer.

THE ILLINOIS PROVINCE. This province which lies in southeastern Illinois and western Indiana was discovered in 1905, and its output reached a peak in 1910 when 33,000,000 barrels were produced. Production had declined to less than 5,000,000 barrels annually by 1937, when deep drilling discovered new sources of petroleum.

The output again increased rapidly until 1940 when 146,484,000 barrels were produced but gradually declined to a production of 58,866,000 in 1953. Annual production, however, has risen to nearly 80,000,000 barrels in recent years due to increased drilling. The production curve in Illinois illustrates the effects of new discoveries on output when no effective conservation legislation had been enacted. The petroleum from this province is largely paraffin base, testing about 30° Baumé, is sulfur free, and is easily refined. The natural gasoline content is about 15 to 20 percent.

THE MIDCONTINENT PROVINCE. This region which includes the oil fields of Kansas, Oklahoma, Arkansas, northern and west-central Texas, and northern Louisiana, is the largest and most productive area in the United States. Large-scale developments began in 1905. Between 500,000,000 and 1,300,000,000 barrels of oil have been produced annually from 1940 to 1962. This tremendous production is due to the large petroliferous area, the complexity of structural conditions, and the variety of sources of origin of the petroleum. All grades from light paraffin to heavy asphaltic oils are produced. This province has had many spectacular developments. The discovery of each new field has stimulated the search for others so that production has been maintained at a high level. A number of times production has been so great, as a result of new discoveries, that the oil market has been flooded and prices fell temporarily. In each instance, however, peak production has rapidly subsided, and the market has recovered. Although early efforts to control production by conservation methods failed, the area in recent times has been developed by efficient engineering methods.

THE GULF COAST PROVINCE. This province came into production in 1900 with the discovery of oil in the famous Spindletop well. Production has at times declined temporarily, but the general curve has been upward to the present. The province ranks second in the United States with an annual output of over 500,000,000 barrels and will probably continue to be a large producer for a considerable period. The oil is usually associated with domelike rock structures, and thus is frequently under great pressure, resulting in many gushers.

The crude oil is of heavy asphaltic base with sulfur impurities and contains little natural gasoline. Fuel oil is the major refined product which is used extensively for heating and in diesel engines. With the use of cracking in refining, the heavy oils have become a good source of gasoline. Some of the oils are excellent for the preparation of heavy cold-test lubricants.

THE NORTHERN GREAT PLAINS PROVINCE. This province is the newest major area of oil exploitation in the United States. Developments are confined to the Williston Basin, which covers portions of North and South Dakota, eastern Montana, and also parts of the provinces of Saskatchewan and Manitoba in Canada. This is one of the largest sedimentary basins in continental North America. Although sporadic explorations have been in progress since 1923, the first oil was discovered in April 1951. Since then progress has been steady, so that by January 1, 1963 about 482,000,000 barrels of proven reserves were known to exist in North Dakota alone. Small local markets and inadequate pipeline transportation for oil and gas have been serious handicaps to rapid development. To facilitate production refinery capacity within the region is growing and a pipeline network is evolving connecting this region with the large petroleum consuming centers. The Williston Basin promises to become a major oil province of the United States.

THE ROCKY MOUNTAIN PROVINCE. This province is composed of scattered fields from Montana to New Mexico. Nearly all grades of oil are present, but light high-quality oils dominate. Production began about 1916, but partly because of the isolation of the area and slight local markets, exploration was limited and output remained small. With increased exploratory work and deeper drilling since 1940 many new significant fields have been discovered and production has increased. Wyoming, now ranking fifth among our oil-producing states with output of about 145,000,000 barrels, is the leading producer, followed by Colorado, Montana, and Utah. In view of the large area and varied structural conditions, there are strong possibilities that a still more intensive exploratory program will discover new and important producing fields.

THE CALIFORNIA PROVINCE. California ranks third with an annual output of less than 300,-000,000 barrels of petroleum. Production has declined in recent years from a peak output of 365,085,000 barrels in 1953. The decrease is due primarily to the paucity of new discoveries. There are only two large producing districts, the Los Angeles Basin and the southern portion of the San Joaquin Valley. Evidence of oil from surface seeps had long been known, but the first successful well was not completed until 1875 in Pico Canyon. Production increased rapidly and in 1903 California became the largest oil-producing state. The State of California has been in first, second, or third place since then.

The oil pools are characterized by high gas pressure so that individual well production is usually large. The oil is predominately asphaltic in character, but small quantities of high-quality crude are produced. Because of great flush production and competition, excessive drilling has characterized the area. After much waste, the oil producers have finally recognized that conservation practices pay dividends. California now has a state conservation law which helps to prevent the waste of natural gas. This gas is conserved not only for industrial uses but also to maintain pressure in the wells, thus increasing the amount of oil that can ultimately be recovered from the producing sands.

ALASKAN PROVINCE. Petroleum and natural gas have long been sought in Alaska. The foothills north of the Brooks Range were long thought to hold the greatest promise. In 1923 the U.S. Navy reserved 37,000 square miles for its own use. Geological exploration and drilling

in the Point Barrow-Cape Simpson area began in 1944. As a result small oil and natural gas deposits have been discovered. Petroleum has not been produced in commercial quantities. Natural gas is used by federal installations in Barrow and in 1962 was made available to local residents.

Commercial production of petroleum began in Alaska in 1957 with the discovery of oil on the Kenai Peninsula. Production of the area has increased rapidly and by 1962 totaled 10,260,-000 barrels. The Swanson River field is the major area of production and is expected to have a billion barrel potential. The field is being developed under modern conservational practices. Repressuring of the field began in November 1962 in order to maintain reservoir pressure.

There are large potential petroliferous basins in Alaska. The sedimentary basins of the Yukon and Kuskokwim rivers are most promising, but little exploration has been undertaken. A smaller area extends for about 350 miles along the southern coast of the Alaska peninsula. Exploration is advancing in this region, including the drilling of wildcat wells.

Trends in Production. The petroleum industry has experienced a continuously rising production curve (Fig. 7). The increase from 1839 to 1900 was relatively modest, rising from 11,963,000 in 1875 to 63,621,000 in 1900. Total production for the period was 1,000,000,000 barrels. The great demands for petroleum were created by the development of automotive transportation. Domestic production rose rapidly after 1900 from 209,500,000 barrels in 1910 to an initial peak of 1,007,300,000 barrels in 1929. After a temporary recession in the early 1930's, the 1936 production exceeded the 1929 peak, and output has continued to rise to an all-time high of 2,676,185,000 barrels in 1962. Although production continues to increase in the nation, the United States has become a major importer of crude oil and petroleum products since 1946. In 1962 the nation imported 419,757,000 barrels of crude oil and an additional 341,607,000 barrels of refined products,

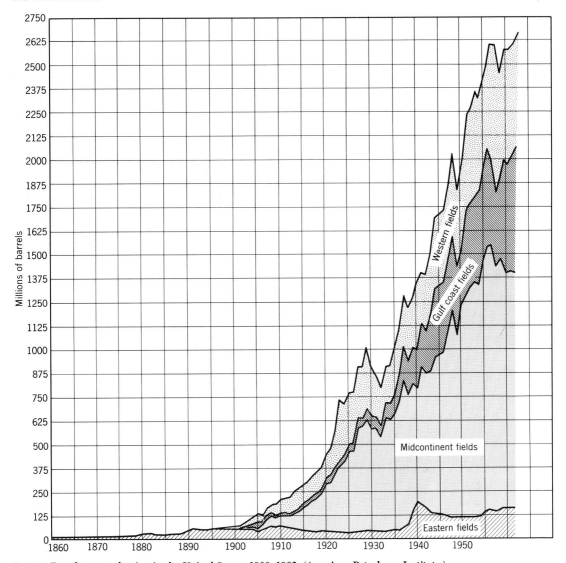

Fig. 7   Petroleum production in the United States, 1900-1962. (American Petroleum Institute.)

or about 29 percent of total domestic demand. About 62 percent of the imports came from Venezuela and an additional 18 percent was from the Middle East. Other important sources include Canada, Libya, and Trinidad.

Migrational Trends. Peculiar to all mineral exploitation is the characteristic of exhausti-bility; oil and gas pools are notoriously short-lived, particularly when exploited under the wasteful practices of competitive drilling. Today the computed centers of oil and gas production are far from the areas where the industry was first important. The line of march has been to the west and south following closely in the wake of discovery.

The center of oil production was located in western Pennsylvania from 1859 to 1889. Commercial production began in Ohio, West Virginia, and California in the 1880's, and by the middle 1890's the center of output was in northwestern Ohio close to the Indiana border. In 1900 more than 57 percent of the crude oil came from the Appalachian district, more than one-third from the Lima-Indiana district, and the remaining 8 percent from California and the Gulf coast.

From 1900 to 1910 the center of production shifted westward from western Ohio to central Kansas, as a result of the remarkable discoveries of new oil pools in the Midcontinent field. By 1919 the center had shifted slightly southward to the Panhandle of Oklahoma. California was the leading state from 1903 to 1915. From 1915 to 1926 California and Oklahoma were about equal in output and first place shifted between them. In 1927 Texas became the largest producer and has maintained the lead since then, producing 35 percent of the national total in 1962. The center of production has consequently shifted, first southwestward in 1929 to northwestern New Mexico and then to the Panhandle of Texas as a result of the outpouring of oil from these fields in the early 1930's. With the great increase in the Louisiana Gulf coast fields and the gradual decline of California production in recent years the center has shifted to west

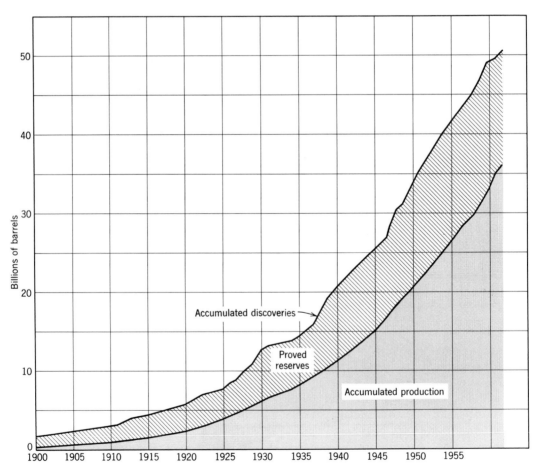

Fig. 8   Accumulated production and proven reserves of petroleum in the United States, 1900–1962. (American Petroleum Institute.)

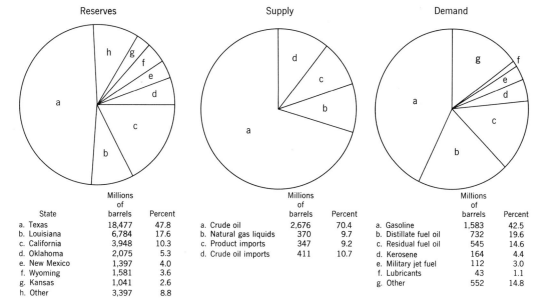

State	Millions of barrels	Percent
a. Texas	18,477	47.8
b. Louisiana	6,784	17.6
c. California	3,948	10.3
d. Oklahoma	2,075	5.3
e. New Mexico	1,397	4.0
f. Wyoming	1,581	3.6
g. Kansas	1,041	2.6
h. Other	3,397	8.8

	Millions of barrels	Percent
a. Crude oil	2,676	70.4
b. Natural gas liquids	370	9.7
c. Product imports	347	9.2
d. Crude oil imports	411	10.7

	Millions of barrels	Percent
a. Gasoline	1,583	42.5
b. Distillate fuel oil	732	19.6
c. Residual fuel oil	545	14.6
d. Kerosene	164	4.4
e. Military jet fuel	112	3.0
f. Lubricants	43	1.1
g. Other	552	14.8

Fig. 9   Reserves, supply, and demand for petroleum in the United States. (U.S. Bureau of Mines.)

central Texas at the present time. In 1962 about 48 percent of the crude oil produced came from the Midcontinent fields, about 25 percent from the Gulf coast fields, 22 percent from the Western fields, and only 5 percent from the Eastern fields.

United States Petroleum Reserves. From the earliest period the conviction of an early exhaustion has haunted the petroleum industry. Because petroleum is a liquid deeply buried in the earth, the only way to measure reserves is to drill into them and estimate possible recovery. The proven petroleum reserves of the United States have been constantly revised upward (Fig. 8). The first estimates were made in 1909 when the automobile industry was beginning to make its first great demands for gasoline. It was estimated that the total petroleum yield of the United States might be as low as 10,000,000,000 barrels or a high as 24,500,000,000 barrels. The first estimates in which the proven reserves were separated from estimates of unexplored fields were made in 1921. In this estimate 5,000,000,-000 barrels were classified as oil "in sight" on January 1, 1922, and 4,000,000,000 barrels

additional as prospective and possibly recoverable by current methods of production. In 1925 the American Petroleum Institute estimated proven reserves to be 5,321,427,000 barrels. The Federal Oil Conservation Board stated in October 1932, that new discoveries raised the known reserves to 10,000,000,000 barrels, and the American Petroleum Institute on January 1, 1939 reported that proven reserves were 17,348,146,000 barrels.

The proven reserves continued to increase until the mid-1950's, and have remained fairly steady in recent years. On January 1, 1963 the American Petroleum Institute and the American Gas Association reported proven reserves of 31,389,223,000 barrels of crude oil and 7,311,-517,000 barrels of natural gas liquids, making total reserves of 38,700,740,000 barrels. New proven reserves in recent years have approximately equaled production. Texas has about 47 percent of the United States crude petroleum reserves, with Louisiana, California, Oklahoma, Wyoming, New Mexico, and Kansas following in that order (Fig. 9).

Proven reserves in any pool include both

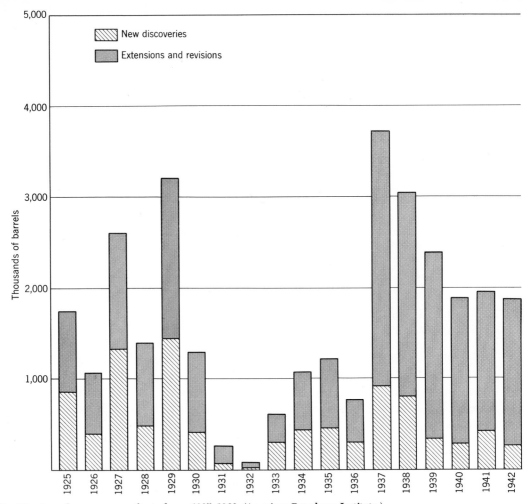

Fig. 10   Annual new reserves of petroleum, 1925–1962. (American Petroleum Institute.)

drilled and undrilled oil recoverable under existing economic and production systems now in operation. For a one-well field, where development has not gone beyond the discovery well, the area assigned as proved is usually small in regions of complex geological conditions, but possibly larger where the geology is simple. In a sparsely drilled field the area between wells is considered to be proved only if the information regarding the geology of the field and the productive horizon is adequate to assure that the area will produce when drilled. Thus, the total of new oil, through discoveries estimated as proven in any given year, will be comparatively small, but the total new oil proven by extension of known fields will be comparatively large (Table 3).

Trends of Petroleum Reserves. The ultimate survival of the petroleum industry depends on the discovery of new fields and deeper oil-bearing zones. The extent to which new sources will be found will depend greatly on whether the price of oil will permit the heavy and increasing expenses of new exploration and still maintain a profit.

Between 1919 and 1930 three major fields,

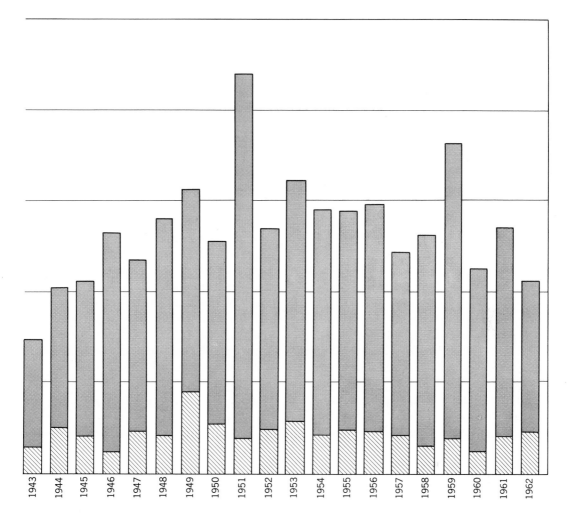

averaging more than 100,000,000 barrels annually, were discovered each year. Since about 1930 we have depended more for our new oil resources on the extensions of known fields rather than on completely new discoveries (Fig. 10). During World War II and immediately following, new discoveries were at a particularly low ebb because of restrictions in drilling exploratory wells. Exploration increased in the late 1940's and early 1950's, but soon an oversupply of oil developed not only in the United States but in the world. The increase in the productive capacity greater than in demand resulted in a lowering of the price of petroleum. This, combined with increasing exploratory costs, had a depressing effect on the United States petroleum industry.

Exploratory activity is the initial step to petroleum discovery. This activity can be measured by the number of geophysical crew months worked each year. The number of crew months worked reached a peak in 1953 at about 8600 and has declined steadily. Crew months worked in 1962 were more than 50 percent below the 1953 level. Another vital activity is the leasing of prospective acreage. Acreage under lease for oil

Table 3. Estimated Proved Recoverable Reserves of Liquid Petroleum (Crude Oil and Natural Gas Liquids) and Natural Gas in the United States

	Reserves Jan. 1, 1963	Assumed Annual Production	Years of Supply (Reserve Divided by Annual Production)
Billions of barrels			
liquid petroleum	38.7	2.7	14.3
oil from shale	92.0	–	–
Trillions of cubic feet			
natural gas	273.7	14.7	18.6

[Source: American Petroleum Institute and American Gas Association.]

and gas, including that already proven productive, reached a peak of 424,000,000 acres, or about 20 percent of the entire land area of the United States in 1959, but declined to about 380,000,000 acres in 1962.

The test well is the next step in oil exploration. The number of exploratory or wildcat wells drilled reached an all time high of more than 13,000 in 1956. This important activity has steadily declined. In 1962 only 9000 wildcat wells were drilled. In the modern period under the best technology, only about one wildcat well in nine is successful in discovering any oil or gas and only about one in forty locates a field which is commercially profitable. After a field is discovered it must be developed by additional drilling. Similar to the trend in wildcat wells, the total number of wells drilled reached a peak in 1956 with 58,000 wells, and steadily declined to only 45,000 wells in 1962. With fewer wells being drilled and with continued improvement in drilling technology and equipment, the number of drilling rigs in use has also declined. This measure of the industry activity reached a peak of 2700 rigs in 1955, and has since declined steadily to about 40 percent below the 1955 level in 1962.

The goal of exploration and development activities is to find new oil and gas reserves. With exploration and development activity declining, the rate of growth of oil reserves has been slowed considerably. The foregoing analysis of trends, however, should not be interpreted to mean that the oil and gas resources of the United States are nearing depletion. For example, when natural gas is converted to barrels of crude oil equivalent on a Btu basis and added to liquid petroleum reserves found, more total reserves per well drilled were found in the period 1959 through 1962 than in the 10-year period before 1962. During the 4-year period an average discovery of 138,000 barrels per well compares with an average of 131,000 barrels for the period 1953 through 1962. The capacity of the petroleum industry to produce has continued to rise to an all-time peak of more than 11,250,000 barrels per day as of January 1, 1963. About 2,850,000 barrels per day, or more than 25 percent of this capacity, was shut-in or idle at the beginning of 1963.

PETROLEUM CONSERVATION PROBLEMS

Applied petroleum conservation lies largely in wise utilization in order to achieve maximum recovery with minimum waste as a result of an advancing technology and a growing social responsibility. In each of the technical branches —exploration, drilling, production, and refining —new scientific advancements have added billions of barrels to our reserves. If our petroleum industry is to serve adequately for its maximum period of existence, a continuing and expanding program in public education and technical research is a necessity.

Petroleum Exploration. DEVELOPMENT OF SCIENTIFIC EXPLORATION. The first oil fields were discovered either by surface evidence, such as seepages or gas bubbles, or by pure luck. It was not unitl after 1900 that the industry considered geological interpretation a definite aid to oil exploration. Beginning about 1912 geologists started to map outcrops to locate favorable drilling locations. By 1920 various kinds of cross sections, subsurface contour maps, and peg-models in three dimensions were being used extensively. The results of the initial explorations were encouraging, and soon the known structures had been drilled to depths permitted by existing equipment.

The most radical change that has come about in exploring for oil and gas has been the introduction of geophysical methods in the early 1920's. One of the earliest was the refraction seismic method developed by German scientists. In this method, scientific use is made of the fact that seismic or earth waves, caused by a charge of explosive detonated at or near the surface, will travel with greater speed through dense rocks than through the surface formations between the starting and recording device. The refraction method was successful in locating a large number of salt domes on the Gulf coast.

American scientists developed the widely used reflection seismic method. In the reflection method the depth and configuration of deeply buried beds are determined from records of waves that originate at the blast and are reflected back to the surface, similar to the echoes that result from reflection of sound waves. The results were phenomenal, and the method is used today in practically all oil-producing countries. This method has been applied particularly to areas where no surface indications are present. It can be used for the deepest drilling possible today.

The gravity method of exploring for oil, which by means of a torsion balance measures local variations in the intensity of the earth's gravitational field, was also introduced in the early 1920's. It is based on the principle that as the density of the rock varies, so does the gravitational attraction at the surface. Thus the pull at the surface of a thick limestone bed in an anticlinal structure is greater over the crest than at a point over the flanks where the limestone is more deeply buried. Gravitational changes are very small so that the instruments must be of great sensitivity. The gravimeter, however, has the advantage of being small, weighing as little as 5 pounds. It can also be used under water. This instrument has been particularly helpful in discovering salt domes and for reconnaissance surveys.

An indication of subsurface structures can also be obtained by measurement of changes in the intensity and direction of the earth's magnetic field brought about by certain mineral deposits as a result of the conductivity or resistivity, and other electrical properties of rocks constituting the earth's crust. The method is useful in determining depths of the magnetic igneous basin and thus assists in the mapping of sedimentary basins. The most significant advance in magnetic surveying was the development of the airborne magnetometer. The instrument is normally towed behind the aircraft and recordings are made of the total magnetic field along a series of grid traverses. The magnetometer is principally used for reconnaissance surveys.

The use of aerial photographs is advancing rapidly in oil exploration for interpretation of structural features such as anticlines, faults, and other features. Plane-table mapping still is of value, but aerial photographs present a direct view of the terrain and make it possible to establish easily the exact position of objects. Aerial maps can be made with a contour interval of approximately one foot which are equal in accuracy to transit and plane-table surveys.

RESULTS OF PLANNED EXPLORATION. The development of geophysical and other methods of surveying has greatly increased the possibilities of discovering oil. The problem of finding additional oil for our expanding market demands an active exploration program. The industry is now spending several million dollars a year in research to develop new techniques and improve old ones.[9] Some of the current problems involve direct oil finding by geophysical and geochem-

[9] Harrison T. Brundage, "Modern Exploration Methods and Field Applications," World Oil, Vol. 158, February 15, 1964, pp. 109-131.

ical methods, adaptation of the seismic method, the origin of petroleum, and intensive studies of subsurface data collected from old and new wells.

Drilling. TREND TOWARD DEEPER DRILLING. Drilling advancements, which have permitted the penetration of all types of formations at ever-increasing depths, have been significant factors in extending the life of the petroleum industry.[10] The pioneer wells were exceedingly shallow, many not exceeding several hundred feet. Gradually the depth increased. By 1890 the deepest well was over 5000 feet and by 1925 nearly 8000 feet. In 1938 a test well in California reached a depth of 15,004 feet, and in 1958 a new record was established with a well 25,304 feet deep in Texas.

Deeper drilling has been responsible for the discovery of new fields in areas where shallow drilling has proved unsuccessful, and of new sands underlying oil-producing fields in which the existence of such sands, if known, was previously considered beyond the limit of drilling. It is estimated that the ultimate recovery from reservoirs already discovered at 5000 feet or more in depth will be in excess of 12,000,000,000 barrels, or about 10 percent of the total ultimate recovery from fields discovered up to 1964.

IMPROVEMENTS IN EQUIPMENT. The outstanding change in drilling techniques, directly responsible for reaching greater depths, was the shift from the cable tool method to the rotary method. Greater speed is an important advantage of the rotary drill. It is not uncommon for a modern rotary rig to drill as much as 1000 feet of soft formation in one day. As a result of the development of "hard-rock" bits and hard-surface alloys, the rotary system has been adapted to practically all formations.

The success of the rotary system has been due to scientific control of the circulating mud fluid and the ability to drill a hole of uniform size. The mud coats the walls of the hole, so that the water sands are sealed without using numerous

strings of steel casing. Thus in rotary drilling a hole of uniform size can be maintained to any depth, whereas with cable tools the hole gets progressively smaller, eventually leading to "running out of hole," a condition that prohibits further drilling.

Other major advancements in drilling include improvements in cements and cementing techniques and development of methods to control high subsurface pressures and temperatures. The application of directional drilling has made it possible to develop offshore fields, such as those in the Gulf of Mexico and along the California coast, where the derricks are on the shore and the oil reservoirs underlie beach resorts or deep water.

There has been a general improvement in the design, strength, and power of drilling equipment. With increased depth the trend has been to heavier rigs. The cable tool derrick has increased in height from 64 to 122 feet, and rotary derricks vary from 122 to 178 feet. Efficient gas-pressure control equipment has been invented which permits drilling in high-pressure areas. The development of these drilling techniques has added thousands of square miles of prospective oil area and has added substantially to our crude oil reserves.

Petroleum Production. The techniques of producing oil from wells have been revolutionized. A scientific analysis of traditional methods has indicated many desirable modifications, for the life of an oil field depends to a large extent on its method of development.[11] Improvement in well spacing, efficiency of reservoir operations, increased importance of production engineering, and secondary recovery methods have enabled constantly larger proportions of the gas and oil in the underground reservoir to be recovered.

UNITIZED DEVELOPMENT. Petroleum, unlike solid minerals, moves underground with shifting pressures. Thus oil will move toward a well when there has been a release in pressure. The long

[10] Mel Hobbs, "Advancements in the Drilling Industry," *World Oil*, Vol. 158, February 15, 1964, pp. 63-79.

[11] R. W. Scott, "Advancements in Production Methods," *World Oil*, Vol. 158, February 15, 1964, pp. 85-101.

established "rule of capture" in oil and gas regions gives the owner of an oil well the right to produce all oil that flows into his well. As a consequence, as soon as an oil well is drilled in an area owned by small landholders, each owner is forced into an intensive drilling campaign if he is not to lose his oil. In the past the fact was largely ignored that oil and gas pools are single units and that for maximum production they should be developed and operated without reference to surface property lines. In hundreds of our oil fields thousands of needless wells have been drilled because of the competitive character of the American oil industry. The greatest disadvantage of uncontrolled drilling is maximum production within a short period of time with resultant loss of the gas pressure and consequently a low ultimate recovery of the oil.

No general rule of well spacing has been devised, for each pool must be considered separately. It may be stated that the optimum number of wells in an oil reservoir is the minimum number to allow proper control of the reservoir energy in order to obtain maximum yield. In recent years there has been a tendency toward wider well spacing. During World War II the federal government required a spacing of one well to 40 acres. At present there is a tendency toward a spacing of up to 600 acres per well.

The most effective solution of the problem of well spacing is the unitization of all oil field operations.[12] Its primary purpose is to conserve the natural resource by treating the complete field as a unit. To be complete, unitization must cover such aspects as preventing overdrilling, the application of secondary methods, and selective production in parts of the field to take the place of competitive drilling over the whole area. Unitization should be established in an oil field as early as possible in its development.

EFFICIENCY OF RESERVOIR OPERATIONS. The increased knowledge of the principles of reser-

voir behavior and of the factors affecting recovery have contributed more to our present reserve position than any other single development. The most efficient operation results from maximum use of natural energy. In the early oil industry, and the practice still exists in certain areas, it was common procedure to produce the oil as rapidly as possible; this practice is now recognized as extremely wasteful. Controlling the production rates and conserving the reservoir energy are likely to increase the ultimate recovery.

Fundamental research on the physical properties of the oil resevoirs has been considerable since 1925. The knowledge of the reservoir energies, free gas, oil and dissolved gas, and free water has been greatly increased. It is now generally recognized that there are three ways in which these fluids behave to release energy: through a simple expansion of gas released from solution in the oil; through displacement of the oil from the sand by downward expansion of a free gas cap, and through displacement of oil by upward influx of water from below the oil sands.

The adoption of methods to maintain as nearly as possible the original reservoir pressures has usually proved successful. The problem is to maintain natural pressures or, if these are exhausted, to create new energy by water or gas repressuring.

INCREASED IMPORTANCE OF PRODUCTION ENGINEERING. Upon completion of a well in most new fields, an efficient production organization is necessary to give the largest ultimate recovery possible. Advances have come so rapidly that oil-producing operations have become highly specialized. From the standpoint of efficient recovery and the conservation of reservoir energy, the use of a particular sized tubing in flowing wells, particularly where natural gas is the chief propulsive agent, is probably one of the most important technical advances. When wells are produced at considerably less than open flow rates, as under a proration schedule, higher efficiencies of flow are attained through tubing of smaller diameter

---

[12] "Unitized Oilfield Conservation Projects in the United States and Canada," Interstate Oil Compact Commission, Secondary Recovery and Pressure Maintenance Committee, 1962, 111 pp.

than would be obtained through large pipe. Modern oil and gas separation, operating under pressure, affects efficient separation of fluids and gases and allows virtually complete recovery of the gas accompanying the oil. This permits the gas to be reinjected into the oil sand, maintaining the reservoir pressure and increasing the ultimate yield.

SECONDARY RECOVERY DEVELOPMENTS. By the primary production methods practiced in the United States as much as 50 to 90 percent of the original oil remained in the oil sand when the wells were abandoned. As a result the oil industry is developing processes by which a greater recovery of oil can be obtained after the free flow has ceased and pumping is no longer profitable. Secondary recovery practices are growing in importance, and the application of these techniques has been the most significant development in oil production in the last two decades. Consequently, millions of barrels of additional oil have been added to our reserves.

Secondary recovery is now practiced in all oil-producing states. In central Pennsylvania production on certain leases has been increased more than 700 percent by gas drives. In the Bartlesville field of Oklahoma the original reservoir pressures yielded a total of 4000 to 6000 barrels per acre over a period of 20 years. With the introduction of gas drive an additional output of 1000 to 1500 barrels per acre has been recovered for a period of more than 10 years. In Texas at the beginning of 1962 there were 1881 secondary recovery projects of which 1568 used water, 252 gas, 43 water and gas, and 18 liquified petroleum gas as the type of injection fluid.[13] New secondary recovery projects are being added in Texas at the rate of more than 300 per year. Secondary recovery projects now account for approximately one-third of Texas crude oil production. These projects have increased the estimated reserves by 20 percent or about 3,000,000,000 barrels.

[13] *A Survey of Secondary Recovery and Pressure Maintenance Operations in Texas to 1962*, Texas Petroleum Research Committee, Austin, Texas, Bulletin 62.

TERTIARY RECOVERY DEVELOPMENTS. After the application of primary and secondary processes most oil fields still contain large quantities of oil that is not recoverable by the traditional methods. For example, according to the Interstate Oil Compact Commission only 26.5 percent of the original oil in California can be recovered by primary and conventional secondary recovery methods. This means that 45,500,000,000 barrels of oil now discovered cannot be produced by using traditional methods. One of the most promising of the new tertiary recovery methods is that of using in-situ combustion, commonly known as fireflooding. The basic principle of this process is to heat the oil sufficiently to decrease the viscosity so that it can, under pressure, be moved to a producing well. This process is particularly important in regions of heavy oil. It is estimated that fireflooding could add 4,100,000,000 barrels to the recoverable reserves of California. Known results indicate that fireflood production can create certain difficulties, including safety problems. The safety problems include disposal of toxic, explosive gases resulting from the combustion process, the handling of high-pressure air equipment necessary to sustain combustion, the handling of high-voltage electricity if an electrical ignitor is used, and protection against well blowouts caused by high pressures induced by combustion.

MAXIMUM OIL PRODUCTION THROUGH CONSERVATION LAWS. The conservation of oil and gas by preventing waste and obtaining the greatest ultimate recovery is the most important single factor in oil and gas production. Control of production rate, preservation of gas caps, injection of gas and water, pressure maintenance, cycling, and the many auxiliary controls have not always been in use. Under our system of government the state has the duty and responsibility to conserve natural resources. However, state governments were slow to act in respect to oil and gas conservation.

With the discovery of the East Texas field in 1930, overproduction, coupled with waste, became so devastating that firm steps were taken to regulate the industry. Thus, as a consequence of wasteful overproduction, the science of modern petroleum conservation began to crystallize. The East Texas field became a national proving ground for experimental laws and methods. As one law was cast aside, a new one was enacted; as one regulation was invalidated, a new one was tried; as one weakness was remedied, a new one was developed.

Finally, in 1935 the Interstate Oil Compact came into being.[14] This is basically a treaty, sanctioned by Congress, entered into by oil-producing states for the purpose of assisting the various states in the formulation of sound oil and gas conservation programs and for the purpose of public education in the necessity and methods for oil and gas conservation. The Interstate Oil Compact establishes no collective power of enforcement and membership is entirely voluntary. However, each state in assuming membership pledges its efforts to enact and enforce laws, rules, and regulations that may be required to bring about the conservation of oil and gas produced in its own jurisdiction.

Thirty-one states have become a member or associate member of the Compact. The Compact functions through the Interstate Oil Compact Commission, whose duty is "to make inquiry and to ascertain the methods, practices and circumstances, which bring about the prevention of physical waste of oil and gas and to report at intervals its findings and recommendations to the States." The Commission is a fact-finding and fast-developing body engaging in studies to determine the most advantageous methods, practices, and conditions of conservation. All members have enacted conservation laws and have issued rules and regulations under such laws. Because of its dominant position as an oil producer, Texas plays a unique role among the oil-producing states as a vital force in the conservation movement. The position Texas takes in regulation of production influences all other oil producing states and even many foreign countries.[15]

Refining. ADVANCES IN REFINING. The technological advances in refining in the twentieth century have also added millions of barrels of oil to our reserves. The greatest advancement in refining has been the development of the cracking processes since 1913, by which heavy hydrocarbon molecules can be broken into lighter fractions by the application of comparatively high temperatures and pressures. By this method the amount of gasoline from a barrel of crude oil has been increased from 5 to 18 percent to 38 to 54 percent of the total yield. With the development of catalytic cracking, the yield of gasoline has been increased to 65 percent, and could be increased beyond this figure.

If it were not for the increased yield of motor fuel made possible by cracking, two or three times more crude oil would be needed to supply the present demands. Besides lengthening the life of our petroleum resources, the conversion of the heavy fraction of petroleum to gasoline by cracking has tended to retard the extent to which coal has been replaced by oil as an industrial fuel. Without cracking, the heavier fractions would have been available in constantly larger quantities from ordinary distillation processes and would have been placed on the market at prices more strongly competitive with coal.

The cracking process not only increases the quantity of gasoline, but also its quality. With thermal cracking, gasoline as high as 80 octane could be obtained. Then through auxiliary processes and catalytic cracking, high octane ratings have evolved. Polymerization, the first of the auxiliary catalytic processes to be developed, yields gasoline of about 90 octane. Alkylation, another catalytic process based on refinery gases, made possible the production of 100 octane gasoline. Catalytic cracking, which came into widescale commercial development dur-

[14] *A Summary of the Background, Organization, Purposes and Functions of the Interstate Compact to Conserve Oil and Gas,* Interstate Oil Compact Commission, 1962, 17 pages.

[15] Erich W. Zimmermann, *Conservation in the Production of Petroleum,* New Haven, 1957, p. 142.

ing World War II, produces gasoline with 88 to 90 octane and gives as high yields as thermal cracking. Even with these processes, refineries would have difficulty in fulfilling the demands for high octane fuels if it were not for a development called catalytic reforming in which low-octane gasolines are upgraded to gasolines which, on addition of tetraethyl lead, have an octane of 95 to 100.

The conservational effects of these developments are tremendous. Also, owing to better fuels, the modern combustion engine is more than twelve times as powerful, weighs about one-quarter as much per horsepower, and has more than forty times as great thermal efficiency as those used in 1920. Thus refining technology has increased our reserves and at the same time made available a product of greater efficiency.

SYNTHETIC LIQUID FUELS. As the natural petroleum supplies are depleted, substitute liquid fuels can be produced to supplement the declining crude oil. This supply can come from a number of sources, such as (1) alcohols from vegetable matter, (2) distillation of oil shales, (3) conversion of natural gas by the gas synthesis process, (4) liquefaction of coal or lignite by the hydrogenation process, (5) conversion of water gas from coal by the Fisher-Tropsch synthesis process, and (6) by-product light oils and tars from coking coal. Because of the vast quantities of petroleum available in recent years only limited attention has been given to the development of the synthetic fuels.

Alcohol, distilled from vegetable matter, has proven satisfactory when blended with motor fuels. At present its production cost is greater than that of gasoline from petroleum, but if the price can be lowered its use may increase greatly.

Petroleum can be obtained from oil shales which contain little or no liquid oil but from which large quantities of oil can be obtained by destructive distillation. The greatest reserves of shale are in western Colorado, southwestern Wyoming, and eastern Utah. Secondary deposits are found in Nevada, Indiana, Ohio, Kentucky, West Virginia, and Pennsylvania. The oil yield from these shales varies from 15 to 60 gallons per ton of shale, and yields of gasoline from 35 to 55 percent have been obtained by the cracking process. Only small pilot plants have utilized oil shales up to 1964.

Natural gas can be converted to liquid hydrocarbon by first changing it to carbon monoxide and hydrogen, which are the raw materials for the gas synthesis process. Small commercial plants have operated in Kansas and Oklahoma for more than a decade. Although gas reserves are fairly large, natural gas is usually considered too valuable as a gas to use it to supplement the petroleum reserves.

In the manufacture of coke and coal gas, 10 to 12 gallons of tar and 3 gallons of light oil are obtained in the high-temperature carbonization of one ton of coal, and 20 to 35 gallons of tar are obtained in the low-temperature carbonization of one ton of coal. Much of this tar is now used as a liquid fuel at the steel plants. At present, however, this is not a practical method to produce large quantities of liquid fuels, for the yield of oil is too low in relation to the quantity of coal consumed.

Two processes for the direct production of synthetic fuels from coal or lignite have been developed. These are the coal hydrogenation, or Berguis-I. G. process, and the gas synthesis, or Fischer-Tropsch process. Liquid fuel is the primary product of both processes with combustible gases and waxes as by-products.

In the coal hydrogenation process the large reserves of high-volatile coal of Ohio, Indiana, western Kentucky, and Illinois and the subbituminous and lignite of the Great Plains are potentially of value. Subbituminous coal is the only grade that can be used at present until improved processes are developed. One ton of high-volatile bituminous coal will yield from 1.43 to 1.79 barrels of gasoline; one ton of subbituminous coal will yield approximately 1.11 barrels of gasoline, and one ton of lignite will yield 0.8 barrels of gasoline. Coal can be hydrogenated directly to gasoline, but it is possible to produce diesel fuels as well as some grades of lubricating oil and wax. By conventional high-pressure hydrogenation, a gasoline of 70- to 75-octane rating can be produced in 20 to 25 percent yield.

The gas synthesis, or Fischer-Tropsch, process has a much wider application to greater varieties of raw materials, including coal, coke, lignite, coal gas, natural gas, charcoal, and wood. The yield of gasoline from bituminous coal is about 2.3 barrels per ton and from subbituminous about 1.7 barrels. The gasoline from American reserves of coal alone would be approximately several thousand billion barrels. The straight-run gasoline, constituting about 60 percent of the total, would have an octane number of about 50 to 55. Other products include diesel oil, lubricating oils, and waxes.

Petroleum Consumption. In consuming petroleum and its products, motorists frequently forget that they are using an irreplaceable natural resource. Largely because of the cheapness of cars and of motor fuel, the United States has become the world's greatest per capita consumer of petroleum. Motoring within the United States during 1963 was equivalent to about 20 million trips around the earth. It is commonly known that greater mileage per gallon of gasoline can be obtained if the speed is only moderately fast. Through reasonable reduction of speed it is estimated that 10 percent of the more than 65,500,000,000 gallons of gasoline consumed in 1962 could have been saved.

It is also estimated that another 10 percent could have been saved by eliminating much needless driving, such as short drives in cities and seeking a parking place, and by keeping pleasure riding within reasonable limits. The conservation of about 13,000,000,000 gallons of motor fuel would be saved for worthwhile projects. It is also common practice for filling station attendants to destroy oil that has motor sludge and dirt in it. This oil has nearly as much fuel value as new oil and should be used in heating plants and incinerators. Most carburetors on American cars are inefficient utilizers of gasoline. It is asserted that if carburetors were properly adjusted on all cars, there would be a saving of another $400,000,000 on our annual fuel bill. Conservation is the effort to ensure the maximum present and future benefits from the use of natural resources. It is the obligation of every citizen to use our rich heritage with maximum efficiency and minimum waste.

NATURAL GAS

Value and Uses of Natural Gas. Natural gas has been called "Nature's most perfect fuel." Its use as a raw material in industry and as a domestic fuel has had a phenomenal expansion in the past decade and promises continuing growth in the foreseeable future. The value of marketed natural gas has risen from nearly $200,000,000 in 1920 to $652,000,000 in 1947, $3,626,046,000 in 1955 to $7,144,690,000 in 1962. The use of natural gas is increasing more rapidly than the use of other natural fuels. The industrial users consume about two-thirds of the total marketed natural gas for the manufacture of gasoline, petrochemicals, and carbon black, as a fuel for Portland cement and electric power utility plants, and in oil and gas field operations.

Domestic and commercial heating and cooling, now using over 30 percent of the natural gas consumed, constitute the second largest outlet. In the space-heating field the increase in the use of natural gas has been striking. In 1962, the four largest consuming states, Texas, California, Louisiana, and Illinois, took 45 percent of the natural gas marketed. Millions of cubic feet of gas were also transported from the southwestern gas fields to the northeastern market.

Trends of Production, Distribution, and Reserves. It has been estimated that commercial gas production from the early 1800's to January 1, 1963 was 210.1 trillion cubic feet. The trend of production has been constantly upward from nearly 339 billion feet in 1906 to a peak of 13.8 trillion cubic feet in 1962.

The United States has an abundant supply of natural gas. Production has been developed in 31 states, but Texas produces about 44 percent of the total. The proven, recoverable reserves of natural gas as of January 1, 1963 were 273.7 trillion cubic feet. The reserves were classified as follows: 199.7 trillion cubic feet of free gas not in contact with crude oil, 43.5 trillion cubic feet of free gas in contact with crude oil, and 29.5 trillion cubic feet of gas in solution in crude oil. Reserves have greatly increased since 1925, largely as a result of discoveries in the Southwest and in California.

There are now important natural gas regions in the United States: Appalachian, Midcontinent, Gulf coast, and California. The Appalachian gas fields include all areas east of central Ohio and northeast of central Alabama. This is the oldest gas-producing area in the United States, and many fields have passed their peak production. West Virginia is the largest producer followed by Pennsylvania and Kentucky.

The Midcontinent and Gulf coast fields have increased their 19 percent of the total production in 1906 to 88 percent in 1962. Developments have been most rapid in Texas, Louisiana, and New Mexico. The California natural gas production rose from 0.03 percent of the nation's total in 1906 to 14 percent in 1948, but declined to about 5.4 percent in 1962.

Conservation of Natural Gas. WASTE OF NATURAL GAS. The ease of recovery and the bountiful supply of natural gas, frequently with a limited market, have often resulted in an exorbitant waste of this valuable mineral fuel. Until 1918 the waste of natural gas was usually equal to the consumption. Although the value of natural gas is now recognized, tremendous waste still continues. It has been estimated that, if the gas wastage in the oil and gas fields of the Texas Panhandle alone were utilized as a fuel for a large electric generating plant, 2,575,000 horsepower could be produced every hour. This power would be almost four times the total output of the Grand Coulee Dam and power plant.

The wastes of natural gas are many and have frequently been intentional. One of the most important causes of waste lies in the common practice of allowing gas to escape freely from oil wells, for this usually increases the immediate yield of oil. Because many oil fields have no facilities for marketing this gas, it is allowed to escape into the atmosphere. In some areas the natural gas has been withdrawn from the reservoir as quickly as possible in order to prevent its capture by adjacent producers. In the making of by-products from natural gas, such as carbon black and gasoline, the residue gases are frequently wasted although they may contain as much as 97 percent of the original heating value of the gas.

CONSERVATION MEASURES. The gas industry is now regulated by local, state, and federal authorities. The power of these commissions is limited to the wording of the legislative acts, by judicial review of the commissions, and the constitutional injunctions against confiscation of property and discriminatory treatment. The local control of natural gas is normally through franchises. These are rights granted by a municipality authorizing a private person to engage in public utility business and to use public property for private profit.

Control of the natural gas industry in a state is today normally by a state commission. The commission with its large staffs has greater ability to cope with the intricate, technical problems of the industry than its forerunner. Today most states have statutes under which a commission is empowered to enforce conservational programs. Although programs vary, provision is generally made for control of the number and location of wells to be drilled, the method of drilling, completing and producing the wells, and the quantity of production. Control of the quantity of production, better known as proration, involves regulation of the level of production as well as the division of production among well owners.

On the national level Congress passed the Natural Gas Act in 1938. The Supreme Court has interpreted the purpose of this act to be "the prevention of the exploitation of the consumer at the hands of the natural gas companies" and thus requires a comprehensive system of controlling the natural gas industry from the individual well to the consumer. Conservation of natural gas has advanced because control of the interstate transportation phase of the natural gas industry under the Natural Gas Act is complete.

ATOMIC ENERGY

Fundamental research and study of atomic energy have been going on for several decades. However, the great concentration of effort has come since July, 1942 with the development of atomic energy in the weapons' program. Although the mineral fuels have been conspicuously developed by private enterprises, it has been recognized almost unanimously from the beginning that nuclear energy must be socialized. In 1946 when the Atomic Energy Commission was established, complete government control of the industry was not disputed. The only question was which government agency should handle this new source of power.

Sources of Nuclear Energy. At the present time atomic energy is developed chiefly from uranium and thorium. Uranium constitutes 0.008 percent of the earth's crust and is therefore twice as abundant as zinc, four times as abundant as lead, and many times more common than tin, silver, or gold. The spectrograph and Geiger-Müller counter detect it in most granite and sedimentary rocks. However, the mineral is rarely found in concentrated form, but ore containing a low content of uranium is practically limitless. The most important ores containing uranium include uraninite, pitchblende, davidite, carnotite, and autunite.

The largest deposits of uranium in the United States are in the carnotite ores on the Colorado Plateau of western Colorado, eastern Utah, northeastern Arizona, and northwestern Mexico (Fig. 11). The ores were first developed between 1910 and 1920. In the 1920's as a result of the lowered radium prices, operations were reduced, and in the 1930's uranium was recovered only as a by-product of vanadium. The ore contains 2 to 4 percent U_3O_8.

In the United States the reserves of U_3O_8 is estimated by the U.S. Geological Survey to range from 2100 billion to 6900 billion tons of coal equivalent. The larger figure is greater than the world's known resources of coal, oil and gas combined. If the much lower-grade ores are included, such as granite, man can be said to have an almost unlimited supply of energy.[16] Thorium deposits are found in northwestern United States at Central, Idaho, and along the southeastern Atlantic coast of North and South Carolina, and Florida.

Peacetime Uses of Atomic Energy. The spectacular development and use of the atomic bomb for war purposes have frequently overshadowed the uses of atomic energy for man's benefits. Nevertheless, a peacetime atomic industry has grown to significant proportion.[17]

A major area of research has been directed toward the development of atomic power stations. At the beginning of 1964 there were seventeen atomic power plants with an electrical capacity of 4000 kilowatts or larger in operation in the United States, five additional plants were under construction, and seven more were under contract negotiation as planned. Up to 1964 the federal government had spent about $1,300,000,000 and private industry approximately $700,000,000 for atomic power plants. There are now 1,025,000 kilowatt hours of installed capacity in atomic plants.

The future growth of atomic power plants will depend on its competitive cost position in relation to that of conventional power plants. A report of the Atomic Energy Commission in 1963 indicated that atomic power would become competitive with conventional sources of power throughout most of the United States in the 1970's and by 1980 would generate nearly 10 percent of the nation's electricity. It also forecast that in 2000 A.D. all new electric power plants and half of all the electricity then being generated in this country would be nuclear.

The development of isotopes has advanced

[16] Sam H. Schurr, "Energy," *Scientific American*, Vol. 209, September 1963, p. 124.

[17] "Exploding Realm of the Peaceful Atom," *Steel*, Vol. 153, August 19, 1963, pp. 44–51.

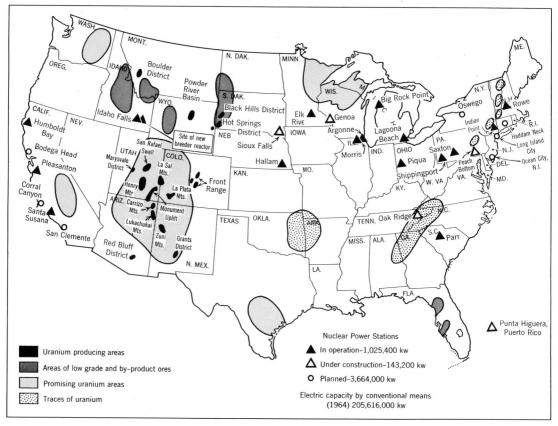

Fig. 11   Sources of uranium and location of nuclear power stations in the United States. (Compiled from various sources.)

rapidly in recent years but is still in its infancy of application. Today the annual value of isotopes is about $5,000,000. The processors of isotopes and the manufacturers of devices to handle them now have an annual business of about $25,000,000. Industry is the leading consumer of isotopes today. Their application is in irradiation and thermal uses. Irradiation can pasturize, sterilize, diagnose, heal, change the atomic structure of materials, and create new materials. Significant applications of isotopes have now been achieved. Radioactive tracers are decreasing the time required to clean rust, mill scale, and other deposits from pipelines. Isotopes in nuclear gauges measure metal thickness and are providing new data in cutting tool wear. Polyethylene pipe and film becomes stronger and more heat resistant when exposed to low radiation doses. A synthetic detergent has been produced by exposing petroleum-derived raw materials to gamma rays. Unlike conventional detergents it is easily decomposed by bacteria in rivers and sewage systems. A new technique known as neutron activation analysis is believed to be the most accurate method known to determine the composition of most materials.

Thermal uses of isotopes by converting the heat generated into electricity may be as significant as that of irradiation. Thermal applications are already in operation. It has been applied to automated, unmanned weather stations. At the present time the United States has isotopic powered stations at both poles. The one in the Arctic is so highly automated that the only moving parts are the hands of a chronometer. Everything else is solid-state electronics.

There have been some significant advances in the use of atomic energy for the propulsion of movable objects. The navy has four atomic ships in its surface fleet, including the carrier *Enterprise*. In 1963 the Navy authorized the building of twelve new atomic submarines, bringing to total built, under construction, and planned to eighty-seven. The atomic submarines are truly submersible in that they can operate completely independent of the atmosphere above the sea's surface. They can operate submerged, therefore, just as long as their personnel can endure submergence. The Atomic Energy Commission and the Maritime Administration also envisage the development of a nuclear merchant marine.

Within the next decade the nuclear space program may become a leading atomic energy market. The National Aeronautics and Space Administration believes that beyond lunar landings, it will be difficult to go anywhere in space without nuclear propulsion. Studies are now in progress to convert heat generated by the reactor into electricity via thermoelectricity, thermionics, or magnetohydrodynamics in order to provide a reliable, large, on-board source of power for spacecraft.

By the early 1960's the importance of the atom to better living conditions in the world had become clear.[18] The use of atomic energy has graduated from the laboratory and has moved into the production plant, with the result that the products of atomic science are being used by the average citizen not only in the United States but in every country of the world.

[18] D. B. Lombard, "Plowshare: A Program for the Peaceful Uses of Nuclear Explosives," *Physics Today*, Vol. 14, October 1961, pp. 23–34.

GENERAL SUMMARY

Our high industrial productivity has been made possible largely by the availability and utilization of our power resources. Our energy consumption has increased more than twelve times since 1870, so that today every man, woman, and child has the equivalent of over 100 slaves working 8 hours each day for him. This has resulted in high productivity which is the first essential of a high standard of living.

Our mineral fuels are still abundant; nevertheless they are irreplaceable and limited in quantity. Coal will retain a substantial position in supplying the nation's fuel. Technical advancements will continue to develop further economies and conveniences in utilization. Because we have a relatively small quantity of coking coals, these should be reserved for metallurgical uses where other coals cannot be substituted. The use of all other coals for steam generation should be encouraged. Our petroleum supply will be depleted relatively soon. Therefore our natural petroleum should be reserved for motor fuels and lubricating needs, and its use as a boiler fuel should be discouraged. This will delay the time when our petroleum needs will have to be satisfied from synthetic oils at possibly considerably higher costs. Natural gas should be reserved for domestic and specialized industrial uses, including conversion into chemicals in regions where coal is lacking. The development of atomic energy in the coming decades may change the energy pattern of the United States. However, this change will be gradual and atomic energy will supplement, rather than displace, our mineral fuels for years to come.

The use of our power facilities can be expected to increase in the future. This will mean a rise in the production of capital and consumer goods to heights never before reached. Consequently, we can expect a higher standard of living to be attained than in any previous period of history.

References

Gatlin, Carl, *Petroleum Engineering: Drilling and Well Completions*, Prentice-Hall, Englewood Cliffs, New Jersey, 1960.

Landsberg, Hans H., Leonard H. Fischman, and Joseph L. Fisher, *Resources in America's Future*, Resources for the Future, Washington, D.C., 1963.

Leeston, Alfred M., John A. Crichton, and John C. Jacobs, *The Dynamic Natural Gas Industry*, University of Oklahoma Press, Norman, Oklahoma, 1963.

Mason, Edward S. et al., *Energy Requirements and Economic Growth*, National Planning Association, Washington, D.C., 1955.

Netschert, Bruce C., *The Future Supply of Oil and Gas*, Resources for the Future, Washington, D.C., 1958.

Nind, T. E. W., *Principles of Oil Well Production*, McGraw-Hill Book Co., New York, 1964.

Petroleum Facts and Figures, American Petroleum Institute, New York, 1963.

Potter, Neal, and Francis T. Christy, Jr., *Trends in Natural Resource Commodities*, Resources for the Future, Washington, D.C., 1962.

Riley, Charles M., *Our Mineral Resources*, John Wiley and Sons, New York, 1959.

Schurr, Sam H., and Bruce C. Netschert, *Energy in the American Economy, 1850–1975*, Resources for the Future, Washington, D.C., 1960.

Sell, George, *The Petroleum Industry*, Oxford University Press, New York, 1963.

Symposium on Petroleum Economics and Valuation, Society of Petroleum Engineers, Dallas, Texas, 1962.

Williamson, Harold F., Ralph L. Andreano, Arnold R. Daum, and Gilbert C. Klose, *The American Petroleum Industry: 1899–1959 The Age of Energy*, Northwestern University Press, Evanston, Illinois, 1963.

Zimmermann, Erich W., *Conservation in the Production of Petroleum*, Yale University Press, New Haven, Connecticut, 1957.

Part 6

CHARLES A. DAMBACH
The Ohio State University

CHAPTER 18

Conservation of Wildlife

The conservation of wildlife means the wise use and management of nondomesticated animals for the benefit of all the people. Both game and nongame species and those that sometimes are inimical to man's interest are included in this definition. Game and fish management are specialized branches of the field of wildlife conservation. Their objective is the maintenance of an adequate supply of game, fish, and fur to meet the demands of those who seek wild animals for sport and profit.

Nongame species are usually considered incidental by-products of game management. Their welfare otherwise is largely dependent on the efforts of interested individuals, private organizations, and such government agencies as the United States Fish and Wildlife Service and the National Park Service, which are supported by funds available through taxation.

IMPORTANCE OF
WILDLIFE RESOURCES

Early History. Native wild animals are an integral part of our American heritage. Their utilization for food, clothing, and barter was vital to the success of the colonists and later to

the opening of the West. They made possible the establishment of many pioneer settlements. Many of the early explorations and discoveries which opened up the interior of the United States were made by trappers seeking new sources of fur for foreign trade. Wild animals were an important source of food for man as recently as the westward expansion of the railroads during the two or three decades following 1830. During this period, for example, about 250,000 bison were killed annually, largely to supply meat for crews building the railroads.

Food. We have long since passed the time when wild animals were of importance in meeting our food or clothing needs. Although the annual kill of present-day game species is enormous in the aggregate, it falls far short of meeting annual food needs. The dressed weight of all big game animals taken annually in continental United States is estimated to be one pound per person. The white-tailed and mule deers account for three-fourths of this total. The dressed weight of all small game is estimated to be less than a pound per person and much of it is wasted.

Fish for Food and Pleasure. The estimated retail value of domestic fisheries in the United

391

States for the year 1962 totaled $1,181,000,000.[1] In the same year fish imports had a retail value $785,000,000. The domestic commercial fish catch for that year was 5,240,000,000 pounds or a little less than 30 pounds per capita. Approximately half this amount was used directly for human food. The other half was converted to such commercial purposes as animal food, fertilizer, marine animal oil, and glue. Although the United States catch of fishes has increased 17 percent in the past decade, it has declined in relation to population growth. In the same period fish and fish product imports have increased substantially and now represent nearly 50 percent of the total United States supply. This country continues, however, to rank fifth among the fishing nations of the world, being preceded by Japan, Peru, China (mainland), and the U.S.S.R.

The principal fisheries industries are located along our Atlantic and Pacific coasts and the Gulf coast. The Pacific region and Alaska alone produced 82 percent of the canned fish pack. The Atlantic coast produced 16 percent, and the Gulf states 2 percent. Our fresh-water fisheries exclusive of the Great Lakes are of importance primarily for recreational fishing.

Although many millions of pounds of fish are taken annually by anglers, they add little in the aggregate to the nation's food supply. Their principal value is the recreation provided for the more than 25,000,000 persons who fish for fun, which in turn generates expenditures for related goods and services approximating $3,000,000,-000.[2] This is a third more than the value of the combined domestic commercial catch and foreign fish imports.

Fur. Wild furs, although no longer a home necessity, still provide a modest source of income for thousands of trappers and part-time

[1] E. A. Power, *Fisheries of the United States*, C.F.S. Number 3200, U.S. Department of Interior, Washington, D.C., 1962.

[2] Anonymous. *1960 National Survey of Fishing and Hunting*, Circular 120, Bureau of Sport Fisheries and Wildlife, Fish and Wildlife Service, U.S. Department of Interior, Washington, D.C., 1961.

income for many farm boys. The aggregate value of wild trapped fur from forty-one reporting states in 1962 was $12,500,000.

Wild trapped furs prior to World War II made up 85 percent of the total raw fur value. Subsequently the fur market became glutted with long-haired furs, such as foxes, wolves, skunks, and raccoons. Prices on these species dropped to such low levels that few trappers troubled to catch them. Prices on short-haired furs, such as muskrat and mink, have remained fairly steady.

Populations of long-haired fur-bearing animals, particularly fox and raccoon, have reached high levels throughout much of their range. Other species, notably otters, martens, and fishers, remain relatively scarce and command good prices. Beaver, at one time the backbone of the wild-fur trade, are again becoming common in areas where they had been absent for decades.

Fur prices fluctuate greatly as styles, economic conditions, and supplies have changed and as acceptable substitutes have been developed. Increased knowledge of genetic principles and nutritional requirements of fur-bearing animals has made fur farming a profitable venture for persons skilled in this field. It is probable that commercial fur farms may within a few decades provide the principal source of raw furs for the American market.

Since the end of World War I, the United States has been the leading producer of furs among the countries of the world and is now the center of the fur industry. The retail fur trade in the United States which results from processing native and imported furs annually exceeds $300,000,000. This is a decline of 25 percent from the estimated value a decade ago.

Biological Value. Modern insecticides, rodenticides, and herbicides, such as DDT, malathion, methoxychlor, and parathion for insects, 2-4D for weed control, and ANTU for rodents, have made possible some control of pests heretofore reduced largely by natural enemies. Forest insects, such as the spruce budworm, larch sawfly and bark beetles, have been brought under control by use of new insecticides.

Many of our native and introduced wild animals consume great quantities of injurious insects, weed seeds, and rodent pests. The following are only a few of the many examples that appear abundantly in the literature of economic zoology. Forbush estimated that birds in 1921 reduced the cost of insect damage in this country by $444,000,000 annually.[3] Bryant credited the meadowlarks in the Sacramento Valley of California when feeding their young with the daily consumption of 193 tons of insects.[4] McAtee estimated that on a single North Carolina farm native finches daily ate more than 900,000 aphids during an outbreak of these insects.[5] During their lifetime, insect-eating mammals, particularly moles and shrews, also consume great quantities of insects.

Many of our hawks and owls feed primarily on such destructive rodents as house mice, rats, meadow mice, ground squirrels, and gophers. Larger mammals, such as foxes, skunks, and weasels, also feed extensively on these injurious animals as do some kinds of snakes. Unfortunately some of these predators occasionally feed on beneficial species of wild animals and domestic livestock, particularly poultry.

Although many birds feed extensively on weed seeds, it is doubtful if they are as valuable in destroying the seeds as are field-inhabiting rodents, which thoroughly grind their food before swallowing it. The seeds of such plants as red cedar, dogwood, and hackberry, for example, pass unharmed through the digestive tract of birds and may in this manner become established in places where they are unwanted.

Injurious Habits. Not all wild animals are beneficial to man. House mice, rats, and other rodents are charged with an annual destruction of $1,000,000,000 worth of property in the United States. Predatory animals take their toll of livestock also. Throughout the country, poul-

try farmers suffer from raids by rats, weasels, mink, skunks, foxes, and predatory birds. The cattle and sheep men of the western plains and mountain ranges suffer losses from large predatory animals, including coyotes, wolves, mountain lions, and an occasional marauding bear. Because of their burrowing habits, muskrats are sometimes responsible for breaks in dams and levees; ground hogs, badgers, gophers, and prairie dogs cause considerable damage by digging dens in crop fields, pastures, and road fills.

A problem of increasing concern in some areas is the damage to grain crops by blackbirds, bobolinks, crows, wild ducks and geese, and to fruit by starlings and other birds (Fig. 1).

Fig. 1   Wildlife, including such species as the red-winged blackbird, the bob-o-link, and certain diminutive warblers may under some circumstances do damage to crops. Ripening corn, as shown in this photograph, is often attacked by red-winged blackbirds, skunks and raccoon, and other animals also may cause serious damage to this crop. Under such conditions control measures are necessary. Wildlife management thus necessitates practices to regulate the abundance of wildlife so that it is beneficial and not harmful to man's interests.

[3] Edward H. Forbush, *The Utility of Birds*, Massachusetts Department of Agriculture, Bulletin 9, 1921.

[4] Harold C. Bryant, *Economic Value of the Western Meadowlark in California*, University of California Agriculture Experiment Station, Bulletin 236, Berkeley, 1913, p. 12.

[5] W. L. McAtee, *Yearbook*, United States Department of Agriculture, Washington, D.C., 1912, pp. 397–404.

Wild animals are known to serve as reservoirs of disease for both man and domestic livestock. Probably the best known is tularemia or rabbit fever, a sometimes fatal disease contracted by human beings from infected rabbits or other wild animals.

Recreational Value. According to a national survey hunters and fishermen annually spend within the United States nearly 4.0 billion dollars in the pursuit of their sport. The significance of these expenditures is apparent when it is noted that it is at a level greater than that expended for any one of such necessary services as household use of electricity, home telephone and telegraph

Fig. 2 An archer from the "States" and his guide in a New Brunswick forest. Millions of dollars are expended annually for guide services, equipment, transportation, lodging, meals, licenses, and other costs related to utilizing wildlife resources for recreation.

service, physicians services, or for radio and television receivers and records. Expenditures for hunting and fishing are much greater than those estimated to be expended for all spectator amusements including movies, theater, concerts, and sports.

The survey showed that more than 30,000,000 persons 12 years of age or older in the United States enjoy hunting or fishing or both, and the number is growing. It has increased by 5,000,000 since a similar study was conducted in 1955. One in every three households in the United States had one or more hunters or fishermen. To enjoy these sports they spent $2,360,000,000 for equipment, such as guns, ammunition, fishing tackle, and special clothing. Another $560,000,000 was expended for travel, and license fees totaled $120,000,000.

Many persons enjoy wildlife for aesthetic reasons only and gain their pleasure through observation and study (Fig. 2). This interest provides a market for the makers of photographic equipment and supplies, for the binocular, field-glass, and telescope manufacturers, the publishers of natural history books, the manufacturers of outdoor clothing, and many other businesses large and small that are dependent on wildlife resources in part, at least, for marketing their services and products.

INVENTORY OF WILDLIFE RESOURCES

The Past. The first white men to set foot on what is now the United States entered a country that abounded with wild animals of many kinds. They found in the eastern seaboard areas an abundance of white-tailed deer, elk, wild turkey, and such smaller animals as ruffed grouse, heath hen, and gray squirrel, which provided food in quantities. A like abundance of fish in the streams and natural lakes also provided food for those who sought to take them by net, spear, poison, and hook. Wild ducks of many kinds, geese, and shore birds frequenting the waterways during their spring and fall migrations and their nesting season afforded another source of food. Inhabiting the waterways and wilderness areas were fur bearers such as beaver, otter, fisher, marten, muskrat, and mink, whose pelts were shipped in great numbers to European ports in exchange for goods needed by the early colonists. Also present were bears, mountain lions, wolves, wildcats, lesser predatory animals, and rodents, which raided the herds of livestock and ravished the gardens and fields of the pioneers.

Under these conditions, a public attitude developed that wildlife resources were limitless, that they could be utilized fully without restraint or concern for the future, and that wildlife inimical to the interests of man was to be eliminated by the most effective means at hand. This pattern of unrestraint was repeated again and again as civilization spread westward. When the Ohio Valley was reached, large numbers of grouse, wild pigeon, waterfowl, and the furs of beaver, otter, muskrat, and other animals were sent to the eastern markets. The supply appeared to be limitless.

Pushing still farther westward, the pioneers found on the great prairies and plains in the heart of America an abundance of grass-feeding animals. American bison in great droves extended as far as a man could see; estimates of their numbers ranged from 15,000,000 to more than 50,000,000. Prong-horned antelope lived on the plains in numbers equal to, if not greater than, the bison. Elk, deer, and small game including quail, prairie chicken, and sharp-tailed grouse were present the year around. In the sloughs, marshes, and waterways, vast flocks of waterfowl and shore birds congregated. This vast abundance of wildlife was quickly reduced by killing for food, sport, and clothing. Grain production and grazing also contributed to the loss until the region is now one of the poorest big-game areas in all North America.

The wilds of the western mountains were opened and exploited before the vast herds of buffalo and antelope had been reduced on the plains. Here animals were fewer but more varied than on the plains. There were elk, mule deer, black and grizzly bear, mountain sheep, mountain goat, wild turkey, grouse, beaver, many kinds of squirrels, and other lesser animals, and large predators such as wolves and mountain lions wherever deer herds were found. In the desert regions game was scarce except for trout in some of the cold streams which had their sources outside the desert area and except for vast flocks of waterfowl in marsh areas. As the westward expansion reached the Pacific Ocean, the last remaining virgin populations of wild animals were tapped. The trout of high mountain streams, the salmon of coastal rivers, the waterfowl of the Pacific flyway, and the sea otters and seals of the Pacific coast were rapidly exploited.

The Vanished and the Survivors. The heavy heel of civilization crushed deeply into our once vast stores of wildlife resources. Among the victims of our expansion were the great auk, the Labrador duck, the heath hen, the Carolina paroquet, the passenger pigeon, the Pennsylvania bison, several races of the grizzly bear, the Audubon big-horn sheep, the big plains wolf, the big sea mink, the Gull Island meadow mouse, and probably the Eskimo curlew, and the Cape Sable seaside sparrow. At the present time about 55 species of wild animals are declining or are in actual danger of extinction. Approximately 100 key deer and 700 trumpeter swans are known to exist in the United States, while the known number of whooping cranes on the North American continent is less than 30.

In a few species, the trend has been reversed. Prong-horned antelope, white-tailed deer, fur-seals, and egrets are examples of animals that have partially or wholly recovered from low population levels.

No single cause can explain the decline of all American wildlife. Market hunting was probably the chief cause for the decline of gregarious birds like the passenger pigeon, Eskimo curlew, and many species of ducks. Passenger pigeons were killed by the thousands in their roosts at night. Eskimo curlews were killed in great numbers during their spring and fall migrations. Ducks and shore birds were killed with specially constructed guns capable of bringing down dozens of birds at a single shot. The great buffalo herds were decimated by hunters seeking the hides for sale or the choice parts for food. Many were killed merely for sport. The whaling, sealing, and fishing industries accounted for the decline of fish, seals, whales, and manatees, and fishermen along the North Atlantic coast were responsible for wiping out the colonies of the great auk and the Labrador duck. Plume hunters nearly caused the extinction of the snowy egret and the reddish egret and reduced many other species before their activities were outlawed. Aquatic resources declined because of the pollution of streams and lakes by industrial and mine wastes, raw sewage from cities, silt from eroding farm fields, and over-fishing of some species. Draining of swamplands, clearing of forests, and the development of grasslands so altered the environment that animals unable to adjust to the changes could not survive. Misuse of the land accelerated erosion and intensified the effects of floods and drought. As a consequence, the capacity of the soil to support both human and wildlife populations was reduced. These factors are of equal or greater importance than the more evident ones previously considered (Fig. 3).

Although the toll of wildlife that fell before the guns, clubs, nets, and traps of man was enormous, not all of it was wasted. Much of the kill was used in helping to meet the food needs of a growing nation and in aiding the development of commerce. We must recognize also that the vast herds of bison which roamed the plains, the deer, elk, bear, wild turkey, the grouse of the eastern forests and central hardwood region, and the mule deer, panthers, and grizzly bear of our western forests could not, even with complete protection, exist now under intensive cultivation and grazing of land necessary to our civilization.

Present Wildlife Resources. Despite the decline of many species, the wildlife resources

Fig. 3   The beaver house, once common on streams and natural lakes in early America, is now found principally in remote areas. Recently, however, under rigid protection, they have returned to some well-populated regions.

of the United States are still vast, and some species are more plentiful today than at any time in recorded history, especially on farms and ranches. The several races of cottontail rabbits, quail, muskrats, field-inhabiting songbirds (Fig. 4), and introduced game birds (pheasants and Hungarian partridges) have been benefited by the clearing of the forests and the development of mechanized agriculture. More than 80 percent of the land available for wildlife production in the entire United States is farm or ranch land.[6] We probably now harvest annually most of the surplus crop of upland game, much of which previously went unharvested for lack of interest or need. Some animals are still being overused, whereas others are not utilized sufficiently to keep their numbers within the capacity of their environments to support them. Big-game mammals such as deer and elk under too rigid protection soon overpopulate their range.

Known wild vertebrate animals total more than 35,000 species.[7] Of these about 18,000 are fish; 5500 are reptiles and amphibians including frogs, toads and salamanders, snakes, lizards and turtles; 8600 are birds (Fig. 5); 3500 are mammals. The North American fauna, especially that of the United States, is unusually rich in number of species. Even in the intensively farmed and highly industrialized midwestern states, the variety and abundance of wildlife is surprising. The State of Ohio, for example, is known to have at least 171 kinds of fish, 32 kinds of frogs, toads and salamanders, 39 kinds of reptiles, 180 kinds of nesting birds, and at least 65 kinds of mammals. On a single well-managed 100-acre farm in the same state, we can expect to find 50 to 60 kinds of wild animals totaling 2000 to 3000 individuals.

Farm Wildlife. Our present wildlife resources can probably best be understood by considering the abundance and variety of ani-

Fig. 4 Many native woodland birds, like this chicadee, have become accustomed to urban areas and utilize manmade facilities for nesting places. They may be found in many residential districts, as well as in parks and remaining natural woodlands. Although there are no available statistics on the subject, it is probable that more people enjoy observing wildlife of this kind than participating in hunting and fishing.

mals in relation to the class of land that they occupy. Of first importance in this classification is farm wildlife, which provides approximately 68 percent of the total game kill.[8] The principal kinds of farm game are the cottontail rabbit, squirrels, bobwhite quail, the ring-necked pheasant, and the Hungarian partridge. These species annually provide the bulk of the recreational hunting throughout the country. Farm wildlife also includes many of our songbirds and other nongame animals which are enjoyed by great numbers of people and such fur bearers as opossums, skunks, and weasels. Farm game animals primarily occupy land owned privately and managed for profit and are often only a by-product of farming operations.

[6] J. Paul Miller and Burwell B. Powell, *Game and Wild-Fur Production and Utilization on Agricultural Land,* Circular No. 636, United States Department of Agriculture, Washington, D.C., 1942, pp. 1–58.

[7] Ernst Mayr, "The Number of Species of Birds," *Auk,* Vol. 63, 1946, pp. 64–69.

[8] Miller and Powell, *op. cit.,* p. 29.

Fig. 5 Migratory birds, including song, insectivors, waterfowl, and shore birds are protected by federal laws. Some of these birds, like the woodcock shown in this photograph, are especially subject to decimation in areas where earthworms have accumulated toxic levels of insecticides applied for injurious insect control. Other earthworm-eating birds like robins may also be affected in such areas.

Fig. 6 A common "city bird" is the eastern mourning dove. This young bird was reared in a spruce tree at the front entrance of a house on a busy city street. It is also a highly prized "game bird" in the South.

398

As increasing areas of farmland are taken over for urban purposes the composition of the wildlife population is subject to changes. Rabbits and squirrels may continue to occupy the same areas, but as dogs become more numerous as the urban area is more closely settled the rabbit population diminishes. Squirrels may continue to be relatively abundant in certain sections of a city providing that nut-bearing trees are abundant and other habitat conditions are favorable. The suburban areas, especially where food is provided, may have a variety of birds including the cardinal, the mourning dove, robins, the mocking birds, and many others depending on the geographical location of the area (Fig. 6).

Wildlife of the Forest and Range. Forest and range wildlife includes most of the important big-game animals: white-tailed deer (Fig. 7), mule-deer, black-tailed deer, antelope, and black bear. Nearly one-half of the total are white-tailed deer, one-half of which are in eastern states (Table 1). Forest and range wildlife also includes wild turkey, sharp-tailed grouse, ruffed grouse, sage hen, western quail, and gray and other squirrels. The coyotes, wolves, gray foxes, bobcats, and black bears that enter the fur trade come largely from forest and rangeland. Although they and the big-game animals are principally species of forest and rangeland, they are relatively abundant on land that is used in

Fig. 7   The white-tailed deer is the most important big-game animal in the United States. They are becoming more abundant in areas recently retired from agricultural use. Where such areas border land used for agriculture, deer damage to crops frequently results. (Photograph by E. E. Good, The Ohio State University.)

Table 1. Big Game Kill in the United States in 1961

Species	Number
White-tailed deer	867,764
Mule deer	814,977
Black-tailed deer	158,253
Elk	77,905
Pronghorn antelope	75,645
Wild turkey	75,398
Black bear	20,430
Moose	13,363
Peccary	5,643
Grizzly bear	515

[Source: Leaflet 446, Bureau of Sports Fisheries and Wildlife, September, 1962.]

part for agricultural purposes. These areas provide about 21 percent of the total annual game kill.

The Wilderness Refuge. Wilderness widlife includes those animals that occupy relatively remote and inaccessible areas like the high mountain ranges and unexploited forested or swampy land. They are greatly restricted in distribution and are nowhere abundant. Among the better-known species are elk, grizzly bear, moose, mountain sheep, mountain goat, ivory-billed woodpecker, and trumpeter swan, and such fur bearers as the lynx, fisher, marten, and wolverine.

Migratory Wildlife. Migratory wildlife inhabits all classes of land. It includes most of our common song and insectivorous birds and such game species as shore birds, ducks, geese, and doves. Although providing only about 11 percent of the total annual game kill, these game birds, because of their spectacular migratory flights and the national and international problems involved in their management, often attract more interest than more abundant species. Various species of waterfowl nest in the wet prairies and marshes of northern United States or Canada and winter in the coastal marshes of southern United States, Mexico, and Central America. Thus at least three countries are frequently involved in the production, protection, and utilization of a single mobile resource. Four well-established flyway routes are followed by these birds in their flights to and from breeding and wintering grounds: the Atlantic flyway along the Atlantic coast, the Mississippi flyway through the Mississippi Valley, the Central flyway through the Great Plains, and the Pacific flyway along the Pacific coast.

Unless drained, the nesting and wintering grounds of waterfowl and shore birds are usually of little or no agricultural or industrial value. Many millions of acres of former duck marshes have been drained and put to agricultural use, with a resultant decline in the area available for breeding and wintering grounds.

Resident Aquatic Wildlife. Resident animals which inhabit our swamps, marshes, sloughs, lakes, ponds, streams, and ditches include some of the most important fur-bearing animals. To this group belongs the muskrat, which is the most remunerative fur bearer in the United States. Beaver, mink, otter, and raccoon also occupy waterways and, like the muskrat, do much of their feeding either along the margins of water areas or in the adjacent agricultural land. Two of these animals (muskrat and the introduced nutria) make up two-thirds of the total annual fur production in the United States, which amounts to about 15,000,000 to 20,000,000 pelts.

BASIC PROBLEMS IN WILDLIFE CONSERVATION

Problems of Ownership. Present concepts of ownership and legal title to wildlife were established during our early history when nearly all wild animals were produced and harvested on publicly owned land. Now more than 75 percent of the annual harvest of game and fur comes from privately owned agricultural land. One of the basic problems in the management of wildlife stems from this change in land ownership. By common law the states hold wildlife in trust for all the people, and the people have the right to use wildlife subject only to restrictions set up by the states and the federal government for migratory species. Thus the responsibility for the welfare of wildlife rests not with each individual but with the government which has practically no opportunity to act beyond limiting the time and manner in which animals can be sought and the number that can be taken. In effect, the government can enforce regulations designed to distribute fairly the wildlife crop among the citizenry, but it can do little directly to improve the crop size since it is produced mainly on land in private ownership, primarily farms and ranches.

Farmers and ranchers have the best opportunity to provide for the welfare of wildlife but have little or no incentive to do so. The farmer who encourages wildlife production on his land runs the risk of abuse by rowdy hunters, personal inconvenience occasioned by even the most considerate hunter, and damage to livestock and crops by both hunters and wildlife; yet he has no greater legal right to use the wildlife he produces than the city sportsman. The only means at his disposal to protect himself from the hunter nuisance is to exercise his trespass rights by closing his land to hunting, trapping, or fishing. A growing number of farm and ranch operators use this means to prohibit hunting on their property. Some farmers charge a nominal fee for hunting privileges. This income often is used to assure better propery protection than state game and fish law enforcement provides. This movement has developed because the public attitude until recently had not generally supported enforcement of trespass laws adequate to afford the farmer the protection to which he feels he is entitled.

Unfortunately many sportsmen still feel that holding of a hunting or fishing license entitles them to full pursuit of their sport wherever they may find it as long as they abide by the regulations pertaining to bag limits, seasons, and legal manner of taking game.

The problem of wildlife ownership is further complicated by the fact that nearly all the state game and fish departments are financed largely by money received from the sale of hunting and fishing licenses. To enforce trespass rights with game protectors or wardens paid from these funds would in effect lead to the closing of more land to hunting and thus to a decline in the number of license-buying hunters. This conflict of interest between sportsmen and landowners is of considerable and increasing importance.

A paradoxical situation exists in that a crop produced by the landowner is widely advertised to the sportsmen by business interests which profit from the manufacture and sale of sporting goods or services.

All hunting licenses sales for continental United States increased from nearly 6 million in 1935 to 14.5 million in 1956. By 1962 the total number of licenses sold reached 18 million.

Thus we have a growing army of hunters and fishermen who annually buy more and more equipment and seek places where it can be used. Economic and social changes leading to fewer working hours, the short workweek, more and longer vacations, and better transportation facilities have all influenced this trend.

Hunting Pressure. The resulting pressure on wildlife and the land is particularly great in heavily populated states. Twelve states have less than 50 acres of total huntable area for each hunting license sold.

Most public designed recreation lands (85 percent) are open to some form of hunting. Most of this land (75 percent) is in the West. The West also has over 95 percent of the public domain lands. Although most of the public hunting land is in the West, most of the hunters (84 percent) are in the other regions. (See Tables 2 and 3.)

For the country as a whole, there are only about 115 acres of potentially huntable land per licensed hunter.

These data do not take into account the many thousands of hunters who do not buy licenses, such as farmers when hunting on their own land, exempted veterans in states granting this privilege, and local people in rural areas in those states where hunting law enforcement is lax. The figures also do not reflect the relative amount of game available per unit of area. The abundance of game is a direct function of the productiveness of the land, and for this reason more game is produced per unit of area in the Midwest than in the rougher and less fertile parts of the country. In few, if any, areas is the supply adequate to provide every hunter with all the game his license permits him to take.

In general, hunting pressure is greatest where the population is highest, but the percentage of the population that hunts and fishes is in inverse ratio to population density. This suggests that the quality of hunting declines as hunting pressure increases.

Although it is becoming increasingly apparent that hunting pressure is not the chief factor affecting the abundance of most species of wildlife, some species are especially susceptible to reduction by this means, particularly wilderness-inhabiting species and those that are intensively sought because of their superior sporting qualities or high trophy value.

Waterfowl, too, are subject to drastic population reduction by overshooting because of the high-quality sport they provide and because of their gregarious and migratory habits. During the droughts of the early 1930's the North American waterfowl population dropped to the dangerously low level of 30,000,000 birds. With stringent hunting regulations and the return of

Table 2. Number and Acreage of Nonurban Public Designated Recreation Areas Open to Hunting, by Level of Government and Type of Managing Agency, Forty-Eight Contiguous States, 1960

Level of Government and Type of Agency	Areas Open to Hunting		Acreage Open to Hunting, in Thousands of Acres	
	Number	Percent of Total	Acres	Percent of Total
Federal	(424)	(17)	(165,818)	(88)
National Park Service	5	(°)	1,787	1
U.S. Forest Service	200	8	158,002	83
Fish and Wildlife Service	80	3	3,590	2
Bureau of Reclamation	18	1	124	(°)
Corps of Engineers	121	5	2,315	1
State	(2,034)	(79)	(21,217)	(11)
Park agencies	223	9	818	(°)
Forest agencies	369	14	15,571	8
Fish and Wildlife agencies	1,407	55	4,693	2
Water development agencies	4	(°)	51	(°)
Transportation agencies	5	(°)	4	(°)
Special authorities	20	1	60	(°)
Other	6	(°)	20	(°)
Local	(95)	(4)	(2,334)	(1)
Park agencies	26	1	17	(°)
Forest agencies	35	1	2,232	1
Water development agencies	1	(°)	–	–
Special authorities	2	(°)	28	(°)
Other	31	1	57	(°)
Total, 48 states	2,553	100	189,369	100

° Less than 0.5 percent.

[Source: U.S. Outdoor Recreation Resources Review Commission, *Outdoor Recreation for America*, A Report to the President and to the Congress, Study Report 1, Washington, D.C., 1962.]

favorable weather, the waterfowl population rose to about 140,000,000 during World War II, when hunting pressure was low.

A rise in duck license sales of a little less than a million to a total of nearly 2.5 million in 1956 raised concern lest ducks again be reduced below the average annual increase and below the carrying capacity of their breeding grounds. Following the imposition of more stringent hunting regulations and higher fees the number of such license sales has dropped to pre-1956 levels.

Pollution. Fortunately, the reproductive capacity of most kinds of fish is so great that their numbers are seldom seriously depleted by ordinary recreational fishing, although commercial fishing reputedly has reduced some once abundant fish of both coastal and inland waters. However, the rendering of streams and lakes uninhabitable for fish because of pollution is a problem of considerable magnitude. Many of our streams are now inhabited only by species of fish such as the carp which is tolerant of the sewage the streams carry.

The chief sources of pollution affecting fishes are agricultural chemicals, domestic sewage, industrial and mine wastes, and fine particles of soil washed from farms. Oxidation of domestic

Table 3. Summary of Acreage of Public Land Open to Hunting, by Regions, Forty-Eight Contiguous States, 1960

| Region | Public Land Open to Hunting, in Thousand of Acres | | | |
	In Designated Recreation Areas	Public Domain	Defense	Total
Northeast	8,066	–	111	8,177
North Central	23,740	343	230	24,313
South	15,660	–	1,978	17,638
West	141,903	148,320	1,443	291,666
Total, 48 states	189,369	148,663	3,762	341,794

[Source: U.S. Outdoor Recreation Resources Review Commission, *Outdoor Recreation for America*, A Report to the President and to the Congress, Study Report 1, Washington, D.C., 1962.]

sewage exhausts the water-borne oxygen necessary to fish life and results in the production of materials toxic to fish. Industrial and mine pollution results from the emptying into bodies of water of waste products which may poison fish directly or interfere with their respiration, thus causing death. Minute quantities of such waste materials may be sufficient to kill fish directly or indirectly by destroying their food supply. For example, phenol, a waste product of gas plants and oil refineries, is toxic to trout at concentrations of but five ppm of water, and potassium cyanide, a waste product of coke ovens, at concentrations as low as 0.1 to 0.3 ppm. Silt in streams covers up spawning beds and bottom-inhabiting organisms which fish feed upon and also reduces light penetration below that necessary for plant growth.

Although some kinds of pollution have been alleviated, the problem still exists on a large scale in many states. Chemicals from coal mines in the principal coal-producing states and the wastes that drain into streams from iron, copper, lead, and other mines, and industrial plants have made hundreds of streams uninhabitable to fish. The treatments necessary to render pollution harmless to animal life are often expensive and

imperfectly developed. For this reason, many states are slow to enforce pollution-abatement measures because they fear loss of important industries to states where pollution laws are less strict. Passage of the federal Water Pollution Control Act in 1948 opened the way for the states to attack this problem cooperatively. The effect on fishes of modern chemicals, especially detergents and agricultural chemicals used for insect, disease, and weed control, is the subject of much controversy. Significant kills of fishes in streams have resulted from careless use of insecticides, and excessive amounts of detergents in streams do create unsightly conditions. The use of these materials appears to be necessary to our economy but caution in their use is also necessary to protect fish and other wildlife resources.

Land Use. Among other conditions affecting the welfare of wildlife are the overgrazing of forested lands and the burning, both intentional and accidental, of forest, range, swamp, and other wildlife habitats. Unwise drainage of vast marsh and swampland areas has also been a factor contributing to the decline of some species. Tractor-powered mowers, binders, combines, and other farm machinery have greatly increased wildlife mortality in crop fields during the reproductive season. Roadside mowing during the same period has also caused severe losses. The electric fence and effective weed-killing chemicals have further accelerated the removal of brushy fence rows which often are the only permanent source of wildlife cover on farms. Decline in productivity of land due to overcropping and erosion has also had a profound effect on reducing wildlife production over large areas of formerly good game lands.

Public Apathy. Prejudice, tradition, misunderstanding, and selfishness are other important problems in wildlife conservation. Many sincere people lacking basic biological knowledge still cling to management of our wildlife resources by outmoded and biologically unsound programs of predator control, bounty payments, "vermin-control" campaigns, introduction of exotic species, and artificial propagation and release of originally wild stock. Vociferous minorities of such uninformed persons sometimes prevent state conservation departments from putting sound wildlife conservation programs into effect. Some states, for example, continue to provide protection to female deer during the hunting season in the face of overwhelming evidence that the herd is becoming too great for its food supply.

Because many state fish and game departments are still subject to political maneuvering by the party in power, it is expedient for them to practice programs of appeasement. However, those fish and game departments that operate under the guidance of truly non-political conservation commissions are generally undertaking farsighted programs of wildlife management based on sound biological concepts and principles.

Lack of technically trained personnel on the staff of conservation agencies is also a problem. A tendency to improve this situation by employing college-trained men for permanent positions carrying moderate salaries has become evident.

MANAGEMENT OF WILDLIFE

Three Basic Concepts. The three basic concepts on which any sound program of wildlife conservation must be built were set forth by Gabrielson,[9] formerly director of the United States Fish and Wildlife Service:

1. Soil, water, forest, and wildlife conservation are only parts of one inseparable program.
2. Wildlife must have an environment suited to its needs if it is to survive.
3. Any use that is made of any living resource must be limited to not more than the annual increase if the essential seed stock is to be continually available.

It should be clear from these concepts that wildlife is primarily a by-product of land use.

[9] Ira N. Gabrielson, *Wildlife Conservation*, New York, 1942, p. vi.

For this reason, its management must be integrated with and largely subordinate to the management of land for agricultural, forest, and mineral use. Management under these conditions requires intimate knowledge of the habits and living requirements of all forms of wildlife.

The basic living requirements of all wild animals are food, water, cover, and a climate to which they are adapted. The particular kind of food, water, and cover required by different animals is usually a fixed characteristic of each species. For example, quail feed primarily on seeds of grain and weeds, fruit, and insects, whereas many birds such as the warblers and vireos, feed almost entirely upon insects and near relatives of insects.

Food Requirements. To be adequate, not only must the food supply be of the right kind, but also it must be available at all seasons of the year and within the daily traveling range of the animal. This problem is particularly acute on the western range where deer, elk, and antelope find abundant food in high mountain ranges during the summer months but are often unable to secure sufficient food to ward off starvation when driven by heavy snows to the valleys where they must compete for food with domestic livestock.

On many of our farms and ranches today there is a greater abundance of food suitable for small animals like quail, pheasant, other seed-eating birds, rabbits, ground hogs, and ground squirrels than was present when the land was covered with forests or unbroken grassland, because of the growing of grain and forage crops, which are utilized by these animals. Although most of these crops are grown for domestic purposes, large quantities of waste grain, forage plants, and weed seeds are left in the fields. For example, mechanically harvested corn fields may contain several bushels of grain and a hundred or more pounds of weed seeds per acre after harvesting is completed. In such areas, lack of cover is frequently the most important factor limiting abundance of wildlife.

Cover Requirements. The specific cover requirements of many animals are varied and complex. Thus the introduced ring-necked pheasant requires for nesting over much of its range open herbaceous cover such as sweet clover, alfalfa, and bunch grasses; dense thicket cover into which it may escape when pursued by natural enemies; tall corn, small-grain stubble, or weeds in which it may feed unmolested; weedy or thicket roosting cover; and exposed ground where it can pick up grit. The common bluebirds and wrens of our farms and gardens, for example, are limited by the availability of such nesting sites as holes in trees and fence posts and artificially constructed bird houses.

An important aspect of the cover needs of wild animals is its distribution in relation to available food and water. To be fully effective, cover must be so distributed that it can be utilized during travel to and from sources of food and water and as refuge which can be quickly reached if an animal is threatened with attack.

Water Requirements. The water needs of aquatic or semiaquatic animals like fish, frogs, ducks, geese, and swans are readily apparent. Not so apparent, however, are the needs of individual species.

Trout require clear, cool water with high oxygen content, whereas bullheads, catfish, and carp are tolerant of silt-laden, moderately warm water. Muskrats are most abundant in shallow water in which cattail, bur reed, and other aquatic plants grow profusely. Waterfowl also favor shallow waters where puddle ducks such as the mallards obtain food by probing the stream or lake bottom with their bills, and where fish-eating birds such as the mergansers and herons find an abundance of small fish. Nearly all species of animals that live in or on bodies of water are dependent upon water that is clean, free from toxic substances, and sufficiently rich in mineral nutrients to support a high population of plants and animals.

Many terrestrial animals like deer, elk, and moose require clear, open water for drinking. Others like quail and pheasant are able to meet their water needs from dew and by eating available succulent plants and fruits.

The absence of suitable water the year around is often the most important factor limiting the abundance of wildlife in areas of low rainfall, particularly in marginal areas where an occasional drought wipes out populations built up during periods of normal or heavy precipitation. Ducks and geese which nest in the marshes of north central United States and the Prairie Provinces of Canada suffer great losses when such droughts occur. In contrast, wildlife of the more humid regions sometimes suffers from an excess of precipitation, especially when it occurs during the nesting season. During such a period, the eggs and young of many ground-nesting species become chilled from drenching rains or are drowned by flood waters.

Capacity to Reproduce. The biotic potential or reproductive capacity of most kinds of wild animals greatly exceeds the carrying capacity of the environment they occupy. If all lived and reproduced, the potential progeny from a single pair of adult bobwhite quail would in 3 years' time number at least 1000 individuals. Even deer which per year produce but one to three young may overpopulate their available range under suitable conditions: theoretically, a density of one pair of adult deer per square mile (640 acres) may in only 15 years result in a population of one deer per acre. Although truly phenomenal increases in population occasionally occur, it is doubtful if the full biotic potential is ever attained under natural conditions.

Decimating Factors. Full attainment of the biotic potential of wild animals is prevented in part by one or more decimating factors: diseases, parasites, predation, starvation, accidents, and hunting. The importance of each factor varies with respect to species, environmental conditions, and human activities; frequently one factor or a combination of factors is more important than any of the others. Thus ducks are generally more subject to losses from overshooting and disease than are raccoon, which suffer from inadequate woodland habitat. Bobwhite quail and deer are subject to losses from starvation during severe winters. Because of their nesting in hay and grain fields, ring-necked pheasants are subject to high mortality from accidental encounters with mowing machines, grain binders, and combines.

Wildlife Management Practices. The primary responsibility of the wildlife technician is to determine whether the decimating and welfare factors are in proper balance with the needs of the species and, if they are not, to devise ways and means of correcting them. This necessitates carefully conducted research into the life history and habits of animals with respect to their natural and potential environment. Although only a beginning has been made in this field of investigation, a considerable body of information useful in prescribing guiding principles is now available.

Regulating the Use of Wildlife. Since Biblical times, limiting the harvest of wildlife to not more than the annual increase has been recognized as a management measure. This is the fundamental purpose of all hunting laws and other regulations restricting the use of wild animals the world over. To accomplish this purpose, various methods have been employed ranging from simple tribal taboos against disturbing the female during the breeding season to the complex regulations in force in the United States at the present time. Although regulations vary greatly from state to state, all are largely based upon limiting the period when animals can be taken to the nonbreeding season (open season); limiting the length of time during which they can be taken (length of season); limiting the number that can be taken in a day (daily bag limit) and in a season (season bag limit); and regulating the manner in which they can be taken (restricting caliber and load of gun, preventing use of decoys, bait, ferrets, fire, snares, nets, and dynamite).

All states now require separate licenses for hunting and fishing or a combined license for both sports. Some states require special licenses of commercial fishermen, live-bait dealers, fur dealers, and game-farm operators. In some states scientific collectors and taxidermists also are required to have permits.

The federal government is responsible for fixing regulations protecting migratory species of wildlife and requires the purchase of a federal duck stamp for hunting waterfowl. The United States has entered into international treaties for the protection of migratory species of wildlife. One of the most important federal laws protecting the welfare of wildlife is the Lacey Act of 1900, prohibiting both the importation of any foreign wild animal without approval of the Department of Agriculture and the interstate shipment of the dead bodies of illegally killed wild animals. The latter provision virtually ended the market hunting of wildlife and the wild-bird feather trade which were theatening extermination of many species. Federal protection of migratory species is authorized under the Migratory Bird Treaty Act of 1918, which replaced the Migratory Bird Act of 1913.

Predator Control. Destruction of animals that prey upon game species and domestic livestock has long been a duty of private game managers and of public employees charged with the welfare of wildlife. Many state game-law enforcement officers spend much of their time killing hawks, owls, crows, foxes, coyotes, and other predatory animals in the belief that the welfare of desirable species is thus promoted. Some states encourage the destruction of predators by paying bounties for each animal killed.

Scientists have accumulated convincing evidence that these efforts not only fail sometimes to promote the welfare of wildlife generally but may actually be harmful. For example, destruction of predators was an important contributing factor in the increase of the Kaibab deer herd in Arizona to the point where it exhausted the available food supply resulting in starvation of much of the herd, serious damage to young trees, and decline in the capacity of the range to support future deer populations.

Unfortunately, our knowledge of prey-predator relationships is not adequate for a satisfactory solution of the many problems involved in this controversial subject. It is common knowledge that predatory animals do kill many desirable species. It is also well known to biologists that a limited amount of predation may be beneficial to some kinds of wildlife by killing off diseased individuals, by preventing overpopulations, by encouraging wariness, and by holding in check less valuable species that may compete with desirable animals for food, shelter, and water. Effective predator control should be directed only at those species and those individual animals actually known to be doing harm.

Artificial Propagation and Introduction of Exotic Species. Since historic times, man has been interested in exotic animals and has attempted to substitute them for native animals displaced by his occupancy of their environment. Of the many attempts to introduce exotic game species into this country, only the introduction of the ring-necked pheasant and the Hungarian partridge can be termed successful. Although the ring-necked pheasant has declined somewhat, it seems to be a permanent addition to the farmland of the nation particularly in the Midwest, the northern Great Plains, and parts of the Pacific Northwest. Filling with foreign introductions gaps left by declining native species does not appear to present a very promising solution to the problem.

In some instances, foreign introductions have caused considerable harm and unexpected displacement of native species. The European starling and the English sparrow, introduced to control certain injurious insects, not only have failed in that mission, but also have become a pest of city and country alike where they occupy nesting sites of bluebirds, woodpeckers, and other hole-nesting birds. The common carp, introduced as a food fish, roil the water in many of our lakes and streams making the habitat unsuitable for other species.

Closely allied to the introduction of exotic game animals are attempts to increase by artificial propagation their numbers and that of native species (Fig. 8). In the United States it has been used both to secure exotic or native stock for establishing new areas or replenishing areas thought to be overshot or overfished and to supply stock for bird-dog field trials, for commercial hunting and fishing preserves, and for sale as food. Many state conservation departments operate one or more game and fish farms and spend as much as one-fourth or more of their total income for this purpose. Ring-necked pheasants and native quail are the game birds generally raised for stocking purposes. Trout, several kinds of bass, bluegills, walleyes, and a number of other fish are commonly reared in artificial ponds for restocking. Most of these are planted in natural bodies of water as fry (recently hatched fish) or fingerlings (fish with one season's growth). Some states attempt to provide public fishing by stocking streams with hatchery-reared adult fish.

Artificial propagation, particularly of upland game species, is an expensive way of providing public recreation. Artificial stocking of fish is usually practical only in new bodies of water. Unfortunately, much of the artificially reared game and fish are released in already adequately stocked areas or in areas not adapted to occupancy by the species released. For many years, artificially reared ring-necked pheasants were distributed equally in all Ohio counties in response to demands by local sportsmen groups. Despite these repeated plantings, huntable populations of pheasants have developed only in the intensively farmed, glaciated parts of that state. A similar approach to stocking fish has been followed in many states. Millions of fry and fingerling fish have been stocked in waters to which they were not adapted or in waters already overpopulated with adapted species.

Wildlife Preserves and Refuges. A few states, Pennsylvania and Michigan for example, have set aside large areas of publicly owned land for public shooting grounds; many states have also acquired and developed lake sites to

Fig. 8   Although the practice of artificial propagation and release of "game animals" as a game
management measure is generally discredited by wildlife biologists, millions of such animals are
raised and released annually in the United States. Raccoon, bob white quail, ring-necked pheasants,
and black and mallard ducks are among the kinds artificially raised. This photograph shows a portion of the quail-rearing pens of a Mid-West Fish and Game Department.

provide public fishing waters. Some extensive
preserves in this country are privately owned by
wealthy persons or by clubs with exclusive
memberships. Frequently these areas encom-
pass the finest hunting territory, such as the
Lake Erie marshes which are largely controlled
by gun clubs for waterfowl shooting. Various
systems of leasing exclusive hunting rights on
farms in the best hunting areas have also become
popular. This practice has been highly developed in the southern and southeastern states
and is gaining headway in the good pheasant
hunting areas of the Corn Belt.

The development of any system of paid hunting has been opposed by organized sportsmen
and conservation departments because they fear
that it will restrict hunting privileges to those
with better than average incomes. Landowners
in general, however, have organized paid hunting preserves more for protection from hunter
abuses than for profit. The fees charged amount
to but a few cents per acre of huntable land.

Unlike preserves, refuges are developed primarily for wildlife preservation. Their history
in the United States is of comparatively recent
origin, although a few such private areas were
probably in existence when the first official
refuge was authorized by the California legislature in the 1869–1870 session. The first federal
wildlife refuge was established by presidential

order on March 17, 1903, when Pelican Island in Indian River, near the east coast of Florida, was set aside for the protection of a waning population of brown pelicans.

Under the dynamic leadership of Theodore Roosevelt, Gifford Pinchot, E. W. Nelson, William T. Hornaday and, more recently, Jay N. Darling, Aldo Leopold, and other conservationists, the refuge movement has so developed that the United States has the greatest wildlife refuge system in the world: 272 federal wildlife refuges, aggregating 17,409,968 acres in continental United States and Alaska. The greatest number of areas (184) is for protection of migratory waterfowl; more than half of the land (10,601,364 acres in sixteen tracts) has been acquired for big game. Other purposes of federal refuges are the protection of nongame birds that nest in large colonies, wildlife in general, and research.

The states, too, have developed a system of wildlife refuges, although the intent has often been to preserve breeding stock of huntable species to establish on adjacent overshot areas. This has proved to be a most useful management method to maintain huntable populations of game in areas of intense hunting pressure but it is practical for only a few species such as waterfowl, deer, and pheasant, which are able to spread out quickly into the surrounding territory, are tolerant of crowding, and can be maintained on cheap land.

Two outstanding private waterfowl refuges are the Andrew Clark Refuge at Santa Barbara, California, and the W. H. Kellogg Bird Sanctuary at Battle Creek, Michigan. Other refuges of outstanding importance are Lake Merritt maintained by the city of Oakland in California, Hawk Mountain Sanctuary in Pennsylvania, Bird City at Avery Island in Louisiana, and the extensive system of refuges maintained by the National Audubon Society. The most important of the latter group are located in Florida with eight refuges and in Texas with seventeen refuges where colonies, chiefly of herons and ibises, are protected.

Management of Food, Cover, and Water. The foregoing wildlife management measures are designed to control those factors that decimate wildlife populations. Except in relation to refuges, they have little to do with providing the food, water, and cover necessary for these animals to live and reproduce. The wise solution of this problem is the key to the future recreational use of the wildlife resources of our farms and ranches.

A partial solution to the problem lies in the fact that good soil, water, and forest conservation contribute greatly to the welfare of wildlife. Permanent reservoirs developed for farm and ranch water supplies, for flood control, and for urban use also provide water for fish, waterfowl, and the many animals that inhabit streams, lake margins, and the shallow fringes of impounded waters (Fig. 9). Only profitable forest management can assure the future of the farm woodlot, which is the permanent home of much farm wildlife and the safe retreat of other kinds. All these measures are vital to the economic security of the farmer and rancher, and they are carried out because it is profitable to do so.

Fortunately a vast program of soil and water conservation has already been initiated on the nation's farms under the leadership of the United States Soil Conservation Service. This agency, working through locally organized soil conservation districts and with the aid of the state agricultural extension programs, has helped thousands of farmers and ranchers to conserve and restore their soil and water and to make their woodlots more productive. As these practices are extended, wildlife will benefit proportionately.

Additional measures are needed, however, to develop fully the potential wildlife productivity of land in agricultural ownership. But other measures of considerable value to wildlife will probably not be carried out on a significant scale unless it becomes profitable for the farmer to undertake them or unless he is safeguarded against the inconvenience and abuse that often attend hunting on his land.

Fig. 9 The lush feeding grounds created by the six Upper Mississippi Headwaters Reservoirs attract numerous waterfowl and game fish. In the autumn thousands of sportsmen flock to the northern Minnesota areas to hunt ducks and rest and relax at resorts and camp sites adjacent to the reservoir waters. In 1961 more than two and a half million hunters and tourists visited the area and the number is increasing. (U.S. Army Corps of Engineers.)

According to estimates made by the Soil Conservation Service, at least 100,000,000 acres of land in continental United States are best adapted to wildlife use, of which at least 33,000,-000 acres are in farms and ranches. About one-half of this area is now making its maximum contribution to wildlife and will continue to do so if it is not disturbed by fire, grazing, or cultivation. The remaining area, in need of some improvement to make it fully productive, includes 6,500,000 acres suited for marsh management, 1,000,000 acres of ponds, 1,000,000 acres of streambanks, 3,000,000 acres of crop-field borders, 6,000,000 acres of oddly shaped fields unsuited to other uses, and 250,000 acres of spoil banks resulting from various surface mining operations.[10]

Careful management of the wildlife areas on

[10] Edward H. Graham, *The Land and Wildlife*, New York, 1947, p. 52.

the nation's farms can establish the cover necessary to hold a wildlife population adequate to utilize fully the food supply that is so often produced as an incidental by-product of highly mechanized agriculture. Such areas are the only land on farms that can be justifiably managed solely for wildlife. They offer the best opportunity for providing the three basic welfare factors of food, water, and shelter which, together with control of the important decimating factors, are the building stones of any successful wildlife conservation program.

Management of food, water, and cover are equally important on other lands if wildlife is to be benefited. Timber production, for example, is given first consideration on both public and private forested land; yet modification of timber management practices can be employed to increase materially forest-wildlife production. These modifications include the leaving of den trees for squirrels, raccoons, and other tree-dwelling animals, the favoring of desirable seed- or fruit-producing trees, the selective or group-harvest method of cutting timber to provide a variety of forest growth from small seedlings to large trees, and the leaving of open areas in reforestation projects for the securing of mixed stands of natural growth and planted trees (Fig. 10).

WILDLIFE CONSERVATION PROGRAMS AND RESPONSIBILITIES

The development of a sound national program of wildlife conservation is dependent on three basic steps:

1. An adequate research program to establish the status of important wildlife species, their needs, and measures necessary for their continued welfare under predicted use.

2. An educational program to acquaint the citizenry with the basic needs of wildlife and with the biological, social, and economic problems involved in its use and to train adequate personnel to administer and manage this resource.

3. An action program to provide the food, water, cover, and protection from decimation needed by wildlife.

Wildlife management is now a well-established profession for which at least fifty-three colleges and universities in the United States offer training at either the undergraduate or graduate level or both.

The states through their divisions of conservation spend for wildlife management purposes the annual revenue from sale of fishing and hunting licenses. A survey conducted in 1961 indicates that over $120,000,000 annually collected from such sales. This amount is supplemented by federal appropriations to the states from an excise tax or arms and ammunition and sport fishing equipment. In recent years these funds have averaged $20,000,000 per year. Approximately 30 percent of this

Fig. 10   The porcupine with defenses peculiarly his own continues to survive in spite of hunting pressures and changes in the habitat.

amount is expended for research, 30 percent for development projects, 35 percent for land acquisition, and 5 percent for administration of the fund.

The United States Fish and Wildlife Service is the federal agency charged with responsibility for migratory species of wildlife and the federal wildlife refuge program. It conducts important wildlife researches in fields ordinarily untouched by state and private institutions. It also participates in a cooperative research program with the American Wildlife Management Institute, state universities, and state divisions of conservation.

Other federal agencies play a leading part in the management of wildlife resources. Of these, the National Park Service and the Forest Service work entirely on public land, whereas the Soil Conservation Service through its technicians develops programs for wildlife restoration on farms managed for soil and water conservation.

Among the many private organizations that contribute to the welfare of wildlife are the National Audubon Society, the Wildlife Management Institute, the National Wildlife Federation, the Sport Fishing Institute, and the Izaak Walton League of America. These and other agencies carry on the educational work of informing the general public of wildlife problems and act as the watchdogs of governmental activities which affect the well-being of our wildlife resources.

SUMMARY

Wildlife is a renewable resource which is subject to management by man. The basic needs of wild animals are adequate food, water, and cover to meet their specific requirements and protection from decimating factors which reduce their numbers. These needs can be met only by proper management of the land upon which they live and by control of such decimating factors as overhunting.

Although many species formerly common or abundant are now rare, the esthetic value of those remaining is great. Public demand for recreational use of wildlife exerts enormous pressure on the supply and in some species necessitates complete protection and drastic restrictions on the use of others to ensure their welfare.

Most of the recreational use of wildlife is provided by agricultural land where the proper incentives for adopting practices beneficial to wildlife are often lacking. Widespread application of soil and water conservation practices may in part fulfill this need. Where these measures are not feasible or adequate, other inducements must be provided if wildlife production is to be maintained at a high population level.

Considerable advancement has been made in the field of wildlife management. Further progress is dependent on continual research and sound educational and action programs unhampered by political interference and the clamor of uninformed or selfish pressure groups.

References

Allen, Durward L., *Our Wildlife Legacy*, Funk and Wagnalls Co., New York, 1954.

Allen, Glover M., *Extinct and Vanishing Mammals of the Western Hemisphere*, American Committee for International Wildlife Protection, New York, 1942.

Beard, Daniel E., et al., *Fading Trails: The Story of Endangered American Wildlife*, The Macmillan Co., New York, 1942.

Connery, Robert H., *Governmental Problems in Wildlife Conservation*, Columbia University Press, New York, 1935.

Gabrielson, Ira N., *Wildlife Conservation*, The Macmillan Co., New York, 1942.

Gabrielson, Ira N., *Wildlife Refuges*, The Macmillan Co., New York, 1943.

Graham, Edward H., *Natural Principles of Land Use*, Oxford University Press, New York, 1944.

Graham, Edward H., *The Land and Wildlife*, Oxford University Press, New York, 1947.

Henderson, Junius, *The Practical Value of Birds*, The Macmillan Co., 1927.

Henderson, Junius, and Elberta Craig, *Economic Mammalogy*, Charles C. Thomas Co., Baltimore, Md., 1932.

Jackson, Hartley H. T., "Conserving Endangered Wildlife Species," *Transactions of the Wisconsin Academy of Sciences, Arts, and Letters*, Madison, Wis., Vol. 35, 1943, pp. 61–89.

Langlois, T. H., "The Role of Legal Restrictions in Fish Management," *Transactions Ninth North American Wildlife Conference*, Wildlife Management Institute, Washington, D.C., 1944.

Leopold, Aldo, "The American Game Policy," *Transactions Seventeenth North American Game Conference*, Wildlife Management Institute, Washington, D.C., 1930.

Leopold, Aldo, *Game Management*, Charles Scribner's Sons, New York, 1933.

Miller, J. Paul, and Burwell B. Powell, *Game and Wild-Fur Production and Utilization on Agricultural Land*, Circular 636, U.S. Department of Agriculture, Washington, D.C., 1942.

Mueller, Eva, and Gerald Gurin, *Participation in Outdoor Recreation: Factors Affecting Demand Among American Adults*, Outdoor Recreation Resources Review Commission Report 20, Government Printing Office, Washington, D.C., 1962.

National Resources Board, *Planning for Wildlife in the United States*, Part IX of the *Report on Land Planning*, Washington, D.C., 1935.

"Outdoor Recreation Resources Review Commission," *Sport Fishing—Today and Tomorrow*, Report 7, Government Printing Office, Washington, D.C., 1962.

"Outdoor Recreation Resources Review Commission," *Hunting in the United States—Its Present and Future Role*, Report 6, Government Printing Office, Washington, D.C., 1963.

Palmer, T. S., *Chronology and Index of the More Important Events in American Game Protection 1776–1911*, Biological Survey Bull. 41, U.S. Department of Agriculture, Washington, D.C., 1912.

Trippensee, R. E., *Wildlife Management*, McGraw-Hill Book Co., New York, 1948.

Troutman, Milton B., *The Fishes of Ohio*, The Ohio State University Press, Columbus, Ohio, 1957.

United States Senate, *The Status of Wildlife in the United States*, Report of the Special Committee on the Conservation of Wildlife Resources, U.S. Senate Report 1203, Washington, D.C., 1940.

Walford, Lionel A., editor, *Fishery Resources of the United States of America*, Fish and Wildlife Service, U.S. Department of the Interior, Washington, D.C., 1945

HOWARD H. MARTIN
University of Washington

CHAPTER 19

Fisheries for the Future

The general American attitude toward fisheries has been that of a pioneer society attuned to an era of plenty. The easygoing assumption that man can never exhaust the bounty of the oceans left nature with the entire responsibility for the renewal and sometimes the survival of a resource. The comfortable concept "just leave it to nature" called for neither care nor restraint on the part of fishermen and the public at large.

Until recently the scientists have lacked precise data concerning most types of underwater life. Marine biology advanced in spite of handicaps, some of them physical and others economic. It was well into the twentieth century before much was known concerning the abundance, habits, growth, reproduction, and migration of the more valuable food fish. Biologists and oceanographers have gradually developed ingenious methods of marine investigation; their continued research on problems of fish populations is now filling in the gaps with exact data of great value.

Although the scientists have been developing new techniques for fisheries research, the commercial operators have not been idle. Deep-sea fishing has become big business, using the best equipment that engineering and electronics can devise, including powerful trawlers with a wide cruising radius, echo-sounders and other fish finders, helicopters for spotting, detailed maps of the best banks, and numerous improvements in gear.[1] Given ample fish populations the mounting efficiency of the operators has been little short of spectacular. Each technical advance has speeded production, but it has also intensified pressure upon the stock.

Marine biologists and resource economists think of fisheries in terms of production for use, a world business worthy of intensive study, and one readily responsive to calculated management. They are sympathetic to present returns for the fishermen but not at the expense of stability for the future. In planning for the long pull they have been deeply concerned over public apathy and with the need for continued research.

---

[1] "Increasing efficiency of fishing gear is one of the embarassments of administrators charged with conservation of the resources. Their problem involves a fishery already too intense for proper management and maximum profits. Increasing efficiency of gear . . . adds to the strain on the resource, forcing the curtailment of fishing periods to the point where economical operation becomes impossible," *Yearbook*, Pacific Fisherman, 1963.

415

Fisheries are perhaps the most poorly managed of all our national resources. Legislative regulations . . . are piecemeal, localized and often based on lay opinion, superstition or snap judgment . . . Yet there is a science of fishery conservation, which is highly specialized and exact . . . It more than pays for itself in increased value and security of wealth which it strives to protect. Nevertheless, federal and state conservation agencies have everywhere been required to do their fishery conservation work on a financial shoestring.[2]

Regional Survey of United States Fisheries. With a maximum of shallow continental-shelf waters in addition to bays, river mouths, and many coastal indentations, the United States has an ideal setting for a large and valuable fishery. It also has a greater variety of fish than any other nation. The North Atlantic and the North Pacific, with their warm and cold currents in close proximity, are natural plankton feeding grounds. With the enlargement of the list of varieties used for food, the value of these well-stocked waters has steadily increased. The annual catch exceeds 5,000,000,000 pounds for which the fishermen are paid about $360,000,000. When the fish are fresh-frozen, filleted, smoked, canned, dried, salted, pickled, or otherwise packaged and prepared for final consumption, the value of the catch is far above this figure (Table 1).

[2] Lionel A. Walford, *Fishery Resources of the United States of America,* Washington, D.C., 1945, p. 131.

New England, the oldest commercial fishing center in America, traditionally regards the cod as its most characteristic food fish, although it is now outranked by at least six other varieties. This historic fish has fluctuated from year to year; an increasing proportion of it now enters the fresh trade rather than the dried or salt fish trade. Speedy and efficient trawlers have increased the catch of ocean perch, flounder, and haddock, the last named now the leading food fish of the Atlantic seaboard. Lobsters, caught chiefly along the coast of Maine, lead all shellfish in value, followed by scallops and clams. The New England market catch includes some sixty separate species—a wider range of commercial fish than is taken in any comparable area of the United States.

The many tidewater bays, inlets, and sunken rivers of the Middle Atlantic states are especially suitable for shellfish, including oysters, crabs, and clams. Chesapeake Bay in particular is famous for its extensive public and private oyster beds, the latter now in the lead; two-thirds of the United States oyster production comes from Chesapeake Bay alone. A so-called scrap fish, menhaden, is caught in purse seines along the mid-Atlantic and Gulf coasts; taken to the extent of 1 million tons in 1962, it is processed into oil, meal, and fertilizer. It has great potential use in the future as a low-cost fish protein concentrate,

Table 1. Fisheries Production by Regions, 1963

Region	Millions of Dollars	Percentage of Total	Millions of Pounds	Percentage of Total
New England and Middle Atlantic	88.8	23	1,347	28
Chesapeake	29.4	8	403	9
South Atlantic	19.4	5	370	8
Gulf	98.2	26	1,387	29
Alaska	48.9	13	378	8
Washington and Oregon	29.3	8	209	4
California	50.0	13	515	11
Great Lakes and Mississippi River	11.6	3	129	3
Hawaii	2.6	1	12	–
Total	378.2	100	4,750	100

[Source: E. A. Power, *Fisheries of the United States, 1963,* Division of Resources Development, Department of the Interior, Washington, D.C., 1964.]

an additive to the diet of undernourished populations.

In the Gulf of Mexico from Key West to the Rio Grande, shrimp trawling is the most profitable single fishing activity. In the United States as a whole it has become a $70,000,000 industry. Other fisheries of the South Atlantic coast and the Gulf include mullet, sheepshead, and the highly migratory red snapper, as well as oysters and crabs.

The Great Lakes have a limited list of food fishes, the more valuable being yellow perch, chubs, and whitefish. The Mississippi River system, even more limited than the Great Lakes, markets almost entirely catfish, buffalo, and carp.

In the 1880's salmon were almost the only fish taken commercially on the West coast. Despite present-day diversification the salmon, now valued at $50,000,000 annually, is still the American favorite; an increasing proportion of the catch now goes to market fresh. Its nearest rival, the warmth-loving tuna, has a much greater world range and is taken in many waters by deep-sea trawlers. Canning tends to be centered in San Pedro and San Diego; the California tuna pack of 75,000 cases in 1912 had increased to 9,000,000 in 1963. The two great food staples, salmon and tuna, together account for well over two-thirds of the total Pacific Coast fishery—$128,000,000 in 1963.

Other leading West coast varieties include bottom fish such as halibut from the carefully conserved stocks of the North Pacific as well as various types of flounder or sole. Two-thirds of the American mackerel supply now comes from waters off California. Shellfish include the Dungeness crab from coastal waters of the Northwest and the deep-water king crab from Alaska; since 1950 the latter fishery has been expanding steadily. The Pacific oyster, grown from seed originally imported from Japan, is kept up by annual imports of fresh seed; it is entirely under private cultivation in certain shallow tidal bays, an example of successful aquiculture.

Exploitation and Depletion in Atlantic Waters. In colonial days salmon were plentiful from the Hudson River as far north as Labrador; they were a staple food taken in large quantities during the annual run and used both fresh and salted. Today only a few rivers such as the Penobscot and others in Maine have appreciable runs, and the Atlantic salmon is regarded as a sports fish, with hatcheries in New England trying to increase the stock. The Atlantic halibut is still regarded as commercial, but is now far below its former production.

Atlantic cod have been taken in quantity for two or three centuries without exhausting the stocks, but statistical records show that present-day catches are far below those of the past. The old-fashioned schooner and handline fishing from dories produced 294,000,000 pounds of cod in 1880. Today with the addition of the latest and most efficient devices, the annual cod catch is 42,000,000 pounds. Atlantic mackerel are still plentiful, but have been subject to wide fluctuations in abundance (Table 2).

A classic example of ruthless exploitation is the giant sturgeon of the Atlantic seaboard; in Chesapeake Bay it was slaughtered indiscriminately for the roe, the bodies being left to decay along the shore. A few sturgeon are still taken from New England to the Gulf, but the species is in danger of extinction. New England is now marketing only one-half as much lobster as in 1890. Alarmed by the decline of this choice sea product, several New England states adopted size-limit laws, and present lobster stocks seem to be holding their own. Since 1952 the Atlantic mackerel catch has declined to a fraction of its former size. Runs of river herring have been reduced by dams and other obstructions impeding access to former spawning grounds. Croaker and weakfish have declined in abundance along the Atlantic coast.

Decline in the Great Lakes and Interior Rivers. Great Lakes fisheries reached their highest levels early in the century, with production decreasing steadily after 1920. The U.S. Fish and Wildlife Service has published a long

Table 2. Fisheries of the United States, 1963

Fish	Thousands of Dollars	Thousands of Pounds
Shrimp	70,000	240,300
Salmon	49,000	279,000
Tuna	41,600	319,840
Oysters	25,800	55,600
Crabs	23,400	243,800
Menhaden	21,900	1,780,000
Lobsters	18,300	34,600
Flounders	11,900	125,200
Haddock	11,700	123,900
Scallops	9,600	20,500
Halibut	7,300	45,500
Catfish[1]	6,178	37,619
Clams	5,400	47,400
Ocean perch	5,100	108,300
Red snapper	3,600	13,300
Cod (Atlantic)	3,100	42,000
Scup or Porgy	3,100	42,200
Mackerel	2,800	135,600
Mullet	2,300	41,900
Whiting	2,200	42,800
Chubs[2]	2,128	16,516
Buffalofish[1]	1,913	18,508
Herring	1,900	183,300
Striped Bass	1,300	9,200
Shad[1]	1,243	7,256
Rockfish[2]	1,137	24,882
Carp[1]	1,047	30,293

[1] 1962
[2] 1961

[Source: E. A. Power, *Fisheries of the United States, 1963*, Division of Resource Development, Department of the Interior, Washington, D.C., 1964.]

list of fishes once plentiful in the five lakes but which are declining, have become commercially insignificant, or are thought to be extinct. Sturgeon and blue pike, once common in the markets, are seldom seen and walleye have been greatly reduced. More important, the formerly plentiful favorites, lake trout and whitefish, are scarce and high-priced; they have been replaced by cheaper varieties such as chubs, yellow perch, lake herring, and introduced species such as smelt.

The debacle in lake trout landings, down from 10 million pounds in 1940 to one-third of a million in 1961, was caused by the depradations of a parasite, the sea lamprey which invaded the three upper lakes. Here the fishkill came close to exterminating lake trout and reduced whitefish abundance to an unprofitable level for operators.[3]

After thousands of tests fishery biologists in 1958 announced the discovery of chemical compounds which were "lethal to lamprey larvae" but harmless to other fishes and animals. Lamprey-infested streams tributary to the lakes are being successfully treated with this larvicide.

Ten years or even five years ago . . . the sea lamprey had destroyed or reduced to low levels the choice species of Lake Huron and Lake Michigan and was making rapid inroads on the lake trout of Lake Superior . . . We now have a control method. Its effectiveness was demonstrated in 1962 when the numbers of sea lampreys in spawning runs were reduced to a mere 14 percent of the 1961 figure.[4]

Fish hatcheries are now providing hundreds of thousands of yearling lake trout for restocking purpose and in time Lakes Superior, Huron, and Michigan should be restored to a good level of abundance. Canada has been cooperating in trout rearing and planting.

Overfishing has not been as persistent in the Great Lakes as in many other regions. Lake Huron whitefish in the 1930's were badly decimated by a new and ruinously efficient type of gear, the deep-trap net; it was prohibited after the fishery showed signs of collapse. Declines of lake stocks, in general, are more directly related to parasites or to pollution. The three upper lakes (with the exception of southern Lake Michigan) are relatively uncontaminated. Lake Erie, however, is rimmed by factories and

[3] The sea lamprey, a notorious predator, is indigenous to the North Atlantic coast from Florida to Labrador. Its active life is spent in salt water but it is anadromous, ascending coastal streams and rivers to spawn. With its powerful sucking mouth lined with sharp teeth, it destroys many coastal fish, including cod, haddock, shad, menhaden, and others.

[4] *Great Lakes Fisheries; Problems and Programs*, 88th Congress, Vol. 109, No. 59, April 24, 1963.

Fig. 1   Razor clams are a highly prized sports and commercial fishery in Washington, Oregon, and Alaska. Dug by hand at low tide the clams are dropped into a surf sack attached to the belt. Heavy inroads on the stock resulted in regulation which now include size limits, bag limits, an annual quota, and a curtailed season. (Washington State Department of Fisheries.)

crowded cities from the Detroit River around its western and southern shores. It is the shallowest of the lakes and receives an ever-increasing burden of domestic and industrial effluents detrimental to fish life.

Also heavily industrialized, the Ohio River system can be eliminated from fishery consideration. The interior lakes and rivers have been overexploited. Catfish and buffalo have survived in the Mississippi, but valuable native game fish, such as the black bass, striped bass, perch, and crappie, have declined. They have been replaced in quantity but not in quality by the sluggish and prolific German carp, introduced into American waters in 1877.

Declines in Pacific Coast Production. Faced with a sharp decline in the great salmon runs and the possible extinction of the halibut resource, the West coast interests have been quick to accept drastic remedial measures for the major fisheries. Both salmon and halibut still face major problems. The diminishing stock of razor clams in Washington has necessitated size limits, quotas, and restricted seasons (Fig. 1 and Fig. 2). Oregon has adopted measures for the conservation of dover, petrale, and English sole.

Fig. 2   Trend in the production of razor clams, 1950–1963. In spite of controls the production has declined steadily over the past 15 years. The conservationist is concerned lest the razor clam become a vanishing resource. (U.S. Fish and Wildlife Service, *Fisheries of the United States, 1963.*)

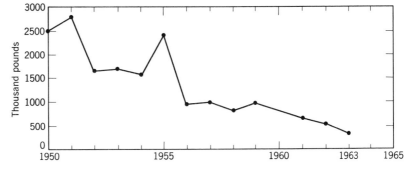

Herring, abalone, spiny lobster, shrimp, and white sea bass, to mention only a few, have become problem fisheries on the West coast, subject to varying degrees of regulation.

Biologists had been concerned about the intensity of sardine fishing in California waters. In 1947 this hitherto infallible fish failed to appear in its usual enormous numbers off Monterey and San Francisco. Alarmed by the disappearance of sardines, the industry asked the California legislature for large appropriations to study the problem.

Although the scientific investigation was in process the runs continued to decline. Former landings had reached 600,000 tons of fish delivered to the canneries at Monterey and San Pedro, and record packs of 5,000,000 cases. As recently as 1958 the California sardine pack was 2,338,000 cases. In 1963 the fishermen caught a bare 1000 tons, the pack making an all-time low of 30,100 cases. Cannery Row at Monterey was wholly inoperative.

Shad of the Atlantic Seaboard. THE SPRING SHAD RUN. This highly prized commercial as well as game fish has been caught in nearly every river along the Atlantic littoral from Florida to Newfoundland, but it is most abundant from the Carolinas to Long Island Sound. In colonial days Chesapeake Bay and the rivers tributary to it had enormous runs each spring; early settlers along the Delaware and the Hudson also caught shad by the thousands. Like the salmon, it is anadromous, with a life cycle that includes both salt and fresh water. Juveniles hatched in Atlantic rivers spend their first summer in fresh water, attain a size of 3 to 5 inches, and then migrate to the ocean. When 3 to 5 years old, adult shad return to the parent stream to spawn.

DECLINE IN ABUNDANCE. So severe were the inroads upon the shad population that as early as 1860 there was a marked decline in the catch. Seines and gill nets at river mouths sometimes cut off entire runs, the level of replacement dropping sharply. Water supply and power dams eliminated many spawning waters and in the late nineteenth century hatcheries began artificial propagation, planting millions of larvae in streams where runs had been decimated. The decline continued, the Atlantic shad catch of 50,000,000 pounds in 1900 dropping to its present 6,200,000 pounds.

Piecemeal measures in individual states having made little progress, the Fish and Wildlife Service was asked to take over the problem. In 1958 it initiated the Atlantic Coast Shad Investigation, a full-scale research project to (1) determine the causes of the decline and (2) make recommendations for better future management. The Investigation found three major causes of the persistent shad decline: overfishing which cut off escapement of spawning adults; the widespread elimination of upstream spawning areas by power dams; and, perhaps most serious of all, the pollution of Atlantic coastal rivers by industrial and urban wastes.

THE REHABILITATION PROBLEM. Using the Investigation findings some progress has been made toward improving the shad situation. Regulations for a larger annual escapement of spawning adults have begun to show results. In the Hudson and the Connecticut rivers shad fishing at a moderate rather than an excessive rate has increased the runs. On the St. Johns River in tourist-minded Florida the sports and commercial fishermen in 1958 were permitted to take only 27 percent of a shad run estimated at over one million. Larger escapements are becoming standard policy for Atlantic shad streams.

A few spawning areas are being opened. On the Connecticut River, the major shad stream of New England, a fish passage device at one dam permits spawning adults to enter 34 miles of waters blocked for the previous 100 years; successful reproduction and returns have been secured here.

The Susquehanna River, 444 miles in length from New York state via Pennsylvania and Maryland to Chesapeake Bay, is obstructed by four large power dams. The three states are asking the power companies to provide fishways which will open many miles of the river to shad migration and reproduction. The companies agreed on a survey to determine the suitability of the river, between and above the dams, for the support of shad populations.[5]

The pollution problem is less hopeful, although certain of the smaller rivers may be decontaminated in time. The Delaware River has shown the most drastic decline in shad, 99 percent between 1896 and 1950; here the Fish and Wildlife Service recommends that municipalities as well as industries clean up their excessive pollution of Delaware Bay. Revived spawning runs in most of the eastern rivers are largely dependent on the ability of the states to change waste disposal practices—not a hopeful prospect in heavily industrialized and densely populated areas.

Oyster Beds of Chesapeake and Delaware Bays. Two-thirds of the nation's oyster production comes from Chesapeake and Delaware Bays where the many river estuaries cut deeply into low coastal plains. Here depth, temperature, and salinity of waters provide optimum conditions for shellfish. The entire output was once tonged or dredged from public oyster grounds open to everyone. The shift has been from public irresponsibility to private responsibility. In Virginia, largest single producer, three-quarters of the landings are now from private oyster beds, planted on public grounds once worked out, and abandoned, now leased to planters. The present trend is toward more private cultivation, better management, and higher returns per unit of effort.

Oyster abundance in the Chesapeake-Delaware area has declined steadily in recent years, and the annual crop is now only one-quarter what it was in the early 1900's. Overdredging of public oyster beds has made many of them unprofitable to work. In Delaware Bay an epidemic

disease which began in 1957 wiped out virtually all oysters. This disaster spread to lower Chesapeake Bay where it reduced production on both public and private beds. The disease has since waned and the depleted areas are being restocked. Parasites and predators, poor setting of spat, and various man-made changes in the environment have also contributed to lower yields. Although few seed oysters are planted in public beds, the State of Maryland has begun a program for possible rehabilitation of its public grounds. Cooperative research projects by federal, state, and private agencies are directed toward disease, setting, predators, and artificial culture.

The pollution problem remains and, as in the case of shad, the fishery may be forced to retreat. Expanding industries and agglomerated populations along the Delaware are hazardous for shellfish dependent on uncontaminated waters. Unless conditions can be improved in the near future oyster growing must of necessity abandon the Delaware. Fortunately, Chesapeake Bay still has extensive stretches of estuarine waters where oysters can be grown safely and profitably.

PACIFIC SALMON

The Salmon of the North Pacific. THE ANNUAL SALMON RUN. Every spring and summer the rivers of the Pacific, from California to the Bering Sea, are the scene of one of the world's most spectacular fish runs. Millions of salmon appear at the river mouths, swarm across the bars, and move steadily upstream. Most rapids and waterfalls are no deterrent. A long run of a thousand miles up the Columbia to the headwaters of the Salmon River in Idaho generally begins in March or April. The short runs of Vancouver Island, where the spawning beds may be only a few hours from salt water, may not begin until late in the autumn. The salmon reach the original stream or lake where they were hatched several years before. Scooping out a shallow nest they deposit and fertilize the

[5] This research project begun in 1963 is financed by the power companies. Eleven million shad eggs from the Columbia River were flown east and planted experimentally above the dams, resulting in a good hatch. Construction of the projected Susquehanna fishways will depend on the final results of the survey.

eggs, then cover them with a layer of protecting gravel. Pacific salmon take no food after leaving salt water. Spent by the journey and the final act of reproduction, the parents lie quietly in eddies and die within a short time.

The eggs generally hatch in about 2 months, the fry emerging from the gravel in the spring. Depending upon species the young salmon remain several months, sometimes as long as 3 years, in fresh water before beginning their trip to the ocean. The salt-water phase of their life cycle lasts from 2 to 6 years, again depending on the variety of salmon. Over 95 percent of their growth is made in the sea. In recent years salmon biologists have discovered the main routes of migration, the major marine feeding and nursery areas, and the general abundance and distribution of salmon in the sea. As a result of tagging and extensive high-seas sampling, the general stocks of both Asiatic and American salmon have been identified and followed in their ocean wandering.

THE SALMON PACK. When adult salmon reach the coasts prior to the annual spawning run, they are in prime condition. Packing plants are located from southern Oregon to western Alaska, usually near river mouths. The average annual salmon pack for the United States and Alaska over a period of 25 years, 1918 to 1943, exceeded 6,000,000 cases (48 pounds to the case), but in the 1954–1963 decade, it declined to an annual average of 3,460,000 cases. In addition to canned salmon several million pounds are marketed fresh, frozen, smoked, and mild-cured.

SPECIES OF SALMON. Five species of salmon are indigenous to Pacific waters. Sockeye or red salmon, weighing 4 to 10 pounds, have long been the favorite. The great Chinook or king salmon, averaging over 20 pounds and sometimes weighing up to 100, are sold fresh as well as canned. Silver or coho are less popular for canning because of their lighter-colored flesh. Pink or humpback salmon, weighing 3 to 5 pounds, are the most plentiful, particularly in southeastern Alaska where they have supplied over three-fourths of the pack to date. Chum or keta, pale in color but high in nutritive value, are also a standard cannery item.

DECLINE OF WEST COAST RUNS. Salmon canning began on the Sacramento River in 1864. The runs at that time were excellent, and the pack increased to 200,000 cases in 1882, then dropped steadily until it disappeared. The decline was caused, first, by overfishing to the point where the adult escapement was insufficient to replenish the stock and second, by power and irrigation dams.

Salmon canning along the small coastal rivers of northern California, Oregon, and Washington reached a peak of about 250,000 cases in 1911; the 1963 pack in the same areas was only 2100 cases. The Columbia River, a steady producer for 90 years, reached its maximum of 629,000 cases in 1883. Since then the teeming sockeye runs of the Columbia have shrunk to a fraction of their former size. The total pack for all varieties on the Columbia was 82,000 cases in 1963.

The Puget Sound area has the richest salmon waters within the United States; canning started here in 1877 and reached its maximum in 1913 with 2,500,000 cases. Minimum output for a 52-year period occurred in 1944 with 38,950 cases; the 10-year average pack, 1954–1963, was 476,000 cases.

The steady decline of salmon in the continental United States was obscured by the rapid rise of Alaskan fishing, which was more than sufficient to keep up the total supply.

The Alaskan Salmon Fisheries. SIZE OF THE CANNING INDUSTRY. The salmon fisheries of Alaska located along 10,000 miles of coast line are one of the richest natural resources of the North Pacific. Caught during their summer runs, the salmon are largely processed in local canneries, the pack being valued at 70 to 90 million dollars annually.

The first salmon cannery in the far north was established in 1878, and by 1888 the Alaskan pack exceeded that of the Columbia River. More and more canneries were established to take advantage of the seemingly inexhaustible supply; under the stimulus of wartime prices production reached 6,677,000 cases in 1918. During the ensuing decade, it dropped to an average of 4,500,000 cases per year, then began to increase, reaching an all-time peak of 8,454,000 cases in 1936. Since then it has decreased gradually to 2,727,000 in 1963.

DECREASE IN SALMON ABUNDANCE. Cutthroat competition was rife among early canners in the territory and legislation enacted by Congress for salmon protection was not effective. Some streams were blocked so completely by traps that few fish reached the spawning beds, and there was apprehension lest the Alaskan fisheries follow the Atlantic salmon industry into oblivion. Behind the scenes there was a struggle between interests in favor of unrestrained operations and fishery experts who pointed out the necessity of restrictions if the industry was to be preserved. After many years of controversy the White Act was passed by Congress in 1924; it gave the Bureau of Fisheries (now the Fish and Wildlife Service) supervision and enforcement powers over all Alaskan fishing.

UNITED STATES FISH AND WILDLIFE SERVICE. Under the control and management of the Service new procedures and regulations were established, including a 50 percent escapement for all salmon entering Alaskan rivers. In addition to collecting much biological data, the enforcement of spawning escapement was delegated to the Service. When the evidence indicated that a given river had been overfished it could be closed entirely; any area which had regained its former level might be reopened. Under these flexible regulations, the Alaskan fishery was stabilized at a profitable level including a minimum of interference with commercial operators.

In spite of well-planned administrative policies salmon stocks and production declined steadily following the high year of 1936. It dropped from 7 million cases to 5 million, finally reaching a production figure less than half that of 25 years ago. Believing that escapement had been evaded under the salmon trap system, which is difficult to enforce, the Service outlawed traps entirely in 1958. Under statehood the following year the Service stepped out of the picture, the supervision and regulation of fisheries passing to the new Alaskan Department of Fish and Game. There is a reluctant feeling in Alaska that firmer measures must be taken if the industry is to be saved (Fig. 3).

One of the major problem areas has been Bristol Bay where catches of salmon of all species are taken, but it is best known for its long-time production of sockeye. These generally mature in a 5-year cycle, but there are also 4-year cycle runs. For 2 years straight, 1963 and 1964, the sockeye runs have been the poorest in history, locally disastrous. Fisheries scientists

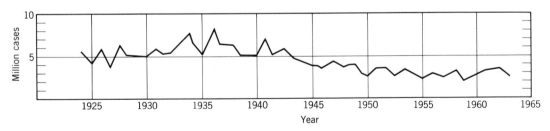

Fig. 3 Total Alaska salmon production, 1924 to 1963. All five species of salmon are canned in Alaska, with pinks the leader, followed by reds (sockeye) and chum. Twenty-five years ago, after several successive record runs, the scientists were confident that the annual pack could be stabilized at an average of five million cases, but there has been a steady decline to half that figure. The 1963 sockeye pack, half a million cases, was the smallest in history. (*Fisheries of the United States, 1963.*)

have been unable to account for the declines in the red salmon stocks, or even to forecast them accurately. Fortunately, southern Alaska with big runs of pinks has made the Alaskan salmon situation less dismal (Fig. 4 and Fig. 5).

Salmon Problems in Canada and the United States: Puget Sound and the Fraser River. All species of salmon are caught in Puget Sound, but the sockeye is regarded as the most important, although runs of pink salmon have sometimes been more valuable. Sockeye entering the Sound are largely migrants on their way to the Fraser River basin of British Columbia, which is well supplied with suitable spawning lakes and headwaters. Poor spawning in the upper Fraser is generally reflected in a poor catch 4 years later. On their way through Puget Sound to the Fraser sockeye were formerly exposed to an array of cannery traps, to numerous purse seiners clustered around the entrance to the Strait of Juan de Fuca and the Gulf of Georgia, and to gill nets in the mouth of the Fraser.

Since both Canada and the United States had a vital stake in the imperiled Fraser runs, a treaty was proposed in 1907. Passed by the Canadian Parliament, the measure was defeated in the United States Senate. During the following 30 years, two similar treaties were approved by Canada but held up by certain American interests.

SOCKEYE SALMON TREATY. It was not until 1937 that a revised treaty was ratified by both countries. By this time ruthless overfishing and poor escapement had reduced sockeye runs to a point where drastic rehabilitation was necessary. The treaty provided for an International Pacific Salmon Fisheries Commission, with three representatives from each country.

The Commission is empowered to investigate the natural history of the sockeye salmon of the Fraser River, hatchery methods, spawning ground conditions

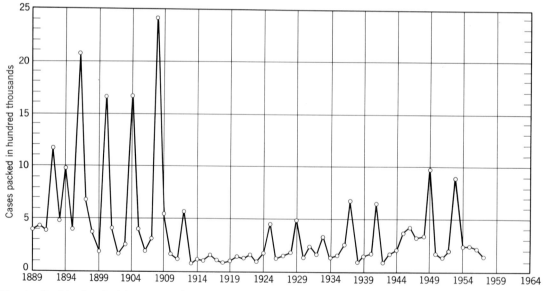

Fig. 4 Combined pack of American and Canadian sockeye salmon, spawned in the Frazer River system. Frazer sockeye mature in a 4-year cycle; prior to 1914 the 1897–1901–1905–1909–1913 runs made Puget Sound one of the world's richest fishing grounds. After a rock slide in Hell's Canyon cut off access to spawning grounds the big runs vanished. In recent years the best cycles have been 1930–1934–1938–1942–1946–1950–1954–1958. The anticipated big-year run of 1962 did not appear due to unexplained mortality in the ocean. (International Pacific Salmon Fisheries Commission.)

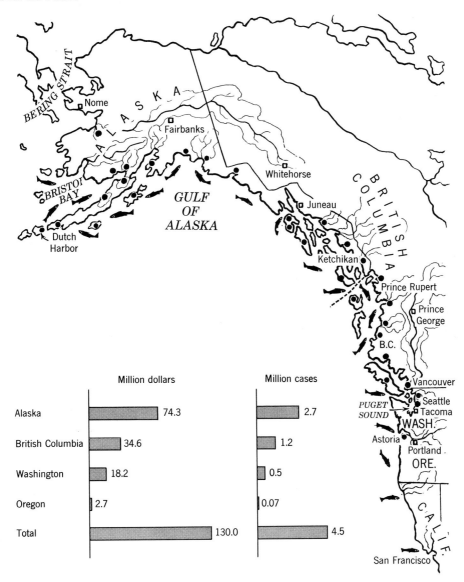

Million dollars

Alaska	74.3
British Columbia	34.6
Washington	18.2
Oregon	2.7
Total	130.0

Million cases

	2.7
	1.2
	0.5
	0.07
	4.5

Fig. 5 North Pacific salmon areas and production for 1963. The fishing areas extend from California northward to the coastal waters in southwestern Alaska and the pack in 1963 consisted of 4.5 million cases valued at $130 million. (*Pacific Fisherman Yearbook,* 1964.)

and related matters. It may conduct fish cultural operations, improve spawning grounds or stock the Fraser with sockeye . . . . and recommend removal of obstructions to migration. It is empowered to limit or prohibit the taking of sockeye in Convention waters . . . . Only such fishing gear may be used in any open season as the Commission may approve. The catch of sockeye shall be distributed as equally between the two countries as is practicable.[6]

Canada agreed to make the entire Fraser basin available for restoration and propagation,

[6] *International Pacific Salmon Fisheries Commission, Annual Report,* 1945, p. 3.

the cost to be borne jointly. The research staff of the Commission began its investigation in 1938 and studied sockeye salmon through two complete cycles lasting 8 years. With the data obtained the Commission drew up the necessary control measures.

FLUCTUATION IN THE SALMON RUNS. Both the American and the Canadian pack of Fraser-spawned sockeye was for many years dependent on a "big-year" cycle, that is, 1901–1905–1909–1913, and three lesser runs in the intermediate years. Tomasevich says:

A mistake made in the exploitation of the sockeye salmon fishery of the Fraser River system . . . was the exploitation of the "off year" runs with the same (or greater) intensity as those of the "big year." The consequence was the overfishing of these runs instead of letting more spawning fish escape with a view to gradually building up these runs in the end, possibly to the level of the big-year runs.[7]

ROCKSLIDE AT HELL'S GATE. During the building of a railroad through the Fraser River canyon in 1913, a rockslide was dumped into the narrow channel at Hell's Gate. The stoppage was so complete that most of the sockeye escapement of that year was cut off from the spawning lakes and streams of the upper Fraser basin and perished below the blockade. As a result, the sockeye pack of 1917 dropped to 500,000 cases.

FISHWAYS FOR A LARGER ESCAPEMENT. Recognizing the Hell's Gate blockade as a permanent obstacle, the Commission decided on a permanent remedy—concrete fishways on both sides of the canyon to facilitate passage through the narrows at unfavorable stages of the river. The year construction began, 1943, the pack of Fraser-spawned salmon sank to 51,000 cases, the lowest figure in 50 years.

With both fishways in operation in 1946 salmon in adequate numbers reached the spawning beds of the upper Fraser and Lake Quesnal. The escapement in 1945 and 1946 was approximately four times as large as in the previous cycle years of 1941 and 1942. Productive lakes

[7] Jozo Tomasevich, *International Agreements on Conservation of Marine Resources,* Stanford, California, 1943, p. 239.

and streams where salmon had been practically extinct were restocked with fingerlings reared in hatcheries. Many years of restricted catches and generous spawning escapements have been part of the rehabilitation plan which has stabilized both the sockeye and pink salmon stocks.

As a major contribution to practical salmon culture the International Commission (IPSFC) has developed an effective basis for forecasting runs in advance. Because of the years salmon spend in ocean depths, such a forecast is difficult to make. It was given a conclusive test on Fraser River sockeye. Based on the great parent year of 1958, the obvious expectation was for a huge run of sockeye in 1962. Using two lines of evidence the Commission scientists concluded that the ocean survival of this class had been poor. Their estimate, made well in advance, was for a run of 4 million fish, far below normal expectancy; this forecast proved correct as have many others since then.

Joint Canadian-American planning for the future of the Fraser includes greatly improved access to spawning grounds, and the opening of many additional areas, now barren or only slightly used. An active construction program is in process (1964) to provide still higher and more efficient fishways which will permit inbound salmon to reach their home waters at any stage of the river. Potential spawning or rearing grounds include such extensive bodies of fresh water as Harrison, Francois, and Kamloops lakes. By opening many square miles of now barren salmon waters the Commission believes that the Fraser system can become the world's most productive salmon river.

CONFLICT OF INTEREST—POWER DAMS ON THE COLUMBIA. Included in the problem of salmon conservation on the Columbia are two gigantic dams, Bonneville and Grand Coulee, each higher than any obstacle previously surmounted by anadromous fish. The 30-foot Rock Island dam on the middle Columbia is equipped with fish ladders which provide passage for salmon on their way to the spawning grounds. The 55-foot Bonneville Dam on the lower Columbia has a system of fish ladders and locks by which salmon can be raised to the upper level. The Bonneville fish-ways have proved successful, spawning salmon having ready access to tributary waters.

The 550-foot Grand Coulee Dam on the middle Columbia, however, is an impassable obstacle. Since it is economically impracticable to convey fish over a barrier of this height, salmon runs are completely blocked at this point. It is estimated that 1100 linear miles of spawning streams in the upper Columbia basin of Washington, Idaho, and British Columbia were lost. To counteract partially this reduction a large federal hatchery with acres of rearing pools has been built at Leavenworth, Washington. Adult salmon on their return journey to the upper Columbia are intercepted at Rock Island Dam, stripped of their eggs, and the eggs fertilized. Salmon were taken by tank truck to suitable planting areas in understocked rivers tributary to the Columbia below Grand Coulee Dam—streams such as the Wenatchee, Okanogan, Entiat, and Methow; the last two are now supplied by hatcheries of their own. Augmented runs and artificial propagation have become a permanent part of sustained spawning stocks.

CONSERVATION OF PACIFIC HALIBUT

One of the most popular food fishes in America is the halibut. This great deep-sea flounder, dark on its upper or right side, white on the left or under side, early became one of the staples of the Atlantic coast fish trade. After the inauguration of fast transcontinental rail service between Puget Sound and the East coast, the first shipment of halibut was made from Tacoma in 1888; since the turn of the century Pacific halibut have been a major factor in the eastern market. Once landed to the extent of 14,000,000 pounds per year, Atlantic halibut have been heavily overfished, decreasing to about 285,000 pounds annually. In the United States the production ratio of Pacific to Atlantic halibut is now approaching 100 to 1.

The Pacific Halibut Catch. The Pacific halibut banks follow the continental shelf from northern California to the Bering Sea (Fig. 6). Halibut are caught on long bottom setlines which are strung with a series of shorter lines baited with herring or octopus; a unit of gear of this sort, called a "skate," is usually set at depths varying from 35 to 200 fathoms. Large and well-equipped vessels with considerable cruising radius operate in the Gulf of Alaska and on both sides of the Alaska Peninsula; these larger vessels carry fifty or more skates of gear, and smaller ones which fish halibut in the coastal waters of the United States and Canada carry 20 to 25. The industry is in the hands of American and Canadian fishermen, with Seattle, Vancouver, Prince Rupert, and Ketchikan as the principal base ports and shipping centers. Cleaned, iced, and landed at one of the Northwest ports, halibut reach United States markets fresh or frozen (Table 3).

Table 3. United States and Canadian Catches of Halibut by Regulatory Areas
(Thousands of Pounds)

Year	Area 1 U.S.	Area 2 U.S.	Area 2 Canada	Area 2 Total	Areas 3A, 3B, North, 3B N. Triangle and 3B S U.S.	Areas 3A, 3B, North, 3B N. Triangle and 3B S Canada	Areas 3A, 3B, North, 3B N. Triangle and 3B S Total°	All Areas U.S.	All Areas Canada	All Areas Total
1931	923	14,609	7,018	21,627	20,907	765	21,672	36,439	7,783	44,222
1961	270	15,756	13,093	28,849	24,039	16,373	40,412	40,065	29,466	69,531
1962	312	14,480	14,183	28,663	25,654	20,490	46,144	40,446	34,673	75,119
1963	210	11,603	14,208	25,811	22,430	22,776	44,756	34,243	36,984	71,227

° Does not include 3,600,000 pounds taken by Japan in Area 3B North Triangle in 1963.

[Source: International Pacific Halibut Commission.]

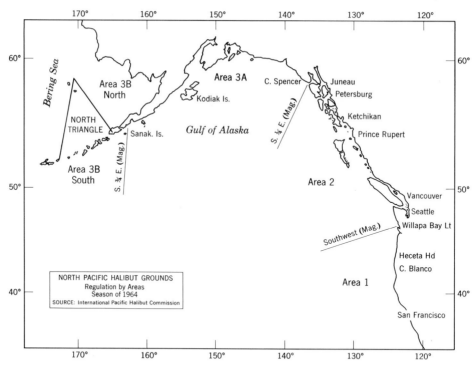

Fig. 6 Halibut fishing grounds of Pacific North America. Six regulatory areas were defined by the International Pacific Halibut Commission in 1963. Largest catches permitted were 34 million pounds from Area 3A and 25 million pounds from Area 2; Area 3B South was given 4 million and there were no limits in Area 1 and 3B North. The new North Triangle shared by United States, Canada, and Japan was allotted 11 million pounds in 1963, 6 million (unfilled) in 1964, and was recommended for closure in 1965 as overfished. (After International Pacific Halibut Commission.)

The halibut lives to more than 25 years old and generally weighs 5 to 200 pounds, although a few giants of 250 to 350 pounds are sometimes taken. During the period of abundance in the early 1900's most of the fishing was done off the coast of British Columbia and southeastern Alaska, within a radius of 500 miles from Seattle and Vancouver, B.C. Peak production was reached in 1915 when the total catch was 69,000,000 pounds. A catch between 50,000,000 and 60,000,000 pounds was considered normal, and in order to maintain this figure both Americans and Canadians worked more and more distant grounds.

CONCEALED DEPLETION. Production figures may give no indication of impending depletion

until after much of the damage has been done. This is especially true of demersal fish with a long life cycle and late maturity. Most female halibut do not arrive at the spawning stage until 12 to 16 years old; about half of them mature at 12 years, and only a small proportion as early as 8 to 10 years. Depletion therefore may be even more insidious than in a salmon run, where the actual shortage of spawners will appear sooner.

EVIDENCE OF DEPLETION. For many years the decline of halibut in the North Pacific was partially concealed because as an area was depleted the fishermen widened their radius of operations and still managed to bring in the usual poundage. Finally the limits of lateral expansion were reached, and, with a greatly increased fishing fleet at work, three definite evidences of depletion began to appear.

1. Despite increased fishing the annual catch was declining on the southern grounds, which had been worked longest and hardest.

2. The proportion of mature fish brought to market was decreasing, a larger share of each catch consisting of "chicken" or small, immature halibut.

3. The catch per skate or unit of gear had declined and was continuing to decline at an alarming rate.

International Pacific Halibut Commission. Although the normal amount of fish continued to reach the market, fishery experts pointed out the basic unsoundness of the situation and the possibility that the Pacific banks were faced with a decline similar to that of the Atlantic. The authorities, both in the United States and in Canada, were convinced that this situation could not continue indefinitely without destroying the Pacific halibut fisheries or reducing them to insignificance.

The International Pacific Halibut Commission was created in 1924 with a membership of two Americans and two Canadians and was given authority to investigate and recommend conservation measures. Comprehensive surveys of the banks were made, using chartered fishing vessels. Thousands of fish were caught, measured, tagged with a metal clip and returned to the water. By offering a bounty for each tagged fish caught, they obtained recoveries and information on as high as 40 percent of the fish released. There were distinct populations of halibut, each living, spawning, and dying within its own area with little migration between areas; a depleted area was unlikely to be restocked from an adjoining one. Artificial propagation of such a deep sea fish is impracticable; it is also impossible to control the food supply or enemies of the fish. Each stock had to be managed so that the catch from it would be fully balanced by natural propagation and growth.

LIFE HISTORY OF THE HALIBUT. Accurate data concerning spawning habits and early growth of any demersal fish are hard to obtain. The Commission research staff spent several winters in the Gulf of Alaska and off the Alaska Peninsula to build up a complete history of the Pacific halibut.

The mature fish gather in schools to spawn along the edge of the continental shelf during the winter season, December to March. The North Pacific expedition took quantities of eggs as well as baby halibut, plotting their location and later migration to deeper water—50 to 100 fathoms. Halibut usually spend their entire life in or near one bank, but after maturity move about freely within it. With these data in hand, it was possible to make recommendations for control and restoration.

REGULATORY MEASURES APPLIED. A treaty giving the Commission authority over the halibut fisheries was signed by Canada and the United States in 1930. Its main regulatory measures included:

1. The division of the fishing grounds into several separate areas which are regulated separately; in 1964 six areas were used (Fig. 6).

2. The application of annual catch limits to be raised or lowered at the discretion of the Commission. Originally set at 46,000,000 pounds (dressed, heads-off weight), the limits have been gradually increased.

3. The closure of each area when its catch limit has been taken. In 1932, the first year of regulation, the fishing season lasted a full 9 months until the closed winter season intervened.

4. The creation of nursery areas where fishing is entirely prohibited.

CAMPAIGN OF EDUCATION. In exercising its new enforcement powers the Commission held and still holds numerous public hearings open to all—fishermen, large- and small-boat owners, and the wholesalers who handle the shipment of fresh and frozen fish. The research staff inaugurated a campaign of education, demonstrating the facts of depletion by means of maps, charts, and graphs, and stressing the need for regulation and restoration of the fishery to its former position, with as little restriction as possible on individual fishing rights.

The restrictions adopted were so successful that the United States Fish and Wildlife Service stated in its 1933 report:

The practicability of the Commission's regulations involving division of the convention waters into areas, limiting the catch from each area, licensing of vessels for the halibut fishery, collection of statistics of abundance and locality of capture, modification of the closed season, and closing of nursery grounds has been satisfactorily proved.

RETURN TO A HIGH LEVEL OF ABUNDANCE. As a result of some 40 years of concerted effort, the North Pacific halibut fishery has become the outstanding world example of rehabilitation and sound management. In 1961 the catch had risen to 69 million pounds; in 1962 it reached 75 million, the largest in its history; and in 1963 it was 71 million. The dedication of a scientific staff plus firm regulation and control have been largely responsible.

In the beginning it took a full 9 months to fill the limit, then 44,000,000 pounds. The much higher catches of the present are taken in varying periods in each area, but generally within a season of 100 days—a great economy of time and effort. Today few halibut fishermen would care to return to the cutthroat competition of the 1920's. Production stabilized at a high level gives them immediate profits as well as an assured future.

Pressure from Other Nations. The high productivity of the revived halibut grounds adjacent to Alaska has not escaped the notice of other fishing nations; both Japan and the USSR operate large fleets in Bering Sea. Under the 1953 North Pacific treaty with the United States and Canada, Japan had agreed to abstain from participation in the halibut fishery, but in 1962 pressed hard for rights in east Bering Sea. Participation was approved, the United States, Canada, and Japan sharing the 1963 catch in the

newly established North Triangle area. They took the quota of 11 million pounds, Japan's share amounting to 3.6 million pounds; a year later they were unable to fill a much smaller allotment and the Commission has ruled that the Triangle has been overfished. Here the three governments face a rehabilitation task of some magnitude. Area 2 has also shown signs of decline and its annual catch figure has been lowered.

At the present stage any additional pressure from outside fishing fleets might easily upset the present balance in halibut.[8] The USSR fleet in Bering Sea is trawling vigorously for bottom fish such as ocean perch, flounder, and sablefish rather than for halibut, but of necessity will pick up large numbers of juveniles; what effect this mortality will have on halibut spawning some years hence is a matter of conjecture. Both the Commission and the commercial industry are sensitive to adverse trends from any quarter. The Commission's objective from the first has been to increase the halibut population to a point where there is a maximum yield and then stabilize it. Any relaxation of the present controls would be regarded as a temptation to indulge in reckless overfishing, with a few highly productive years, followed by a lapse of the fishery into its quondam state of insignificance.

PELAGIC SEALING: THE PRIBILOF ISLANDS

Like the whale, the Northern fur seal has long been a problem in conservation. The rocky Pribilof Islands of the Bering Sea make up the largest seal rookery in the world. In winter the seals swim far south in the ocean, returning in early summer to their home grounds where the pups are born. In the past seal hunters of all

---

[8] The halibut problem bears a certain resemblance to present-day oyster growing in Chesapeake Bay. The planter leases a tract of old worked-out public grounds, replants and rehabilitates it at considerable expense, and when his oysters are ready to harvest, must protect his beds from neighbors who have contributed nothing to the enterprise.

nations congregated around the Pribilofs to indulge on indiscriminate killing. After an unsuccessful attempt in the early 1890's to have the Bering Sea recognized as a closed area subject to its sole jurisdiction, the United States in 1911 negotiated a treaty with Great Britain, Russia, and Japan. This agreement, the North Pacific Sealing Convention which prohibited pelagic sealing, was signed just in time, the herd having been reduced from an estimated 1,500,-000 to a scant 216,000 in 1912.

CONTROL AND RESTORATION. United States' control includes both protection and scientific management. Coast Guard cutters accompany the herd on its annual migration. Since seals are polygamous and sexes are born in equal numbers, a large proportion of the bachelor seals is surplus and can be killed without impairing the natural increase. Three-year-old bachelors provide the major share of the Pribilof skins which now average some 80,000 per year; Canada and Japan each receive 15 percent of the skins. Sold at St. Louis fur auctions annually the United States' share brings some $4,000,000, netting the government a million dollars above expenses. Under this system of control by agreement, the seal herd had been restored to its original size by 1947.

THE WHALING INDUSTRY

The whale has been pursued so ruthlessly for more than a century that a conservative estimate of the present world whale population is 200,000, a mere remnant of the hordes which once frequented the seas. This great deep-sea mammal has been particularly vulnerable to the mechanized efficiency of modern methods.

The shift of whaling operations—from Norway and Iceland to the shores of New England, thence to the North Pacific with headquarters in the Hawaiian Islands, and finally south to New Zealand, the Falkland Islands, and the Antarctic—provides a graphic progression in the mismanagement of a resource. A few whales widely scattered throughout the marine world

are processed at small shore stations. Two areas with concentrated stocks, Antarctica and the Aleutian area of the North Pacific, are targets for modern, mechanized whaling on a large scale.

FACTORY SHIPS IN THE ANTARCTIC. Seventy percent of the world whale catch comes from the Antarctic. The most active center is Ross Sea, where the cold waters are rich in tiny crustacea and other minute sea organisms. During the short Antarctic summer, December to February, the great mammals feed along the edges of the southern ice floes. Whaling in this ocean, begun by the Norwegians in 1904, soon attracted the major fishing nations.

Vessels averaging 20,000 tons are equipped with all necessary machinery for whale carcass reduction. They carry helicopters for spotting, and each employs ten or twelve small but high-powered catcher boats. A catcher hunts down and harpoons a whale, which is towed back to the ship and drawn up a slipway to the flensing floor. In addition to oil this seagoing factory prepares whale beef which finds a ready market in the Orient and to a lesser extent in Europe. Bone and scrap are made into meal or fertilizer and the oil is used in margarine, soap, cosmetics, or lubricants.

The Conservation Problem. Whales range the oceans freely between Arctic and tropical waters and are not under the direct jurisdiction of any country. They are common property available to the first comer and heavy inroads have been made into world stocks. Japanese scientists report that the gray whale is seldom seen in the North Pacific and several other varieties are rare. Sperm, right, and humpback whales are diminishing all over the world, with finback, sei, and blue whales accounting for the bulk of the recent catch. Too many immature whales are being taken, and all varieties are being killed faster than they can reproduce.

INTERNATIONAL WHALING CONVENTIONS. Convinced that several species were facing early extinction biologists and oceanographers proposed an international convention to protect the remaining whale stocks. Signed by twenty-six nations, this 1935 treaty halted the killing of certain species, set size limits for others, established a 3-months season, and provided sanctuaries where whaling was prohibited. World War II abrogated these agreements. Following the war eighteen nations signed a new International Whaling Convention (1946) which created a Commission with headquarters in Norway and set a seasonal catch limit of 16,000 whale units. A unit consists of one blue whale, two fin-whales, or two and one-half humpbacks. Participating countries were given quotas proportionate to their fleets. Catches are reported weekly by radio, the season closing when quotas have been filled.[9]

WHALE STOCK MANAGEMENT: PRESENT VERSUS FUTURE. Before World War II the Norse oceanographer, Hjort, estimated that there were not over 300,000 whales in Antarctic waters; scientific advisors to the Whaling Commission estimate the present stock at not over 100,000. Under the Convention of 1946 it was assumed that a seasonal catch of 16,000 units would stabilize the resource at a safe level. Research data collected by the Commission's scientific staff soon indicated that this figure was too liberal; certain species were being killed too rapidly and were endangered. After reducing the annual kill to 10,000 units, the scientists soon called for further readjustment to 5000 units. This met firm opposition from countries with heavy investment in new vessels and equipment. To supplement the findings of the Commission staff a special committee of scientists analyzed all data, coming to similar conclusions.

Grey- and right-whales have been fully protected throughout the world; the fishing countries agreed to add humpback and blue whales to the abstention list, but refused to accept a seasonal limit to 5000 units. Sei- and fin-whales

[9] In 1962–1963 five countries operated seventeen fleets in the Antarctic, Japan leading with seven, followed by Norway and the USSR with four each. Lesser participants have since dropped out leaving a three-country fishery in Antarctica, Japan-Norway-USSR in a 50-30-20 ratio.

will provide most of the future catch, intensifying the pressure on those two species which in turn will deteriorate. In disregarding scientific findings, the operators have placed present profits in a higher category than future stability.

THE ALEUTIANS. In the Aleutian area of the north Pacific, with the second largest whale population, Japan and the USSR operate highly efficient fleets. They have an agreed 6-month's season and a minimum whale length of 35 feet, a measurement difficult to guarantee in practice. There are no restrictions on species or on numbers killed. With three fleets each Japan took 4700 whales in 1963, the USSR slightly more; the Russians added a fourth fleet in 1964. Sperm, sei- and fin-whales are plentiful, providing the bulk of the catch; blue whales are more limited and humpbacks are scarce. No other restraints are in prospect and Japan has indicated concern for whale survival in the Aleutians.

Although not a direct participant in world whaling, the United States is concerned with marine conservation as well as with viable international agreements. Norway and Japan are vitally interested in stabilizing this resource at a favorable permanent level. It is generally recognized that sharper restrictive measures must be adopted and respected if this unique mammal is to survive.

MANAGEMENT OF FISHERIES

The Abundance-Depletion Cycle. The foregoing accounts of shad, salmon, halibut, seals, and whales may be regarded as fairly typical of the conservation problem inherent in most American fisheries, as well as illustrating the methods by which restoration may be achieved. In most commercial operations, where fish are regarded as free goods of nature and the only law is the law of capture, a well-defined pattern is now recognized.

1. A period of abundance, with large catches per man, per boat, or other unit of effort. The apparently inexhaustible supply of a common

property resource attracts competitive operators and leads to overfishing.

2. A period of declining catches, with the return per unit of effort falling off to a marked degree.

3. Intensification of fishing efforts. This understandable attempt of the fishermen to keep up the poundage generally means more and larger boats, more efficient gear, and a wider cruising radius.

4. Depletion and abandonment of the grounds. Depletion often occurs with scant warning, because, by the more intensive combing of the sea or by taking constantly larger percentages of schooling fish, such as sardines or anadromous runs of shad or salmon, the impending exhaustion may be concealed for some time.

Many varieties of fish have gone through this cycle, which begins to operate just as soon as the original abundance drops below a certain level. In some instances, if a scant spawning stock remains, a ground may rebuild naturally but slowly to a point where fishing may be resumed years later.

Even though certain fluctuations in abundance of marine life are caused by biologic factors or by physical and chemical conditions within the sea or in fresh-water spawning grounds, overfishing is still the outstanding cause of depletion. Consequently, restriction on overfishing is the most direct remedy that can be applied to marine life management.

The Pollution Problem. Industrial development has placed an additional handicap on the many streams and rivers formerly utilized as fishing areas. (See also Chapters 12 and 18.) Sewage from cities, oil from ships in harbors, and mill wastes of all kinds have been poured into streams and bays, particularly along the heavily industrialized North Atlantic seaboard. Also destructive to fish life are the effluents from coal and metal mines, chemical plants, rayon mills, pulp mills, fruit and vegetable canneries, and sugar refineries. One of the recognized

causes for the decline of shad runs is the contamination of streams flowing into Chesapeake Bay. The lessened herring, pike, and perch catch in Lake Erie is partly the result of industrial pollution. In 1963 the death of some 5,000,000 fish in the Mississippi River Delta was traced to rain runoff from farmlands which had been sprayed with a DDT-type insecticide.

Factories and fisheries are conflicting interests, and the industrial necessities of a given locality may prove greater than its need for uncontaminated shad waters or oyster beds. In the future, however, it should be feasible to have purity of waters without placing any real handicap on industry. Scientific research has solved some of the problems of factory wastes, so that industrial plants are increasingly willing to cooperate in keeping streams free from poisonous or offensive materials. The fouling of coastal waters by oil-burning and oil-carrying ships is now prohibited by federal laws. Since stream pollution is also undesirable from the social and esthetic standpoint, public opinion is now calling for considerable future improvement.

Agencies for Scientific Research. Control work in fisheries falls into two broad divisions: (1) investigation and (2) regulation. The restoration of any declining species must always be preceded by a thorough investigation of the life history and habitat; these studies are the prerogative of the fishery biologist, limnologist, and oceanographer.

Concerning investigational work there is little difference of opinion. The accumulation of biologic data as well as the economic facts of exploitation is usually favored by all interests. Within the limitations of its appropriations, the Fish and Wildlife Service has made innumerable studies; others have been made by international commissions for halibut, tuna, Great Lakes fisheries, and sockeye salmon. The commercial fishing interests, with millions of dollars invested, are willing to cooperate with survey work and frequently assist in financing it.

Most states have fishery commissions with research staffs, most of them specializing on local problems. California began the study of the valuable sardine industry about 1919, intensifying it after 1947 as the fishery declined. The Washington State Department of Fisheries, originally interested mainly in salmon, has made numerous studies of shrimp, oysters, herring, and razor clams (Fig. 1). Among the valuable agencies is the International Commission for the North Atlantic Fisheries, which includes the countries especially interested in the North Atlantic littoral and the Newfoundland banks. This Commission carries on biologic and economic investigations, collecting and correlating all data that are valuable to its members. The Bureau of Commercial Fisheries operates a dozen widely scattered biological laboratories, the one at Boothbay Harbor, Maine, specializing on herring and lobster; one at Beaufort, North Carolina, on menhaden, shad, striped bass, blue crabs; Gulf Breeze, Florida, is doing research on oysters and pesticides; Galveston, Texas, shrimp, red tide, and pesticides; and Honolulu, Hawaii, the tunas. Other laboratories, including many in universities, are making significant contributions to marine research; included are Scripps Institution of Oceanography in California, the Fisheries Research Institute of the University of Washington, the Chesapeake Biological Laboratory at Solomons Island, Maryland, and the biological laboratory of Ohio State University at Put-in-Bay. This is, however, by no means a complete list.

Restrictive Legislation and Enforcement.
Fishing is an outgrowth of the old hunting economy, and there is probably no occupation in which the worker is more intensely individualistic and more opposed to any type of restriction. The natural tendency of the fisherman, as an area begins to decline, is to fish even harder. Individuals or small companies with a heavy investment in boats and gear, with families to support and taxes to meet, are in no position to agree voluntarily on any conservational policy that calls for a restricted catch. The industry therefore is generally unable to take a long-range view of the matter.

For many years any attempt to follow investigation with restrictive legislation was fought by groups who believed their immediate interests demanded wide-open fishing. After carefully planned legislation was secured, it was often difficult to enforce it. Most of the regulatory agencies are using their powers with the utmost discretion and are permitting the industry to take the maximum amount of fish commensurate with a sustained supply for the future. In certain areas the industry has been educated to accept a carefully regulated catch, a larger escape of spawning fish, more eggs, more fingerlings, a larger stock of mature fish, and eventually a larger surplus for commercial capture.

Control of an entire fishery by a single bureau or commission with discretionary powers has so far proved to be the most effective type of regulation. In the United States the legal control of fisheries is vested in the states, and various commissions have been successful in regulating the season, the types of gear, excessive diversion for irrigation, and the operation of state hatcheries.

In many states there is a sharp legislative conflict between the commercial and the sports fishermen over the allocation of fishing rights and privileges. In general, any declining species tends to become the subject of a determined legislative drive to reserve it exclusively for the sportsman, a somewhat questionable interpretation of the principle of conservation.

Interstate Control of Fishing Waters.
Some of the richest fishing rivers, bays, and coastal waters of the United States are administered under two or more sets of rules, sometimes at cross purposes. Regardless of political boundaries, New York shares certain fishing grounds with Connecticut, others with New Jersey. A similar situation prevails in the Great Lakes and elsewhere. Stocks of fish may migrate across a state line, sometimes spawning in one state and feeding in another.

The states traditionally exercise full jurisdiction over their coastal and interior waters, setting up the regulations under which fisheries are operated. The legislative approach to interstate migration of fish has often been unrealistic, and its results controversial. The Maryland-Virginia friction over oyster beds is of long duration. "Maryland crabs migrate to Virginia waters to spawn, and hence legislation established in the upper state will have little effect on crab rehabilitation unless corresponding and cooperative enactments and enforcement can be instituted by the lower state." [10]

On the Atlantic coast the highly migratory shrimp move south in winter through state waters with diverse regulations and, while still undersized, are taken in excessive quantities along the Florida coast. Under the present system, progressive laws of one state may be nullified by obsolete laws of a neighboring commonwealth. There is a growing tendency, however, for states sharing the same stocks of fish to strive for uniformity in legislation as in Washington and Oregon.

Freedom of the Seas and Fishing Rights. Fisheries throughout the world including both coastal and deep-sea are beset with problems of jurisdiction. The ancient and honorable 3-mile limit, generally accepted as standard maritime practice, is of doubtful validity when applied to certain questions of fishing rights. The more migratory the fish, the more complicated the jurisdiction, and even relatively sedentary stocks pose certain problems. Anadromous varieties such as salmon and shad, hatched in inland lakes and streams but deriving most of their growth from planktonic pastures in the ocean, return as adults to their original waters. In the ocean they have long been subject to the law of open capture, although not in large numbers; even a few miles from their home streams they may be taken by anyone. Does the parent hatchery have any vested right in them? Can bottom fish such as the halibut, rehabilitated and conserved by agreement between two nations, be harvested freely by a third?

THE ABSTENTION PRINCIPLE. At various times Japanese and Russian vessels including floating canneries have encroached on Alaskan halibut grounds and salmon runs. In the 1930's Secre-tary of State Cordell Hull pointed out that alien interests which bore none of the cost and had been subjected to no conservation restrictions were not entitled to share in the returns from conservation practices. He included another principle which is as well established as freedom of the seas: the right of a nation to protect its own vital interests to any essential distance off shore. In 1953 by a treaty between Japan, Canada, and the United States, the Japanese agreed to abstain from American salmon, halibut, and herring fisheries. This treaty defined what is now known as the abstention principle: if a nation has exclusively developed a coastal fishery, has subjected it to conservation research and regulation, and is making full use of it on a sustained yield basis, other nations should abstain from permitting their fishermen to enter it regardless of the distance the fishery extends off shore.[11]

THE THREE-MILE AND OTHER LIMITS. The international implications and problems of fisheries have continued to engross nations, and the answers have varied widely, leading to treaties, agreements, conventions, reliance on historic fishing rights, and attempts to define marine jurisdiction in terms of distances and boundaries.

Sovereignty over home waters within the 3-mile limit has had the widest general acceptance despite its origin as a maritime dictum never intended as a directive for resource management. There is now a growing disagreement on the 3-mile concept. Many nations, for example Norway, have pointed out the absurdity of a broad coastal embayment, a 700-mile estuary such as the St. Lawrence, or a deep fjord penetrating 40 miles into the land, all fished by foreign fleets keeping just outside a 3-mile ribbon of shore. In 1964 the Twelve-Mile Treaty of London was approved by thirteen European nations. Accepted by every country in western Europe, it adopted a 12-mile limit for fisheries, measured from headland to headland. Australia

---

[10] Julian D. Corrington, "Reorganization of Conservation Work in Maryland," *Science,* February 5, 1943.

[11] Edward W. Allen, Chairman, International North Pacific Fisheries Commission.

has taken similar action and Canada leans in the same direction.

The present international trend is toward more joint agreements and treaties with many nations participating. The United Nations called two "Law of the Sea" conferences at Geneva in 1958 and 1960. In addition to compromises between those who sought protection for their own coastal fisheries and those who wished to exploit all coastal fisheries throughout the world, there have been various developments of value to conservation (Fig. 7).

The United States has a new law (1964) asserting jurisdiction over all shell fish on the continental shelf, and making it unlawful for vessels of other nations to fish within its territorial waters. Many nations are asserting firmer con-

trol over broader areas of their adjacent waters. Although self-interest is obviously paramount, sustained yield programs will benefit.

The Freedom of the Seas concept, as we know it, originated with Hugo Grotius who is called the father of modern international law. His objectives were to break the navigation monopolies asserted by Portugal and Spain and to ward off the threat of James I of England to suppress Dutch fishermen from fishing off the Scotch and English Coasts.

There is as much reason today as ever why navigation and trade should enjoy the greatest freedom, but it is now known that certain varieties of ocean fish are subject to severe depletion; hence it is no longer reasonable that aggressive nations should be permitted to fish as they please, wherever they please, regardless of the detrimental effects on local stocks and damage to local communities.[12]

[12] Contributed by Edward W. Allen.

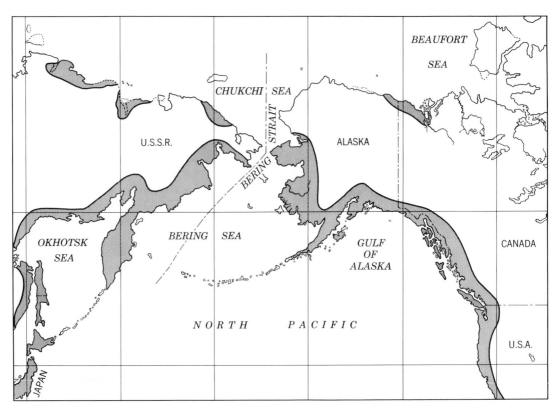

Fig. 7 Conflict of interest in the North Pacific where the United States, Canada, Japan, and the Soviet Union are rivals. The areas shown with horizontal lines include the world's best salmon rivers. Here anadromous and demersal fish are common property and international agreements become imperative. (After U.S. Fish and Wildlife Service.)

AQUICULTURE FOR THE FUTURE

The science of land utilization has progressed rapidly since about 1900, and agriculture is now in possession of a body of exact knowledge concerning crop production. The technique of underwater research has been gradually perfected to the point where it is now possible to make reasonably accurate and extensive examinations of the ocean at any given depth. Scientists hope that it will thus be possible to lay the basis for agriculture's companion industry, farming the continental shelves so that fishing will develop into real aquiculture.

Scientific fish farming in the United States is on the increase, including the construction of artificial ponds that are stocked with suitable varieties of game or pond fish, such as bass, crappie, bluegill, and catfish. By adding chemical fertilizers to the water, microscopic plants and insects multiply, serving as the base for a highly productive pyramid of underwater fish food. Under proper management the annual return averages 200 to 600 pounds of fish per acre.

Oyster farming in Chesapeake Bay, Willapa Bay (Washington), and other shallow inlets is already far more profitable than the unrestricted exploitation of public oyster grounds. The soft-shelled crab industry of Tangier Island, Virginia, is a systematic business with the fish under control. Mollusks and crustaceans seem especially adapted to aquiculture. Pelagic and anadromous fish present more obvious difficulties in management, and it may be impossible to apply this method to demersal types. In the not too distant future, however, man may find it profitable to cultivate the sea as carefully as he is now cultivating the land.

Program of Restoration. It is impossible to apply identical conservation measures to all fisheries. Each must be regarded as a separate problem. The remedial measures for all fisheries, however, tend to have certain similarities, which may include:

1. A program of scientific research until the complete life history is known.
2. Flexible regulations which may include one or more of the following corrective measures: (*a*) provision for adult escapement; (*b*) a quantity limit on the catch; (*c*) restrictions on the size or the age of the catch; (*d*) a closed season for part of the year, or possibly for a term of years if the stock is badly depleted; and (*e*) refuge zones or nursery areas where fishing is prohibited.
3. Restrictions on types of gear to eliminate too-intensive exploitation.
4. Removal of obstacles to migration or the construction of fishways.
5. Artificial propagation by means of hatcheries and the stocking of barren areas if practicable.
6. Abatement of stream and coastal pollution.
7. Licensing of vessels or other fishing media to ensure more effective control.
8. Securing the cooperation of the fishing industry and the public by a program of education.

It is always easier to preserve an original stock than to rebuild an exhausted fishery. Preservation of fisheries depends largely on public willingness to recognize the danger, grant adequate appropriations for research, and submit to reasonable regulation. The ultimate goal of all such measures is a sustained yield and a permanent abundance.

References

Official Publications, both scientific and economic, of: U.S. Fish and Wildlife Service; International Fisheries Commission; International Pacific Salmon Fisheries Commission; Departments of Fisheries (or Conservation and Resources) of the various states.

Baker, Ralph C., Ford Wilke, and Howard Baltzo, *The Northern Fur Seal Circular 169,* Bureau of Commercial Fisheries, Washington, D.C., 1963.

Committee for Whaling Statistics, *International Whaling Statistics*, Annual. Oslo, Norway.

Davidson, Frederick A., and Samuel J. Hutchinson, *The Geographic Distribution and Environment Limitations of the Pacific Salmon*, Bulletin 26, Bureau of Fisheries, Government Printing Office, Washington, D.C., 1938.

Hobbs, Carl L., and Karl F. Lagler, *Fishes of the Great Lakes Region*, University of Michigan Press, Ann Arbor, 1965.

Innis, H. A., *The Cod Fisheries; the History of an International Economy*, Yale University Press, New Haven, Conn., 1940.

Koo, Ted S. Y., Editor, *Studies of Alaska Red Salmon*, University of Washington Press, Seattle, Washington, 1963. This is the first in a scientific series entitled Publications in Fisheries.

Molluscan Shellfish, Hearings of the Committee on Merchant Marine and Fisheries, 88th Congress, First Session, Oct. 2 and 3, 1963. Serial No. 88-13, Washington, D.C., 1963.

Pacific Fisherman, Yearbook. Annual.

Power, E. A., *Fishery Statistics of the United States, 1961*. Department of the Interior, Fish and Wildlife Service, Washington, D.C. Similar but condensed statistics are published annually.

Rounsefell, G. A., and G. B. Kelez, *The Salmon and Salmon Fisheries of Swiftsure Bank, Puget Sound, and the Frazer River*, Bulletin 49, U.S. Bureau of Fisheries, Vol. 27, 1938, pp. 693–823.

Russell, E. S., *The Overfishing Problem*, Cambridge University Press, Cambridge, 1942.

Smith, Frederick G. W., and Henry Chapin, *The Sun, the Sea, and Tomorrow;* potential sources of food, energy, and minerals from the sea. Charles Scribner's Sons, New York, 1954.

Thompson, W. F., and N. L. Freeman, *History of the Pacific Halibut Fishery*, Report 5, International Fisheries Commission, Vancouver, B.C., 1930.

Thompson, W. F., *The Effect of Fishing on Stocks of Halibut in the Pacific*, University of Washington Press, Seattle, Washington, 1950.

Tomasevich, Jozo, *International Agreements on Conservation of Marine Resources, with Special Reference to the North Pacific*, Stanford University Press, Stanford, California, 1943.

United Nations Department of Economic Affairs, UNSCCUR, Volume, VII, Wildlife and Fish Resources, United Nations, New York, 1951.

United States Fish and Wildlife Service, *Commercial Fisheries Review*. Monthly.

United States Fish and Wildlife Service, *Fishery Statistics of the United States*, Department of the Interior, Washington, D.C., Annual, 1918—.

Walford, Lionel A., *Fishery Resources of the United States*, 79th Congress, 1st Session, Senate Doc. No. 51, 1945.

White, Donald J., *The New England Fishing Industry*, Harvard University Press, Cambridge, Mass., 1951.

Part 7

MARION CLAWSON
Resources for the Future, Inc.

CHAPTER 20

Recreational Resources

The demand for outdoor recreation is booming. One need only look at any popular park on a pleasant summer Sunday afternoon for dramatic evidence of this; or one may look at the statistics of visits to various kinds of outdoor recreation areas.[1] The one shows a comparatively large number of people, often filling to overflowing the facilities available for them; the other shows a steady upward trend in the figures. Today people demand and get much more outdoor recreation than they demanded and got 20 years ago.

Why do people seek outdoor recreation in such large and growing numbers? What kinds of natural resources are most in demand for outdoor recreation use? How are these natural resources used for this purpose? These are some of the questions to which this chapter is directed.

A Few Preliminary Definitions. In the voluminous literature about outdoor recreation, there is often confusion and apparent divergent conclusions, arising in no small part from the lack of commonly accepted definitions of some of the chief terms. In the hope of avoiding some of this confusion, we give three definitions as basic to this chapter[2]:

1. *Recreation* means activity (or inactivity) undertaken because one wants to do it. As such, it contrasts with work, done primarily to earn money or otherwise to provide the "necessities" of life, or what have come to be so considered, for one's self and one's family. It also contrasts with the mechanics of life, such as eating, sleeping, operations to keep house, dishes, clothing, and person clean, whether these are for one's self or for his or her family. There is not a sharp line between recreation and all other activities. The same activity may sometimes be work and sometimes recreation. Cooking, dressmaking, embroidery, furniture-making, and many other specific activities may fall into either classification.

The distinguishing characteristics of recreation is the attitude with which an activity (or

[1] A basic reference source in this field is *Outdoor Recreation for America,* a Report to the President and to the Congress by the Outdoor Recreation Resources Review Commission, Government Printing Office, Washington, 1962; and the 27 Study Reports prepared under the direction of the Commission and published by the Government Printing Office subsequent to the Commission's report. These reports contain a wealth of detail and references to many related publications.

[2] These definitions are taken from a study, as yet unpublished, by the author.

inactivity) is undertaken, not the specific kind or nature of that activity. If undertaken because one wants to do it, with no feeling of compulsion or "ought to," then it is almost surely recreation. In the modern complex world, recreation is often a major opportunity for self-expression. Since one more freely chooses his recreation than he does his job or his necessary chores of living, his choice is more nearly a personal one and less a socially determined one.

Recreation is closely related to leisure. If leisure is taken to mean time in which activities (or inactivity) consciously decided on are undertaken, then the relation of recreation and leisure is very close. On this basis, mere idleness is neither leisure nor recreation.

2. *Outdoor recreation* is simply those kinds of recreation typically undertaken in the outdoors. As such, it contrasts with the various forms of recreation typically carried on indoors. There are some borderline activities, since some recreation may be either outdoors or indoors. Outdoor recreation obviously requires space and resources, sometimes much space and large resources, for its enjoyment. Some outdoor recreation is best carried on where the natural landscape has had the minimum modification, other activities require extensive investment.

3. *Resources*, for outdoor recreation include areas of land, bodies of water, forests, swamps, and other natural features which are in demand or likely to become so, for outdoor recreation. The physical characteristics of these natural elements of the landscape affect their use for outdoor recreation, but they become resources for outdoor recreation only as they are useful for this purpose. Land, water, forests, and other natural features which for any reason are not or cannot be used for recreation are not part of the outdoor recreation resource. In this respect, outdoor recreation is no different from farming, forestry, grazing, mining, or any other use of natural resources. There is nothing inherent in the physical landscape or features which makes it a recreation resource; it is the combination of the natural qualities and the ability and desire of man to use it, which makes a resource out of what otherwise may be a more or less meaningless combination of rocks, soil, and trees.

The Statistical Record. The statistical record for every major kind of public outdoor recreation area, and most individual parks or other kinds of areas, shows a mounting use year after year. For most areas, the annual increases are a relatively constant percentage of the number of visits; the higher the level of visits, the greater the absolute size of the increase. The more people enjoy outdoor recreation, the more they want it, it seems.

Actual data on usage of public outdoor recreation areas are rather poor—they are available only for recent years for many areas, and their accuracy is not always above criticism. The best data relate to the postwar years. An upward trend in visits is evident in these data as there are for the prewar years. For the national parks, data are available since 1910, and the earlier data show the same tendency toward a constant percentage increase from year to year. The tendency toward increased usage leveled off somewhat during the severe depression years of the early 1930's, but showed growth again before the war. During the war, visits to the national park system and to national forests declined by about two-thirds, for travel restrictions and other wartime situations inhibited the usual recreation developments.

Since the war, a marked upward rise in recreation has occurred on each major type of outdoor recreation area (Table 1). Total visits to all units of the national park system more than doubled from 1946 to 1954, and doubled again from 1954 to 1963; total visits to the national forests increased somewhat more than twofold in the earlier period, but by threefold in the latter period. Large increases were shown on the reservoirs, constructed by the Corps of Engineers—nearly threefold in the 9 years from 1954 to 1963. TVA reservoirs and all state parks experienced generally similar increases in visits also (Fig. 1). The increase in use was apparently least for city parks, but it is also true that our data are poorest for these, and perhaps the actual increase in visits was much more than these data suggest.

Although the trend varies somewhat from one kind of area to another, and even more from one specific park to another, and also somewhat from year to year, yet the rate of increase is remarkably close to a median figure of 10 percent annually. A constant percentage increase of this magnitude means a doubling in about 8 years. It can be seen that this rate was actually reached or exceeded in several of the instances in Table 1. No constant percentage rate of increase can go on unchanged forever; in time, the figures reach astronomical heights. If the past percentage trend in visits to Corps of Engineers reservoirs continued unchanged to the year 2000, every man, woman, and child on the entire nation would be spending 2500 days annually at Corps reservoirs! Some leveling off in past growth rates simply must take place sometime; but when, and from what level of use? This is a question to which we shall return later in this chapter.

Fig. 1 The TVA lakes are widely used for recreational purposes. Recreational facilities and improvements valued at more than $168 million have been placed on lakes and lakeshores by states, counties, cities, and private individuals and companies as well as by the Authority. Boats kept on TVA lakes now number more than 52,000. The lakes are popular for boating (including sailing), water skiing, and fishing. (Bureau of Outdoor Recreation, Department of the Interior.)

Table 1. Annual Visits to Major Public Recreation Areas 1946, 1954, and 1963

(Millions of Visits)

Kind of Area	1946	1954	1963
National park system	22	48	94
National forests	18	40	123
Corps of Engineer reservoirs	[1]	56	147
TVA reservoirs[2]	7[3]	25	46
All state parks	93	166	292[4]
City parks[5]	503	724[6]	[1]

[1] No data available; visits to Corps reservoirs totalled 26 million in 1952.

[2] Visitor days, not visits.

[3] 1947.

[4] 1962.

[5] Visits to selected facilities only; data unavailable for total use of city parks.

[6] 1955.

[Source: 1946 and 1954, *Statistics on Outdoor Recreation*, by Marion Clawson, published by Resources for the Future, Inc., Washington, D.C., 1958.]

One additional point should be borne in mind in considering the figures in Table 1. The number of specific areas and the total acreage of each kind of area increased during the years under consideration. This was especially marked for the Corps reservoirs. A major part of the increased visitation record is probably the result of this larger number and acreage. However, changes in the acreage and number of national forests during this period were minimal; yet recreation visits to them increased almost as much as to any other kind of area except Corps reservoirs. It is by no means clear that all the visits to a new area are a net addition—some may be merely a diversion to this area of visits that otherwise would have occurred on one of the older areas. The future trend in total outdoor recreation activity will depend in part on the acreages available and their location. If relatively few overcrowded areas are available, the visits will not rise as much as will be the case if many new areas are provided.

Basic Factors Underlying Recreation Trends. Although various factors may be operative in particular situations, four basic factors seem to be generally operative and to underlie the large and continuing increases in outdoor recreation activity: population changes, income changes, increased leisure, and improved transportation. These deserve a closer look.

One of the most persistent and pervasive forces in American history has been the steady growth of population. From less than 4 million persons in 1790, when the first Census was taken, we have increased to over 190 million. There has apparently never been a year in our national history when total population declined. The annual rate of growth was roughly 3 percent, until about the middle of last century; then it declined slowly to a low of roughly ¾ of 1 percent during the 1930's; and it has since risen to about 1.7 percent. Many countries have experienced long secular declines in population growth; ours is one of the few, if not the only one, that has experienced a reversal of such a long-term trend. The death rate has declined steadily; although additional modest declines seem probable in the future, yet no spectacular changes seem possible. The big and erratic variable has been birth rate. Although this is somewhat responsive to prosperity and depression, and to war, yet it has changed in the past in ways not easily understood or predictable. The consensus among experts is that the rate of population growth for the next generation will not differ very greatly from the present rate; this means a total population in excess of 300 million by the year 2000.

Although changes in total numbers of people has been the major population change, yet changes in the rural-urban balance and in the age distribution merit comment, as affecting outdoor recreation. There has been a steady move from rural to urban areas for a long time in the United States, but in recent decades it has reached such proportions as to mean an actual loss of people in many rural areas. During the decade of the 1950's, while total United States population was increasing by 18.5 percent, more than half of all counties lost people, and many additional rural areas did also. Within the large urban complexes, the move has been away from the city center, toward the suburbs.

City people, on the average, patronize public outdoor recreation areas far more than do rural people; hence a move of people from rural areas to cities is likely to mean increased demand for outdoor recreation. We have also acquired both far more older people and a far larger proportion of them. An increasingly large proportion of these is retired. Although total outdoor recreation activity often declines with age, yet the large number of such people, with time and modest incomes, creates special demands for outdoor recreation.

Real income per capita has also trended upward in the United States for a long time. However, this trend has been somewhat irregular, being broken by major depressions and becoming steeper in periods of rising prosperity. Moreover, the basic trend has often been obscured by changing price levels. However, in terms of constant prices real income per capita has about doubled from the mid-1920's to about $2000 now. For the past several decades, the average annual rate of increase in per capita income, measured in constant dollars, has been nearly 2 percent—roughly the same as the present rate of increase in total population. The best outlook today is for a continued rise in real income per capita, at roughly the present rate. Average per capita incomes, measured in present-day dollars, may well reach $4100 annually by the year 2000.

Another aspect of this rising income situation has special importance to outdoor recreation. Although expenditures for the so-called necessities of life—food, shelter, and clothing—tend to rise as real incomes rise, yet a larger and larger portion of total income falls into the "discretionary" class. People have more choice about how to use some of it. As a matter of fact, as nearly as we can tell from rather unsatisfactory data, the percentage spent on outdoor recreation has risen considerably since the war. A rising percentage of a rising average income obviously means a lot more money spent for this purpose. Total expenditures for outdoor recreation in the year 2000 may well reach six times what they were in 1960.

There has been a rising trend in total leisure in the United States for several decades. This has been manifest not merely in shortened average or typical work weeks, which indeed have become shorter over a long period, but also in other factors. At one time, many men and women worked 7 days a week and most of the others worked 6; now most work 5, with some 6, and some shorter. At one time, 10 and 12 hour days were common; now 8 is typical. As recently as the end of World War I, steel workers were on an 84 hour work week: 12 hours a day, 7 days a week. The work week has shortened irregularly—a good deal in the 1930's, but some lengthening during the war, and no major trend in recent years away from the prewar situation.

Other changes have been taking place also. One dramatic change has been the rise in the paid vacation. Once the privilege of some white collar workers, it is now nearly universal in union labor contracts and common among many other classes of workers. The length of the paid vacation has also increased. In addition to the increase in numbers of older retired persons, noted above, there has also been some increase in the proportion of young people not yet in the labor force, and, of course, a great increase in their actual numbers. Whereas boys often began work at 15 years or even younger in an earlier day, today few begin before 18 and some not until older. These older and young people often demand far more outdoor recreation than they would want if they were working.

The fourth major force has been the improvement in travel facilities. When travel was predominantly by public transport or by horse and buggy, as before World War I, then a trip to a park only a few miles away was a major undertaking. The great rise in private automobile ownership and the concomitant improvement in highways have opened great opportunities to average persons for convenient, comfortable, and relatively inexpensive travel. Total travel for all purposes has increased from about 500 miles annually before World War I to about 6000 miles per person annually today. Although we do not know how much of this travel is for rec-

reation, yet it seems probable that a larger percentage is for this purpose today than was true in an earlier time. Many a family today drives 1, 2, or even 5000 miles while on their vacation trip. Few areas are inaccessible any longer. The supply of outdoor recreation has opened up greatly to the individual, while at the same time the demand for any area has increased greatly.

Interestingly enough, the upward trend in each of these four major factors has been at nearly the same rate (Fig. 2). That is, the annual growth in each has been somewhat less than 2 percent, as far as our somewhat imperfect data will permit us to calculate. This is to be contrasted with the upward trend in use of many outdoor recreation areas of about 10 percent annually, which we noted earlier. It seems highly probable that these four basic factors have interacted, so that the upward trend in one has reinforced the upward trend in another. For instance, had the improvement in roads and automobiles occurred without any rise in real income per capita—an improbable situation,

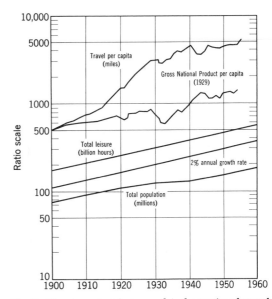

Fig. 2   Four important factors explain the continued growth in outdoor recreation activities since 1900; more people have enjoyed more leisure, higher income, and greatly improved travel facilities. (*Land and Water for Recreation*, Rand McNally and Co., Chicago, 1963.)

because roads and autos improved in large part as a result of the demand created by the higher incomes and were financed out of those higher incomes—then it is probable that people would have been unable to afford to travel to outdoor recreation areas in the great amounts that actually did. As a matter of fact, during the war when travel was restricted but incomes were high, the number of visits to national parks and national forests declined by more than half. Even if incomes had risen and transportation had improved, use of outdoor recreation areas would not have risen as much as it did if working hours had remained at their level of a generation ago. It has been the combination of factors which has been most significant.

The best current prospects are that the upward trend in each of these basic factors will continue. In the year 2000, we shall probably have from 300 to 350 million people, compared with 190 million now; average per capita incomes, in terms of present prices, will then average about $4100, compared with about $2000 now; paid vacations will be longer and more common, typical work weeks somewhat shorter, more people will be retired, and otherwise total leisure in the whole society will be greater; and as transportation will be improved more and more, people will typically travel considerably more.[3] All of this will lead to a materially higher level of demand for outdoor recreation. The Outdoor Recreation Resources Review Commission estimated that total demand in the year 2000 would be three times what it was in 1960; the author has estimated that in 2000 it would be ten times what it was in 1956 (which is equivalent to about six times what it actually was in 1960).[4] As we have noted earlier, present trends simply must flatten out sometime, somewhere; but we cannot be sure where or at what level this will occur. Almost everyone at all familiar

with the recreation scene agrees, however, that future demand for outdoor recreation will be much greater than present demand. Outdoor recreation is, and will continue to be, a growing use of natural resources.

The Nature of the Recreation Experience. In order to understand the use of natural resources for outdoor recreation, one must consider carefully the nature of the recreation experience. In any kind of marketing or economic research, we need to understand the nature of the transactions that take place. The whole recreation experience is analogous to the marketing transaction. Every outdoor recreation experience consists of five rather clearly identifiable phases, as follows (Fig. 3).

1. *The anticipation or planning phase.* This takes place before the family or other recreation group leaves home. This is when the decision is made as to where to go, when, how long to stay, what equipment to buy, how much to spend, and the like. It seems probable that more than half of all money spent for outdoor recreation is spent at this time, in the user's home town.[5] This planning may be careful or careless, informed or uninformed; and in any case plans may be modified as the experience later unfolds.

2. *Travel to the recreation site itself.* The length of the trip and the distance traveled vary according to the kind of area visited, but it is not uncommon for as much time and money to be spent in this phase as is spent later at the site itself. Some people regard this travel phase as enjoyable because some people travel for the pleasure of traveling itself; but it seems probable that others regard this with less enthusiasm, as something necessary in order to reach their destination, but not enjoyable for itself alone. The travel may take a few minutes, to visit a nearby park, or a few hours for an all-day outing, or several days for a longer vacation (Fig. 4).

3. *On-site experiences.* This is a part of the whole experience that most persons think of

[3] See report of Outdoor Recreation Resources Review Commission, *op. cit.*, p. 45. See also Hans H. Landsberg, Leonard Fischman, and Joseph L. Fisher, *Resources in America's Future*, The Johns Hopkins Press, Baltimore, 1963.

[4] Commission report, *ibid.*, p. 47; and Marion Clawson, R. Burnell Held, and Charles H. Stoddard, *Land for the Future*, The Johns Hopkins Press, Baltimore, 1960.

[5] Marion Clawson, "Private and Public Provision of Outdoor Recreation Opportunity," in *Economic Studies of Outdoor Recreation*, ORRRC Study Report 24, Washington, D.C., 1962.

In anticipation of an outdoor recreation experience, a family plans where it will go and what it will do, and buys equipment and supplies.

Back home again, the family recalls its recreation experience, often with great pleasure. Memories may be an important part of the whole experience.

In order to reach the outdoor recreation area of its choice, a family must travel. Considerable expense is involved in such travel, and often as much time is consumed in travel as later on the site. Travel is often not as pleasurable as experience on the site.

When the activities at the site are through, the family must travel back to its home. Often tired, frequently in a hurry, sometimes broke, the family is in a different mood than when it travelled in the opposite direction.

When it arrives at the recreation site, the family may engage in many activities. Bodies of water are especially valued for outdoor recreation. The activities at the site generally provide the basic purpose for the whole experience, even when they occupy less than half the time and require less than half the total expense.

Fig. 3　Phases of the whole outdoor recreation experience: anticipation, travel to recreation area, on-site activities, the return trip, and recollection. (*Land and Water for Recreation*, Rand McNally and Company.)

Fig. 4   The Yakima Project, Washington, provides fine picnic and camping sites along the shores of Kachess Reservoir. Many tourists as well as local people find here conditions favorable for quiet relaxation. (Photograph by Rasmussen, Bureau of Reclamation.)

when outdoor recreation is mentioned; it is indeed the chief reason for the whole experience and the chief user of natural resources; we shall consider it in more detail later in this chapter. But the on-site part of the whole experience is only a part of the whole—whether one considers time required or used, money spent, or satisfactions obtained. The range in activities at the site is very wide, and we shall consider some of them in detail later.

4. *Travel home again.* Although the end points of this journey are the same as travel to the site, the intermediate route may be different. Moreover, the recreationists are quite probably in a different mood now—their vacation is gone, their money has been spent, they may be tired, and, for the moment, at least, they may be in a much less buoyant mood than when they ventured forth on this recreation experience. Nevertheless, considerable time and money must perforce be spent on this phase of the whole experience.

5. *Recollection is the last major phase of the whole experience.* Back home again, the family or others who went on the trip tell of their experiences to the stay-at-homes, neighbors, friends, co-workers, and others. The memories may not exactly coincide with the experience

itself—the fish get bigger, the mosquitoes more fierce, the camping more primitive, etc. It is probable that very often more satisfaction is achieved in this phase than in any other. Less money is spent here, and the time requirement is not rigid. Perhaps most important, it is the nature of the recollections of one experience which do most to determine the timing and the character of the next experience.

These five phases are indispensable parts of the whole experience; none can be omitted ordinarily, although the time and money spent in each might vary considerably. The costs of all phases must be included as part of a package; so must the satisfactions and annoyances of all parts. What happens en route may affect users' attitudes toward a park fully as much as what they find on the site itself. When the economist strives to measure costs and benefits from outdoor recreation, he must consider the whole experience; so must the recreation planner or the legislator or administrator responsible for designing and promoting a recreation system.

Systems of Outdoor Recreation Areas. Recreation areas of different kinds and in different locations form highly complex systems. In this, they are not unlike the plants and animals in an ecosystem. Each has its particular role or function; the relationships between different units may be complementary, competitive, or partly each. When people go to one lake or water body, they may thereby be reducing their recreation use of other ones. But the presence of more than one lake or water body may lead recreationists as a group to develop more water sports than would be the case if there were but one lake. The amount of use a particular area receives is likely to depend to a large extent on the availability of alternative areas for the same users.

There are so many different kinds of outdoor recreation areas that it is helpful to group them into a few broad classes. Some loss in detail is more than offset by greater simplicity for readier understanding. Classifications can be based on one or more of various factors. The Outdoor Recreation Resources Review Commission clas-sified areas largely on the basis of their management problems and objectives.[6] These classes were established: (1) high-density recreation areas, (2) general outdoor recreation areas, (3) natural environment areas, (4) unique natural areas, (5) primitive areas, and (6) historic and cultural sites. Criteria for evaluating each were established, and management guides set forth for each.

A different basis of classification is according to economic characteristics.[7] A threefold grouping of user-oriented, intermediate, and resource-based has been established on this basis (Table 2). User-oriented areas must be located near where people live, are used typically after work or after school, consist individually of rather small tracts, and are often city parks. Intermediate areas can lie farther from where people live, but should ordinarily be within one or two hours driving time. They are typically used for day-long outings and are often part of a state park system. Within the restrictions of distance, they should be on the best sites available. Resource-based areas include the outstanding mountain, shore, swamp, or other natural features, and in practice are often located relatively far from where most people live. They are often visited during vacations. National parks and national forests fall into this category.

Outdoor recreation areas could be grouped according to the type of natural resources included. Thus extensive water surfaces, shores, streams, forests, mountains, caves, and many other natural features could be grouped separately. In practice, many recreation areas contain more than one kind of natural resources; sometimes it is the combination of resources that makes an area most attractive. Within some limits, resources can be created for recreation use. Trees can be planted to create forested areas, or dams may create artificial lakes to provide for water sports.

Whatever the basis of classification, there is, in

[6] *Op. cit.*

[7] Marion Clawson, R. Burnell Held, and C. H. Stoddard, *Land for the Future*, The Johns Hopkins Press, Baltimore, 1960.

Table 2. General Classification of Outdoor Recreational Uses and Resources

| Item | Type of Recreation Area | | |
	User Oriented	Resource Based	Intermediate
1. General location	Close to users; on whatever resources are available	Where outstanding resources can be found; may be distant from most users	Must not be too remote from users; on best resources available within distance limitation
2. Major types of activity	Games, such as golf and tennis; swimming; picnicking; walks and horse riding; zoos, etc.; playing by children	Major sightseeing; scientific and historical interest; hiking and mountain climbing; camping, fishing and hunting	Camping, picnicking, hiking, swimming, hunting, fishing
3. When major use occurs	After hours (school or work)	Vacations	Day outings and week ends
4. Typical sizes of areas	One to a hundred, or at most to a few hundred acres	Usually some thousands of acres, perhaps many thousands	A hundred to several thousand acres
5. Common types of agency responsibility	City, county, or other local government; private	National parks and national forests primarily; state parks in some cases; private, especially for seashore and major lakes	State parks; private

fact, a continuum from one extreme to another. If one element of the classification system is distance from users, then there are obviously areas ranging from the nearby local park to the most distant wilderness area. Or if size of the tract is the basis of classification, parks run from an acre, or at least from a very few acres, up to a million or more acres for large national parks. Even the ORRRC management classification system has intermediate types—an area may be somewhat intermediate between a general outdoor recreation area and a natural environment area, for instance. This continuum from one type to another facilitates transfers of use from one area to another; if one area is crowded, part of its potential use load is likely to be diverted to another somewhat similar area.

This continuum among recreation areas, and the interchangeability in use within limits, emphasizes the system aspect of all the areas. If a new park or area is added, it not merely offers some use, it also affects the use of many others, directly or indirectly. In this respect, the various parks in a general area or region are somewhat like the different dams along a single river; the operation and value of each dam are affected by the existence and operations of all the others. Or the situation is not unlike that of a large electricity supply system, where each new generator affects the operation of all the others. This system aspect of outdoor recreation is particularly complicated, because the different kinds of areas are frequently owned and operated by different units of government. Later in this chapter we shall return to the problems of intergovernmental relations in recreation.

Characteristics of Public Recreation Areas.
The areas of mass use for outdoor recreation are often publicly owned, as well as many areas which have relatively light use. Our information about publicly owned areas is better than it is about privately owned areas, and so we shall take up the public areas first.

Among the resource-based publicly owned outdoor recreation areas, the national parks are outstanding. Beginning with Yellowstone National Park, which was set aside in 1872, a number of areas have been established over the years as national parks. Each has been outstanding in one or more respects, and each has had national, as contrasted with local, importance. Several include outstanding mountain scenery; Yellowstone, Mt. Rainier, Mt. McKinley, Glacier, Yosemite, Rocky Mountain, and others include large mountain areas. Grand Canyon is noted for its tremendous canyon, the Everglades are a great swamp, Sequoia has its famous trees, etc. Most, if not all, contain many natural features. In them, all commercial uses are excluded (with minor exceptions) and each area is for outdoor recreation in the broadest sense of the word. The national parks average nearly ½ million acres each. To these national parks have been added national monuments, historic areas, and other units. The total area of the national park system in 1960 was about 26 million acres, or slightly over 1 percent of the total land area of the nation. The average intensity of use of this whole system is about three visits annually per acre, but this average conceals great variations, often within the same park. Some parts are intensively used, others have scarcely any visitors. As we have noted earlier, the trend in use has been upward at about 10 percent annually. The long-run future of many of these areas may be in jeopardy as a result of this use trend; it is difficult to see how the national park system can absorb ten to twenty times its present volume of visitors, which the present trends will bring in 30 or 40 years, without serious damage to the areas themselves. Although a number of proposals is pending now for additions to the national park system, it cannot possibly be extended indefinitely simply because there is not an unlimited supply of suitable additional areas.

Another major resource-based kind of public recreation area is the national forests. These are multiple-use areas; recreation is only one use, sometimes not the major use. Relatively limited areas have been set aside for exclusive or chief use for recreation; the remaining areas are nearly all open for this purpose. Although the national forests were started somewhat later than the national parks, their area has long been larger, about 180 million acres at present. On the average, national forests have about 1 million acres each. On the average, their use is about one-half visit per acre annually, but they, too, have some intensively used tracts and relatively large areas used very little indeed. Timber production and harvest are the chief purpose on much of the national forest area, and livestock grazing on other large areas. Although the national forests probably will not expand greatly in total area, because of rather general opposition to large increases in federal land holdings, the acreage set aside for outdoor recreation within them could be increased greatly.

The federal wildlife refuges provide a unique kind of resource-based outdoor recreation area. Wildlife today have little economic value beyond their recreation value. The area in all federal wildlife refuges actually exceeds the area in the whole national park system, but this includes several huge game ranges in Alaska and in the West, where relatively few visitors can or wish to go. Average rate of visitation is lower on wildlife refuges than even on the national forests, but many refuges get large numbers of visitors each year. Other uses are subordinate to the main purpose of protecting wildlife. Some expansion in this system is desirable for strictly wildlife purposes, and additional recreation use of the whole system can and undoubtedly will be made.

Of the intermediate type of recreation areas, state parks are the most popular publicly owned kind. Although some states have had parks for a long time, the system as a whole got a major boost during the 1930's. Many states, in order to qualify for employment programs financed out of federal funds, substantially added to their park acreage then. More than half of the whole state park acreage is included in a few very large (over 50,000 acre) state parks: Baxter in Maine, Adirondacks, Catskill, and Allegany in New York, Porcupine Mountains in Michigan, Custer in South Dakota, and Anza Desert and Borrego in California. More than a third of all the state parks are less than 50 acres each, and 60 percent are smaller than 250 acres. In recent years, total visits to state parks have exceeded visits to all kinds of resource-based public recreation areas. Visits per acre in recent years have averaged nearly 50 per acre—more than fifteen times the average rate of use of national parks and one hundred times the average rate of use of national forests. State parks offer the greatest possibility for increase in acreage of any major kind of public outdoor recreation area. Their acreage could be increased tenfold or more by converting suitable areas to this use and by improving other areas for this purpose. In the past half dozen years, New York, New Jersey, Pennsylvania, Wisconsin, California, and Washington have embarked on major programs to increase their state park acreage, and other states have also shown notable progress.

Reservoir areas and surrounding lands, of reservoirs built by TVA and the Corps of Engineers, are another kind of public owned intermediate type of outdoor recreation area (Fig. 5). These reservoirs are built for flood protection, navigation improvement, and hydroelectric power production primarily, but recreation is coming to be an increasingly important by-product. The total area of this type is somewhat greater than the total area of all state parks, but use is definitely less, so that average use per acre is around thirty visits annually. Partly because of increasing areas in Corps reservoirs and partly because of the tremendous increase in popularity of water sports, use of these areas for recreation has grown faster since the war than has any other kind of area. The same pur-

poses underlying present reservoirs are almost sure to lead to the construction of many more reservoirs in the years ahead, and they will be probably used as recreation areas even more extensively. Moreover, construction of moderate-sized reservoirs primarily for recreation and only secondarily for the traditional uses of reservoirs is likely to become common in the future.

City parks are the chief kind of user-oriented, publicly owned outdoor recreation area. They began in the latter part of the nineteenth century, and their acreage has expanded roughly in proportion to the growth in city population. As we have noted, the prime requisite of such parks is a location close to where people live. Individually, most such parks are small, averaging less than 40 acres each, and with many less than 10 acres. The total area in all city parks is less than 1 million acres. We lack accurate data on the number of visits to them, but it probably exceeds those to all other public areas combined. The extent used probably exceeds 1500 visits per acre annually, on the average. Like the other areas, this average includes some tracts used much more widely and some much less. Although ample land exists in the expanding suburban areas, where city parks might be developed, the big problem is to see that it is reserved for this purpose before it becomes covered with houses. With the almost certain large and continuing growth in urban population, major increases in city parks will be required in the future, and their provision will be a major resource management problem.

Use of Private Land for Public Recreation. We have much less data, especially historical statistical data, about use of privately owned land for recreation purposes than we have for public land. Various situations exist.[8] A common one is the man who owns a piece of land for the use of his family and perhaps a few friends, but

[8] Marion Clawson, "Private and Public Provision of Outdoor Recreation Opportunity," ORRRC Study Report 24, *Economic Studies of Outdoor Recreation*, Washington, D.C., 1962.

Fig. 5   Clark Hill Dam and Reservoir, Savannah River, Georgia and South Carolina. More than 3 million people annually visit the Clark Hill Reservoir. This is a view of swimming activities at the Elijah State Park on the Georgia side of the project. (United States Corps of Engineers.)

who on occasion may rent it out to others. Although we do not precisely know how many private tracts are owned primarily for such recreation, the number may well run more than a million, for there are more than a million very small forest holdings, many of which must be owned primarily for recreation.

Many landowners permit hunting and fishing by the public on their lands, sometimes without charging a fee, sometimes only on payment of fees, which in some areas may be rather large. In the more thickly settled parts of the country, private land is increasingly being prohibited from private hunting, at least without the per-

mission of the owner. Many landowners have had unfortunate experiences from allowing hunting on their land, such as fences cut, gates left open, livestock shot, and machinery damaged. Sportsmen's groups and others have sought to promote better hunters' manners in the woods and on the farms.[9] In other parts of the country, most private land is open to hunting.

Other private landowners permit other rec-

[9] The Izaak Walton League has put on a campaign to this end, for instance. See *Outdoor America*, June 1958, August 1959, November 1959, September 1960, October 1960, and January 1961.

reational uses of their land, sometimes providing considerable facilities for doing so.[10] Large lumber and other timber-owning companies, in particular, have provided camping and other facilities. So have some large electric utility companies. These landowners have also had unfavorable experiences from their lands being used privately, but they recognize that the public wants to use large, extensive, forested areas and they have sought to make such lands available.

In some cases, clubs or other private groups own land that they use for their own enjoyment. A group can own a larger tract, and develop it more fully, than could an individual. Most clubs are on a nonprofit base; their land and facilities are generally available only to their members and guests. Such recreation developments include a wide range of activities, from swimming pools and golf courses to hunting lodges in relatively inaccessible territory.

In still other instances, owners of land conduct major businesses to provide outdoor recreation opportunity to the general public.[11] We have no data on the total extent of such activity. Many of these are located on water bodies and offer water sports of different kinds to patrons. Others offer camping, horseback riding, and other extensive land-use activities. These various operations go by many different names, which sometimes accurately describe their chief activities: resorts, dude ranches, campgrounds, commercial beaches, yacht and boat clubs, shooting preserves, vacation farms, etc. Many of these private areas are so located that their guests or patrons can also take advantage of publicly owned areas; a boating club is on the shores of a public lake, for instance, or a dude ranch is near or actually within a national park or national forest. Scattered private holdings within the latter are often the basis for a recreation business.

Many problems are connected with this type of business. One major one is that so much of their business is highly seasonal. Buildings must be maintained on a year-round basis, and even some staff is maintained year round when most or all the business is confined to a season of 3 months or less. Another obstacle is that so much public recreation area is open without charge or for a very low fee. Although the private providers often charge primarily for the service they render, rather than for their resources as such, the competition from public areas is certainly a factor. The American public, or at least a large part of it, has become accustomed to free or low-cost outdoor recreation and does not realize the value of the resources it so obtains. But there are many business problems in this type of enterprise also, just as there are in the running of hotels, motels, and other businesses catering to the general public.

There are also great opportunities for greater public use of private land for outdoor recreation. After all, more than two-thirds of all land in the United States is privately owned and much of it has a large recreation potential. The large amount of the probable future demand for outdoor recreation makes it probable that public areas will not expand fast enough to satisfy this demand. Recreation could well develop as the dominant use for some private areas or as one use among several on larger areas.

Outdoor Recreation Activities. Americans engage in various activities outdoors which are termed recreation. The simple ones of pleasure riding in automobiles, walking for pleasure, picnicking, and swimming are the most popular, whether we judge by the numbers of people who engage in them or by the numbers of days spent at them.[12] More than half of the total population apparently engage in riding, walking, and picnicking. Boating, canoeing, fishing, hunting, camping, and other relatively common activities are participated in by fewer people for fewer days per year. So are still others, such as horseback riding, water skiing, sailing, and ice sports. In addition to these reasonably common

---

[10] *Recreation on Forest Industry Lands*, results of a survey by American Forest Products Industries, Washington, D.C., 1960.

[11] *Private Outdoor Recreation Facilities*, ORRRC Study Report 11, Washington, D.C., 1962.

[12] ORRRC report, *Outdoor Recreation for America*, *op. cit.*

activities, there are many in which far fewer people participate and for relatively few days in total—mountain climbing, cave exploring (spelunking), and many other specialized activities. Some are too expensive or too strenuous for mass participation or lack a general appeal, but they still have ardent devotees. There are, of course, many kinds of participator sports also, but these we exclude from this consideration of outdoor recreation.

Most people take their vacations in the summer season or during the warmer months of the year. Many older people follow the sun and spend their vacation time in the South. Florida, the Gulf Coast states, New Mexico, Arizona, and California have become the destination of thousands of people every winter. Some, particularly the older people, are seeking comfort in the sun; others are seeking the diversion, the excitement, and the entertainment available in these resort areas. But there are people who seek recreation in the cooler latitudes and higher altitudes where there are opportunities for hunting, ice fishing, skating, skiing, ice sailing, and other winter sports (Fig. 6). The development of ski resorts with suitable slopes, lifts, lodges to ac-

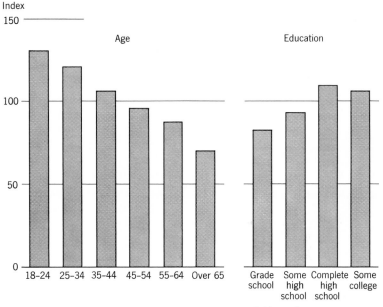

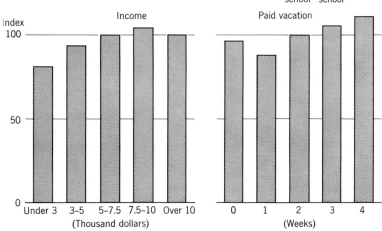

Fig. 6 Net effect of various socio-economic factors on relative participation in all forms of outdoor recreation. (*Land and Water for Recreation,* Rand McNally and Company.)

commodate the guests and other necessary facilities requires an investment of many thousand of dollars. The tourists themselves must spend considerable sums to be properly outfitted and equipped to participate in the sports programs. In recent years the use of ice machines has brought skiing and skating to warmer latitudes and lower altitudes than was thought possible a few years ago.

It is impossible in this chapter to attempt to describe these activities in any detail. The essential fact to keep in mind is that "outdoor recreation" is not a single activity, but many, with different groups interested in each, with different and sometimes conflicting demands for natural resources. The fisherman and the water skier may have divergent interests in their use of a body of water as will the most ardent hunter and the rancher have for using grazing land, for instance. Some outdoor recreation activities ap-

peal primarily to one age group or another; hunting, for instance, is primarily an adult male activity. However, very often, the family goes as a group to outdoor recreation areas. In this case, there must be something at the site to appeal to each member of the family. Dad and the older boy go fishing, the younger children swim and play on the beach, the tots use the playground equipment, mothers sit quietly in the shade, etc. Many activities require water bodies or are more enjoyable near water. This fact, plus the need for a variety of activities, lends special importance to the presence of attractive water bodies in outdoor recreation areas.

Effect of Socio-economic Factors. Not everyone participates in outdoor recreation to the same degree; part of the differences is because of personal preferences, but a considerable part depends on easily observable socio-economic characteristics (Fig. 7). As people get older, they participate less in outdoor recreation, on the average, and the kind of activities also change. Persons over 65 have about half the total activity of persons 18 to 24.[13] Swimming declines rapidly with age, whereas nature and bird walks increase with age. Total recreation activity rises with family income, at least within the range up to $10,000; over that level, outdoor activity per family seems not to rise and may actually decline a little. Even more striking are the variations in kinds of activity with changes in income; in general, these activities involving comparatively high costs increase much faster as income rises, whereas the less expensive kinds increase less or actually decrease.

Total outdoor recreation activity also rises with education, at least up to the point of finishing high school. People with more education participate more in outdoor recreation, but this may not be a simple cause and effect relationship; those personal qualities which lead someone to get education may also be the qualities which make him enjoy the outdoors. Total recreation activity also rises with amounts of paid

Fig. 7 Winter scene at Squaw Valley high in the Sierra Nevada Range in east-central California. View shows the 5000-foot KT-22 double chair lift. This famous winter sports area averages 450 inches of snow annually. (Bureau of Reclamation.)

[13] See Marion Clawson, *Land and Water for Recreation*, Rand McNally and Co., Chicago, 1963, where data from ORRRC Study Reports have been summarized.

vacation; an even greater response is evident for those kinds of activities which can well be carried on only during vacation, mountain climbing, for instance.

All the foregoing are net relationships. That is, older people of the same income level will engage less in outdoor recreation than will young people; but older persons sometimes have higher incomes and their effect may more than offset the effect of greater age, so that one group of older persons may participate more in outdoor activity than a particular group of younger persons. The wide variations in individual tastes should always be kept in mind also. Thus it is very difficult to predict what a particular individual will do, even if we know his age, income, education, and other characteristics; but we can estimate what the average participation of a group will be, depending on these same factors.

Resource Characteristics for Outdoor Recreation. The characteristics making for a good outdoor recreation area depend on the kind of use the area is planned for.

A resource-based outdoor recreation area requires, by definition, unusual natural qualities. These may be outstanding mountains, lakes, swamps, sea or lake shores, geologic formations, or other kinds of areas. They must be truly outstanding by national, not by local, standards. It is not easy to define "outstanding" in quantitative or objective terms, so that every observer would arrive at the same judgment. But anyone who has seen Grand Canyon, or the Yellowstone geysers, or the Yosemite Falls, or any one of numerous other areas set aside in the national park system or included within some of the national forests, will agree that these are superlative by any standards.

The same is true, generally, of historic sites. We all agree that Independence Square in Philadelphia is a part of the basic history of the United States. Again, the standard of national rather than of local interest must apply.

The difficulty with these two classes comes with many areas that are on the borderline. In the Great Plains, where mountains are lacking,

the Black Hills is a most unusual feature. Parts of it deserve recognition, as they have achieved in the Custer State Park of South Dakota, even if they lack national significance. The same is true of many historical sites.

When it comes to the intermediate-type outdoor recreation area, attractive water areas, woods, and related natural resources are important, but now *location* becomes more significant. We have noted earlier that good intermediate recreation areas should be within two, and preferably within one, hours driving time from where people live. But in most cases this locational requirement gives a rather large range for exercise of choice. Within that range of choice as to location, natural qualities should dominate. The importance of water bodies for recreation has been mentioned. An attractive lake or stream permits swimming, boating, fishing, water skiing, and other water sports, singly or in various combinations. A fairly high degree of water quality is often necessary for these uses; in the future, avoidance of water pollution in order to permit recreation will often be a major resource management problem. Trees for shade or for general enjoyment are also important; so are some areas of modest topography for picnicking, camping, and other uses.

One characteristic of intermediate outdoor recreation areas is that they can often be *made* —they need not be only found, as is true with the resource-based areas. Attractive lakes can often be made by constructing dams with fixed overflow outlets, so that the shores develop the characteristics of natural lakes. An adequate but not excessive watershed is required. Trees can be planted: even beaches can sometimes be constructed by filling with sand. Worn-out or relatively unproductive farm or forest land, somewhat uneven in topography, can be converted into quite attractive parks by relatively modest expenditures of money and a few years time. Thousands of suitable sites exist in the United States. The possibilities of expansion are better for intermediate-type recreation areas than for any other.

When it comes to the user-oriented areas,

location is all-important. By and large, people live where they do for reasons other than the availability of local recreation—and largely independent of the availability of other types also. The user-oriented recreation must be moved to where people are, and not require people to travel far for it. For neighborhood parks and playgrounds a distance of a quarter to a half mile is as far as people will go; other kinds of local parks can be a little farther away. Obviously, the choice of an area is now sharply limited, and is in practice limited still further by the present buildings on each tract. With very limited exceptions, we have not been willing to spend the money to clear dwellings or other buildings from sites in order to make them into parks or playgrounds. Most user-oriented recreation areas require modest topography and medium soil conditions for their best use and development. Some areas, however, have been developed on lands too steep or too swampy for dwellings or other buildings, or on areas too subject to flood overflow. Some excellent local parks have been made on sites abandoned for other purposes, such as abandoned quarries. If the space exists in the proper location, modern earth-moving and other technologies can often convert odds and ends of land into attractive local parks.

The foregoing has made it clear, we hope, that it is difficult to judge the recreation usefulness of a tract of land merely by looking at it. One can come nearer doing this for resource-based areas than for others; but even here, it is how this area compares with others of somewhat similar characteristics which may be decisive. For other kinds of areas, where location is more and more important, one must look beyond the specific tract to form a judgment about it. Tracts can be, and have been, used for recreation when a view limited to the specific tract would reject it as entirely unsuitable for the purpose. If something better is unavailable, we shall often make the best of what does exist, for the demand for outdoor recreation is usually quite strong.

The Role of Government. As we have noted, outdoor recreation takes place on both public and private lands and waters. In the latter cases, the value of an area often depends on the availability of public areas reasonably nearby. Thus the role of government in providing outdoor recreation is very great, often crucial.

Public recreation areas are provided by almost every level of government. The federal government provides national parks and related areas, national forests, various reservoir areas, and wildlife refuges. The states provide parks, forests, highway waysides, and various recreation services to local government and to citizen groups. Cities and other units of local government provide parks and various recreation services. There is no clear, sharp line separating the activities of these various kinds of government, although there are general fields of interest or specialty. One of the major policy questions in the recreation field, to which we shall return later, is the proper role of government at different levels. This has concerned many persons in recent years; the Outdoor Recreation Resources Review Commission gave attention to this problem, among many others.

In considering this matter, it is helpful to realize that government (at any level) may and usually does operate in two rather distinctly different roles. On the one hand, it is an "entrepreneur"—a planner who acquires, develops, and manages a particular area for outdoor recreation purposes. Only government can carry out this role adequately in many cases. Government can consider the needs for all people for outdoor recreation, not merely the needs of those who can afford to pay well; it can use its legal powers to acquire needed land, when private individuals often could not acquire the same land at any reasonable price or even at all; and the large capacity of many recreation areas makes it imperative that they be managed for relatively large groups of people, which often government can do very well. For all these reasons, government has a special, although not exclusive, role to play in the outdoor recreation field.

The other role that government usually plays is that of financier of outdoor recreation. Funds are raised by various means of taxation, to buy, improve, and manage recreation areas. By and large, until now, users have paid very little of the costs through charges levied on each use. There has been no correspondence between the taxes one paid to help provide outdoor recreation and the use which he got out of the public recreation areas. One reason many people have pushed for public outdoor recreation is that it is "free"; obviously, of course, it is not free, because someone must pay for it some way. The costs are submerged in the general tax bills.

These two roles of government could be separated largely or wholly. This could be done if the government, which planned and developed the recreation area, required its users to pay all the costs, through entrance fees or other charges based on use of the area. There may be good reasons of public policy why we wish to provide free outdoor recreation to some groups in the population who cannot afford to pay. However, in practice, most of the public outdoor recreation areas have been provided for the groups who can afford to pay entrance fees sufficient to pay the costs involved. This seems clearly true for those types of recreation where the users must incur substantial other costs to visit the areas anyway—the resource-based and intermediate areas, in general. But, even with cities, parks have been provided far more liberally in the higher income sections where people can afford modest charges than they have been made available in the lowest income neighborhoods where the capacity to pay is much lower.

Some Problems for the Future. We may well conclude this chapter by raising briefly a few of the questions about outdoor recreation that are almost sure to rise in the future.

First, how might our country become better coordinated but not centralized planning for outdoor recreation? We have noted that outdoor recreation is one function of many units of government, at federal, state, and local levels, and also of many private organizations. None can adequately plan its program without taking into consideration the plans and programs of all the others, but there is no mechanism whereby

this can be done. It is most unlikely—and this author would argue, undesirable as well—that we should have highly centralized planning in this field. Americans simply resist such centralization. But there is a very real problem here that will demand attention as the use of outdoor recreation areas grows.

Second, how might we estimate, with reasonable accuracy, the future demand for outdoor recreation, and the areas of land and water required to meet those demands? As we have noted, it is not easy to estimate future demands. We cannot simply extend past trends indefinitely, for they lead to ridiculous figures; but we are far from sure as to what should be substituted for such trend extensions. Even if we knew how many million visits there would be, in some future year, to a particular kind of outdoor recreation area, we are still not fully certain as to how much land and water are required to meet this demand properly. We may be forced to accept heavier use ratios in the future than we have thought desirable in the past, and yet there is surely some point at which satisfactions from outdoor recreation decline because of overcrowding.

Third, how can we encourage greater public use of private land for outdoor recreation? Most land is privately owned, especially in the densely settled regions of the nation. Some of this land can be used for recreation, either as the major use or as one use which is not incompatible with other uses. But there are many difficult problems, both for the recreationist and more particularly for the landowner. Can we devise better and fairer arrangements whereby the wishes of the one can be satisfied while protecting the legitimate rights of the other? This is a field for research and experimentation.

Last, how can the money necessary for the provision of the public areas be raised best? There will almost surely be considerable resistance to a greatly increased use of general tax revenues for this purpose. The fact that some people rarely use outdoor recreation areas, while others often use areas located outside the political units in which they pay taxes, raise serious problems of equity. One way to avoid these problems would be to raise more of the necessary money from entrance fees or other charges levied on those actually using the recreation areas. But this is strongly opposed by still other groups in the population, who firmly believe that outdoor recreation should be free to all who seek it. This is obviously a political issue which will have to be settled by argument and votes, as are many social issues in this country.

These and other problems that could be posed are another way of emphasizing that outdoor recreation is a rapidly growing activity in the United States. Unless something very drastic, like a thermonuclear war, intervenes, then we shall surely see outdoor recreation continue to grow as a human activity and as a user of natural resources.

References

Brockman, Christian Frank, *Recreational Use of Wild Lands*, McGraw-Hill Book Co., New York, 1959.

Butler, George D., *Introduction to Community Recreation*, McGraw-Hill Book Co., New York, 1949.

Clawson, Marion, *Land and Water for Recreation*, Resources for the Future Background Series, Rand McNally and Co., Chicago, 1963.

Clawson, Marion, *Statistics on Outdoor Recreation*, Resources for the Future, Washington, D.C., 1958.

Clawson, Marion, R. Burnell Held, and Charles H. Stoddard, "Land for Recreation," Chapter 3 in *Land for the Future*, Resources for the Future, The Johns Hopkins Press, Baltimore, 1960, pp. 124–193.

Langton, Clair Van Norman, *Principles of Health, Physical Education, and Recreation*, Ronald Press, New York, 1962.

McClellan, James C., *Recreation on Forest Industry Lands*, American Forest Products Industries, Washington, D.C., 1962.

McCune, Ellis, *Recreation and the Parks*, Haynes Foundation, Los Angeles, 1954.

Meyer, Harold D., and Charles K. Brightbill, *State Recreation: Organization and Administration*, A. S. Barnes and Co., New York, 1950.

Miller, Norman, *The Leisure Age: Its Challenge to Recreation*, Wadsworth Publication Co., Belmont, California, 1963.

National Conference on State Parks, *Yearbook, Parks and Recreation Progress*, Washington, D.C. Annual.

United States Department of the Interior, *Community Recreation and the Public Domain*, Government Printing Office, Washington, D.C., 1963.

United States National Park Service, *Annual Reports*, Department of the Interior, Washington, D.C.

United States National Park Service, *State Parks: Statistics, 1960*, Washington, D.C., 1961.

United States National Park Service, *Water Recreation Needs in the United States, 1960–2000*, Government Printing Office, Washington, D.C., 1960.

United States Outdoor Recreation Resources Review Commission, *Outdoor Recreation for America*, A Report to the President and to the Congress, Washington, D.C., 1962.

LAWRENCE A. HOFFMAN
The Ohio State University

CHAPTER 21

The Conservation of Man

Natural resource problems have recently been viewed more and more in terms of what they mean to people, indicating increased recognition that the country's greatest resource is people.

The strength of the nation lies less in numbers than in quality. Excellent health, high skills, and effective institutional organization taken together are fully as important as any of the other factors of production, that is, material capital, management, government, and natural resources, in effecting large per capita production and great national power.

Conservation of man may be interpreted to mean the avoidance of waste in reproduction and in rearing and educating children, together with the maintenance at minimum cost of good health and high productivity in the adult working population and the aged. With all our failings, we have become relatively low-cost replacers of life. Compared with the past, we are also relatively efficient in maintaining life and health among both children and adults. Our treatment of the aged may be inferior to that of past generations in nonmaterial considerations. Our educational efforts and our use of the average adult worker are probably intermediate in quality: better than previous generations, but still mediocre compared with present and prospective needs.

Most of our knowledge relating to past efforts to conserve man comes from aristocratic societies, in which treatment of the majority of people was mainly ignored in assessing deficiency and progress. Therefore we really have no dependable base points for purposes of accurate comparison, and pessimism is easily attainable by those forgetful that living in the first stages of a quantitatively comprehensible world can easily lead to erroneous comparisons between today's median accomplishments and yesterday's best accomplishments.

PROBLEMS OF POPULATION REPLACEMENT

The two major changes that shape population change in a nation are mortality and fertility. The growth of our population would not be affected much by reduction of infant and child mortality, for infectious diseases are essentially under control. We might still lengthen life expectancy by reducing mortality among

461

adults through learning how to control degenerative diseases.

Waste in Population Replacement. The wastage of life in replacing each generation is very low in our society. Infant mortality is now only 2.5 percent. Mortality among older children is even less; thus at current rates of survival more than 95 percent of those born will at least reach age 15.[1] More than 60 percent will live to age 65.

Progress in medical science, hospital deliveries, and prenatal and postnatal care have largely taken the hazards out of childbirth, with the maternal death rate now less than 0.1 percent, only a fifth of the rate a generation ago.[2]

Eliminating most premature deaths has led to a rising median age: it was only 19 years a century ago, had risen to 23 half a century ago, and was 28.5 in 1964.

The major determinant of our population change is now fertility, or the trend in birth rate. The events of the past generation have made this very difficult to forecast with precision, with the chief variables being the following:

1. The long-run surge in the number of families being formed.[3] In the 1940's an average of 0.5 million new households was formed each year; in the 1950's it was about 1 million; and by the mid-1960's it is approaching 2 million.

2. The married proportion of the adult population is now over two-thirds of all 14 years of age.[4] Even by age 40 only 8 percent of the men and 6 percent of the women are still single (this is but half the proportion at the turn of the century).

3. Only a tenth of young married couples are now childless, compared with double that proportion before World War II. (However, if all families are considered, some two-fifths have no children at home.)

4. Women are starting childbearing while young, the result partly to the lowering of the average age at marriage (23.1 years for men, 20.5 years for women in 1964).

5. Families remain small (3.7 persons per average family). Of the some 30 million families with children at home, roughly a third have one child, another third have two children, and the last third have three or more children. There is no evidence of an abandonment of the small-family system by any appreciable group, and the number of very large families is dropping.

6. The increase in births (over 4 million annually since 1954) has been achieved by somewhat more even fertility than in the past. The increase has been due mainly to more families having children or adding a second or third child. The groups that were historically the most fertile had the smallest increases.[5] Over 85 percent of all families stop at four children.

There is still a very uneven distribution of fertility in the nation, although less so than during the great depression of the 1930's (Fig. 1).

---

[1] Although accidents are largely amenable to control, they outrank every disease as a killer among children and young adults.

[2] Even when only women in the reproductive ages are considered, maternity causes less than 4 percent of all deaths at those ages (accidents take three times as many lives among them as childbearing). By region, the same general pattern of maternal mortality exists today as two decades ago (that is, much higher than the average in the rural South and rural West).

[3] The Bureau of the Census defines a family as two or more people living together who are related by blood, marriage, or adoption.

[4] Over 70 percent of young women between 20 to 24 years are or have been married, compared with fewer than half in 1900.

[5] Fertility is still much higher than necessary for replacement. If the average wife were to have 2.27 babies, the population would be stationary in a few decades. But wives in their early 30's are expected to have an average of 3.4 children by the time they have completed their families. Among wives in their early 30's, all large groups exceed the necessary number:

white wives	2.6	urban wives	2.5
nonwhite wives	3.1	rural wives	3.3

Even if average fertility should drop somewhat in the forseeable future, the increase in young Americans (for example, 50 percent more 18 year olds by late 1960's over 1950's) would keep absolute increase at a high level for decades. Some authorities believe that the fertility of young married couples will be much lower than in the past because of the increased use of oral contraceptives.

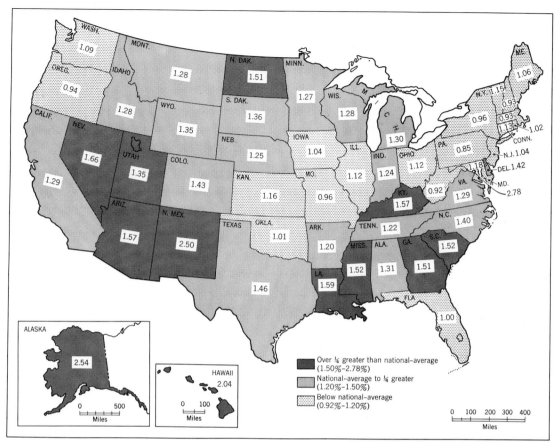

Fig. 1 United States: percent natural increase, by states, 1963. (Public Health Service, U.S. Department of Health, Education, and Welfare.)

Regionally, the 6 million people of the southern Appalachians have fertility twice that of the national average. In respect to the size of a family, less than a tenth of the mothers still adhere to the big-family pattern. There are many who fear "genetic erosion" in our society, because few of the very fertile families are among the wealthy or culturally most advanced segments of our population.[6]

Genetically there are few valid reasons for such fears. We cannot measure the mental ability of children through measurement of

[6] Actually nearly a third of the families with six or more children have an income above the national-average, with about the same proportion of such families having to get along on less than half that national-average.

their parents. Every newborn child receives a unique pattern of genes, and the only reliable way to discover how good this new pattern may be is to measure directly the intellectual growth of the child under favorable circumstances.

There is a good correlation between environmental factors and intelligence. The structure of the brain allows for a wide range of delivered mental ability. A child born into a secure family, sent to a good school, and continually exposed to a high level of aspiration approaches maximum mental power. The same child placed in degrading, frustrating situations will approach a minimum of its potential because of the cultural impoverishment. Thus mental efficiency or intelligence is a product of inherited factors, the age, experience, and physiological development of the individual, and the adequacy of the culture in which he grows up.

It follows from all this that the key to fuller utilization of human resources is to provide more enrichment and to give each person the best possible education in the widest sense of that term. A differential birth rate might pose a social danger in a caste-organization society, but in one where the superior classes' culture is continually being diffused to the lower socio-economic classes, the danger of genetic erosion would seem to be minor.

Cost of Population Increase. Throughout its history, the United States has not only replaced its population, but increased it. During the past century, the American population increased more than sixfold, whereas the world's population only doubled. The national average annual rate of increase was almost 2 percent, whereas the world as a whole averaged only three-quarters of one percent.

However, our rate of growth has been falling, as a long-range trend. It dropped from 3 percent yearly in the decade preceding the Civil War to a low of 0.7 percent during the Depression of the 1930's, but since has been increasing at about double the depression rate (Fig. 2).

The population estimate for 1965 is 196 million. Of the 2.5 million annual population increase, some 90 percent is due to natural in-

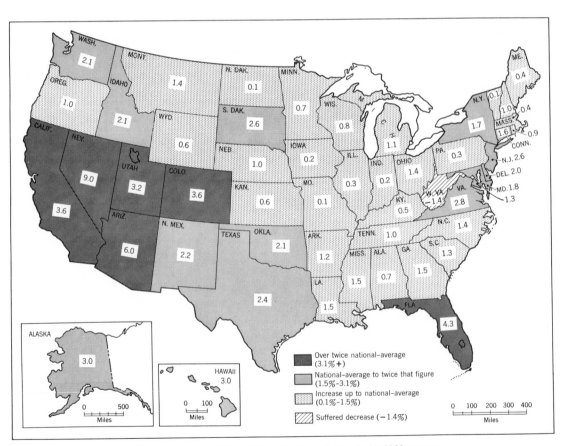

Fig. 2   United States: annual percent increase in the total resident population, 1960–1963 average.
(Bureau of the Census, U.S. Department of Commerce.)

crease and 10 percent to net immigration. Of the net immigration, about 55 percent was from Latin America, about 37 percent from Europe, and the remaining 8 percent from the rest of the world.

The period of infancy and early childhood obviously represents a drain upon family and community resources, an investment made toward a productive return in later life. The demographers, Dublin, Lotka, and Spiegelman, assume that for the United States this nonproductive phase of life extends to the age of 18, on the average, and estimate the investment in a child up to that age at some 4 years' average-family income. In agricultural areas and those in which child labor still persists, the child begins to be productive at a much earlier age. It would probably be safe to estimate, however, that up to the age of 15 years the investment made in a child greatly exceeds its economic return, even in rural areas.[7]

Premature death represents a net economic loss to society from about $1000 at birth to perhaps $15,000 at young adulthood. A death at the age of 40, on the other hand, represents a net economic gain to society, whereas one at 65 represents a net gain to society of more than twice what was invested in that individual.

The whole economy is under pressure because of the rapid growth in the two groups at the extreme ends of the age scale. The number of young and aged dependents is growing three times as rapidly as is the group between. The percentage of these dependents compared to the productive age groups is rising steadily.[8] In the near future, about two-fifths of the expected increase in the national income will go to take care of the increasing number of dependents.

There are many who hold the idea that such population growth provides a firm basis for prosperity. Their reasoning is that our ability and willingness to consume tends to lag behind our productive potential. An increase in the number of consumers is thus thought to offset this tendency by stimulating demand for personal consumption, through bringing continuous pressure for expansion on most sectors of the economy.

Trends in Education. An outstanding social achievement of the past half century has been the raising of the general educational level of the American people. For nearly 30 percent of all Americans, education is a full-time occupation or a time-consuming avocation.[9] Total costs (public and private) amount to nearly 6 percent of the annual gross national product (3 percent in 1929).

There is still incomplete coverage in our educational system. Currently, only half of the adults 25 years and older have completed a high school education, and less than 10 percent have completed 4 or more years of college. Even at the appropriate younger age groups, about a tenth of our youth still fail to complete grade school, about a third fail to complete high school, and only a seventh complete 4 years of college.[10]

---

[7] Per confinement, the average private expenditure is some $300, not including lost income from inability to work. On the average, American couples spend over $600 on a child during the first year of its life, a sum which mounts, apparently by geometric progression, with each succeeding year. The $600 income tax deduction per child saves about $120 in actual tax for most families, or about 33 cents a day, hardly enough to meet the needs of a growing child.

[8] When the dependent age groups—persons under 18 and those 65 and over—are lumped together, they constitute about the same proportion of the total population as was the case at the beginning of the century.

[9] There are some 127,000 institutions, controlled by some 0.2 million trustees, manned by over 2 million teachers and administrators, teaching some 53 million students (35 million primary, 13 million secondary, and 5 million college students).

[10] One of the weakest links in our educational system is the failure of present methods to reach about 20 percent of big-city children. They never learn what they should, even the 3 R's. Vocational schools generally spend 50 percent of the time on academic subjects and 50 percent on shop subjects, so those who cannot handle the first are not allowed to attempt the second. To compound the problem, traditional apprenticeship systems in the United States are dying fast, being strangled by shortsightedness on the part of unions and disinterest on the part of industry, by nepotism, and by racial prejudice. The "dropout problem" is a great waste not because of the inability of nongraduates to perform the more or less menial tasks in society, but because most employers will not hire dropouts even for low-grade jobs if they can possibly avoid doing so.

However, the expanding program of secondary education in the twentieth century has permitted the typical young adult of the 1960's to complete 4 years of high school; his father probably had less than 1 year in high school; and his grandfather, no doubt, did not go beyond grade school.

The second half of the twentieth century bids fair to see higher education become nearly as common. At the turn of the century, only 4 percent of the population 18 to 21 years of age were enrolled in institutions of higher education, compared with ten times that fraction today. In metropolitan areas, commonly over half of this age group start college, although little more than half of them complete 4 years and receive a baccalaureate degree.

In the fall of 1964, some 1.2 million freshmen arrived on campus, about 45 percent of the high school graduates. Of the high school graduates, those in the top 2 percent in terms of academic achievement practically all go to college, but from there on down family income is the main determinant of who goes. Federal aid to students is now confined to a loan program serving perhaps 5 percent of college students (a 1965 law will help more students get low-interest loans from commercial sources by guaranteeing repayment). About 1 million qualified high school students do not attempt to enter college: some cannot afford it, some do not understand the later values to be derived, and some just do not want to go to college in the face of other more immediate goals. Thus the problem is two-

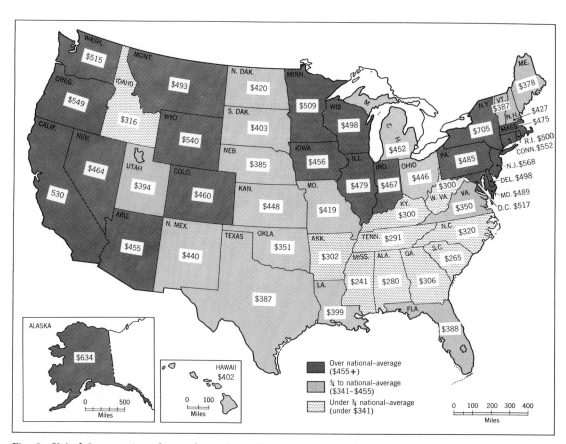

Fig. 3 United States: estimated expenditures for public schools, 1963–1964, in average daily attendance. (Research Division, National Education Association.)

fold: how to aid the needy and how to motivate the uninterested.

Regional and ethnic inequalities in organized education are still impressive (Fig. 3). In general, education in rural areas is inferior to that in urban areas, especially outside the Northeast and the West coast, although there appears to be a narrowing of the gap between rural and urban school systems. With some exceptions, the quality of education for nonwhite Americans is somewhat inferior to that for whites, although narrowing the gap in the 1960's has been a major objective.

CONSERVATION PROBLEMS IN THE ACTIVE ADULT POPULATION

Much of the increased human conservation in the United States in the past generation is related to the phenomenon of millions of families being lifted from poverty to middle-class levels of consumption. In one way, it can be said that one important new American frontier has been opening up the purchasing power of the poor.

However, poverty restricts the amount of welfare that the poorest American family units can afford. The share of the nation's income going to the top one-fifth of families is 45 percent; the share of the poorest fifth is some 5 percent. The remaining half of the nation's income goes to middle-class families (those in the $3000 to $7500 annual income range), making up three-fifths of all families.

Obviously, the poorest fifth of all families will include the overwhelming number of families requiring subsidization. That fifth includes 30 million people in families, and 5 million unattached persons. The per capita disposable income of the 35 million Americans in the lowest fifth of the population is only $600 (compared with the national average disposable income of $1900)—it would take $11 billion to bring all poor families up to the $3000 level, which is now considered the minimum to sustain lower middle-class status.

Of the poor families, 47 percent live in the

South, 25 percent in the Middle West, 17 percent in the East, and 11 percent in the West. Nearly half of all nonwhites are poor, and more than 40 percent of all farm families are poor; in both categories, such families are mainly concentrated in the South and in the nonwhite West (Fig. 4).

More than 11 million children live in families whose incomes are less than $3000 yearly. The heads of more than 60 percent of all poor families have received only a grade school education. A third of all poor families are headed by a person over 65 years of age. More than 3 million unattached persons (mostly elderly) had incomes below $1000 yearly. The poor unattached individuals are mainly older workers and retired persons widely scattered in both rural and urban areas.

Not all adult problems are caused by poverty, but most that are not caused are intertwined in complicated cause-effect interrelationships. This is especially true of illness, accidental death, physical handicaps, and disability related to ethnic prejudice, assessed more fully below.

Cost of Illness. Morbidity and premature death cost the nation a staggering total each year. According to Ewing, the cost of premature death, of total disability, and of partial disability each cost the equivalent of about 5 percent of the national income yearly, whereas short-term illness costs the equivalent of about 2 percent of the annual national income.[11] On any one day, about 5 percent of the total population is so disabled by illness or by physical or emotional handicaps of some kind as to be unable to go to work. Minimum cost of this short-term illness is estimated at some ten billion dollars annually, of which a fifth is accounted for by prolonged illness.

The share of the national income going to private medical care (narrowly defined) has risen from 3.5 percent in 1930 to 5.5 percent in 1964. In the latter year, benefits paid to insured

---

[11] O. R. Ewing, *The Nation's Health: A Report to the President*, Washington, D.C., 1948. Fragmentary checks indicate this pattern of cost remains substantially the same for early 1960's.

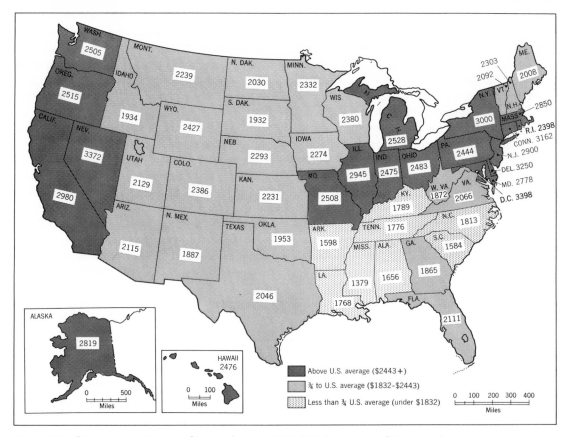

Fig. 4   United States: per capita personal income, by states, 1963. (U.S. Department of Commerce.)

persons for hospital-surgical-medical expenses by all voluntary insurers was about 8 billion dollars, about a quarter of the total private medical bill.[12] The other three-quarters had to be covered by reorganizing the budget, using savings, or going into debt to pay. Both in the early 1930's and in the mid-1960's some 10 percent of the population was burdened with 40 percent of the total personal expenditure for medical care. These 5 million families find themselves in serious financial straits, with costs running between 20 percent and more than 100 percent of their total annual income.

By 1964 more than three-quarters of the total population had some degree of protec-

[12] Governmental, industrial, and philanthropic medical costs were about half as much as the total private medical costs.

tion furnished by private health insurance groups. Blue Cross and Blue Shield provided about 39 percent of the hospital expense coverage, about 36 percent of the surgical expense coverage, and some 46 percent of the regular medical expense coverage. Insurance companies provided 56 percent, 58 percent, and 46 percent of the three types of coverage, and independent plans the remainder, 5, 6, and 8 percent, respectively.

The accompanying map of the United States depicts what proportion of each state's resident population had some form of voluntary health insurance in 1964 (Fig. 5). Most states with high centralizations of population—including practically all the states in the Manufacturing Belt—have greater proportions of their population protected by some form of voluntary health insurance. The relative ease by which health insurance is provided to heavily populated areas through the group insurance mechanism accounts for these heavier areas of coverage. In recent years, however, extension of the group mechanism to include more and more types of businesses and similar activities, and the greater availability of other insurance programs, has accounted for gains in less densely populated states and regions.

There are still some glaring gaps in this voluntary health insurance system: (1) farmers and other people in rural areas are neglected because they are hard to reach; (2) only 30 percent of those households with annual incomes under $2000 (and under half in the $2000 to $4000 range) are covered; (3) the aged are left out of most insurance plans (or have extremely high rates to pay) because their high sickness and injury rates make them poor risks; (4) few plans have regular coverage for long-term "catastrophic illnesses," such as tuberculosis, cancer, and polio; (5) most plans do not make provision for treatment of mentally ill, although this is half of all long-term hospitalization (there are now some 0.5 million patients in public mental hospitals, and only 10 to 15 percent of the 17 million Americans needing some sort of mental care are getting it); (6) most plans do not include peripheral but necessary medical benefits (for example, dental care, nursing, ambulance service, etc.).

Everywhere the deficiency in medical personnel and institutional facilities falls more

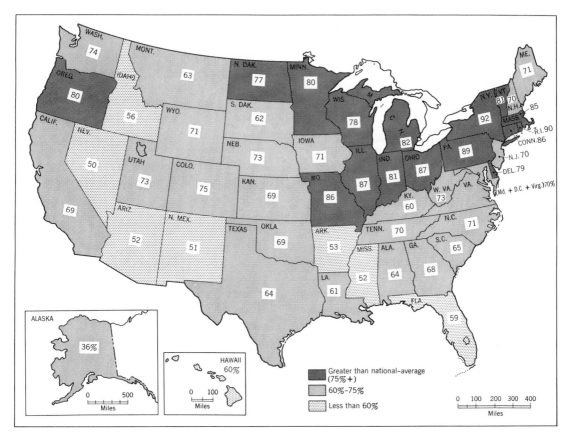

Fig. 5   United States: percent of resident population with some form of voluntary health insurance, by states, 1963. (Health Insurance Council.)

heavily on the rural population. Some 70 percent of American physicians live in the metropolitan areas, which have less than half of the total population. Urban-industrial states regularly report over twice as many days of hospital care per 1000 population annually as do the more rural states.

Accidental Death. Although accidents are largely amenable to control, they account for nearly 7 percent of all deaths each year. They are among the first five causes of death at every age period, and outrank every disease as a killer among children and young adults. Motor vehicle deaths account for two-fifths of all accidental deaths, with a tenth of the loss among those under 15 years of age, about three-quarters of the loss in the productive age period (15–64), and the remaining among persons 65 years of age and over.

The accidental death rate at all ages combined is over twice as high among males as among females, reflecting not only greater exposure to occupational and recreational hazards, but also greater daring.

Motor vehicle mishaps are dominant at every period of life under age 65—at the older ages they are outranked only by falls. Among males, motor vehicle accidents account for about a third of all accidental deaths in every age group (at ages 20 to 24 they account for two-thirds of all such deaths). Among females, motor vehicle deaths are relatively more important than among males during the greater part of life—however, in terms of actual death rates, females consistently have the more favorable experience.

Neglect in Using Handicapped Adults. Nearly 1 of every 10 Americans in the productive age group has a disability that limits activity: there are about 5 million with heart disease, another 5 million with ambulatory problems; hearing difficulties affect 6 million; and 7 million have arthritis, to mention just the largest groups. About 7 million draw paychecks; those who do not collect more than $0.8 billion annually in public assistance payments. Since the government, in cooperation with business and labor, began an intense pro-

motional campaign about 15 years ago, over 4 million handicapped workers have been placed in jobs (including 1 million rehabilitated and retrained, and about 0.6 million disabled veterans of World War II and the Korean conflict helped to obtain private employment).

About 2 million workers are injured each year in job accidents, of which 75,000–85,000 suffer permanent disability. There is a backlog of some 2 million workers with handicaps incurred in past years.

The Office of Vocational Rehabilitation, one of five major programs in the U.S. Department of Health, Education, and Welfare, aids financially state agencies to help place the handicapped in jobs. Some 0.2 million are now placed yearly under this program. However, of the severely handicapped (for example, by blindness, loss of a limb, tuberculosis, epilepsy, and other crippling diseases), only a relatively few are permanently employed.

Cost of Prejudice. The Negro and other nonwhite people throughout the United States have advanced along many fronts in recent years: (1) their longevity has increased, (2) their educational level has been raised, and (3) their social and economic status has been measurably improved. However, the Negro's economic gains have not come up to his dramatic progress in the political and social fields. On the farm there has been little, if any, improvement. Off the farm, at least in the South, the colored man has not done much better than hold his own, if you first discount the gains that industrialization has brought to the population as a whole.

The white man has had two reasons for discriminating against the Negro since he brought him to the United States. The first was economic; the second was social.

The first "need" is disappearing more swiftly than the second, but half of the Negroes are still poor by the government's official definition.[13] More than 75 percent of Negro families earn

---

[13] The government counts as "poor" families whose purchasing-power is less than $3000 or individuals having less than $1500 yearly. These United States poor are not poor by world standards, or by the standards of United States history, but in relation to middle-class ideals.

less than the $6500 average annual income of white families. About 60 percent of Negro families still earn less than $4000 a year, against only 25 percent of white families. About 5 percent of Negro families earn $10,000 or more a year, against 20 percent among white families.

Because of inferior medical and environmental conditions, the life expectancy of the Negro population is 6 years less than that of whites at birth, 4 years less at age 20, 3 years less at age 40, and 0.5 year less at age 60.[14] With increasing urbanization (now over three-quarters) and improving levels of living, the gap between the Negro's and the white man's life span is narrowing.

Improvement in housing comes slowly. Of new, privately financed dwellings built by private builders in the past generation, only 1 percent were inhabited by 10 percent of the population which consists of Negroes. About a third of urban Negro families now own their own homes.

The foundation of the Negroes' economic progress is the fact that large numbers have left farm and domestic work and have gone into industry since the cessation of European immigration in the 1920's. Of the Negro farm-work force before World War II, about one-third has been pushed or pulled off the farm.

About 35 percent of all Negroes now live in southern urban areas, and 40 percent in urban areas elsewhere.[15] About 23 percent of all Negroes now live in southern rural areas, and nearly 2 percent in rural areas elsewhere. Just over 40 percent of the total Negro population now live in the North and West, whereas just under 60 percent still live in the South (Fig. 6).

The vast majority of the nation's 7 million Negro workers are massed in low-paying jobs.[16] Among Negroes with jobs, roughly a fifth are in white-collar jobs, compared with about half among white workers. Over a tenth of all industrial workers now are Negroes, but among skilled workers and foremen, the Negro proportion is still less than 5 percent. Negroes still comprise but 3 percent of college teachers, 2 percent of physicians, and 1 percent each of lawyers, reporters-editors, and managers. In general, Negroes get less pay for the same education, have a higher unemployment rate,[17] and a growing income gap[18] compared with whites.

In some ways, the problem of the Negro is still mainly concentrated in the South, since nearly three-fifths of the country's Negroes still live there. Considered as a whole, the South was more than one-third Negro at the turn of the century, was less than one-fourth Negro in the early 1950's, and is now less than one-fifth Negro (the Southeast is now about one-fifth Negro, the Southwest about 15 percent). The Middle Atlantic and eastern Middle West areas are nearly one-tenth Negro, with other regions (New England, western Middle West, Mountain, and Pacific areas) under 5 percent Negro.

Most important, the changes now occurring in the South—urbanization, Negro outmigration, and the breakdown of social isolation—are rapidly narrowing the differences between the South and the North.

PROBLEMS OF MAINTENANCE AMONG THE AGED

Under mortality conditions prevailing in 1850, the expectation of life at birth was less

[14] Currently, two-fifths of the nonwhite male babies fail to survive to age 60, compared with only one-quarter of the white. Among females, the disparity is even greater. In fact, all during the childbearing period and well beyond, the mortality rate for nonwhite females is double or more than for white females. Since 1900, the life expectancy of the Negro infant has doubled.

[15] Over half of all Negroes now live in central cities (the other quarter of urban Negroes live in small cities and towns). Washington, D.C. is now over 60 percent Negro. Within 15 years, if present population trends are arithmetically projected into the future Negroes will be in the majority in Baltimore, Chicago, Cleveland, Detroit, and St. Louis; and in the decade following, Philadelphia. This Negro "population explosion" in the central city matches the white population explosion in the suburban ring.

[16] About half of the men and two-thirds of the women are still below the semiskilled level.

[17] For example, in the summer of 1963, 24 percent of all Negro youngsters were unable to find work, whereas this was true of only 9 percent of all white adolescents.

[18] The median income of Negro families dropped from its high of 57 percent of white income in 1952 to 53 percent in 1962, at which level it has remained.

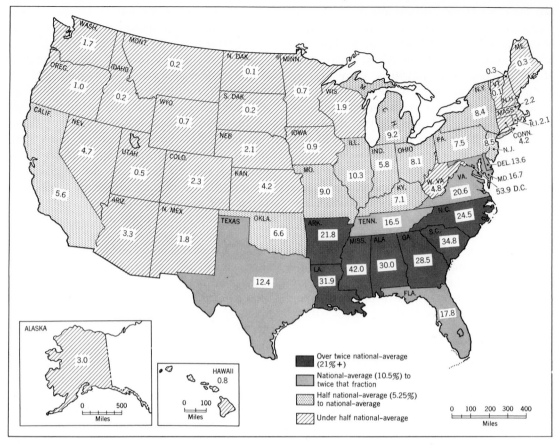

Fig. 6 United States: Negroes as a percent of the population, by states, 1960. (*1960 Census of Population*, U.S. Department of Commerce.)

than 40 years. By 1963, the figure had risen to 70 years (67 years for males, 74 years for females). The average American who now reaches age 25 has more years of life before him than did the average newly born baby at the turn of the century. The average American who now reaches age 50 has a presumable life expectancy of 75 or more years.

This remarkable longevity record is the result of many factors: (1) The striking advances achieved in the medical and allied sciences have been made widely available throughout the country. (2) At the same time, official and voluntary public-health agencies have multiplied in number and broadened the scope of their activi-

ties. (3) In addition, our health and general well-being have benefited greatly from the rapid rise in the level of living.

The extraordinary progress made in prolonging life during the past century reflects, in the main, the effective control gained over the communicable diseases, such as pneumonia and influenza, tuberculosis, diarrhea, nephritis, etc. Three out of ten children born in 1900 were all that could expect to reach the age of 70; four out of ten children born in 1925 were expected to reach 70; five out of ten children born in 1950 will live to be 70. Future gains will be more difficult to achieve because they will depend largely upon reducing the toll from diseases which, in the present state of knowledge, are for the most part of obscure or unknown origin.[19] Yet there is reason to believe that some advances will be made in fending off such causes of mortality as the medical and sanitary sciences continue to develop new knowledge and to make more effective use of what is already known.

Neglect of Older Workers. The nation has made less and less use of its older citizens in the past half century. As compared with over two-thirds of the men 65 years of age or older counted in the labor force then, only one-third are now employed. One reason for the decline is the shift of the population from the farm to the city, where it is more difficult for an old man to keep working, either full time or part time. A second reason is the development of social security and other pension systems which encourage retirement at 65.[20] A third reason is the premium which our present industrial system puts on younger workers.

The number of persons in the population of the United States age 45 or older is now nearly 50 millions, and by 1975 may make up approximately half of the adult population.

For the most part, the prejudice against older workers goes back to a period when physical effort was relatively more important in the labor force than at present. Actually, younger men and women are better only in physically exhausting jobs, the type of job where the machine is more and more substituted for human effort. In more highly skilled jobs, there is a tendency for skill and judgment to increase with experience. The older workers have greater "knowhow," display greater patience, cause less waste, and are less frequently absent.

[19] If it were possible to prevent all deaths before age 40, expectation of life at birth would be increased about 5 years. Substantial gains in the future will be dependent largely on our success in preventing or postponing the cardiovascular-renal diseases and cancer, which are the preponderant causes of death in the middle and later years of life. The difficulties are indicated by the fact that, in the past generation, the expectation of life at age 60 has increased 1 year for white men and 3 years for white women.

[20] Among males aged 60–64, three-quarters of all separations from the labor force are due to retirement, and only one-quarter to death.

Economics of the Aged Dependent. The problem of the aged, once dealt with adequately on the family or local level, has become a national problem affecting economic, social, and political affairs. The growing number of aged affects the economy by altering the consuming market, influencing union demands, making an impact on finance through investments of insurance and pension funds, and by possible development into a cohesive, special-interest political group.

During the past half century, the number of people over 65 has been increasing twice as fast as the general rate of population-growth. This group of retired or retirable now constitutes about 9.3 percent of the total population (Fig. 7). As a bloc, this group is growing older, is predominantly white, is predominantly female, and is commonly no longer part of a family group. Since the majority of such people is not wholly self-supporting, they represent a burden on society already faced with increasing pressure from young dependents.

The arithmetical average income per person over 65 in 1963 was about $2,000, only a bit below the national average of $2443. However, much is obscured by the term, "average": the median was less than half that figure, and the distribution is much more revealing. Actually, 1 in 5 had an income of under $1000 a year,[21] and half had less than $3000, with only 5 percent having an annual income of over $5000. About 2 out of 5 had liquid assets of under $200, over two-thirds had liquid assets of less than $2000, and only 1 in 5 had such assets in excess of $5000. About two-thirds owned their own houses but the value was usually small and a single long illness could wipe them out financially (those over 65 use two to three times as much medical care as those under 65).

Nearly half of the 18 million elderly had no health insurance coverage in 1965. About 15

[21] Over half of this group had no income and were dependent on their children and public assistance. Overall, 90 percent of the elderly who did not live with their children received no cash contributions at all from members of their family.

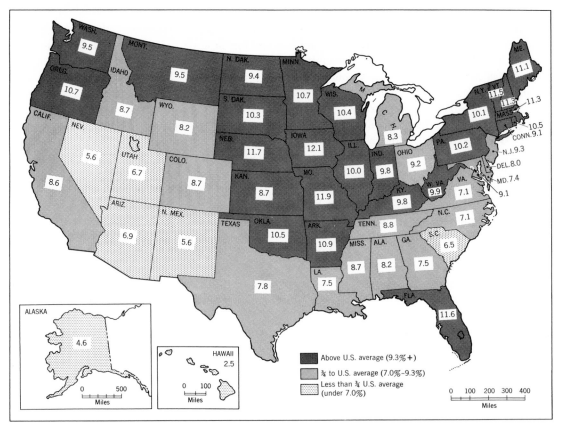

Fig. 7   United States: percent of the total population at age 65 and over, by states, 1962. (Bureau of the Census, U.S. Department of Commerce.)

percent were very sick and unable to pay for their medical expenses; of this group, 60 percent were insured and 40 percent depended on children, other relatives, or charitable and welfare agencies.

Some 3 percent of the nation's elderly have been forced to give up the fight for self-reliant existence and have entered one of the thousands of institutions for the aged that range from expensive, private maintenance to public squalor.

Slightly less than two-thirds of the elderly citizens' income is from private sources. Less than 10 percent of the elderly are receiving payments from a private pension plan, and these account for less than 5 percent of the total monetary income of the aged. The remainder of the income is from social security, railroad, and civil service pensions.

The federal government in 1963 distributed more than $15 billion in benefits and services to persons 65 years of age or older.[22] About 14 million (including some under 65) received monthly social security benefits; the average weekly social security pension for a couple was only $29.

However, older people may be less of a problem as time goes on. For one thing, although older dependents are increasing rapidly, there will be fewer total dependents, since the rise in aged is counterbalanced by smaller families, more working women, and perhaps greater use

[22] In 1964, some 20 million persons received social security payments; 1 million more families will average $129 a month in aid to dependent children; 7 million are getting federally supported relief payments. This federal welfare costs each American 80 cents each week (expenditure on highways $1.35).

of older workers. The gross national product may rise even faster than the number of old people, so it may cost less to provide for the aged. Even if welfare for the aged should be greatly improved, maintenance is unlikely to rise above 5 to 6 percent of the gross national income, about twice the present fraction.

PERSPECTIVE

Gradually, American society is providing protection against the five major hazards of economic security: unemployment, sickness, disability, old age, and death. More and more it is accepted that a healthy and prosperous society cannot be established and maintained by constituent members handicapped by overwhelming burdens of poverty, disease, and ignorance.

Progress made in the public-health sciences during the past half century has made it clear that the heavy burdens of disease can, in large measure, be lifted by the application of scientific knowledge already available, and each year the results of public-health research are broadening the areas of possible control. Future advances in health and reduction of mortality should give us a growing pool of older workers who will add greatly to our potential of manpower and experience.

From the point of view of economic productivity, the age distribution of our population is such that an increasing proportion of our workers will be old, so much depends on our making effective use of our older workers. The working-population possesses high skill and initiative, has excellent technical and management leadership, and is tooled with the most productive industrial machine in the world. The average level of formal education and oc-

cupational training has risen constantly during the past half century, and the trend suggests that it will rise to much higher levels in the future. We still have a growing population, and the ratio of the labor force to the total population is still capable of expansion, mainly because technical progress is continually relieving older women from routine household tasks and excessive childbearing so that they can work outside the home if they wish.[23]

We are not exploiting sufficiently the intellectual resources of the nation. Much more can be done to identify the brightest youngsters, encourage them to plan on higher education, offer them opportunity to work in their chosen fields, give them financial and moral assistance when necessary, and give them the kind of education that will allow them to go ahead rapidly to take their places among the intellectual elite.

We are not using to the best advantage the judgment potentialities of our older people. We do not wish to have a social framework in which the elders and old traditions are inviolate nor a situation in which oldsters become beggars, or suffer from social isolation. New ways of maintaining economic solvency and self-respect for the old people will have to be worked out as an increasing segment of our population becomes aged.

[23] On average, today's American woman marries at 20, has only two or three children, and can expect to live to the age of 73, which leaves her 30 useful years even after her children grow up. Some 40 percent of all women worked in 1963, compared with only half that fraction in 1900. In 1963, women in the labor force increased by 2.25 percent, men only 1.4 percent. That year women made up 51 percent of the population and held 36 percent of the B.A. degrees, 31 percent of the M.A. degrees, and 11 percent of the Ph.D. degrees. They comprised 85 percent of all elementary school teachers and 47 percent of all secondary school teachers, but only 6 percent of all physicians and less than 3 percent of all lawyers.

References

Corson, John J., and John W. McConnell, *Economic Needs of Older People*, The Twentieth Century Fund, New York, 1956.

Dewhurst, J. Frederic, and associates, *America's Needs and Resources: A New Survey*, The Twentieth Century Fund, New York, 1955.

Dublin, L. I., A. J. Lotka, and M. Spiegelman, *The Money Value of a Man*, Ronald Press, New York, 1946.

Eldridge, Hope T., *Population Policies: A Survey of Recent Developments*, The International Union for the Scientific Study of Population, Washington, D.C., 1954.

"Human Resources of the United States," *Scientific American*, Vol. 185, 1951, pp. 27–116.

Kutner, Bernard, and associates, *Five Hundred over Sixty: A Community Survey of Aging*, Russell Sage Foundation, New York, 1956.

Landis, Paul H., *Population Problems: A Cultural Interpretation*, American Book Company, New York, 1948.

Lorimer, Frank, and associates, *Culture and Human Fertility*, United Nations Educational, Scientific, and Cultural Organization, Paris, 1954.

Metropolitan Life Insurance Company, *Statistical Bulletin*, New York. Monthly.

Perlman, Mark, and associates, *Human Resources in the Urban Economy*, The Johns Hopkins Press (distributed for Resources for the Future), Baltimore, 1963.

Schultz, Theodore W., *The Economic Value of Education*, Columbia University Press, New York, 1963.

Spiegelman, Mortimer, *Introduction to Demography*, Society of Actuaries, Chicago, 1956.

Thompson, Warren S., and assistant, *Population Problems*, McGraw-Hill Book Company, New York, 1953.

United Nations Department of Social Affairs, *Economic Measures in Favour of the Family*, New York, 1952.

United Nations Department of Social Affairs, *The Determinants and Consequences of Population Trends*, New York, 1953.

United States Department of Agriculture, Economic Research Service, *Recent Population Trends in the United States with Emphasis on Rural Areas* (Agricultural Economic Report No. 23), Washington, D.C., 1963.

United States Department of Commerce, Bureau of the Census, *Vital Statistics*, Washington, D.C., Monthly.

United States Department of Commerce, Office of Business Economics, *Survey of Current Business*, Washington, D.C. Monthly.

United States Department of Health, Education, and Welfare, Public Health Service, *Vital and Health Statistics—Analytical Studies*, various series, Washington, D.C.

United States Department of Labor, *The Economic Situation of Negroes in the United States* (Bulletin S-3), Washington, D.C., 1962.

Winslow, C. E. A., *The Cost of Sickness and the Price of Health*, World Health Organization, Geneva, Switzerland, 1951.

Woytinsky, W. S. and E. S., *World Population and Production*, The Twentieth Century Fund, New York, 1953.

Part 8

HAROLD V. MILLER
Tennessee State Planning Commission

CHAPTER 22

State and Local Planning

We are an urban nation and daily becoming more so.

That some seven-eighths of our nation's population live in the urban manner, at least divorced from the soil as a direct source of livelihood, is a fact that cannot be overlooked in any intelligent approach to conservation and wise use of our resources. The distribution of the bulk of the population in the urban manner, as opposed to the older rural pattern, inevitably introduces a new set of values to many of the natural resources. The concentration of population in localized areas means greatly increased land values in particular localities as well as a high density of population and investment on those lands. This becomes dramatically evident as a rain-swollen stream spreads over a valley floor. If this occurs at a season when crops are not in the field, the inundation of agricultural land may cause only the mildest of inconvenience and may actually increase the productivity of the bottomlands. On the other hand, when these same waters in the same valley spread into a great city at any season of the year, the economic loss and general disruption may be immense.

Also, conveniently located bodies of water, or land, or forests, or even such intangibles as enjoyable scenery, take on added economic, psychological, and therapeutic values to the extent that they may be available for recreation of a segment of the population living in high density situations in the urban manner.

True, food and fiber still come largely from the soil. But it is in the cities where most of our goods are processed and our wants are satisfied.

THE RISE OF ORGANIZED PLANNING

There has always been planning of sorts in virtually every aspect of human affairs and human endeavor. Planning of sorts characterizes daily decisions of individuals, young and old alike. But the kind of planning discussed here is the organized, and usually official, looking-ahead and the application of professional effort in orienting the decisions, actions, and developments of society in a manner best suited to achieve what will be needed or desired tomorrow.

Some Early Examples of Planning. City planning of a specialized sort characterized the conscious design and layout of a number of the European cities, even those dating back 2000 years. The compact design and remnants of the surrounding fortification walls of ancient and medieval cities are still observable. Planning in those cases was mainly to secure a close-knit urban unit susceptible of defense against opposing ground troops.

In this country, conscious premeditated design characterized early planning of Philadelphia, Detroit, Washington, D.C., and a scattering of other cities.

In the 1920's designs for reconstruction and extension of a number of cities were made. Some of these were carried out in whole, or in part, but many remained primarily as designs on paper. There was widespread recognition of the public interests in the proper and compatible use of land, and the zoning of lands for specific uses was undertaken in a number of the larger cities.

Organization of State Planning. The early 1930's saw considerable federal stimulus to organized and official planning among the states. Establishment of the National Resources Board, and later the National Resources Planning Board, constituted federal recognition and set the stage for stimulation of the states to organize counterparts. It was a time of much experimentation for there was relatively little in the way of achievement to use as a guide save work such as that which had been done in the 1920's in the cut-over lands in the Great Lakes area.

By 1936 there were forty-seven state planning bodies across the country. Under federal stimulation and limited leadership, these engaged in a great deal of vigorous activity, especially in the collecting of data, the making of resource inventories, the publishing of findings, the making of special studies of resource problems, the drafting of legislation, and in kindred activities. Many of the states had set up state planning agencies primarily as the result of federal stimulation, and in some states there was little or no understanding of the productive functions which the state planning agency might perform, nor real consciousness

of a need for such a body. Under these circumstances, some of the agencies functioned until the public insisted on constructive action, or until withdrawal of the appropriations supporting the agency.

Only relatively few of the state agencies set up in the middle 1930's survived and functioned continuously to date. Outstanding among those re the Tennessee State Planning Commission, with its continuing strength in city-planning services to the small cities, the Alabama State Planning Board long achieving a balance of planning and economic development, and the Pennsylvania State Planning Board which has performed signal work in planning services to the office of the governor.

During World War II many long-range programs were shelved, either because of shortages of materials and workers or because of withdrawal of federal aid (WPA, PWA, etc.). The activities or form of many state planning agencies were changed either to gain immediate objectives of national defense or to contribute more significantly to the war effort. These circumstances meant the demise of many planning efforts both at local and state levels.

As the fortunes of war began to turn, concern over planning problems became very widespread, even popular, in cities and state capitals across the nation. Questions regarding the economic future of cities and states found expression in a flurry of public and private organizing for the purpose of providing jobs for veterans when they should return. State-level activity found expression in varying forms. In some states, the industrial-location efforts of established state-planning agencies were stepped up; in other states, departments of commerce were created, and advertising programs aimed at industry and tourists were inaugurated. But there was neglect of many worthwhile aspects of resource or area development. As a result many states are now moving in the direction of more comprehensive efforts in planning and development, either in a single agency or through parallel organizations.

For best results in the legislative and administrative programs of state government there should be a strong planning staff addressing itself to work and problem solution, which must be done by a planning office high in state government and operating as a close staff arm of the governor. Types of functions falling into this category are illustrated herewith.

PLANNING ON A STATE-WIDE BASIS. Into this class of activity fall the planning operations on which many state-wide programs should be based. If state parks are considered as a state service to the citizens, state parks should not simply be clustered either in a scenic corner of the state or in a politically pivotal group of counties. Rather, they should be located and developed in a pattern designed to render reasonable service to all of the citizens. Hospitals and other institutions ought to be distributed across the state in patterns related to the population density. Planning for site acquisition, for the size of establishment, and for function to be performed should be settled in advance of an appropriation.

COORDINATION BETWEEN PROGRAMS AND BETWEEN AGENCIES. Coordination can take a variety of forms under varying circumstances. In one agency several years ago, without a formalized, capital-budgeting procedure at the state level, state-planning personnel visited various institutions and agencies other than the highway department well in advance of a meeting of the legislature to collect information on the probable requests for appropriations. The total derived by this approach was nearly 50 million dollars, and, obviously, there was not that amount of money in sight. The various offices were revisited, and revised estimates were secured which reflected much more realistically the needs of each agency and which totaled 10 million dollars less. When these requests were finally laid on the governor's desk and were transmitted to the legislature for consideration, the task of making decisions and appropriations had been vastly simplified. As a result, no agency or institution was wastefully oversupplied with money, and no agency or institution was stifled for want of money occasioned by exorbitant amounts being channeled in other directions.

PLANNING ASSISTANCE TO THE VARIOUS OPERATING AGENCIES. Relatively few state agencies, except perhaps in the very largest states, have maintained or could maintain justifiably professional planning personnel on their own staff to give the proper attention to projecting their plans and outlining their needs into the future, to do advance work in site selection or site planning, or to perform related work. Just as the office of the attorney general is the source of legal advice for a variety of state departments (as opposed to maintaining their individual legal staff) so a comparably competent planning agency should be available for professional planning advice and assistance to other state agencies.

A STAFF SERVICE TO THE GOVERNOR. As state government grows larger, more complex, and more expensive, so the governor's needs for staff assistance increases. Few governors relish the prospect of adding indefinitely to their own personal staffs, if no reason other than the probability of criticism from political opponents. Yet the governor needs access to a technical planning staff to which he can refer appropriate matters for investigation and can receive a reply in whatever degree of confidence he may specify. His position is immeasurably strengthened if such a staff has been developed and if that staff has earned a reputation which will give great weight to its findings.

The Council of State Governments has suggested that each state consider an office of planning services in the executive branch, with a trained staff, to function in an informational and advisory capacity to:

1. Assist the Governor in developing objectives for current and emerging trends.
2. Compile an inventory of current basic data and undertake research in various problems of state government.

3. Review and suggest means for coordinating the plans of state agencies.

4. Suggest to the Governor alternative courses of action, indicating the consequences of each course.

5. Assist the departments in their planning efforts.[1]

SERVICE AS FEDERAL-LOCAL INTERMEDIARY. In the welter of federal regulations, federal standards, federal aid programs, and even direct federal projects touching areas that are normally under the jurisdiction of local governments, there is rarely appreciable coordination among the various federal elements before the full impact of their programs, construction, or influence bursts upon the locality. Oftentimes even when things seem to be working at cross purposes, the local government has neither the technical staff facilities to insist on coordination nor is there much inclination to question a project, especially when the undertaking is being financed either entirely by federal funds or on what appears to be a very favorable matching ratio.

PLANNING IN CITIES AND URBAN AREAS

The growth of city planning as a professional field has been little short of phenomenal since the middle 1930's. True, there were a number of city planning commissions, dating from earlier years, but some of these were direct lineal descendants of the "City Beautiful" movement which developed after the Columbian Exposition in 1892. This exposition had the effect of introducing into the consciousness of many political and civic leaders the possible grandeur and enjoyment of a form of civic art expressed in monumental public buildings, boulevards, and landscaped open spaces. More practical officials were confronted with pressing problems of finance, of avoiding mistakes

such as too-narrow streets, and of wanting to be able to foresee more clearly the character and direction of urban growth and the accompanying need for community facilities, such as schools, parks, and utilities. In 1937 the National Resources Planning Board had identified over 1700 local planning commissions in cities and towns. By 1964 that number had more than doubled, and in addition a majority of these official bodies offered employment to one or more professionally trained staff members. The competition for professionally trained personnel has meant at least two jobs are available for every professionally trained man; the field has become one of many opportunities with substantial salaries.

Organization for City Planning. Authority to undertake and to enforce planning in cities or other localized areas comes as a grant of power from the state. The enabling legislation necessarily covers a series of specific aspects, both powers and duties.

There will be one body of law dealing with the establishment of the official planning body, outlining the method of choosing the body's membership and number and establishing the place of the planning body in local government. In most cities the planning work is carried on through the establishment of a board or commission, usually dominated by citizens, which exercises direct administrative and policy-making supervision of the technical staff. Thus, the planning process becomes at one and the same time a technical and professional contribution, as well as affording a forum for civic thought and a tangible outlet for civic service and expression on the part of a group of citizens.

Another body of law will deal with the establishment and administration of zoning within the local jurisdiction. It will provide the means for arbitrating or adjusting those cases where the strict application of the zoning regulations may work undue hardship on the individual due to particular and peculiar circumstances beyond his control. Ordinarily adjustment is allowed only in relation to such unavoidable circum-

[1] *Planning Services for State Government*, The Council of State Governments, Chicago, March 1956, p. 42.

stances as unusual shape or size of a parcel of land or difficult topography rendering a parcel unusable if the zoning regulations were arbitrarily applied.

Another body of law will deal with local control over the subdivision of land. The way the land is subdivided has a more or less permanent effect on the community. Persons come and go, live and die, and otherwise move in and out of an individual house. Even houses are built, grow old, are torn down, and replaced within the general framework of lots and streets with relatively little impact thereon. In order to cope intelligently with the many aspects of the problem of land subdivision, the state enacting legislation generally will convey fairly broad powers so that realistic treatment can be given to the width of lots, width of streets, street grades, set-back lines, and to the extent to which the developer will make physical improvements in connection with his lots.

Because of the many facets of urban construction and urban life touched upon by a good planning program the legislation ordinarily will require that public hearings be held before some of the more important regulatory steps growing out of the planning program are taken.

In some few cities the planning staff is more nearly an adjunct of the office of mayor or of the city manager. In Greenville, South Carolina, for example, the staff reports much more directly to the chief administrative officer and to the legislative body of the municipality than do the planning technicians in most American cities. There is no denying the efficiency of such an administrative relationship and there is little room to demur as long as the planning is done *with* people rather than *for* people.

Scope of City Planning Work. Official planning agencies, as arms of local government, number several thousand across the country. Virtually every municipality of 25,000 or over has an official planning body, as do many smaller municipalities, towns, townships, or counties. In many of the counties with official planning agencies, the agency may concern itself with

basic public works, such as the county road system, and with the zoning of rural land to prevent unsightly development along highways, to achieve compatibility among land uses, or to encourage conservation of the soil. In the municipalities and in the urbanized but unincorporated suburban areas, planning studies ordinarily are essential to wise development. Even though the most widely known product of the planning process may be zoning, devoted and unpaid laymen are at work continuously in behalf of the community. Their work constantly leads to decisions regarding the use of land and other resources, decisions that are essential in an effective conservation movement.

City planning work often finds its principal expression in the form of plans for perfecting, rearranging, or projecting the physical aspects of the community. Though the plans may deal largely with physical things, they are not likely to be good plans unless many historical, economic, sociological, and psychological factors have been taken into account.

Good planning and plan preparation seem like a slow process because of the intricate interrelationships which must be taken into account before arriving at individual planning decisions. To illustrate: to drain a swamp may be a step in the direction of achieving more land for agricultural tillage, but the draining of the swamp and the elimination of that water body will have ramifying effects on fish and game, including migratory water fowl. It will mean the disappearance of the swamp as a water retention basin and ground water recharging area. Also, the drainage action may ultimately increase flood hazards, accelerate erosion and siltation, and may affect adversely the falling water table over a considerable area.

Planning decisions in urban areas usually have even more complex and immediate ramifying effects. In the subdivision of a particular fringe area, perhaps a particular street ought to be extended as a major street of generous width. To have such a street may be very desirable, but with this decision the planning does not stop.

By virtue of its generous width and good alignment the street soon carries a considerable volume of traffic. Businesses may be established along that street because the heavy travel would make this frontage a good place for business. The street will also give better access to outlying sections, and the owners of the land in those areas may begin to take an interest in subdividing. As lots are sold, residences are built. These call for new or enlarged schools. More people and more institutions out that way mean new facilities such as water, sewer services, and bus services. It is to be hoped that these ramifying developments can be sufficiently foreseen so that the water and sewer lines can be laid in adequate size before the streets are paved.

Procedures. The first step in developing a plan is the accumulation of some of the working tools of planning. Predominant among these are maps of various sorts. They constitute an inventory record of the status of the community at that time. Many of these maps are common to, or used by, a number of disciplines and professions—geographers, engineers, and insurers. There would be adequate base maps showing streets and lot lines. There should be maps showing installed utilities, including both the network of the various systems and the capacities of their various branches. Maps showing land in public ownership and semipublic holdings will help contribute to an understanding of the community's institutions. Land-use maps will show at least the major groupings of uses, such as residential, commercial, industrial, and vacant (Fig. 1). Topographic maps are virtually a necessity.

Taking into account the past movements and the evident trends of the population, charts and assessments should be made of the prospective future population so that they too will benefit by present decisions. An understanding of age-sex distributions of people and racial or national groups is important in planning.

A study of the economic base is essential to good planning. An examination of economic trends will necessarily take into account both site and situation of the local jurisdiction and will involve understandings including such fundamentals as the natural resources within the hinterland of the particular community. Economic elements such as transportation facilities and the general competitive position of the community also enter into final decisions regarding future developments.

Having established a general picture of the community's future in terms of population and economic function, with an understanding of the attitudes and aspirations of the people, it is possible to think in terms of space for the people, of transportation facilities, of quantities of water, electricity and gas to be provided, of sewage to be disposed of, and of institutions and community facilities such as parks and playgrounds. Total space will be dependent somewhat on the space units desired by the community. In Baltimore or Philadelphia the people are accustomed to less land per family than in St. Louis, Detroit, or Kokomo. Land per family for residential purposes will be influenced by zoning and will be provided under the subdivision regulations. Land for industry needs to be provided and protected by intelligent zoning. And to be competitive with other communities under the new standards and practices of industrial plant construction, space must be available for five to ten times the floor area of new plants. No longer is an appreciable segment of industry equipping itself with loft space or locating in multi-storied factory buildings such as those built about 1850 along the Connecticut River and other local water-power sites in New England.

Land must be provided for commercial uses. Inevitable questions arise such as the extent to which expressways should be provided to encourage the movement of vehicles into a central business district or whether outlying shopping centers should be encouraged, admitting that the central business district is destined to remain a place for specialized shopping and for office buildings, professional offices, and major financial institutions. On the basis of these

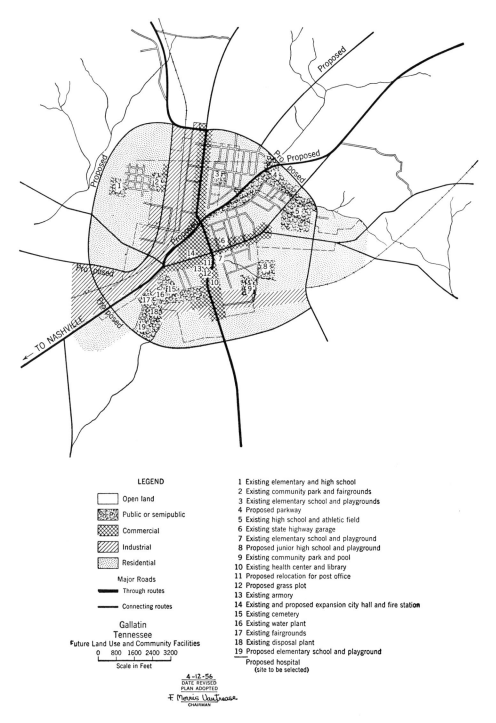

LEGEND

☐ Open land

▦ Public or semipublic

▨ Commercial

▨ Industrial

▨ Residential

Major Roads

━━ Through routes

━ Connecting routes

Gallatin
Tennessee
Future Land Use and Community Facilities

0 800 1600 2400 3200

Scale in Feet

4-12-56
DATE REVISED
PLAN ADOPTED

F. Morris Vautrease
CHAIRMAN

1 Existing elementary and high school
2 Existing community park and fairgrounds
3 Existing elementary school and playgrounds
4 Proposed parkway
5 Existing high school and athletic field
6 Existing state highway garage
7 Existing elementary school and playground
8 Proposed junior high school and playground
9 Existing community park and pool
10 Existing health center and library
11 Proposed relocation for post office
12 Proposed grass plot
13 Existing armory
14 Existing and proposed expansion city hall and fire station
15 Existing cemetery
16 Existing water plant
17 Existing fairgrounds
18 Existing disposal plant
19 Proposed elementary school and playground
Proposed hospital
(site to be selected)

Fig. 1   This map of a small town shows a number of land uses and also the plans for the road system, yet the scale is uncomplicated. (Gallatin Regional Planning Commission.)

and other data, it is possible to begin the drafting of a major thoroughfare plan to secure the passage through, or the by-passing of, through traffic and to handle the traffic to and from the center of the city and to designate the appropriate routes to interconnect the various portions of the city.

A community-wide, future land-use plan can now be constructed. It will take into account the major space needs and distribute these needs logically and in relation to each other on a map anticipating the spread of the future community at the target date agreed upon for the comprehensive plan. Advance planning of schools will allow the acquisition of land before it is absorbed for something else, and the presence of the schools, or at least school sites, will encourage the subdividing and development of property in a manner contemplated by the plan. Parks and playgrounds should be similarly planned in advance, both for economy in land acquisition and for the assurance of having what is planned available where it is needed.

In all of this, plans should go forward for caring for the parking of an anticipated number of vehicles. An automobile or truck that cannot stop is as useless as one which will not start.

When all of these space needs can be foreseen and when major decisions have been made regarding the desirable density of population, then it is possible to proceed intelligently with the drafting of the zoning plan. The zoning plan consists of, first, a map of the area showing the various land-use districts into which the community is divided, and second, a text which outlines the permitted land uses in each district. It is through zoning that areas are designated for residential, industrial, or commercial purposes, and each legitimate use of land is protected against invasion by other uses. Property values can thus be stabilized, investments can be made with assurance, and a place can be provided for every legitimate use of land with every use reasonably allotted to its proper place.

The inevitable question ultimately arises as to how the public works called for in the plan are going to be paid for. A most sensible approach, and one which is increasingly being utilized as part of the comprehensive plan, is the long-range capital budget. This involves a review of the present fiscal position of the municipality, of its income and expenditures, of its outstanding indebtedness, and of the legally accessible revenues not now being collected. Then follows a projection of future operating costs, the listing and estimating of capital costs for individual future public-works projects, the assignment of priorities to same, and the projection of the resultant financial program, say, 5 years into the future with annual revisions and reprojections anticipated.

Urban Renewal. In the past, the sequence of different land uses, building occupancy, and building conditions came to be regarded as a rather inevitable cycle in most American cities. The sequence in a particular city ordinarily began with the establishment of a cross-roads or waterfront settlement in which, as it grew, the central area was gradually converted to business establishments. The houses adjacent to the stores were not only older but, being next to commercial places, were less desirable for residential purposes. As the village grew into a town, there was a gradual elimination of the old houses as new commerical establishments sprang up. Old commercial establishments in the center were gradually eliminated in favor of taller buildings, housing a concentration of offices, financial establishments, and department stores (Fig. 2 and Fig. 3).

As time passed, the central business district of the city would get larger, and the decaying blighted area adjacent became broader. Islands of very old residences, unfavorable to profitable conversion by private enterprise, simply became worse and worse slum areas.

Since World War II there has been a decided increase in outlying shopping centers and super markets in all but the very smallest cities, and this has contributed to stemming the increasing spread of the central business district. This has

Fig. 2 A view of Penn Center, Philadelphia, looking west and showing the complex of railroad tracks. Photograph was taken in 1952 before redevelopment of this important down-town section of the city. (Philadelphia City Planning Commission. Photography by Lawrence S. Williams, Inc.)

slowed down the conversion of the blighted and slum areas to commercial use.

From the mid-1930's to the mid-1950's some demolition of slums was accomplished through public action by tearing down some of the worst, and reusing cleared areas for low-cost public housing which was made available to those unable on their own to secure safe, sanitary, and adequate housing.

President Eisenhower was well advised early in 1954 when he said, in essence, that there simply is not enough money to tear down all the slums as they develop. Public expenditures should be directed toward preserving good portions of the city, rehabilitating those that have deteriorated, and as a last resort tearing down those areas that have degenerated beyond repair. It was in keeping with these concepts that

Fig. 3   An aerial view of Penn Center, Philadelphia, looking northeastward. Note the redevelopment of area formerly covered by a broad pattern of railroad tracks. Photograph taken in 1963. (Philadelphia City Planning Commission. Photography by Lawrence S. Williams, Inc.)

the Housing Act of 1954 was passed and the Urban Renewal Program became a reality. Under this program, there is a very real opportunity for inhibiting the spread of slums and blight and in making cleared slum lands available for any of a variety of uses according to the needs of the community. There are incentives for the creating of parks and playgrounds in places where they are needed the most. Lands not needed for public purposes which have been assembled and cleared in the process of developing may, according to local needs, be sold for residential, commercial, or industrial pur-

poses. High-rise apartments, many in the luxury class, occupy reassembled lands, and represent a return from suburban to urban living. In many instances the locating of non-noxious industries near the center of the city, as a by-product of urban renewal, will make possible increasing employment opportunities close to the residence of many employees and thus limit the need for expensive street construction, which becomes necessary when residences and places of employment are distant from each other.

Since communities are in competition with each other just as surely as individuals or corporations are, the communities which do not take constructive steps in urban renewal and do not participate in these programs will find themselves at a competitive disadvantage in the future. With the average life of buildings in our cities being only 40 to 50 years, it means that we are rebuilding American cities each 40 to 50 years. It makes good sense that to do the job well there should be enlightened urban planning.

PROBLEMS OF THE URBAN REGION

Immense problems have arisen in many of our major metropolitan regions simply as an outgrowth of the complexity of local governmental jurisdictions represented therein. The Greater Boston area, Cuyahoga County surrounding Cleveland, and St. Louis County, Missouri, are examples (Fig. 4).

Some of these, as in the case of the metropolitan region of Boston, began as entirely separate towns and villages scattered over a countryside which has subsequently been built up until the whole area has become a great urban mass virtually continuous in urban land occupancy but tantalizingly separated by jurisdictional lines (Fig. 5). In other instances, such as in the Chicago area, residential communities sprang up in the countryside and along the lakeshore at points where rapid transit or good highways made feasible commuting to the central city to work.

Since 1940, the mounting costs of urban government in larger, older, central cities have led to local initiative to incorporate sections of urban fringe areas as separate municipalities in order to avoid incorporation into, or annexation by, the central city. Many of the satellite

Fig. 4   A recent view Memorial Plaza Park in St. Louis, Missouri, showing the modern structures and open spaces in a once-crowded and old section of the city. (St. Louis City Plan Commission.)

Fig. 5   Redevelopment in downtown Boston has been very dramatic in recent years. The photograph shows demolition in old Scolley Square area preceding construction of Government Center. Historic Faneuil Hall is shown in the right background. Photograph taken in January 1964. (Boston Redevelopment Authority.)

communities are unable to supply themselves with municipal services of their own. Many are forced to become customers of the central city for services such as water supply and sewage disposal. Also, with the jurisdictional differences, it is impossible to plan responsibly for the entire urban area and thus attain some uniformity in land use, taxation, utility services, schools, and an integrated system of streets.

The execution of major projects such as expressways, interregional urban highways, or highway links through urban areas becomes fantastically complicated in these jungles of duplicated administration. It becomes much more expensive in terms of public funds to execute such projects. Compromises often must be made in route location, in nature of construction, and in remedial attention to utilities in order to gain local approval of the project (Fig. 6).

Meanwhile, blight and slum conditions spread across areas regardless of jurisdictional boundaries.

A variety of solutions to pressing metropolitan problems are being advocated. Nashville and Davidson County, Tennessee, have consolidated into a single Metropolitan Government. Miami-Dade County is an example of partial consolidation, and various cities have created special districts or services for area-wide functions such as sewers or transit.

Also, virtually all comprehensive plans for

the development of the major cities now are covering urbanized areas, including satellite municipalities; and a growing number of federally aided or state-sponsored public works programs are requiring as prerequisite a comprehensive development plan for the entire metropolitan area (Fig. 7).

REGIONAL PLANNING

Regions have been variously defined depending chiefly upon the criteria used in their determination and the purposes for which they are delineated. Therefore, no simple definition of regional planning will be accepted universally.

A region is inescapably a portion of the earth's surface. By ordinary usage it implies a substantial portion of the earth's surface, transcending in area the ordinary municipality and in most instances exceeding the area of a county. Some degree of homogeneity is an essential consideration in delimiting a region. Depending on the basis for delimitation, regions may vary greatly

Fig. 6 Los Angeles, California. The modern city is confronted with the serious problem of integrating streets with the major highways and freeways which serve the urban community. (Division of Highways, Sacramento, California.)

Fig. 7 The Midtown Plaza, Rochester, New York, provides in the downtown area much of the atmosphere and convenience of a modern suburban shopping center. (Rochester City Planning Commission.)

in size, but a region must always have a boundary.

Representatives of the various scholarly disciplines constantly recognize and delineate regions according to their needs. Plant ecologists will be guided by typical plants or plant associations; geologists, by the earth materials finding surface expression in a given territory; and climatologists, by climatic conditions. Also sociologists painstakingly divide larger areas on the basis of chosen indices meaningful to them.

For political or governmental purposes, regions represent areas of common interest or convenience, the boundaries for which are ordinarily drawn along political lines, thus making them groups of counties, states, major portions of states, or groups of states. The state is the region for many conservation and other governmental activities where state law, administrative regulations, or finance play a substantial part.

Choosing Planning Regions. From the foregoing discussion of regions and the variety of political and scientific indices by which regions can be delimited, it can be correctly assumed that similar latitude exists for delimiting regions for planning purposes.

Prudence and logic will characterize the delimiting of a region for planning purposes and both will be exercised in the light of goals to be achieved and available tools with which to work. In 1929, Wisconsin's plans highlighted the agriculturally submarginal character of the cut-over portions of the state and, through a combination of rural zoning and public purchase, large areas were essentially depopulated. About 1950, through the medium of the New England Council, states of that area banded together on a program of economic planning and business financing. The U.S. Department of Commerce and other federal agencies traditionally divide the country for program purposes into regions either on the basis of problems (for example, Bureau of Reclamation serving the semi-arid West) or on the basis of communication (Atlanta is the regional headquarters of many agencies serving the Southeast). The Tennessee Valley Authority is granted jurisdiction and responsibilities coinciding logically with the territory drained by the Tennessee River. More recently, at the direction of Congress, regional studies of major river basins have been undertaken which inquire broadly into the future economic and population possibilities as a basis for assessing the role of water resources development in such areas.

During several years the governors of states represented in the Appalachian area have been engaged in joint study and in consultation with the federal government in an effort to improve the economy and living conditions in this region of 165,000 square miles. This situation holds the promise of a new approach, with each of the ten states preparing comprehensive plans for their respective areas, and, on coordination, to proceed with effective results, acting jointly with the federal government and contiguous states, under legislation passed by Congress in March 1965.

Some problems susceptible of planning treatment transcend state boundaries but can be handled by means short of national action. This is well illustrated in the field of stream pollution. For example, Tennessee is signatory to an interstate stream pollution control compact under which the several states pledge interstate action on preserving the quality of waters of the Tennessee and Cumberland rivers. The seven states involved have become an administrative region for the accomplishment of these purposes in the two watersheds.

In the field of interstate action in the control of forest fires, however, the boundaries of the region of common interest embrace a larger territory and are much more flexible. This author acting for the State of Tennessee, negotiated an Interstate Forest Fire Protection Compact to which all states south of the Ohio and east of the Mississippi are signatory, and which agreement makes possible the bringing together of the combined fire-fighting facilities of all these states to control a major conflagration, thus extending greater protection to the forest resource than any one state could possibly finance and maintain. By interstate action a great step forward in conservation of natural resources has been taken.

References

American Institute of Planners, Washington, D.C., *Journal.* Quarterly.

American Society of Planning Officials, *Planning Advisory Service*, Chicago. Monthly, topical monographs since April 1949.

Duncan, Otis Dudley, W. Richard Scott, Stanley Lieberson, Beverly Duncan, and Hal H. Winsborough, *Metropolis and Region*, Resources for the Future, The Johns Hopkins Press, Baltimore, 1960.

Dyckman, John W. and Reginald R. Issacs, *Capital Requirements for Urban Development and Renewal*, McGraw-Hill Book Co., New York, 1961.

The Editors of *Fortune, The Exploding Metropolis,* Doubleday and Company, Garden City, New York, 1958.

Gibbs, Jack P., editor, *Urban Research Methods,* D. Van Nostrand Co., Princeton, New Jersey, 1961.

Gottmann, Jean, *Megalopolis,* Twentieth Century Fund, New York, 1960.

Hawaii State Planning Office, *The General Plan for the State of Hawaii,* Honolulu, Hawaii, 1961.

International City Managers' Association, *Local Planning Administration,* Third Edition, Chicago, 1959.

Kent, T. J., Jr., *The Urban General Plan,* Chandler Publishing Co., San Francisco, 1964.

Lautner, Harold W., *Subdivision Regulations,* Public Administration Service, Chicago, 1941.

Mayer, Harold M. and Clyde F. Kohn, *Readings in Urban Geography,* The University of Chicago Press, Chicago, 1959.

Miller, Harold V., *Mr. Planning Commissioner,* Public Administration Service, Chicago, 1954.

Mumford, Lewis, *City Development,* Harcourt, Brace and Co., New York, 1945.

Mumford, Lewis, *The City in History,* Harcourt, Brace and Co., New York, 1961.

Palo Alto, California, *Interim General Plan,* City Planning Commission, Palo Alto, California, 1955.

Perloff, Harvey S., Edgar S. Dunn, Jr., Eric E. Lampard, and Richard F. Muth, *Regions, Resources, and Economic Growth,* The Johns Hopkins Press, Baltimore, 1960.

A Place to Live, The Yearbook of Agriculture, U.S. Department of Agriculture, Government Printing Office, Washington, D.C., 1963.

United States Department of Agriculture, *Rural Zoning in the United States,* Washington, D.C., 1952.

United States National Resources Planning Board, *State Planning,* Washington, D.C., 1942.

Walker, Robert A., *The Planning Function in Urban Development,* Second edition, University of Chicago Press, Chicago, 1950.

Yokley, E. C., *Zoning Law and Practice,* The Michie Co., Charlottesville, Va., 1948.

GUY-HAROLD SMITH

The Ohio State University

CHAPTER 23

National Planning
and the Conservation of Resources

The national government, by its legislative acts, administered by the chief executive and tested in the highest tribunal of the people, provides equal opportunity for all the people of the United States. Since the founding of the Republic the Congress has given attention to the needs of the nation, but inevitably certain acts of Congress have been advantageous to selected groups or particular areas. But in the government there have always been men of high principles whose great ambition has been to contribute to the general welfare of the nation.

The Responsibility of Congress. In the Congress, both in the House of Representatives and in the Senate, the members in general may be said to entertain two major objectives. As would be expected, these elected representatives of the people are the protectors of the interests of the people whom they serve. At the same time they are aware of the needs of the nation, and their legislative actions reflect their interests in the national welfare.

The improvement of rivers and harbors, the reclamation of lands requiring irrigation, the control of floods, the development of power, the protection of coastal areas against erosion, the conservation of the soil resources, the pres-

ervation of the dwindling forest resources, the conservation of the mineral treasures, and provisions for recreation have received Congressional attention.

Inequality in the Distribution of Resources. The abundant resources of the country have not benefited all the people equally. Many people have been enriched because they have been successful in securing control over the material resources of the country. Others in humble circumstances have not shared in the great wealth of the nation. Certain pioneers settled the new farmland when the rich prairies were available. At a later period the settlers were not so fortunate, for the richer lands were gone. The abundant timber and mineral resources were developed and exploited by private capital, and a fortunate few were enriched. Other people came into possession of poor land and found it difficult to earn a decent living. The material resources distributed unequally over the country have benefited the people unequally.

Private Enterprise and National Planning. Concurrently with the political growth of the United States private enterprise and personal initiative were responsible in a large measure for the development of the natural resources.

495

Because of great abundance, rapid and wasteful use of resources became a characteristic feature of the national economy. From the time of settlement and particularly after the frontier moved westward beyond the Appalachians, there was for many decades a prodigality about the exploitation of the great resources of timber, grass, water, coal, iron, oil, and natural gas. But two world wars with their enormous wastefulness and a great economic depression have made us aware of the necessity of husbanding our resources. Planning among other things must be directed toward the wise use of resources and the ordering of the economy in the best interests of all the people. Planning is both a public and a private responsibility. People as property owners, whether as private citizens or as shareholders in large corporations, must join with the federal government in reducing or avoiding the wasteful exploitation of natural resources.

There have been brief periods of economic stress with widespread unemployment and insecurity. Fear has replaced hope, and people have entertained doubt about the stability and the soundness of the national economy. The Ameican economy, characterized by its great capacity for production, has been unable to achieve by itself certain necessary reforms and attain stability and full employment; as a result the federal government has participated increasingly in the economic life of the nation.

It has become evident that the federal government has become more paternalistic and now takes a leading part in planning for the full use and conservation of the material resources of the country. The national government has become in effect a gigantic planning agency and participates in many ways in the economic life of the nation.

THE NATURE OF NATIONAL PLANNING

Planning on a Nationwide Basis. It is not always evident that certain acts of Congress may change in a significant way the utilization of natural resources. The tariff regulations or duties applied to imports may affect all the people in much the same way. The import duty on foreign sugar increases the price of sugar everywhere in the United States. The duty on wool has a similar effect on the price of all woolen products whether they are made of imported wool or wool of domestic origin. In these instances the government was not primarily concerned with the increased price of sugar and wool to all the people but in the protection provided for the domestic producers of these products.

Although certain acts of Congress may operate selectively for the benefit of the few, many laws have nationwide application. The Pure Food and Drug Act, the insuring of bank deposits, the establishment of uniform postal rates, the operation of the Federal Reserve System, and many other acts and regulations apply more or less uniformly to all the people (Fig. 1).

Benefits or disadvantages may accrue selectively to certain people, but the national welfare requires on occasion that the federal government take definite action. No doubt the best interests of the people were served when the federal government endorsed stockpiling of strategic materials, and required that all uranium-bearing ores be sold to the government. During World War II and during hostilities in Korea, a large number of resources and industrial materials were brought under control of the federal government. The jurisdiction of the government extended from production and procurement through processing and allocation to civilian and military agencies. This was well illustrated by rubber, the ferroalloys, copper, aluminum, and a great number of products. In times of national stress the participation of the federal government in the economic affairs of the nation is greatly expanded in the best interests of all the people.

However in times of peace and international calm the federal government, depending on the party in power, may encourage private interests to take on a larger responsibility in ordering the national economy.

National planning is regarded by many as

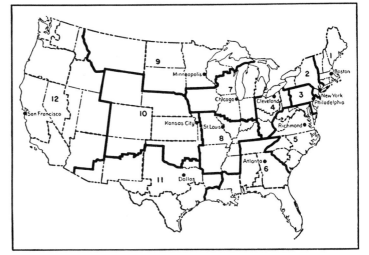

Fig. 1   The Federal Reserve Board: Districts. These divisions were originally set up to serve the banking and financial interests of the country. The boundaries are essentially political and arbitrary in character. (National Resources Committee.)

a step toward a kind of totalitarianism which is in conflict with free enterprise and personal liberty. The states that pay more into the federal treasury in taxes than they receive in benefits are disposed to complain about inequities. Generally it is accepted as good governmental planning to use the greater wealth and resources of richer and more fortunate states for the benefit of the poorer areas.

In the broad field of planning for the security and the defense of the nation, and planning for the security and health of the people individually and by groups, the federal government must be concerned with the physical or material resources that are fundamental in security planning. The government extends its protection to all the people and otherwise recognizes the nationwide application of its laws and regulations. The conservation and wise use of the material heritage of the nation require vigilance and dynamic action against waste of the physical base of the national economy.

Government Must Take the Long View. In the long-range development of the economy of the United States the material resources have been or will be depleted unequally. Certain industrial raw materials occur in such great abundance that there is little danger of immediate exhaustion. The use of enormous quantities of

iron and petroleum, on the other hand, has threatened our ultimate supply of these basic resources. The heavy demand for lead, zinc, and copper has made us aware of the possibility of exhaustion of these essential metals.

The federal government and other agencies, both private and public, are giving attention, through research, to extending the productive life of many of the raw materials so necessary in the complex economy of the United States and the world.

Standard of Living and Resource Utilization. The high standard of living attained by the people of the United States is related to a number of factors. The volume and value of material resources in relation to the number of people are favorable to the development of a high standard of living. The capacity of the people, with an urge to improve their physical well-being and raise their cultural standards, has been an important factor. The inventive genius of the people made possible the development of machines that can utilize the great power resources of the country for the welfare of the people. In spite of an imprudent drain upon the material base of the nation the economic and political leadership has been equal to its opportunity to bring favorable conditions of life and security to the American people. To maintain these conditions is the challenge which recurrently confronts the people and their government.

Planning, a Definition. Planning is the development of a program of ultimate objectives and a schedule of operations to achieve the desired results. In the development and wise use of resources a clear statement of the objectives to be attained is essential to the execution of a plan. It is also very important that the several operations in the plan be scheduled so that the key projects are given priority. This simple statement encompasses most of the essentials of planning whether local, state, regional, or national.

Planning is not regimentation or may not be. In the United States democratic planning should emerge from community or national discussion of issues that require collective action. Planning should be continuous, or at least there should be a periodic review of previous plans so that obsolete objectives may be abandoned. Also it may be necessary to reschedule the projects in terms of recent developments. A long-term plan characterized by rigidity instead of flexibility may be doomed to failure. It is important that planning, as a community program, should be responsive to the will of the people who may wish to re-examine their earlier plans and revise their schedule of projects.

REGIONAL PLANNING

In an area as large as the United States where the geographical diversity is so great, it was inevitable that resource development and use would be distinctly regional in character. For example, the harvesting of the great white pine forest of the Great Lakes states placed upon the lumber markets one of the finest building materials in the latter decades of the nineteenth century and the first decade of the twentieth. When this harvest was consumed the lumber industry moved on to other forests, and the cut-over lands became a problem area. In a similar manner the grasslands of the Great Plains were first

the natural grazing lands of the indigenous buffalo. Then overpasturing and the breaking of the sod for agriculture weakened the natural defenses of the area, and in the dry years of the 1930's and the 1950's the area took on dust-bowl characteristics.

What Is a Region? There are many kinds of regions. Some regions are essentially physical in character, such as soil regions, physiographic regions, climatic regions, and drainage basins. Others are cultural regions, such as language areas, regions with a dominant religion, and areas with a particular mode of government. Whether physical or cultural a region must have one or more distinguishing characteristics that are more or less co-extensive with the area, and it should be set apart from other regions with distinct or arbitrary boundaries.

Many easily recognized regions in the United States have emerged because of certain dominant characteristics. A region, to have validity and usefulness as a planning area, may or may not have exactly defined boundaries or enumerated common characteristics. For administrative convenience it may be useful and desirable that regions, whether physical or cultural, have boundaries that are easily identified and demarcated.

Most Americans are familiar with such regions as New England, the Piedmont, the South, the Middle West, the Great Plains, the Upper Lakes area, the Columbia Plateau, the Great Basin, the Yukon Basin, and many more restricted areas or regions such as the Mohawk Valley, the Delta country, the Tennessee Valley, Appalachia, the Salt Lake oasis, the Central Valley of California, or the Puget Basin (Fig. 2). Some of these are physical regions or were originally, but have taken on composite characteristics reflecting something of the natural conditions in combination with the economic and cultural attributes. People living, working, and shaping the destiny of an area give to it characteristics that transcend the natural conditions which at the outset may have been dominant.

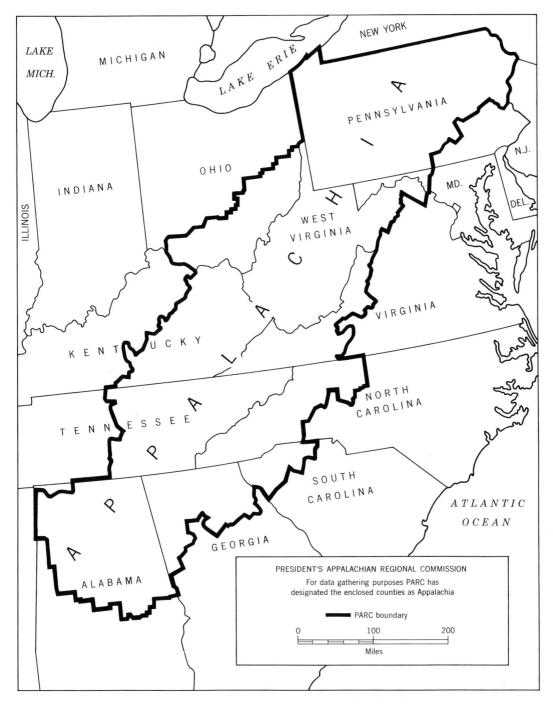

Fig. 2 Appalachia as delineated for the purpose of gathering and assembling data that may be useful in planning programs will require action by the Congress and approval by the President. (Area Redevelopment Commission, U.S. Department of Commerce.)

PRESIDENT'S APPALACHIAN REGIONAL COMMISSION

For data gathering purposes PARC has designated the enclosed counties as Appalachia

━━━ PARC boundary

0   100   200
Miles

499

Most regions have a central or core area which may be regarded as the type location. However, the core may not represent all the characteristics of a large area or in the same proportion. No small area in New England could be truly representative of the forested highlands of northern Maine, the truck farming area of the Connecticut lowland, the sandy beach areas of Martha's Vineyard, or the industrial community of Worcester, Massachusetts. With all its regional or sectional differences New England is a region in the minds of most people.

In regional planning, which in effect is national planning by regions, it is necessary that the areas set up as planning regions should have something of the unity of spirit that characterizes New England, the South, or the Middle West. From this sense of regional unity will come the leadership and the energy that will achieve results.

Frederick Jackson Turner, historian of the frontier, recognized the importance of pioneer life as a significant force in the development of fundamental political character of the United States. Although the moving frontier tended to bring some common experiences, the pioneers were adventuring into different geographical regions. Sectionalism was from the outset a concomitant characteristic of the settlement and development of the United States.

Regionalism or sectionalism in a narrow provincial sense may be an undesirable characteristic of the national economy. But regionalism, if it is a unifying force which transcends the restricted limits of a small area, may be a vital factor in the development of national character. Out of the diversity of states and regions a spirit of national responsibility emerges. "The diversity of regions rather enriches the national life than impoverishes it . . ."[1] Regional planning is in effect national planning expressed or developed areally.

Regional Divisions of the United States. The federal government has found it desirable,

[1] Donald Davidson, "That This Nation May Endure, The Need for Political Regionalism" in Herbert Agar and Allen Tate, *Who Owns America?*, Boston, 1936, p. 116.

and in particular cases almost a necessity, to decentralize or regionalize certain functions. The concentration of many agencies in Washington has been looked upon as undue centralization of administrative activities in a single urban center. The rapid expansion of governmental agencies in wartime and during the difficult depression years placed a heavy burden upon the metropolitan area of Washington. Housing for government employees, transportation to and from work, office space for personnel, and related problems became the insuperable difficulties of a rapidly expanding metropolitan area. There was no time for planning, but it was obvious that decentralization of certain governmental functions was an urgent necessity.

The Census Divisions. The Bureau of the Census has established nine arbitrary but statistically useful regions. Each of these divisions includes states that have many characteristics in common. They include New England, Middle Atlantic, South Atlantic, East North Central, West North Central, East South Central, West South Central, Mountain, and Pacific groups of states. The new states of Alaska and Hawaii are included in the Pacific division. These regions have statistical convenience and through long use have become well established.

Functional Divisions of the United States. For the purpose of decentralizing certain administrative functions of the government a number of agencies have a regional pattern of organizaion. This is well illustrated by the United States Circuit Court of Appeals which consists of ten Circuit Districts and the District of Columbia. These regions or districts are judicial areas and serve this function only.

In 1914 during the administration of President Woodrow Wilson the Congress enacted the legislation that created the Federal Reserve System. For the purpose of carrying out the provisions of the act the United States was divided into twelve Federal Reserve districts each consisting of a number of states or parts of states and each having a Federal Reserve bank to serve the banking, industrial, and commercial interests of its area.

Many other agencies of the federal government have been organized on a regional basis, or have established outpost or field offices to facilitate their administrative activities.

Planning Regions. The establishment of regions for the planned development and use of resources emerges as a necessary concomitant of national planning. Certain steps have already been taken and may indicate the nature of the regions that are most suitable for planning and developmental programs. It is obvious that no single type of region will be suitable for all purposes. Several kinds of regions, differing in dimensions, overlapping perhaps in certain instances, and encompassing a number of vital activities, may be necessary to achieve the several objectives of a well-balanced program of national development.

The Watershed as a Planning Region. It has been recognized that the hydrographic basin or watershed is an appropriate and manageable planning area. In many of the drainage basins of the United States the principal problems that require constructive action are closely related to the river in each watershed. The control of the master stream becomes the key project in a basin-wide program of resource development which will under proper management extend to other problems not directly related to the river (Fig. 3).

The Tennessee River basin, developed under the administrative jurisdiction of the Tennessee Valley Authority, may be regarded as the model drainage-basin planning region. Other watersheds have been designated as well suited for regional development. These include the Ohio Valley, the Missouri Valley, the Colorado Valley, the Columbia Valley and others (Fig. 4).

The Tennessee Valley development is an achievement that has been the envy of other regions. People in other areas are reluctant to wait until adversity requires a program of action. The needs of the United States in respect to highways, housing, automobiles, and new productive equipment to meet consumer demands are so great that material, the labor force, and the managerial skills may not be available at all times for major public-works projects.

Before the need arises for immediate action comprehensive surveys can be made so that plans will be ready when the need arises. As an integral part of the plans a schedule of projects should be developed. It may be necessary to proceed immediately with certain plans for a region or watershed and reserve for later periods the completion of the project. That is well illus-

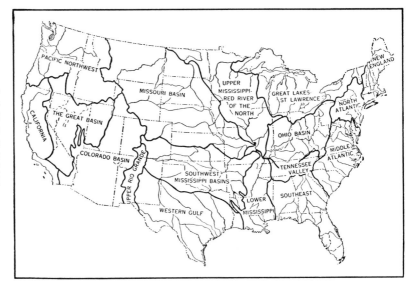

Fig. 3   Major drainage basins of the United States. Drainage basins are naturally well suited for water planning, but in spite of their limitations they have been considered appropriate for the more inclusive regional planning programs. (National Resources Planning Board.)

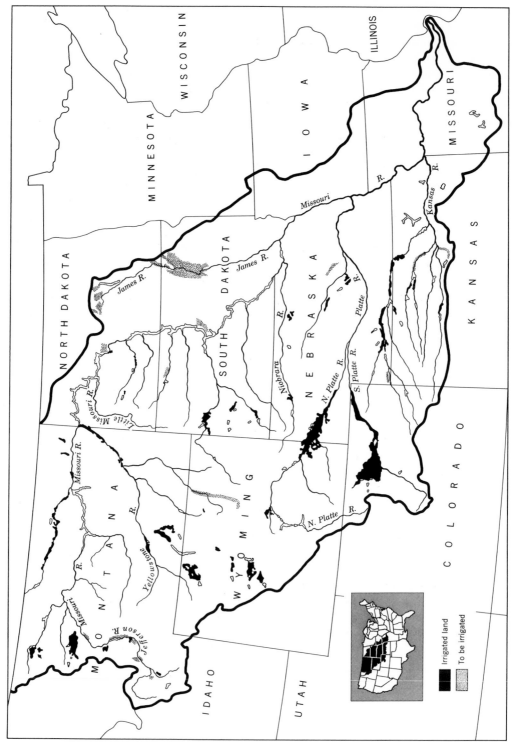

Fig. 4   The Missouri River basin. The basin of the Missouri presents a series of problems which seem to require careful basin-wide planning for their proper solution. (After the Corps of Engineers, U.S. Army.)

trated in the signing of the Ohio River Valley Water Sanitation Compact at Cincinnati, Ohio, on June 30, 1948. Navigation on the Ohio has long been a part of the program of river development. Floods remain a great menace, and many years will be required before the excess waters can be brought under control. But the Ohio is more than an artery of commerce. It is a source of water for millions of people, and at the same time it is a great sewer. Sanitation in the Ohio Valley continues to be a problem.

Groups of States as Planning Regions. Other types of areas have been suggested as suitable for regional development. The New England area consists of a group of states rather than a number of drainage areas; yet the water problems of the several major streams such as the Connecticut and the Merrimack require a number of multiple-purpose projects to meet the situation.[2] The Middle Atlantic area, like New England, is largely a group of states extending from New York to North Carolina and fronting on the Atlantic. It is an area with many problems, but it lacks the regional consciousness so characteristic of New England.[3] This is a region highly developed industrially and commercially, and many of the most urgent problems of today are related to the lack of careful planning in the past. Urban blight and the related ills of the industrial communities require plans and programs of action that will rehabilitate the unfortunate people who live in such areas and redesign the land-use pattern in terms of the long-range needs of the urban areas.

Other groups of states have been considered appropriate planning regions. Some of these include the Southeast, consisting of South Carolina, Georgia, Florida, Tennessee, Alabama, and Mississippi. Part of this area is already included within the jurisdiction of the Tennessee Valley Authority. In spite of industrial develop-

ments in the Piedmont, in the Birmingham district of Alabama, and in the Tennessee Valley, this is also an agricultural area with some of the agrarian problems associated with the cash crops of cotton and tobacco.[4]

The Mountain states planning region consists of Colorado, New Mexico, Wyoming, and parts of several other states in the Rocky Mountain area. This large area, because of the character of its resources, has been exploited rather than developed. Minerals have been mined until the rich treasures have been exhausted; grasslands have been overgrazed to supply meat products to the eastern markets; and in many areas the limited timber resources have been cut so that watershed protection has been reduced. The scant rainfall, in most places inadequate for either forests or agriculture, becomes a resource of great importance in the water courses where the water is available for power and for irrigation. The co-ordination of the several water-use projects is the major regional problem of the mountain states.[5]

The Pacific Southwest and the Pacific Northwest regions are similar planning regions because each consists of a number of states and parts of states. In both areas large tracts of dry land without adequate water are characteristic, though the Southwest has less rainfall than the Northwest. The Southwest has access to the power and the water of the Colorado while the Northwest taps the resources of the Columbia.

In the Pacific Southwest water is the universal need. "Cities, farms, mines, and factories depend directly on perpetuation of their water supplies, which must often be brought from distant sources. The desert is ever striving to recapture the territory that has been wrested from it."[6] In such an area the individual, whether he is a farmer, a miner, or a city dweller engaged in activities that seem to bear little relationship to the basic industries, may be unmindful of the fact that he is in a large measure dependent

[2] National Resources Planning Board, *Development of Resources and Stabilization of Employment in the United States, Part II. Regional Development Plans*, Washington, D.C., 1941, p. 14.
[3] *Ibid.*, p. 29.

[4] *Ibid.*, p. 50.
[5] *Ibid.*, p. 174.
[6] *Ibid.*, p. 198.

upon projects sponsored and developed by collective action.

The Pacific Northwest as a planning region consists approximately of the three states of Washington, Oregon, and Idaho, though the regional limits have not been sharply defined. The several problems related more or less directly to the natural resources include the settlement and reclamation of arable lands, the utilization of water for irrigation and power, flood control, the establishment of the sustained-yield principle in the lumbering industry, forest protection and rehabilitation, and the preservation and development of the scenic resources.

NATURAL RESOURCES AND NATIONAL SECURITY

The basic raw materials so necessary in maintaining the highly developed economy of the United States are available in very unequal quantities. Fortunately America is richly endowed with most of the essential raw materials of industry, but there are notable exceptions. The rapidly expanding economy has increased greatly the demand for raw materials and hastened the exhaustion of certain resources initially in short supply. A people mindful of the real or ultimate scarcity of the resources that are essential to the national economy should take the necessary steps to attain security. The economy of peace should be convertible to war in all possible haste in times of emergency. Whether the United States is a neutral or belligerent, the nation's best interests will be served if the economy is based upon adequate supplies of essential raw materials.

Complete independence in respect to the basic resources of industry is an impossibility for the United States. Dependence upon resources imported from other countries is and has been a significant feature of the American economy. Staley has stated clearly and forcefully, "There is no escape from international raw material interdependence . . ." [7] and this applies

[7] Eugene Staley, *Raw Materials in Peace and War*, New York, 1937, p. 238.

to the United States as well as to the less richly endowed countries.

New Discoveries. The available supply of many important resources will be increased by new discoveries if the history of mineral exploration can be used to forecast the future. In spite of the prospect that new discoveries will add substantial supplies of many resources to the total available for industrial use, there is also the grim truth that the rate of discovery will fall below the rate of use. National security is related to the continued search for additional supplies of essential resources and to an expanded program of research designed to make available industrial raw materials from deposits now known.

During World War II it was recognized that private mining interests would not be able to carry out the necessary exploration for, and development of, new mineral deposits rapidly enough to meet the needs of a nation at war. As a consequence the federal government by various means became involved in the exploration for new mineral resources and the expansion of the mineral processing industries. For example, the United States Geological Survey and the Bureau of Mines carried out investigations of domestic deposits of strategic minerals, such as chromite, mercury, manganese, and several others.

Direct Subsidies. In addition to the scientific work of the Bureau of Mines and the Geological Survey and the loans made by the Metals Reserve Company, direct subsidies were paid to the high-cost producers of copper, lead, and zinc amounting to several hundred million dollars in the period 1942 to 1947. Both by indirect methods and direct subsidies financial assistance can be used to increase production of a material in short supply.

Energy Resources and the Strength of the Nation. The fuel and power resources of the United States have made possible the high development of power-driven machines and have been responsible in a large measure for the highly productive facilities that have brought material conveniences and comforts to the American people. Inanimate energy released by the consumption of coal, petroleum, gas, and water power has multiplied manyfold the energy of human hands. The continued use of these power resources should give the United States a material civilization of a high order (see Chapter 17).

It is difficult to state just what fraction of the total power produced in the United States will be developed from uranium and from other nuclear sources by 1975 or the year 2000. Power plants using nuclear fuel are in operation and a small contribution is being made to the total supply of electrical energy available. Others are under development or are being planned. The ultimate importance of atomic energy as a power resource is related to a number of significant factors including the relative cost of the power resources, the continued availability of adequate quantities of uranium-235 and other nuclear fuels, and the relative importance of the weapon's program to the plans for the peaceful use of nuclear materials in medical science and in commerce.

The Metals in a Power-Using Economy. Because the United States is the major consumer of metals and many other mineral products, it is essential that every effort be made to assure the nation adequate supplies from both domestic and foreign sources. The United States normally uses more than half of the world's aluminum, cadmium, beryllium, cobalt, lead, molybdenum, the platinum-group metals, and a number of others. Consumption varies between a quarter and a half of the world's production of antimony, copper, iron ore, magnesium, manganese, mercury, nickel, tin, and others. Important quantities of these strategic materials are imported currently and in the future will have to be secured from foreign areas. As a consequence the Congress and other agencies of the federal government will carry a large responsibility for national and international planning designed to maintain the flow of essential metals and minerals to the United States. (See Chapter 16.)

As the supplies of metals are drawn increasingly from foreign sources privately owned mineral industries will be unable to assume full responsibility for assuring to themselves suffi-cient supplies of metals and minerals to meet the requirements of peace, the necessities of national defense, or the emergency of war. The maintenance of adequate reserves, stockpiling of strategic materials, and the development of substitutes become, in part at least, a responsibility of the national government.

It is also important that the stockpiling operations of the national government do not permit a number of companies or individuals to profit unduly. President Kennedy, at a news conference held on January 31, 1962, reported that he had reviewed the stockpile program and that it was apparent to him that the storage of costly materials has been "a potential source of excessive and unconscionable profits."[8] Senator Symington and his committee examined the situation as it had developed over the years and in a number of instances the committee's findings seemed to support the President's contention.

Resources of Organic Origin. The United States is normally dependent on imports for an important list of products of organic origin. During World War II fats and oils were in short supply. The expansion of the production of peanuts and soybeans offset in large measure the loss of coconut and palm nut oil regularly imported from the Far East. The cordage fibers such as henequen, Manila hemp, and jute are not only important in civilian industries but are essential in time of war. Other fibers such as kapok, bristles, and wool are imported to meet domestic requirements.

The list of materials of organic origin can be extended to include timber and wool pulp, condiments, tanning materials, rubber, and hides and skins. Our dependence upon oversea's sources may be reduced by the development of substitutes, particularly rubbers developed from petroleum and alcohol. The increased use of plastic wood, resin-impregnated woods, wallboard, and preservatives may extend greatly the forest resources of the country.

Unlike the nonperishable mineral resources these organic materials cannot be stockpiled

[8] See Draft Report of the National Stockpile and Naval Petroleum Reserves Subcommittee (Senator Stuart Symington, Chairman), Washington, D.C., 1963.

without danger of deterioration. Stockpiling requires continual renewal of supplies to meet or offset withdrawals from the nation's hoard of essential materials.

PLANNING BY FEDERAL AGENCIES

Both the legislative and executive branches of the federal government recognize their high responsibility for the long-range planning for the general welfare of the people and the security of the nation. Their objectives have been achieved by legislative action by the Congress authorizing the creation of agencies, prescribing and limiting their functions, and finally, after their functions are no longer necessary, terminating their activities. The President may, under legislative authority and by executive order, establish agencies whose responsibilities may be related to long-range planning in the areas of resource use and national security.[9]

In the executive branch of the government the Council of Economic Advisers must be ready at all times to keep the President informed concerning the national economic situation and to discern developments that may affect the growth and stability of the economy. The Office of Science and Technology has a similar function and it must continually evaluate plans and programs in science and technology. The National Science Foundation and the National Aeronautics and Space Administration have been vitally concerned with research and education in science and particularly with those branches of science and engineering that are essential in establishing the United States in a position of leadership in space science.

Bureau of the Budget. The Bureau of the budget created on June 10, 1925, consists of a director and approximately twenty officials as well as a staff necessary to prepare the budget which the President presents to the Congress. This agency is in a position to examine critically the asking budgets of the major departments,

divisions, offices, services and other branches of the federal government. The Bureau of the Budget is in effect a major planning agency and its recommendations are presented to the Congress who must initiate and pass the legislation necessary for both the short-run and the long-range programs of the federal government.

The National Security Council. By Congressional action the National Security Council was created in 1947. The National Security Act has been amended to change slightly the composition of the Council which presently consists of the President, the Vice President, the Secretary of State, the Secretary of Defense, and the Director of Emergency Planning. The Special Assistant to the President for National Security and an Executive Secretary are officials rather than members of the Council. This important agency has as its chief functions the integration and interpretation of all domestic, foreign, and military policies that have significant bearing on national security.

Office of Emergency Planning. The Office of Emergency Planning with approximately fifteen important offices, divisions, and centers is one of the most important agencies concerned with or involved in the field of national planning. This important agency of the federal government stands ready to advise the President and Congress on the capacity of the nation to convert the peacetime economy to a wartime footing if this became necessary. If a serious international situation should require a quick appraisal of the material resources available to meet the challenge, the Chief of the National Resource Evaluation Center, the Chief of the Stockpile and Requirements Division, the Chief of the Resource Management Division, and the officials of several other offices and divisions could, under the leadership of the Director of the Office of Emergency Planning, present strong and meaningful recommendations to other agencies of the federal government concerned with national security.

Central Intelligence Agency. Created by the National Security Act of 1947 the Central Intelligence Agency has as its principal purpose

---

[9] *United States Government Organization Manual, 1964-1965*, Government Printing Office, Washington, D.C., Revised June 1, 1964.

the coordination of all the intelligence activities of its own organization as well as similar activities of the several departments of the government. Naturally, much of the work of this agency is classified and is not readily available to the public.

Atomic Energy Commission. The Atomic Energy Act of 1946 created the Atomic Energy Commission. This Act as amended in 1954 sets forth the purposes of the Commission and established in general as well as specific terms the nature of its activities and the areas where it has jurisdiction. In essence the purpose of the Act was to bring control of nuclear energy under the jurisdiction of the federal government so that this enormously important source of energy would be used to serve the interests of national security, world peace, and the general welfare. The Commission must be concerned with the use of atomic energy in the development of a weapons system, the use of isotopes in medical science and in industry, and the allocation of nuclear fuels for use in the generation of electricity.

The Department of the Interior. Probably no other single division of the federal government considering its areas of responsibility is as concerned with natural resources as is the Department of the Interior. In each office or division the routine activities of the staff may be concerned with the collection and publication of data that will be useful to other agencies of the government as well as to the private sector of the national economy. Many of these offices and divisions of the Department must be ready with long-range plans for the future so that the Secretary can advise the President and the Congress on the resource situation in terms of national needs.

Some of the divisions of the Department of the Interior that are vitally concerned with national resources include the Fish and Wildlife Service, Office of Mineral Exploration, Office of Saline Water, Office of Coal Research, Bureau of Commercial Fisheries, Bureau of Mines, the Geological Survey, National Park Service, Bureau of Reclamation, Bureau of Outdoor

Recreation, and many others. The personnel of these agencies, bureaus, offices, and services must maintain the joint attitudes of the custodian of the nation's wealth and of the planner concerned with the nation's welfare in the future.

Other Agencies Concerned with Resources and the National Welfare. It is not appropriate here to list all the agencies of the federal government that are concerned with the material resources of the country. The numerous agencies can be identified and listed by reference to the manual previously mentioned.[10] Other major divisions of the government—such as the Rural Electrification Administration, the Forest Service, the Soil Conservation Service, the Agricultural Stabilization and Conservation Service, and others in the Department of Agriculture; the Corps of Engineers of the Department of the Army; the Coast and Geodetic Survey, the Weather Bureau, the Area Redevelopment Administration, Bureau of Public Roads (Fig. 5), and others in the Department of Commerce; and the Office of Naval Research in the Department of the Navy—are concerned with resources for both the present and the future welfare of the nation.

PLANNING IN THE PRIVATE SECTOR OF THE ECONOMY

In these times of big government, big business, and big labor unions, planning for the future development and use of resources is a widespread concern of the people. The large corporations, whether they are primary creators of wealth as mining companies and lumber companies or whether they are involved in the later manufacturing processes such as the making of automobiles or chemical products, must have both short-range and long-range plans for the future. In the larger firms a division may be assigned the responsibility of maintaining adequate reserves of raw materials so the parent company can continue in business over an ex-

[10] *Ibid.*

Fig. 5 A view of the major highway connecting Kansas City, Missouri (in the background), and Kansas City, Kansas. One of the major problems confronting the nation is development of a transportation system that will link the cities with the suburbs, the rural areas, and other cities. (Photo courtesy Armco Steel Corporation.)

tended period of time. A petroleum company as a producer, a manufacturer of petroleum products, and a distributor must carry on more or less continually the search for new deposits. A firm using timber and other products of the forest must be prepared to utilize the resource fully and move on to other areas that have not been exploited or to adopt a schedule of forest harvest and reforestation which will maintain the lumbering and wood-processing industries over a long period of time. On occasion the responsible officials in a company may yield to

short-range goals to keep the firm in a competitive position, but at every opportunity the long-range plans of the company will receive careful attention.

It is important that the federal government and the large resource-using industries carry on research and planning programs that are mutually advantageous. The federal government can hardly be expected to develop an important fishery resource by restocking an area, by reducing pollution, and by other means to improve the resource situation and then without restrictions to permit private enterprises who have little concern about the future to overfish the area and actually deplete a fishery that should be managed productively. The long-range interests of the government acting in behalf of all of the people and the commercial interest of a private company may be served by cooperation and mutual understanding.

National Problems That Lie Ahead. As the United States has become increasingly an urban and industrial nation a number of problems emerge that require attention. Many people have been concerned about the demand for additional rural lands to meet the needs of the urban communities for living space. Many manufacturing plants are a part of the urban sprawl, and extensive areas of agricultural land have been taken over to serve the needs of industry. Careful studies of this problem seem to indicate that highly productive land is entirely adequate to meet the needs of the nation for several decades for food, fibers, and other agricultural products.

National and local concern about the continued availability of adequate supplies of potable water and unpolluted air has focused attention on two problems that will require the attention of national, state, and local governments in the immediate future. As much as 97 percent of the water of the earth is in the sea. If potable, agricultural, and industrial water is to be developed from this source the desalinization program will have to be greatly expanded. In the immediate future the solutions to the problem of inadequate water supplies will include greater storage of surface waters, reduction of pollution, filtering and processing water to make it reusable, the reduction of waste in use, slowing the return to the sea, recharging the aquifers, improving the cover and soak-in in the headstream areas, and by other water-conserving measures.[11]

Primarily air is for breathing, but it serves many other purposes as well. It is a source of nitrogen for agricultural and industrial use. Oxygen for medical and industrial purposes is derived from the air. Like water the air is the medium in which an important mode of transportation is carried on. It is the pollution of the atmosphere that has attracted local, national, and international attention. The concentration of people and industry in closely settled urban communities has resulted in pollution. Both particulate and gaseous materials are emitted from the stacks of fuel-using plants, from smelters, factories, automobiles, and other producers of contaminants.

The heavier particulate materials may be removed from the air by gravity, but they may remain in the atmosphere for days and weeks, and under stable atmospheric conditions may become a part of the pall of smoke or smog that hangs over many industrial communities. If the smog contains gaseous substances as well, the quality of the air for breathing may be greatly diminished.

In a 5-day period from October 27 to November 1, 1948, Donora, Pennsylvania, experienced the ill effects of a severe smog related to the output of pollutants by the local smelters and other fuel-using industries and to the stagnation of the air resulting from a long-extended period of thermal inversion. Nearly 6000 people or 43 percent of the total population suffered from respiratory difficulty and 20 deaths in this period were caused by the high concentration of pollutants and the extended period of air stability. Many cities being in depressed areas where thermal inversion may develop can expect to be confronted with the smog problem.[12]

The problem of air pollution involving both the prevention of smog and the cleansing of the atmosphere may be largely a state or local prob-

[11] Abel Wolman, Chairman of the Water Resources Study, *Water Resources*, Publication 1000-B, National Academy of Sciences, National Research Council, Washington, D.C., 1962.

[12] *Air Over Cities*, Symposium sponsored by the Division of Air Pollution, U.S. Department of Health, Education, and Welfare and the Robert A. Taft Sanitary Engineering Center. Held November 6–7, 1961, Cincinnati, Ohio (SEC Technical Report A62-5).

lem, but the federal government becomes an interested and responsible party because weapon-testing may result in dangerous fallout.

INTERNATIONAL CONTROL OF NATURAL RESOURCES

The federal government by treaty and by other kinds of international agreements participates in the partial control of a number of resources. This is well illustrated by the Migratory Bird Treaty Act of 1918 (See Chapter 18).

Beginning in 1933 and continuing at intervals of 3 or more years, the United States has been a participant in a number of international agreements relating to wheat. The United States is a major producer of wheat and certain readjustments in acreage allotments have been related in part to the establishment of export quotas and prices by the members of the conference which draws up the terms of the International Wheat Agreements. The operation of the Acreage Reserve Program of the Soil Bank of 1957 is related to the problem of agricultural surpluses.

Because of the danger of depleting an important marine resource, the principal whaling nations are now adherents to an international convention which limits the take of whales in the Antarctic waters. The International Whaling Commission meets at regular intervals and establishes quotas for the several signatory nations.

As the United States participates increasingly in international affairs it may be expected that agreements will be entered into involving the international control of other activities or materials. In addition to wheat, coffee, sugar, seals, whales, migratory birds, and minerals, other resources are likely to be subject to international agreements.

RESEARCH AND THE PROBLEM OF DIMINISHING RESOURCES

In the conservation of the natural resources of the nation one of the great hopes of the future is the intensive search for the solution of the problems related to the exhaustion or decline of the material wealth long so abundant and easily available to us. Organized research must be brought to bear upon this problem, and human talent must be mobilized so that the security of the nation will never be in doubt for want of the essential raw materials.

Individual Research. It is traditional that the individual scholar at work in his laboratory or in his study represents scientific progress in a free society. Scientists working alone in their laboratories or in the field have found ways of utilizing more fully or more cheaply our material resources. The scholar in isolation has become relatively less important, but his work should be encouraged and supported.

Industrial Research.[13] Many years ago certain industries anxious to maintain their competitive position established research laboratories and employed a staff of scientists to carry out their investigations. Initially the industrial research laboratories or divisions were largely concerned with practical problems related to the industry that supported them. But industrial research has become both practical and fundamental. The findings do not always need to have immediate and practical usefulness. At the outset research carried on by industry was largely directed toward more economical manufacture of commercial products or the development of new and better products.

Some of the best-known industrial research organizations include the Research Laboratories Division of General Motors Corporation, the General Electric Research Laboratories, the chemical, development, and engineering departments of the E. I. du Pont de Nemours & Co., The Standard Oil Development Co., Monsanto Chemical Company, the Mellon Institute, the Battelle Memorial Institute, Arthur D. Little, Inc., and many others. These research organizations have become increasingly important in the industrial progress in the United

---

[13] John H. Gribbin, John H. and Sue Singer Krogfus, *Industrial Research Laboratories of the United States,* Eleventh Edition, Publication 844, National Academy of Sciences, National Research Council, Washington, D.C., 1960.

States. Research activities have moved forward from the restricted objectives to more comprehensive programs. Better products for the ultimate consumer remain important, but research is being directed toward the solution of the raw material problems. The beneficiation of low-grade ores is an important development and indicates the direction of research in the field of natural resource utilization. The recovery of aluminum from common clays and other aluminum-bearing minerals is a research enterprise of major importance. The transformation of the rubber industry as a result of the loss of access to adequate supplies of natural rubber is a notable example of the capacity of American industry to solve a raw material problem.

In the field of industrial research integration can be achieved for the reason that government-sponsored programs have been allocated to those research foundations or organizations best qualified to carry on the investigations. Continually there emerge from the industrial laboratories achievements which the National Security Resources Board can examine and appraise in terms of the needs of the nation.

Research in Colleges and Universities. Research in the major educational institutions of this country has been overshadowed by the great industrial research organizations. In fact research in the universities is in many instances indistinguishable from the research in industry. Many universities receive support from industry for their research programs, and generally the achievement of practical results is a major objective. In the universities there can be a detachment that is conducive to long-range research of fundamental character where practical application is not immediately envisioned. The universities are peculiarly well suited for this type of research.

It is appropriate that certain research programs in the universities should be concerned with the many aspects of the resource problem. In the physical and biological sciences, in political science, and in economics both the scientific and the social aspects of natural resources may be investigated with scholarly objectivity.

The Government and Research. The federal government and to a lesser extent states and municipalities have conducted and supported research activities over a long period of time. During World War II and in the postwar period research in agencies of the federal government has been greatly expanded. In a similar manner research in the universities and in private research organizations has been generously supported by the federal government. Much of the research is related directly or indirectly to the problem of national security and in one way or another is concerned with the resource situation.

The Agricultural Experiment Stations, the Bureau of Mines, the Soil Conservation Service, the Bureau of Animal Industry, the Forest Service, the regional laboratories and the Agricultural Research Center of the Department of Agriculture, the Office of Naval Research, the Research and Development Board, and many other bureaus and agencies of the federal government are devoted to research programs which will lead eventually to a wiser use of our basic resources.

In a nation of diminishing material resources there are still new frontiers to be explored. New lands are no longer available to challenge the pioneering spirit of the youth of America, but the new frontiers of science present an opportunity for adventure and achievement for those who would serve the needs of their country. Through the resourcefulness of the people in making a full and appropriate use of the more abundant materials, a high standard of living for the people and security of the nation can be achieved. Out of the materials of the earth people create resources.

References

Eisenhower, Milton S., "Federal Responsibilities in Total Conservation," *Conservation of Renewable Resources*, University of Pennsylvania Bicentennial Conference, University of Pennsylvania Press, Philadelphia, 1941, pp. 175–189.

Gaus, John M., Jacob Crane, Marshall E. Dimock, and George T. Renner, *Regional Factors in National Planning and Development*, National Resources Committee, Government Printing Office, Washington, D.C., 1935.

Landsberg, Hans H., *Natural Resources for U.S. Growth*, The Johns Hopkins Press, Baltimore, 1964.

Landsberg, Hans H., Leonard L. Fischman, and Joseph L. Fisher, *Resources in America's Future*, Resources for the Future, The Johns Hopkins Press, Baltimore, 1963.

Lilienthal, David E., *TVA, The March of Democracy*, Harper and Brothers, New York, 1944.

Lorwin, Lewis L., *Time for Planning*, Harper and Brothers, New York, 1945.

MacKenzie, Findlay, editor, *Planned Society, Yesterday, Today, Tomorrow*, Prentice-Hall, Englewood Cliffs, New Jersey, 1937.

Millett, John D., *The Process and Organization of Government Planning*, Columbia University Press, New York, 1947.

National Planning Association, Committee on New England, *The Economic State of New England* (Directors of research and editors: Arthur A. Bright, Jr. and George H. Ellis), Yale University Press, New Haven, 1954.

National Planning Association, *Long-Range Projections for Economic Growth: the American Economy in 1970*, Washington, D.C., 1959.

Odum, Howard, and H. E. Moore, *American Regionalism*, Henry Holt and Co., New York, 1935.

Rodgers, Cleveland, *American Planning*, Harper and Brothers, New York, 1947.

Shah, K. T., *National Planning, Principles and Administration*, Vora and Company, Publishers, Ltd., Bombay, India, 1948.

Stanley, Timothy W., *American Defense and National Security*, Public Affairs Press, Washington, D.C., 1956.

Terral, Rufus, *The Missouri Valley*, Yale University Press, New Haven, Connecticut, 1947.

United States National Resources Committee, *Regional Planning*, Government Printing Office, Washington, D.C., 1936–1939.

United States National Resources Committee, *Research—A National Resource, 1: Relation of the Federal Government to Research*, Government Printing Office, Washington, D.C., 1938. 255 pages.

United States National Resources Planning Board, *Industrial Locations and National Resources*, Government Printing Office, Washington, D.C., 1943.

United States National Resources Planning Board, *Research—A National Resource, II: Industrial Research*, Government Printing Office, Washington, D.C., 1940. 369 pages.

Wootton, Barbara, *Freedom under Planning*, University of North Carolina Press, Chapel Hill, N.C., 1946.

Wriston, Henry M., *Goals for Americans*, Prentice-Hall, Englewood Cliffs, New Jersey, 1960.

General Works on Conservation

Allen, Shirley W., *Conserving Natural Resources*, Second Edition, McGraw-Hill Book Co., New York, 1959.

Barnett, Harold G. and Chandler Morse, *Scarcity and Growth: The Economics of Natural Resource Availability*, The Johns Hopkins Press, Baltimore, 1963.

Bromfield, Louis, *Out of the Earth*, Harper and Brothers, New York, 1950.

Brown, Harrison, *The Challenge of Man's Future*, Viking Press, New York, 1954.

Burton, Ian and Robert W. Kates, editors, *Readings in Resource Management and Conservation*, University of Chicago Press, Chicago, 1965.

Callison, Charles H., editor, *America's Natural Resources*, The Ronald Press Co., New York, 1957.

Ciriacy-Wantrup, S. V., *Resource Conservation*, Revised Edition, Agricultural Publications, University of California, Berkeley, 1964.

Clawson, Marion, R. Burnell Held, and Charles H. Stoddard, *Land for the Future*, The Johns Hopkins Press, Baltimore, 1960.

Conservation Foundation, *Annual Reports*, New York.

Conservation of Renewable Natural Resources, Proceedings of Inter-American Conference, U.S. Department of State, Publ. 3382, Denver, Colorado, 1948.

Coyle, David Cushman, *Conservation: An American Story of Conflict and Accomplishment*, Rutgers University Press, New Brunswick, New Jersey, 1957.

Dasmann, Raymond F., *Environmental Conservation*, John Wiley and Sons, New York, 1959.

Dewhurst, J. Frederic, and Associates, *America's Needs and Resources, A New Survey*, The Twentieth Century Fund, New York, 1955.

Fairchild, Wilma Belden, "Renewable Resources: A World Dilemma; Recent Publications on Conservation," *Geographical Review*, Vol. 39, 1949, pp. 89–98.

Firey, Walter, *Man, Mind and Land, A Theory of Resource Use*, The Free Press of Glencoe, Illinois, 1960.

Flynn, Harry Eugene and Floyd E. Perkins, *Conservation of the Nation's Resources*, The Macmillan Co., New York, 1941.

Franklin D. Roosevelt & Conservation, 1911–1945 (4 Vols.), compiled and edited by Edgar B. Nixon, General Services Administration, National Archives and Records Service, Franklin D. Roosevelt Library, Hyde Park, New York, 1957.

Glacken, Clarence J., "The Origins of Conservation Philosophy," *Journ. Soil and Water Conservation*, Vol. II, 1956, pp. 63–66.

Graham, Edward H., *Natural Principles of Land Use*, Oxford University Press, New York, 1944.

Gustafson, A. F., C. H. Guise, W. J. Hamilton, Jr., and H. Ries, *Conservation in the United States*, Third Edition, Comstock Publishing Company, Ithaca, New York, 1949.

Hatt, Paul K., editor, *World Population and Future Resources*, American Book Co., New York, 1952.

Hays, Samuel P., *Conservation and the Gospel of Efficiency, The Progressive Conservation Movement, 1890–1920*, Harvard University Press, Cambridge, 1959.

Higbee, Edward, *American Agriculture, Geography, Resources, Conservation*, John Wiley and Sons, New York, 1958.

Highsmith, Richard M., J. Granville Jensen, and Robert D. Rudd, *Conservation in the United States*, Rand McNally and Co., Chicago, 1962.

Huberty, Martin, R. and Warren L. Flock, editors, *Natural Resources*, McGraw-Hill Book Co., New York, 1959.

Jacks, G. V., and R. O. Whyte, *Vanishing Lands: A World Survey of Soil Erosion*, Doubleday, Doran and Co., New York, 1939.

Jarrett, Henry, editor, *Perspectives on Conservation*, The Johns Hopkins Press, Baltimore, 1958.

Jarrett, Henry, editor, *Science and Resources: Prospects and Implications of Technological Advance*, The Johns Hopkins Press, Baltimore, 1959.

Kauffman, Erle, *The Conservation Yearbook*, Monumental Printing Company, Baltimore, 1956.

King, Judson, *The Conservation Fight, from Theodore Roosevelt to the Tennessee Valley Authority*, Public Affairs Press, Washington, D.C., 1959.

Kreps, Juanita Morris, editor, *Our Natural Resources*, The Reference Shelf, Vol. 22, No. 2, H. W. Wilson Company, New York, 1955.

Krug, J. A., *National Resources and Foreign Aid*, Report of the Secretary of the Interior, Government Printing Office, Washington, D.C., 1947.

Landsberg, Hans H., *Natural Resources for U.S. Growth*, The Johns Hopkins Press, Baltimore, 1964.

Landsberg, Hans H., Leonard L. Fischman, and Joseph L. Fisher, *Resources in America's Future, Patterns of Requirements and Availabilities, 1960–2000*, Resources for the Future, The Johns Hopkins Press, Baltimore, 1963.

Lyons, Barrow, *Tomorrow's Birthright*, Funk and Wagnalls, New York, 1955.

Marsh, George P., *Man and Nature; or Physical Geography as Modified by Human Action* (1864), Revised Edition, *The Earth as Modified by Human Action*, Charles Scribner's Sons, New York, 1884.

Mather, Kirtley F., *Enough and to Spare*, Harper and Brothers, New York, 1944.

Mouzon, Olin T., *International Resources and National Policy*, Harper and Brothers, New York, 1959.

National Resources Committee, General reports and publications on regional planning, state planning, public works, land planning, and water planning (see also the reports of the National Planning Board and the National Resources Board), Government Printing Office, Washington, D.C., 1934–1943.

National Resources Security Board, Reports and press releases, Government Printing Office, Washington, D.C., 1948–1953.

Ordway, Samuel H., Jr., *Conservation Handbook*, New York, 1949.

Ordway, Samuel H., Jr., *Prosperity Beyond Tomorrow*, The Ronald Press Co., New York, 1956.

Ordway, Samuel H., Jr., *Resources and the American Dream*, The Ronald Press Co., New York, 1953.

Osborn, Fairfield, *Our Plundered Planet*, Little, Brown and Co., Boston, Mass., 1948.

Osborn, Fairfield, *The Limits of the Earth*, Little, Brown and Co., Boston, Mass., 1953.

Parkins, A. E., and J. R. Whitaker, *Our Natural Resources and Their Conservation*, John Wiley and Sons, New York, 1936 and 1939.

Parson, Ruben L., *Conserving American Resources,* Second Edition, Prentice-Hall, Englewood Cliffs, New Jersey, 1964.

Perloff, Harvey S., Edgar S. Dunn, Jr., Eric E. Lampard, and Richard F. Muth, *Regions, Resources, and Economic Growth,* The Johns Hopkins Press, Baltimore, 1960.

Pinchot, Gifford, *The Fight for Conservation,* Farmers Bull. 327, U.S. Department of Agriculture, Washington, D.C., 1909.

Potter, Neal and Francis T. Christy, Jr., *Trends in Natural Resource Commodities, Statistics in Prices, Output, Consumption, Foreign Trade, and Employment in the United States, 1870–1957,* The Johns Hopkins Press, Baltimore, 1962.

The President's Materials Policy Commission, *Resources for Freedom,* Vol. I: *Foundations for Growth and Security,* Vol. II: *The Outlook for Key Commodities,* Vol. III: *The Outlook for Energy Sources,* Vol. IV: *The Promise of Technology,* Government Printing Office, Washington, D.C., 1952.

Raushenbush, Stephen, "The Future of Our Natural Resources," *The Annals,* Vol. 281, 1952, pp. 1–275.

Renner, George T., *Conservation of National Resources,* John Wiley and Sons, New York, 1942.

Report of the National Conservation Commission, Senate Document 676, Vol. 1, 60th Congress, 2nd Session, Government Printing Office, Washington, D.C., 1909.

Resources for the Future, *Annual Reports,* Reprints, Monographs, etc.

Resources for the Future, *The Nation Looks at Its Resources,* Report of the Mid-Century Conference on Resources for the Future, December 2–4, 1953, Washington, D.C., 1954.

Reuss, L. A., H. H. Wooten, and F. J. Marschner, *Inventory of Major Land Uses in the United States,* Misc. Publ. 663, U.S. Department of Agriculture, Washington, D.C., 1948.

Schurr, Sam H. and Bruce C. Netschert, *Energy in the American Economy, 1950–1975,* The Johns Hopkins Press, Baltimore, 1960.

Scott, Anthony, *Natural Resources: The Economics of Conservation,* University of Toronto Press, Toronto, Canada, 1955.

Sears, Paul B., *Deserts on the March,* Revised Edition, University of Oklahoma Press, Norman, Oklahoma, 1947.

Staley, Eugene, *Raw Materials in Peace and War,* Council of Foreign Relations, New York, 1937.

Straus, Michael W., *Why Not Survive?* Simon and Schuster, New York, 1955.

Thomas, William L., Jr., editor, *Man's Role in Changing the Face of the Earth,* University of Chicago Press, Chicago, 1956.

United Nations Department of Economic Affairs, Proceedings of the United Nations Scientific Conference on Conservation and Utilization of Resources, August 17—September 6, 1949, United Nations, New York, 1951. Vol. I: *Plenary Meetings,* Vol. II: *Mineral Resources,* Vol. III: *Fuel and Energy Resources,* Vol. IV: *Water Resources,* Vol. V: *Forest Resources,* Vol. VI: *Land Resources,* Vol. VII: *Wildlife and Fish Resources,* Vol. VIII: *Index.*

United States Congress, House of Representatives, *A Program to Strengthen the Scientific Foundation in Natural Resources,* House Document 706, 81st Congress, Second Session, A Supplemental Report to Accompany Hearings on H. R. 6257 and H. R. 6900, Government Printing Office, Washington, D.C., 1950.

United States Congress, House of Representatives, Interior and Insular Affairs Committee, *The Physical and Economic Foundation of Natural Resources,* I. *Photosynthesis, Basic Features of the Process,* II. *The Physical Basis of Water Supply and Its Principal Uses,* III. *Groundwater Regions of the United States—Their Storage Facilities,* IV. *Subsurface Facilities of Water Management and Patterns of Supply—Type Area Studies,* Government Printing Office, Washington, D.C., 1952.

University of Pennsylvania Bicentennial Conference, *Conservation of Renewable Natural Resources,* University of Pennsylvania Press, Philadelphia, Pa., 1941.

Van Hise, Charles Richard, *The Conservation of Natural Resources in the United States,* The Macmillan Co., New York, 1910 and 1921.

Van Hise, Charles R., and Loomis Havemeyer, *Conservation of Our Natural Resources,* The Macmillan Co., New York, 1935.

Vogt, William, *Road to Survival,* William Sloane Associates, New York, 1948.

Wales H. Basil, and H. O. Lathrop, *The Conservation of Natural Resources,* Laurel Book Co., Chicago, 1944.

Whitaker, J. Russell, and Edward A. Ackerman, *American Resources,* Harcourt, Brace and Co., New York, 1951.

White, Gilbert F., "Toward an Appraisal of World Resources: New Views of Conservation Problems," *Geographical Review,* Vol. 39, 1949, pp. 625–639.

Wilbur, Ray Lyman, and William Atherton Du Puy, *Conservation in the Department of the Interior,* Government Printing Office, Washington, D.C., 1932.

Zimmermann, Eric W., *Introduction to World Resources,* edited by Henry L. Hunker, Harper and Row, New York, 1964.

Index